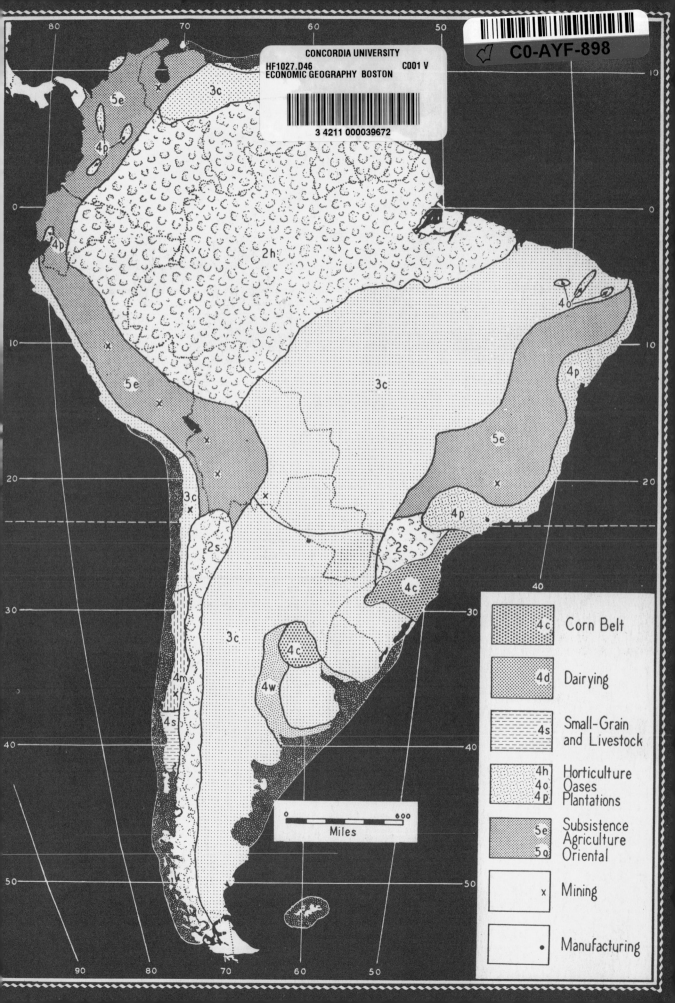

5e

3c

4p

4p

2h

4o

4p

5e

3c

5e

x

x

x

x

x

x

3c

2s

4p

2s

4c

3c

4c

4w

4m

x

4s

Miles

0   600

Corn Belt
4c

Dairying
4d

Small-Grain
and Livestock
4s

Horticulture
4h
Oases
4o
Plantations
4p

Subsistence
Agriculture
5e
Oriental
5q

Mining
x

Manufacturing
•

ECONOMIC GEOGRAPHY

Economic Geography

By SAMUEL NEWTON DICKEN

PROFESSOR OF GEOGRAPHY AND
HEAD OF DEPARTMENT OF GEOGRAPHY AND GEOLOGY
UNIVERSITY OF OREGON

BOSTON: D. C. HEATH AND COMPANY

LIBRARY OF CONGRESS CATALOG CARD NUMBER: 55–7397

[5L4]

Offices: BOSTON · NEW YORK · CHICAGO · ATLANTA · SAN FRANCISCO · DALLAS · LONDON

Preface

ECONOMIC GEOGRAPHY is the successor to A RE-GIONAL ECONOMIC GEOGRAPHY, published in 1949. Readers who are familiar with the latter will find that ECONOMIC GEOGRAPHY incorporates many improvements: latest available statistics throughout, improvements in organization, new text material, and a larger and more useful appendix. Many of the new features were suggested by users of the previous book. The author is grateful to all those who contributed suggestions. All suggestions were carefully considered, but unfortunately, not all could be followed.

Frequent revision of an economic geography text is necessary in order to keep pace with production changes. This book includes available data from the censuses of 1950 and 1951 and later. For some countries, unfortunately, statistics as well as recent on-the-ground descriptions are still very meager. Statistical references in the text are usually stated in round numbers and are somewhat at variance with those in the Appendix.

It is possible to give here only a brief outline of the organizational and content changes. A new chapter (Chapter 4), "The Geographic Background of Production in Other Continents," is a companion for Chapter 3, "The Geographic Background of Production in America." These chapters provide a brief geographic background of all the continents, especially for those students who have not taken a course in elementary geography. Surface features, drainage, climates, soils, peoples, and production regions are reviewed. Fish and fisheries are covered in one chapter (Chapter 5), "Products of the Seas." Minerals, fuels, and power are treated in a series of five chapters: Chapter 31, "The Metallic Minerals"; Chapter 32, "The Non-metallic Minerals"; Chapter 33, "Coal: A Primary Fuel and Chemical"; Chapter 34, "Petroleum and Natural Gas"; and Chapter 35, "Water Power and Water Supply." Chapters 31, 32, and 35 are entirely new. The chapters on manufacturing and trade have been revised to include new sections. Throughout the book are new maps, graphs, and photographs.

To the Reader

Many people would like to know more about other lands, inhabitants, and products. These people are often discouraged, however, by some such statement as this: "If you wish to know more about the world, do not study books; go and find out for yourself." On the surface the quotation appears to be good advice, but reflection reveals that it is based on the doubtful assumptions that one can learn nothing worth-while from books and maps and that a person will understand without previous experience or preparation any country which comes under direct observation. Further, it suggests that the world is small enough and that an individual's time and resources are large enough to permit firsthand examination of wide areas.

On the contrary, geographic facts are significant only to those prepared by study and thought to observe them. Many people have traveled far, seeing much but understanding little; many who have traveled little are well informed. Fortunate indeed are they whose travels have been prefaced by even an elementary study of man's earth. It is more realistic and appropriate to say: "If you wish to know about some region or country, read the best descriptions available and obtain as much additional information as possible from maps, interviews, and correspondence. Then visit the region, make observations, and check them with what you have read." Firsthand observations will suggest and encourage further reading.

Economic geography is not for travelers and casual students alone; it has dollars and cents value for the businessman, farmer, manufacturer, and even for the consumer. All people who deal with commodities need to know conditions in competing regions as well as in their own neighborhood and since production is constantly changing, the student must acquire enough skill in the techniques of economic geography to aid in estimating the trends.

Practical applications of economic geography are all around us, although some of them are not very obvious until they are pointed out. Forecasting a freeze in the orange groves of California; surveying conditions in the "Dust Bowl" in order to formulate government policy; investigating a tropical plain to determine its suitability for bananas; these are merely random examples. The scope of practical economic geography is suggested by the uses made of it by students. One student upon graduation went to work in the bond department of a bank. He was called upon to investigate County H— in an irrigated region which was offering bonds for sale. The financial affairs of County H— were in good condition, but in looking over the geography of the region the investigator discovered that a neighboring district was in a position to divert most of the water from County H—, thus making it practically unproductive. On this basis the bank refused to sell the bonds. Another student who became manager of a small paint factory found that a knowledge of the sources of the various pigments, oils, and other materials used in making paint not only aided him in the purchase of raw materials, but was of help in advertising his product. A third student became interested in urban geography—the location and functions of the various parts of cities and the exact distribution and movement of the people within them. Continuing his studies he worked out a method for locating retail stores scientifically, and today he is head of the research department of a large company and employs assistants who are trained in economic geography.

To the student who must for the moment confine his studies to book and map, economic geography offers a variety of approaches. It may be studied by individual products or commodities, with or without regard to their interdependence. The material may be arranged by countries, in which case there is usually some sort of subdivision of the larger countries. The method used in this book involves first the study of production types or occupations, such as grazing, plantation farming, grain farming, fishing, lumbering, and manufacturing. Then, under each type, specific regions are studied—Russian Turkestan, the Gobi of western China, the Great Plains of the United States, and the Argentine Pampa, to mention a few under the grazing type. The ultimate goal is an understanding of the distribution of world production seen against the

geographic background of the natural and cultural environments and viewed in the perspective of time. Such a goal is worthy of a lifetime of study. The primary purpose of this book, therefore, is to develop a frame of knowledge which will sharpen observation and into which additional facts acquired by reading and travel may be properly fitted.

As a survey of the table of contents suggests, this book is organized by regions of production. In this way all of the important kinds of production within a given area can be integrated (if they are related) and studied against the background of physical and cultural environments within which the production has developed. Production regions are grouped under seven major types, an arrangement which simplifies the presentation and avoids much repetition. The types are based, in general, on the kind of production which in any given region employs the most people.

The study of economic geography requires a thorough knowledge of countries, states, cities, rivers, and mountains. The background of most students in this respect must be supplemented by the study of maps, in both text and atlas. It is advisable to cultivate the "map habit," not necessarily the constant use of the atlas but rather the habit of studying all pertinent maps in connection with the current topic.

In addition to the maps in the text and atlas, it should be observed that the base map is a simple and effective tool for note-taking in geography, often more satisfactory than the usual methods. The boundaries of the "Corn Belt," for example, can be sketched on a base map in a few minutes. A written description of its boundaries with an equal standard of accuracy would probably require almost an hour. Furthermore, placing the data on a map tends to bring out significant patterns and relationships.

Before studying the first chapters of this book it is suggested that you make an inventory of some familiar region. Most people have acquired a miscellany of geographic facts from general reading—newspapers, books, and magazines—as well as from direct observation. For example, ask yourself what you know about the Great Plains

Region of the United States (discussed in Chapter 9). Do you know its exact location (parts of what states)? What do you know about the towns, railroads, people, and products? Turn to an atlas and study the appropriate maps; note the "place geography," also the surface configuration, rainfall, population density, and the relation to adjacent regions. Then read the text, study the maps therein, and fit the material into the pattern of your previous knowledge. Make brief notes, on a base map if possible. Above all, endeavor to be specific. Do not be content to note: "population sparse." A much better kind of statement would be: "population about five persons per square mile."

After the study of the text and atlas is completed, there will be gaps in your knowledge which may be filled partly by asking questions of your instructor or consulting the references at the end of this book. Do not be disappointed if you are unable to find a satisfactory answer to your questions. The general outline of world production is well known, but a great many details remain to be studied. The questions at the end of the book are designed to point up the discussion and to suggest topics for further study.

It is scarcely necessary to point out to students of economic geography that no one book or course can hope to cover adequately all phases of the subject. Products are too varied in character and distribution, and the geographic background is too complex for all aspects to be treated fully. It has been the author's endeavor to produce a text which emphasizes the geographic aspects of production rather than the purely economic, to write it in such a form that previous training in college geography on the part of the student will not be necessary, and to arrange the material so that some parts can be omitted and others expanded. In practice the author has rarely had an opportunity to expand, except at the expense of drastic omissions later on in the course. In fifteen years of teaching economic geography in more than fifty separate classes, it has usually been necessary to omit some of the material presented in this book. Several chapters may be omitted at the discretion of the instructor without destroying the fundamental structure of the course. On the other hand, if more time is available, it is not difficult to expand the treatment of many chapters, giving more attention to minerals, to cities, and to trade.

In the course of the preparation of this book, which has occupied much of the author's spare time for several years, it is difficult indeed to recall all the sources of information, suggestions, comments, and criticisms that have contributed to its completion. To those familiar with the literature of economic geography it will be apparent from references at the end of the book that many workers in this and allied fields have contributed to the final result. Whatever originality the author can claim lies in the arrangement and method of presentation of the material. Even here ideas have been borrowed from many sources and many people. The preparation of a planographed syllabus (1934) in collaboration with Professor Richard Hartshorne led to an extension of these and other ideas. Special thanks are due to Professor Hartshorne for permission to use parts of this syllabus and for many other helpful suggestions. The work of Professors Wellington Jones and Derwent Whittlesey in the delineations of agricultural regions marks an important milestone in studies of this kind. The above are simply the high lights in a long list of contributors to the author's education in economic geography.

Special thanks are due to Professor J. H. Burgy and Professor John C. Weaver for critical reading of the manuscript. In the early stages of planning, most valuable suggestions and criticisms along with judicious encouragement were offered by Professor J. R. Whitaker. The author is indebted, most of all, to Emily Fry Dicken for both editorial and clerical assistance throughout the preparation of the book.

SAMUEL N. DICKEN

Table of Contents

ECONOMIC GEOGRAPHY

FIGURE 1.1. *Map of selected United States imports and exports. Items listed in the margins are imports, those located within the United States are exports. Our imports are more diverse in character than the exports, but the total value of the latter is usually greater.*

1

The New World

THE stirring events of recent years have focused our attention sharply on the affairs of the world. A few years ago we said with pride, "This is our *country*." We let it go at that. Today we think with more than a little concern, "This is our *world!*" The turn in world events has called attention to matters which long ago deserved our thought. Some of us are producers of goods which must be sold in competition with goods from other lands; others are engaged in the distribution of domestic or imported products; all of us are consumers of goods from near and distant lands. See FIGURE 1.1. Where and how these goods are produced and consumed is a subject which concerns us all, no matter how selfish the point of view. Furthermore, if there is to be a lasting peace, everyone must be concerned with the production and movement of goods, as well as with the political attitudes of the various peoples, since the two factors are intimately related.

Production changes in distant lands affect our own country profoundly. The discovery of high-grade phosphate in North Africa, for example, put many a worker in Florida out of a job. The African phosphate is so much closer to the fertilizer-hungry farms of Europe. When cotton production was increased in Russia, Brazil, and other countries, the price of cotton in our own Cotton Belt fell, and a government program was inaugurated to stabilize the price. When the production and prices of goods are relatively stable, the consumer is more interested in the quality and cost of an article. When the sources of some commodities are cut off, when quality declines and prices advance, however, interest arises in the conditions of production, in the sources of the

raw materials, in the nature of the manufacturing processes, and in the methods of distribution to the consumer.

Even before our entrance into World War II, our concern for world-wide production was greatly heightened. An embargo on Japanese goods had cut off our supplies of raw silk and restricted the sale of raw cotton. Later the Japanese blockade of southeastern Asia created a scarcity of rubber and focused attention on the development of synthetic rubber at home, and on the increase of natural rubber production in Brazil. The loss of manila fiber turned our attention to Mexican sisal (agave) and to domestic hemp as substitutes. On the other side of the world, the partial blockade of Europe caused a scarcity of optical goods, olive oil, mercury, manganese, and many other products. The efforts to compensate for these scarcities has had a permanent effect on our productive economy, and one important result of these blockades is our new awareness of the interdependence of all parts of the world.

OUR PLACE IN THE WORLD

It has always been a tendency of man to believe that his world is larger than it is and that beyond his immediate horizon the affairs of the world are of little concern. What did it matter to the early Greeks that primitive peoples roamed the plains of Britain? The eastern Mediterranean was the Greek world, and yet that day came to an end. For centuries the people of China enjoyed a rich culture and cared little for distant lands until the Mongols overran most of the country. The Japanese were able to avoid contact with the outside world until as late as 1840.

Modern communication, especially the radio and the airplane, has reduced the effective circumference of the earth to a fraction of what it used to be. Today every country, every island, every person is, in a fundamental sense, a world citizen. Isolation is no longer a reality or even a possibility. It is a dream of a day that is past. In many ways the earth appears to be the same as it was a generation ago, but the realization that from now on our existence is linked with even the most distant peoples of the earth has been emphasized by World War II.

POPULATION AND PRODUCTION

People produce. It is inevitable that, in a broad survey of production, one should think of population also. Obviously production is where the people are, and yet a preliminary glance at maps of world production and world population raises a number of questions. Why are production and population so unequally distributed? See FIGURE 1.2. Is this distribution proportional to re-

sources? Who are the "haves" and who are the "have nots"?

The estimated population of the earth was more than 2,400,000,000 in 1950, an average density of about 43 persons per square mile. In Europe and Asia there are about one third of the world's resources and almost three fourths of the people. In some rural districts of the Old World there are more than 1500 persons per square mile. In similar areas in the New World there is almost no population. It would be simple enough to say that population depends on production and that the amount of production depends on resources, but this is not always true, as may be judged from the graphs drawn in FIGURE 1.2.

On the basis of population and area alone, it appears that Asia and Europe are overpopulated and that the other continents are underpopulated. Few thoughtful people would suggest that the population of the earth should be suddenly redistributed; but the fact is that in some regions of the earth production is pushed to the limit of the

FIGURE 1.2. *Graph of area, population, arable land, coal production, and petroleum production by continents. Notice the inequalities of resources and production compared with population.*

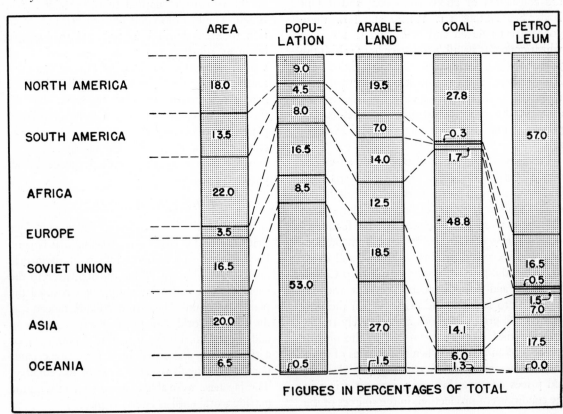

FIGURE 1.3. *A sparsely populated district in northeastern Mexico. The light rainfall and the rugged terrain are unfavorable for production, but notice the small irrigated plots, lower left. Here, as in many other parts of the world, the marginal lands are occupied by a few people. From Cia Mexicana Aerofoto, S. A.*

resources, at least with present techniques, while in others the surface has barely been scratched. Pressure of population causes people to seek "living space" elsewhere, but few lands are now open to settlement. Migrations are restricted to small "quotas," and certain peoples are excluded from many of the comparatively "empty lands."

Not all of the "empty lands" are capable of supporting additional millions of people under present systems of world production. Australia, for example, is almost as large as the United States but has only 8,000,000 people. A careful study of the resources of Australia, taking into account the small area of humid land, suggests that large-scale immigration is possible only if new forms and techniques of production are in-

troduced. If the tropical northern part of Australia could be utilized more effectively, it is quite possible that the continent could support an additional 8,000,000. It seems likely that the United States could absorb an additional 50,000,-000 with few changes in the production system.

When the problem is examined in some detail, as it will be in succeeding chapters, it is apparent that not only have the inequalities of population distribution helped produce world tensions, but that the distribution of strategic commodities, such as petroleum, coal, iron ore, wheat, sugar, cotton, gold, and rubber, play lesser, but important roles. At the onset of World War II, five great powers or coalitions were struggling to control a large share of the world's production:

the United States, the British Empire, Germany plus Italy, Russia, and Japan. Japan, of course, was a part of the Rome-Berlin-Tokyo axis, but her sphere of influence was separate and distinct. Each of these powers had a sphere of influence so far as production was concerned; a part of the sphere was well defined but there was also, in each case, a fringe over which the control was only partially established. The United States played a leading role in most of North America and endeavored, by peaceful means, to extend this influence to Latin America. Great Britain fought desperately to maintain commercial control of her far-flung empire, the products of which were so important to the homeland. The people of Germany and Italy, long considering themselves the "have not" victims of circumstance and faced with rapid increases in population, sought "living space" in Europe, Africa, and perhaps in Latin America. Russia showed her designs for conquest in certain areas of strategic importance from the military and production standpoint, especially along the borders of her extensive territory. The chief goals of the Soviet Union have been more raw materials and machinery for her growing industries and better outlets to the warm seas. The oil of Iran, Iraq, and Arabia, the industrial potential of Germany, the raw materials and manpower of China, and complete control of the outlet from the Black Sea are especially desirable. Moving toward these objectives the Soviet Union has found most of the rest of the world arrayed against her.

VARIETY OF PRODUCTION

The inequalities and maladjustments of production are even more apparent when specific kinds of production are examined. Why is there such an amazing variety, from the primitive agriculture of Amazonia in the equatorial belt of South America to the highly organized tropical plantation, from the nomadic life of the Eskimo to the uranium mines of Great Bear Lake in Northern Canada? It is easy to answer that the variations are associated with the particular resources found in different parts of the earth and, indeed, that is a partial answer. See FIGURE 1.4. Contrasting forms of production, however, are found in similar environments. Why is the rubber production in Malaya vastly greater than that in Brazil, the home of the rubber tree? Why is so little coffee produced in Ethiopia, the original habitat of the coffee tree? Along with the distribution and variety of world production, one must study the factors in the physical environment, such as land forms, climate, and soils; these elements should be interpreted in the light of the cultural background of the people who occupy the land.

CLIMATE AND PRODUCTION

Climate is the great conditioner of production. Very few of the economic activities of man are free from its limiting influence, although agriculture, grazing, and forestry are more profoundly affected than mining and manufacturing. Climate also limits the character of the natural vegetation, landforms, and soils. Through these factors climate influences production.

The generally gradual variation of climate from place to place facilitates the comparison of climatic regions with types of production. (Compare Chapter 2 and Appendix A.) Much of the land with Steppe (semiarid) climate is used for grazing. The subhumid climates, the transition between the arid and humid climates, are correlated with the commercial wheat belts, although wheat yields are higher in somewhat moister localities. Mediterranean agriculture and the Mediterranean climate are closely associated. Correlations are more difficult in the tropical rainforest climate, where excessive rainfall is a handicap to some forms of production. But the rainforest also "permits" a variety of crops to be grown. In western Java, for example, three crops of rice are harvested in one year; also corn, cassava, rubber, sisal, sugar, coffee, tea, and many others. Climate limits the productive activities of man, but it does not determine them. In some climates the choice is decidedly limited, in others quite wide.

THE IMPORTANT PRODUCTS OF THE WORLD

The variety of products is almost endless, but what are the *important* products of the world? Is wheat an important product? Most people would agree that it is. Is silver important? It is certainly not important in the same sense or in the same degree as wheat. Products are commonly compared by money value since it is not easy to compare the relative importance of a bushel of wheat and a pound of silver. Furthermore, in a brief

FIGURE 1.4. *Loading Chilean nitrate for export. In Chile there are large reserves of this material— a necessity in the fertilizer, chemical, and munitions industries. The development of synthetic nitrate, however, has caused a serious decline in Chilean production. From CIAA.*

FIGURE 1.5. *Mahogany logs in the Escondido River near Bluefields, Nicaragua. These logs are ready to load on a steamer for shipment to New Orleans or some other port in the middle latitudes where they will be converted into veneers and plywood. From CIAA.*

discussion it is best to separate primary products or raw materials from manufactured items, since it is scarcely logical to compare a bushel of wheat with the flour produced from it. The method of comparison by values is not without objections. Prices vary in different parts of the world, but allowances can be made for these variations and the small inevitable errors will not distort the picture of world production very much.

A complete list of the important products of the world would run to great length. In the list below, the more valuable products are grouped in 16 categories.

1. Milk
2. Meat
3. Hay and forage
4. Cereals and sugar
5. Fruits and vegetables
6. Coffee, tea, and cacao
7. Wine and hops
8. Tobacco
9. Vegetable oils
10. Textiles
11. Rubber
12. Wood products
13. Metals
14. Nonmetallic minerals
15. Fuels and power
16. Manufactures, highly varied

Milk includes all kinds used by man but not butter and cheese, which are manufactured products. Meat includes beef, veal, pork, ham, bacon, lard, mutton, goat, and fish. Hay and forage include fodder, barley, oats, corn, root forage, and oil cake; obviously some of these items are used also for human food. The cereals—wheat, rye, and rice—are grouped with cane and beet sugar because all are used largely as energy foods. Coffee, tea, and cacao are used as beverages. The chief vegetable oils are cottonseed, linseed, rapeseed, hempseed, sesame, soybean, copra, peanut, palm nut, babassu, olive, and (for the sake of convenience) whale oil. The principal wood products are softwood lumber, pulp, cabinet woods (FIG. 1.5), and tanning materials. The nonmetallic minerals include cement, asbestos, salt, graphite, mica, sulfur, natural phosphates and nitrates, guano, potash, and basic slag. Fuels and power are derived from coal, lignite, petroleum, natural gas, and hydroelectric energy. Manufacturing

is the most varied of all production types. In this discussion it includes only the products of complex manufacturing. Commodities which are only slightly processed are considered as raw materials.

STRATEGIC MATERIALS

In many respects it is right and proper to evaluate the importance of a product by its total dollar value. By using this method we emphasize the common everyday things, such as milk, meat, and coal, which are widespread and comparatively abundant. Many people are more interested in items which are scarce and difficult to obtain. The term "strategic" came into general use in 1939 when the Army and Navy Munitions Board issued a report entitled "Strategic and Critical Raw Materials," in which "strategic materials" were defined as those essential in wartime to the national defense, but which must be obtained in large part from territory outside continental United States. A list of 72 items was included in the report, divided into first, second, and third priorities, depending on what proportion of the commodity, if any, could be obtained in the United States. For example, in the first priority were tin and rubber (FIG. 1.6) since practically none of these are produced in the United States. In the third priority was aluminum, which later became more abundant as new refining plants were constructed. Other minerals on the list were antimony, chromium, manganese, tungsten, mercury, mica, and quartz crystal. Tropical products included rubber, manila fiber, and quinine. Other products were wool, optical glass, and silk. It will be noted that, in spite of the fact that many of the sources of the articles were cut off by the war, the scarcity of some has been felt more acutely than that of others, either because larger quantities were needed, or because stock piles were small, or because of the lack of substitutes.

In addition to concern for these strategic war materials, more interest was aroused in certain peacetime products because of the scarcity arising from war conditions. Thus the interest in sugar, coffee, and bananas (FIG. 1.7) was much greater as these commodities became scarce than it was in wheat, corn, and cotton, which are usually more abundant. To this list of "peacetime" strategic materials we must add palm oil, cacao, tea, copra, and many other tropical fruits and vegetable oils.

Obviously many of the wartime strategic materials are also of great peacetime significance.

As strategic materials become even scarcer, substitutes are sought and frequently found. The new material may then become a competitor with the old. Rayon competes with silk; hemp and sisal with manila fiber. Wood and plastics may replace metal in part. Some of the substitutes are improved to the point where they permanently replace the original product. For example, nylon, a synthetic fiber, has proved more satisfactory for many purposes than silk.

SHIFTS IN WORLD PRODUCTION

Nearly thirty years ago the productive activity of a small iron mine in eastern Kentucky came suddenly to an end. From the local point of view the reason was obscure: the mining operations were simple, and the ore was close to the surface, making it necessary to remove only a few feet of soil and loose rock to expose the iron-bearing formation. By means of steam shovels, tiny in comparison with those of today, the overburden of soil was scraped away, and the ore was scooped up and loaded on cars bound for the steel mills. The cost of mining was low, but the ore was not of high quality and production in large quantities was not possible, although the deposit was by no means exhausted. Today the open pits are all but obliterated by the briars, weeds, and thickets of scrub oak and sassafras. Why did production stop? Some years earlier, men seeking ore had discovered and developed the Mesabi Range in Minnesota, as well as other iron mines in the Upper Great Lakes Region. There the ore was excellent, it was easy to mine in large quantities, and furthermore it could be transported cheaply on the Great Lakes to the vicinity of the coalfields. As a result, this mine and scores of other small mines in the Appalachian Region could no longer compete.

Changes in world production are not always

FIGURE 1.6. *Tapping rubber trees and collecting latex on a rubber plantation in Honduras. Synthetic rubber has made heavy inroads on the natural rubber market. From CIAA.*

FIGURE 1.7. *Harvesting bananas on a Guatemalan plantation. One man cuts the "stem" with a knife attached to a long pole while the other worker catches it. Bananas are heavy and perishable, and most plantations are located near the coast. From CIAA.*

unfortunate, either for the region directly concerned or for any other district. Many changes are
slow, all but imperceptible to the people involved.
For example, fifty years ago southern Minnesota
was a great wheat country; most of the cropland
was devoted to this crop, and there were many
local flour mills. Little corn was grown and only
slight attention was paid to livestock. Gradually
a change took place. Not only were the crops
changed, but an entirely new type of farming was
introduced. The growing of wheat was decreased;
the growing of corn and hay was increased. Livestock for meat and milk became the focus of the
farmers' attention. In short, farmers replaced the
"wheat belt" with the "corn belt" and the
"dairy belt," and in turn they advanced wheat
growing into the grazing region, which caused the
cattle range to be moved still farther west. On
the whole, the effect was a general increase in the
intensity of production without serious loss to
any of the regions involved.

Usually, however, what is one region's loss is
another's gain. In the early days of rubber production, Brazil had what amounted to a monopoly.
It had the climate, the land, and millions of wild
rubber trees, from which latex could be had for
the tapping. Skilled labor is required for tapping
on a permanent basis, and such labor was not
available in Brazil, at least not in the rubber region. As a result, the Brazilian rubber tree was
transplanted to Malaya and the East Indies, where
there was an abundance of docile and teachable
labor. Earlier the coffee tree, native to Ethiopia,
had been shifted to Arabia, India, Java, and eventually to Brazil—a sort of advance payment,
perhaps, for the loss of rubber. The potato, native to the Andean Highlands of Peru and Bolivia,
finally found its greatest development in northern
Europe, where it is used widely as feed for livestock, as well as food for man.

These are individual examples in the changing
world pattern of production, which like a mighty
maze is complex but has order and reason. It is
easy to say that all changes are caused by competition, but the generalization is not very meaningful. In particular, the shifts in world production
are associated with changing demands, new inventions and discoveries, substitutions of cheaper
or better products, improved transportation,
tariffs, trade agreements, and boycotts. These
factors reach the most remote regions and affect the most primitive as well as the most complex forms of production.

Because of World War II the pattern of production was changed, not only in the countries
involved in the war but in the whole world. The
effects on production have yet to run their course.
The most obvious result of the war was the interruption of communications. Commodities which
were carried by ships were affected. People who
depended on the export of a few commodities for
a large share of the national income suffered
heavily. People of countries which had a well-
rounded production and were most nearly self-
sufficient suffered the least, immediately, from
the indirect results of the war; those depending
most on the import of raw materials were the
hardest hit. Another powerful factor in changed
production was the shift from peacetime to wartime production. In many countries this meant
merely the stepping-up of certain types of production which formerly were nearly static, such
as the production of larger quantities of milk,
meat, and eggs in the United States for export in
the Lend-Lease program. It is worth noting that
in the early years of the war the wheat regions
benefited little because of the enormous reserves
of wheat already available. After the war, wheat
(FIG. 1.8) became scarce, temporarily. Another
important effect of the war on production was the
stimulation of the production of strategic materials of all kinds, and also the search for substitute products and new areas of production.

Some of the effects of the war were temporary,
while others will last indefinitely. The development of synthetic rubber, new fibers, and, above
all, atomic energy will have long lasting effects.
So will the partial exhaustion of the iron ore in
the Mesabi Range and of the bauxite of Arkansas.

SOME IMPLICATIONS OF WORLD PRODUC-
TION FOR THE UNITED STATES

From the United States we export surplus products, and we import some of the surpluses of
other countries. This practice is similar to that of
most countries. We are almost unique, however,
in having surpluses that consist both of manufactured goods and of agricultural and mineral
products in the raw state. This combination of
surpluses introduces a number of problems. Our
surplus of cotton competes in the markets of
Europe with that of Brazil, Egypt, and India. Our

FIGURE 1.8. *When wheat became scarce after World War II, the acreage and production in the United States expanded rapidly. This field near Sturgis, South Dakota, produced 20 bushels to the acre in a district too dry for cultivation in some years. From Soil Conservation Service.*

wheat competes with that of Argentina, Canada, and Australia. At the same time, we export manufactured goods—automobiles, machinery, iron, and steel—to the countries with which we are in competition for the raw material markets Since we are well supplied with most of the raw materials and the manufactured products which we need, it is difficult for the people of other countries to export to us, particularly since both our own manufacturers and producers of raw materials demand tariffs protecting the price of their products.

Although we are more nearly self-sufficient than people of any other country, we are dependent on various parts of the world for certain products. From Canada comes nickel, copper, asbestos, lumber, paper, and part of our refined aluminum. From Middle America we receive cane sugar, bananas, sisal, oil, manganese, and other minerals. Cane sugar from Cuba competes with beet sugar produced in Colorado, Utah, and other states and also with cane sugar produced in Louisiana and Florida. If it were not for a protective tariff, beet sugar could not be grown profitably in the United States.

Oil, tin, nitrate, coffee, cacao, wool, and some rubber are exported from South America to the United States. Since coal is lacking in both Middle America and South America, it will be very difficult for extensive manufactures to be set up there. Raw agricultural and mineral products for the most part will continue to be exported from these regions, and certain manufactures will be imported, but the people of South America are becoming more and more self-sufficient in certain industrial articles, such as iron and steel, textiles, clothing, and processed foods.

Africa, the second largest and in many ways the least developed continent, consists almost entirely of colonial possessions of European powers. By position and political affiliation, Africa apparently means little to the United States. Increasing quantities of cacao, palm oil, diamonds, copper, and other minerals are exported from Africa to the United States, however. With the coming development of the "dark" continent, more tropical products can move to the United States in return for industrial products, upon which the progress of Africa depends. In a very real sense, the undeveloped portions of Africa and South America are rivals as potential suppliers of tropical products, such as rubber, cacao, palm oil, and cabinet woods, to the United States. On the other hand, we face especially keen competition from the British and other European people in selling our manufactured goods in their colonies or dominions.

About one fifth of the external trade of the United States has been with Europe, a continent which is clearly deficient in raw materials but well provided with resources and "know how" for industrial production. A great variety of manufactured products ranging from woolens to scientific instruments, and from furs and newsprint to wines, is exported from Europe to the United States. In turn, we supply Europe both with raw materials, such as wheat, meat, and cotton, and with finished goods, such as automobiles, agricultural machinery, and petroleum products.

In many respects our trade with Asia has been more significant than that with any other continent, both in terms of dollar volume and in the strategic nature of the commodities. Formerly raw silk was the most important import, but war-interrupted imports of rubber, tin, tung oil, manila fiber, tea, copra, and quinine were felt most severely in the United States. Because of the large labor supply in southeastern Asia and the favorable climate for tropical production, more plantation crops are produced there than in any other part of the world. It will be a long time before similar production will be possible in the tropical portions of Africa and South America.

The whole pattern of trade with Oceania was changed by World War II. Formerly the products of Australia and New Zealand were traded largely with western Europe, partly because of political, cultural, and economic ties and partly because of the limited demand for these products in North America. With Europe cut off during the war and weakened afterward, the peoples of Oceania turned to North America for much of their finished goods, exporting in turn wool, meat, hides, dairy products, and some minerals.

The preceding paragraphs have indicated that a significant part of the normal life of the United States is essentially international life. The problems of the world must be solved by a realistic approach, taking into consideration the physical and human resources of each major region. Not all problems are those of production and trade,

MATERIALS CONSUMED BY FREE COUNTRIES

(From *Resources for Freedom*, a report by the President's Material Policy Commission, 1952, Vol. I, p. 1.)

The United States in 1950 Consumed These Materials		Other Free Countries in 1950 Consumed These Materials
2,350,000,000 barrels	PETROLEUM	1,274,000,000 barrels
1,320,000 long tons*	RUBBER	825,000 long tons
1,800,000 short tons**	MANGANESE ORE	1,400,000 short tons
130,000,000 short tons	IRON ORE (50% Fe)	105,000,000 short tons
1,081,000 short tons	ZINC	1,061,000 short tons
1,255,000 short tons	COPPER	1,343,000 short tons
784,000 short tons	LEAD	844,000 short tons

 * 2240 pounds per ton
** 2000 pounds per ton

but these items are of fundamental concern in any discussion of international adjustment. We do need to know more of how the "other half" lives.

In war or peace the inquiring student of production geography finds himself in a world far from static. The geography of yesterday is not that of today or tomorrow, even though some of the elements are relatively changeless. The first question is: "Where are goods produced?" Other questions follow. "Under what conditions?" "Why are these goods produced here?" "What changes in production are taking place there?" "What are the implications of production?" The last two questions are more difficult, but even partial answers contribute to a vivid awareness of our world.

2

The Major Types of Production

Most people are fairly familiar with the district in which they live and with the nature and background of production in that district. They know the hills and valleys, the rivers, the climate, the people, the important products, and the conditions under which they are produced. A farmer in our Corn Belt, for example, knows his own county. He knows the standard crops—corn, wheat, oats, and hay—how they are grown and also the significance of livestock for meat and milk production. If mines and factories are present, he knows about them too. Everyone thinks of production in terms of individual items such as wheat, coal, electricity, or shoes. Likewise production *units* are generally understood. Familiar production units are farms, ranches, plantations, logging camps, mines, and factories. The recurrent features of similar production units may be described as a production *type*, a corn belt, for example. Each production type, in turn, is represented by one or more production *regions*, such as the Corn Belt of the United States or of Argentina. Some characteristics of the type, to be sure, vary from region to region, just as they do from unit to unit. The fundamental qualities remain reasonably constant, however, making it possible to organize the study of production around a few types, rather than in terms of a long list of single products. Other production types, widely known, although not usually clearly defined, are wheat farming, dairy farming, grazing, fishing, lumbering, mining, and manufacturing. It should be noted that the names of *types* and *regions* are often similar or identical. The context usually makes the distinction clear.

In practice each production type is characterized by its chief products or product combina-tions. A corn belt, for example, is not merely a type in which corn is the major crop; the significant quality is the production of corn, hay, oats, and other forage crops used to fatten meat animals, or for sale. The usual final product of the corn belt is meat: beef, pork, lamb, and poultry. Corn is exported from some regions while in others it is used for food. Cash crops such as wheat, soybeans, and tobacco add substantially to many farmers' incomes but are of secondary importance in defining the type.

In order to avoid undue length and complexity in the study of economic geography, the number of production types described is kept at a minimum. No attempt is made to cover all possible combinations of production, but rather to present the major kinds of production on the earth. In some areas, such as ice caps, tundras, and the driest parts of the deserts, very little or nothing is produced, and these areas are passed over without mention. Minor differences are given little attention, although an effort is made to point out significant contrasts in the various production regions of the same type. It will be shown (Chapter 19), for example, that in the Argentine Corn Belt, unlike the United States Corn Belt, "flint" corn is grown rather than the "dent" variety and a large proportion of the crop is exported. Considering, therefore, the limitations of space as well as the complexity of the subject, it seems advisable to describe world production under seven major categories, subdivided to form nineteen types. The types are designated by number and letter to facilitate note taking and representation on maps and graphs. It should be remembered that the definitions of the types and their representation on maps are generalized.

```
┌─────────────────────────────────────────┐
│            PRODUCTION TYPES              │
│                                          │
│   1. COMMERCIAL FISHING                  │
│                                          │
│   2. FOREST PRODUCTION                   │
│        2h  Hardwood forest production    │
│        2s  Softwood forest production    │
│                                          │
│   3. GRAZING                             │
│        3c  Commercial grazing            │
│        3n  Nomadic herding               │
│                                          │
│   4. COMMERCIAL AGRICULTURE              │
│        4w  Wheat belt farming            │
│        4c  Corn belt farming             │
│        4s  Small grain and livestock farming │
│        4d  Dairy farming                 │
│        4m  Mediterranean agriculture     │
│        4h  Horticulture                  │
│        4p  Plantation farming            │
│        4o  Oasis farming                 │
│                                          │
│   5. SUBSISTENCE AGRICULTURE             │
│        5e  Extensive subsistence agriculture │
│        5rp Oriental agriculture: rice and │
│            plantation crops              │
│        5rg Oriental agriculture: rice and │
│            winter grains                 │
│        5m  Oriental agriculture: millet  │
│                                          │
│   6. MINING                              │
│                                          │
│   7. MANUFACTURING                       │
└─────────────────────────────────────────┘
```

DESCRIPTION OF PRODUCTION TYPES

1. COMMERCIAL FISHING, the production of fish and related products for sale, is represented by a variety of production units. A salmon trap with a nearby cannery in a narrow sea inlet in Alaska called a fjord; a "fisherman's wharf" on the coast of Newfoundland and in most of the harbors of the world; a Diesel-powered trawler on the Iceland "banks," searching the bottom for cod; all these and many more are variants of commercial fishing. The Alaskan fjord (FIG. 2.1) will serve as a specific example. The fjord itself is a sort of funnel-like trap on its narrow inland margin. The salmon, seeking the fresh water of the river, strike for the upper end and there, in the narrow passage, are easily trapped. A scow brings tons of the fish to the cannery since the fjord is so remote that it is difficult and expensive to market fresh fish. Most commercial fishing is limited to the shallow margins of the oceans, the "salmon rivers," and to a few inland seas such as the Caspian and the Great Lakes. Some commercial fishing is found in almost every sizable river and lake, but the value of such fisheries is small. Under Commercial Fishing, products of the sea which may not properly be called fish, such as oysters, shrimp, sponges, pearls, and whales, are usually included.

The chief fishing grounds of the world are in the Northern Hemisphere, in fairly high latitudes. Most productive are the "banks" near New England and eastern Canada, the coastal margins of northwestern North America, northwestern Europe, and the east coast of Asia. Most fish are taken in waters with a depth of 600 feet or less and within a hundred miles of shore.

2. FOREST PRODUCTION extends from the Equator to the Arctic Circle and includes a variety of products from lumber and pulp to chicle, wild rubber, quinine, and palm oil. Two broad types of forest, hardwood and softwood, are readily distinguished, but in many areas mixed forests are to be found. In the middle latitudes it is common practice to define the hardwoods as the deciduous varieties, such as oak, maple, birch, poplar, and gum, and the softwoods as the coniferous varieties, such as pine, fir, and spruce. This distinction will not hold, however, in the tropical areas where the broad-leaved trees are evergreen. It is better to define the hardwoods simply as broad-leaved and the softwoods as needle-leaved.

In the regional discussions to follow, it will be necessary to distinguish forest production from agriculture and grazing. Since agriculture usually represents more intensive use of the land, the limit between agriculture and forest may be set at the line where 10 per cent of the land is used for agriculture. The distinction between grazing and forest production is generally easy because of the striking difference in vegetation, although in some districts grazing invades the forests.

Hardwood Forests (2h) are widely scattered from the equatorial rainforests to the higher latitudes, but most of the middle latitude areas have been cleared to make way for agriculture. The largest stands today are in the tropics. In Amazonia in South America, in the Congo country of Africa, and in southeastern Asia there are large areas of tropical forests where lumber, cabinet woods, dyewoods, quebracho for tanning, Brazil

FIGURE 2.1. *A scow load of salmon at the cannery in an Alaskan fjord. In narrow portion of the fjord seen in the distance, there are many favorable sites for fish traps, while because of the deep water, steamers are able to come into the cannery. From U. S. Fish and Wildlife Service.*

nuts, rubber, and palm oil are produced. Production in most of these areas is still essentially a gathering economy. The natives collect the wild fruits, nuts, and other materials for their own use or for sale. Agriculture, although difficult for a number of reasons, is possible in most parts of the tropical forest. In many areas shifting cultivation can be seen, as the natives move their small patches from time to time because the fertility of the tropical soils is quickly exhausted. In some districts the planters have invaded the rainforest since the demand for some tropical products, such as cacao, bananas, and rubber, far exceeds the wild supply.

In the middle latitudes hardwood forests are limited to remnants of the original areas, but production is greater than in the tropics because of nearness to the markets, purer stands, and better working conditions. Good though small stands of oak, maple, and gum are still to be found in North America in areas not suited for agriculture, while in Europe certain areas of forest are carefully tended and replanted after the manner of a tree crop. But it is obvious that the scarcity of temperate hardwoods will lead to the increased exploitation of the tropical forests in the immediate future.

Softwood Forests (2S) occupy a broad zone in the Northern Hemisphere from Alaska to Labrador and from Norway to eastern Siberia. Smaller areas often mixed with hardwoods occur as remnants in the agricultural regions and in some middle latitude districts not suitable for farming. Only a few small areas are to be found in the Southern Hemisphere, mainly in Brazil and Chile. The softwood forests are of great importance commercially but lack the variety of products found in the hardwoods. The chief products are lumber (FIG. 2.2), pulp for paper, furs, and minerals. Since much of the land is rough or mountainous, it is a major source of water power. Production is on a highly organized and competitive basis and large parts of the forests in Canada, northern United States, Sweden, Finland, and northern Russia have been cut over. The lakes, the rivers, and the cool summer climate

attract millions of tourists and the numerous resorts and hotels account for more income than the lumber and pulp in some districts.

3. GRAZING is the dominant form of land use in the drier lands where neither forestry nor agriculture is feasible. Some humid regions where agriculture has not yet been established are also used for grazing. Grasses and other forage plants will support cattle, sheep, goats, or other grazing animals although large areas of land are necessary. The two main requirements are grass and water. In the drier lands, the deserts, these are usually insufficient.

Two types of grazing are distinguished: commercial, in which most of the products are sold; nomadic, in which the pastoral peoples wander from place to place in search of grass and water, selling very little. The limit between agricultural and grazing regions generally is drawn through points with 10 per cent of the land in crops. It should be emphasized here that the density of livestock in the grazing lands is very low and

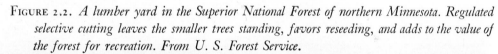

FIGURE 2.2. *A lumber yard in the Superior National Forest of northern Minnesota. Regulated selective cutting leaves the smaller trees standing, favors reseeding, and adds to the value of the forest for recreation. From U. S. Forest Service.*

FIGURE 2.3. *Sheep raising in western Canada near Kamloops, B. C. Grasslands on the margins of the forests furnish excellent pasturage. From National Film Board of Canada.*

that most of the meat animals of the world are to be found in the *humid* agricultural regions.

Commercial Grazing (3c) is limited largely to the semiarid parts of the more recently settled continents, North America, South America, Africa, and Australia. In these lands meat, wool (FIG. 2.3). mohair. and hides are produced for export on ranches. The ranch sites are permanently located and, although the livestock may range over rather wide areas, the "migrations" are restricted. If sufficient water is available, forage crops for winter feed are irrigated. If water is more abundant, fruits, sugar beets, and other cash crops may be irrigated. Dry farming of small

grains is possible in some districts, especially in the wetter years, but commercial grazing is the characteristic form of production. The Great Plains of the United States, the Dry Pampas of Argentina, the Great Karoo of South Africa, and the Artesian Basin of Australia are outstanding examples of commercial grazing.

In the tropical grasslands Savanna Grazing represents a slight variant of the commercial type. In these lands with summer rain and winter drought, such as the Llanos of Venezuela, the Campos of southern interior Brazil, and the Sudan south of the Sahara in Africa, conditions are less favorable than in the middle latitudes. In many places the winters are too dry, the grasses are too coarse, and the livestock diseases too destructive for grazing. Nevertheless some hides, hoofs, horns, and meat are exported. Sheep do not generally thrive in the savanna lands although they have done fairly well in West Africa. Most of the savanna lands are not used intensively at the present, except in the Orient, where rice is grown on the wetter lands, millet and small grains in the drier sections. In the future development of the relatively empty savanna lands, agriculture will probably become more important than grazing.

Nomadic Herding (3n) is the tribal grazing of domestic animals principally cattle, sheep, and goats, with some donkeys, horses, camels, and yaks. It is the primitive subsistence form of animal husbandry confined largely to the desert borderlands of the Old World, where the land is too dry for crops but supports a sparse growth of grass. Two elements are necessary for nomadic existence—grass and water. In no part of the Nomadic Herding regions are both sufficient all the year round. Therefore, the people migrate seasonally, or whenever grass or water becomes scarce in one locality.

Animals furnish most of the food and the raw materials for clothing, shelter, and simple implements of the nomads. Their diet is mostly milk, cheese, and meat, together with the grain which may be obtained from agriculturists in the neighboring oases. Barter and trade are limited, however.

Few statistics are available for the Nomadic Herding regions so it is difficult to show them all correctly on a map. The largest region extends all the way from the western Sahara to Mongolia, and from the Urals to southern Arabia. Smaller regions are to be found in northern Siberia, Lapland in northern Europe, and in parts of North America inhabited by reindeer Eskimo.

4. COMMERCIAL AGRICULTURE includes various types of farming in which a large proportion of the crops or other products of the farm are sold; in many cases they may be exported. On a coffee plantation, for example, most of the coffee is exported, only a small part of the crop being consumed locally. On a Corn Belt farm if meat is the chief item sold, then the corn is fed to the livestock and is considered a subsistence crop. All gradations are to be found, from the nearly pure commercial unit such as a wheat farm to a subsistence economy in which all the products are consumed locally. Obviously numerous borderline examples will be encountered. In the eight types of Commercial Agriculture described in the following pages more than half of the principal products are sold from the farm in one form or another. Some crops, cotton, rubber, sisal, sugar beets, and many others, are not suitable for consumption until processed in a factory. See FIGURE 2.5.

The *Wheat Belt* (4w) is a highly specialized type of agriculture, in which small grain is the dominant element. Wheat belts are usually located in areas too dry for the production of forage crops, such as hay and corn. Farms are large, often exceeding 1000 acres, but the yields are low chiefly because of the light rainfall. Heavy power machinery is used to till, sow, and harvest the crops; therefore only a few men and generally no draft animals are required. Livestock for meat or dairy purposes is of little significance and those present in the region are likely to belong to commercial grazing rather than to the wheat farms. Some units, however, are essentially combinations of wheat farms and ranches. Nearly all the wheat, barley, oats, flax, and other crops are exported from the wheat belts, largely to manufacturing districts. See FIGURE 2.5. Very little of the product is consumed on the farm, and this is probably the most completely commercial type of farming in the world. It is, therefore, highly dependent upon and sensitive to world market conditions. The chief regions of this type are the great surplus wheat producing districts of the world, including the winter and spring wheat belts of North America, the wheat belts of Argentina, southern Russia, and Australia. Wheat is grown in other types of agriculture, usually as a secondary crop. The wheat belts are distinguished from the grazing regions by having more than 10 per cent of the total area as crops, and from the more humid farming regions by low proportion of livestock to crops, less than 20 animal units per 100 acres of cropland. (An animal unit is one cow or one horse, five hogs, or seven sheep.)

The *Corn Belt* (4c) is sometimes designated as the corn, hay, wheat, and livestock belt, in order to emphasize the fact that corn is not the only product. But corn is usually the major crop because of its value in fattening beef cattle, hogs,

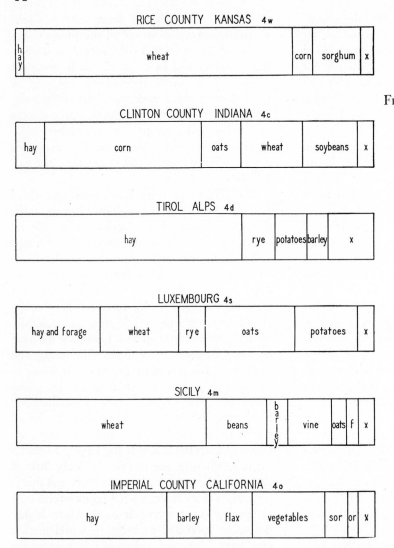

RICE COUNTY KANSAS 4w

| hay | wheat | corn | sorghum | x |

CLINTON COUNTY INDIANA 4c

| hay | corn | oats | wheat | soybeans | x |

TIROL ALPS 4d

| hay | rye | potatoes | barley | x |

LUXEMBOURG 4s

| hay and forage | wheat | rye | oats | potatoes | x |

SICILY 4m

| wheat | beans | barley | vine | oats | f | x |

IMPERIAL COUNTY CALIFORNIA 4o

| hay | barley | flax | vegetables | sor | or | x |

FIGURE 2.4. *Crop graphs for six types of commercial agriculture, wheat belt (4w), corn belt (4c), dairying (4d), small grain and livestock (4s), Mediterranean Agriculture (4m), and oasis (4o). Areas are proportional to the percentage of cropped land. Note especially the varying proportion of hay, wheat, and corn. Abbreviations:* f, *forage crops;* sor, *sorghum;* or, *orchards;* x, *miscellaneous crops.*

lambs, and poultry for the market. Furthermore, the cultivation and harvesting of corn is one of the chief tasks of the farmer. Oats, wheat, barley, and grain sorghums are used as supplementary feeds, but hay is the second crop in value. A portion of the cultivated land is also used for pasture. In addition to the large numbers of animals bred and raised on the farms, many corn belt regions import young meat animals ("feeders") from the nearby commercial grazing regions for fattening and resale. The principal business of the corn belt farm is the production of meat or corn for sale, but if the unit is near a city there is often considerable milk production. Wheat, soybeans, tobacco, flax, and other cash crops are frequently grown, supplementing the farmer's income. Most of the corn belts of the world are located on fertile

humid plains (FIG. 2.6) with warm summers, such as the middle west region of the United States, the humid Pampa of Argentina, and the plains of the Po and Danube rivers in Europe. The corn belts are differentiated from the other types of commercial agriculture by having more than 20 per cent of the cropland in corn and with no cash crop more than one half the corn acreage.

The *Small Grain* and *Livestock* (4s) type resembles the corn belt in many respects, but the crop and livestock patterns differ enough to deserve separate treatment. The type is represented by one large region which stretches from northern Spain to eastern European Russia. The crops (FIG. 2.4) include wheat and rye for bread, either of which may be the dominant crop, potatoes for food and feed, oats, barley, and hay. Sugar beets, flax, grapes, deciduous fruits (fruits from deciduous trees) and other cash crops are grown in some localities. The products sold from the farm include meat, dairy products, and grain, but the farms in the eastern part of the region consume a large portion of the produce. The great handicap of this region is the cool summers not suitable for the growth of corn or similar crops, but since a large portion of this region is near the great manufacturing belt of Europe there is a large market for grains, meat, milk, and other foods. This type is distinguished by the almost complete absence of corn. Wheat and rye together occupy more than 10 per cent of the cropland, and the tilled crops are greater than hay and pasture combined. It is essentially a mixed type of farming, producing grain, potatoes, meat, and milk for sale.

Commercial Dairying (4d) is characterized by intensive milk production with large acreages of hay and pasture and smaller areas of grain and other crops. This type appears in regions too cool

or too wet for wheat or corn, or in the vicinity of large cities where the demand for milk and milk products is very heavy. The cultivated crops (FIG. 2.4), grown largely for dairy feed, are silage corn, oats, barley, potatoes, beets, and coarse turnips. The potato and some other crops are used for food also. The product sold from the dairy region depends on the location with respect to the market but in any case the fundamental product is milk whether exported in the fluid form, dried or condensed, or in the form of butter and cheese. Most dairy farms also have some meat animals for sale.

Many variations in detail are shown in the large dairy regions of the Alps, northwestern Europe, Australia, and in northeastern United States and the smaller regions in Washington, Oregon, and Argentina. All may be distinguished from the other types of Commercial Agriculture by the large milk production in proportion to the cropland, more than 50 gallons per acre per year. The ratio of hay to grain is also high, as is dairy

FIGURE 2.5. *Harvesting sugar beets near Woodland, California. The level floor of the Sacramento Valley lends itself to irrigation and the use of machinery. From the Sugar Research Foundation.*

FIGURE 2.6. *A cornfield in Franklin County, Ohio. Notice the height of the stalks and the length of the ears. This field yielded 139 bushels to the acre. From Soil Conservation Service.*

cows to meat cattle. Although dairying is the dominant type of agriculture in the regions mentioned above, it is found, in a secondary role, in many other regions.

Mediterranean Agriculture (4m) was begun around the Mediterranean Sea and later was extended to other areas having the same type of climate. This is one of the most distinctive and universally recognized types of agriculture. The production pattern, in fact, depends on the climate with the dry season in summer, when most crops ordinarily grow, and a wet season in winter too cool for some crops but favorable for the small grains. The climate, with its dry season and a limited quantity of rain, sets a severe limitation on agriculture, but if the mountains nearby can supply additional water for irrigation a very profitable form of agriculture is possible. One quality which distinguishes this type from other commercial types is the emphasis on tree and bush crops (FIG. 2.4): the citrus and other fruits, as well as the olive which is not produced in any other production type. In addition, there is a system of winter crops such as cereals, beans, and vegetables, and a set of irrigated summer crops including vegetables, grapes, bush crops like the small berries and the deciduous fruits, which make most of their growth in the summer season. Livestock is not abundant because of the limited pasturage and forage crops. The people as a rule do not eat much meat or many dairy products. The crops with the largest acreage are the cereals, usually wheat and barley, but they do not always have the highest value. The principal regions of this type are in Spain, Italy, Greece, Turkey, North Africa, California, Middle Chile, South Africa, and to a limited extent in southern Australia. Mediterranean Agriculture is distinguished from other types by the large percentage, more than 15 per cent, of the cropland in tree and bush crops, in addition to the sharp contrast between the summer and winter crops.

Horticulture (4h) includes the truck farms, market gardens, commercial orchards and other small areas of miscellaneous agriculture not belonging to the types listed thus far. Vegetables of various kinds in season are supplied from market gardens in the vicinity of most large cities. From truck farms, often located in regions remote from markets where early vegetables and fruits can be produced, similar products (either fresh or canned) are supplied. Fruit orchards are common in many parts of the corn and dairy belts and other areas of large-scale agriculture. Other horticultural areas are often found on rough land not suitable to ordinary cultivation. Usually large quantities of fertilizer are used in the horticultural districts, and very little livestock is supported. The horticultural districts (FIG. 2.7) may be distinguished from other types by the large acreage of vegetables and fruits (more than 25 per cent of the cropland) and by one-season cropping as distinct from the Mediterranean type. Small irrigated districts in the arid regions are classified as oases for the sake of convenience, although some of them are definitely horticultural and are indicated on the maps with the symbol, 4o. In other words they are horticultural oases.

The *Plantation* (4p) is a large agricultural unit developed in the tropical or subtropical regions, which, with the aid of outside capital and management and native or cheap imported labor, produces a cash crop. In this book the term "plantation" also includes small farms in the tropics and subtropics which produce the usual plantation crops, even though all the conditions listed above are not present. Most plantations are located near coasts or on inland waterways so as to facilitate export of products. Plantations, on which are produced commodities of relatively small bulk, such as coffee (FIG. 2.8), are sometimes located inland. Also on plantations are produced most of the natural rubber, tea, cane sugar, bananas, cotton, jute, manila fibers, sisal, and many other commodities. In addition, some subsistence crops are usually grown to feed the workers (FIG. 2.7); in the New World corn, beans, and cassava; in the Old World principally rice. The regions of plantation crops are most difficult to define briefly, but in practice they may be distinguished as areas of tropical or subtropical cash crops, with subsistence crops playing a minor role.

Here and there in the arid and semiarid lands where the over-all use of the land is for grazing, there are many *Oases* (4o), small islands of irrigation standing out against the thinly scattered production of the deserts and steppes. Local supplies of water from wells and streams make it possible to cultivate a variety of crops, depending on the temperatures. Rainfall is light and of little meaning in most of the oases. Scattered, as they are, over vast expanses of the dry lands in both

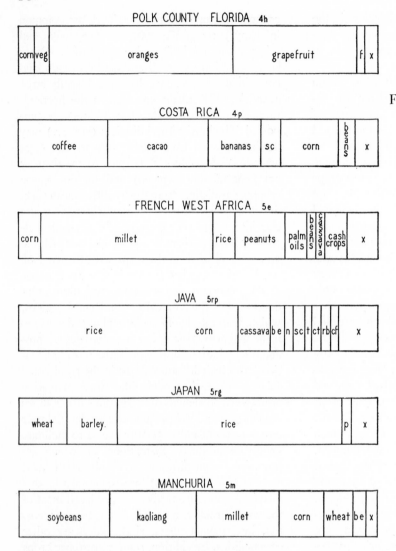

FIGURE 2.7. *Crop graphs of two commercial types of agriculture, horticulture* (4h) *and plantations* (4p); *and four subsistence types, extensive subsistence* (5e), *rice and plantation* (5rp), *rice and winter grain* (5rg), *and millet* (5m). *Notice the variety of food crops. Abbreviations:* f, *forage crops;* sc, *sugarcane;* be, *beans;* n, *nuts;* t, *tea;* ct, *cotton;* rb, *rubber;* cf, *coffee;* p, *potatoes;* veg, *vegetables;* x, *miscellaneous.*

high and low latitudes, the oases cannot be defined in terms of crops. In the Old World, from the Sahara to Mongolia, the oases are associated with Nomadic Grazing and are mostly on a subsistence basis. However, the lower Nile, the oases of Central Asiatic Russia, those of the Indus, Iraq, and some others are commercial. The oases of the New World are also commercial in character, such as the Imperial Valley in California and Mexico, with its production of alfalfa, barley, melons, lettuce, and cotton; and the Utah oasis, with alfalfa and sugar beets.

The most common crop in the oases of the New World is alfalfa, which finds a ready market in the nearby ranches. The oases may be delimited on a map as small areas of intensive irrigation in the steppe and desert lands.

5. SUBSISTENCE AGRICULTURE is widely distributed throughout the tropical and subtropical lands and can be found in some areas of the middle latitudes. In the New World corn, beans, and cassava are staples. In the Old World rice, cassava, bananas, millet, sugar, and various oil seeds are the most common crops. Since the crops are largely for home consumption, they do not enter into world trade in any quantity. Livestock are used for draft purposes but only to a slight extent for meat or milk. As a consequence, forage crops are almost lacking. The highlands of the low latitudes and parts of adjacent lowlands represent the extensive type of subsistence agriculture. In southeastern Asia subsistence agriculture is much more intensive since large amounts of labor are applied to small areas of land. Subsistence agri-

culture may be divided into four types according to kind of climate and crop:

5e   Extensive subsistence agriculture.
5rp   Oriental agriculture, rice and plantation crops.
5rg   Oriental agriculture, rice and winter grains.
5m   Oriental agriculture, millet.

Extensive Subsistence Agriculture (5e) is dominant on the uplands of Middle and South America, on the low plateaus of Africa, and in the more favorable parts of the tropical lowlands not yet invaded by the plantation. Population is generally sparse except where irrigation favors a local development of more intensive cultivation. Corn, beans, the white potato, small grains, some cotton, and tobacco are common crops (FIG. 2.7). Most crops are grown for food and all are mainly for local consumption. In the higher altitudes of this type, the conditions for crop production are similar, in many respects, to those of the middle latitudes. In a few localities Europeans have introduced their own staple crops, especially the small grains. The people of the tropical highlands, however, have not become exporters of these staple products. In the tropical lowlands much of the agriculture is intermediate in character between the shifting cultivation of the rainforest and the plantation. Some of the subsistence crops have become plantation crops, sugar and bananas, for example. Here and there within the regions of extensive subsistence agriculture, small areas of plantation tillage occur. This type is very difficult to delimit satisfactorily on a map because of the great variety of products and the lack of statistics in many areas. It includes all cultivated areas with sparse or moderate population, from which few agricultural products are sold.

Intensive subsistence agriculture with *Rice* and *Plantation Crops* (5rp) is found in the more humid parts of southeastern Asia, including southern India, Malaya, and the East Indies. Food crops (FIG. 2.7), rice, cassava, and oil seeds are cultivated intensively and, in favorable locations, plantation crops such as sugar, jute, and manila fiber, are grown for export. Rice cultivation overshadows the cash crops. Rice is grown in the wetter season in small plots or paddies by means of careful planting and, unless the rainfall is very great, with irrigation. In some places two crops of rice and a third crop of vegetables may be produced on the same land in one year. In Java are found good examples of this type of intensive production of rice, corn, and cassava for food, and of sugar, sisal, coffee, and tea for export.

FIGURE 2.8. *Coffee plantation on the plateau of São Paulo, Brazil. Coffee on gentle slopes in foreground and middle distance. The owner's house is near the center, and the smaller houses of the workers are to be seen at the left. From Rembrandt.*

FIGURE 2.9. *An oasis near Boise, Idaho. Apples and other deciduous fruits grow well on the gentle slope, while grain and hay are produced on the level land in the upper right. From Bureau of Reclamation.*

The *Rice* and *Winter Grain* (5rg) type occurs in the middle latitudes of eastern Asia, including northern India, south China and southern Japan. In these areas a distinct dry season in winter together with moderately low temperatures precludes production of most plantation crops, but the small grains will grow in the winter. Therefore, the growing of rice is alternated with wheat, barley, millet, and other similar crops (FIG. 2.7) along with smaller acreages of mulberry, cotton, tea, tobacco, sweet potatoes, and vegetables.

The *Millet* and *Grain* (5m) type of subsistence agriculture is found in those parts of the Orient where the summers are either too cool or too dry for efficient rice production. For this reason it is sometimes called the Non-Rice type. Wheat, barley, the millets, grain sorghums, which are winter crops (FIG. 2.7) in the *Rice* and *Winter*

Grain type, become summer crops (spring planting) in northern China and Manchuria. There the soybean is also a staple crop. In western India the small grains are usually grown in winter. Rice is not completely absent from this type but is grown only in small quantities.

When the definitions of the agricultural types described previously are applied casually to specific areas, there is some possibility of confusion. The regions of plantation crops, for example, appear to merge insensibly with extensive subsistence agriculture. The oases seem sometimes to conflict with horticulture, the dairy belts with small grain and livestock, and so on. A careful study of the major qualities, especially of the crop and livestock patterns, the use of the products, the methods used, and the intensity of production will usually serve to distinguish the various types, provided sufficient data are available for the area in question. In areas where two or more types are intermingled making it difficult to separate them on a map, a combination type is indicated, as suggested in the discussion of horticulture, page 25.

6. MINING is so widely distributed over the surface of the earth and in such variety that not all of the production can be assigned to regions. Many important mines are mere points on the map, mixed in with agriculture, forestry, and grazing. See FIGURE 2.10. A few definite mining regions such as the major coalfields and oilfields can be recognized and outlined on the map, but even important mining regions like the iron mines of the Mesabi of northern Minnesota and Lorraine in eastern France, the gold and diamond fields of South Africa, and the copper mines of Montana and the Belgian Congo scarcely appear as "regions" on a small-scale map. In the regional descriptions to follow, most of the mineral production will be considered along with the other types of production which cover larger areas.

For example, the minerals of the northern part of North America will be studied in Chapter 6 on North American forest production. Major attention will be given to coal, iron, petroleum, copper, and gold, although other minerals deserve special attention in some regions.

Mining is a robber economy in that the resources of a given district tend to become exhausted rather quickly. The production of oil is often exhausted from oilfields in a few years; on the other hand, coal and iron are still being produced from some fields and mines after a century of exploitation.

7. MANUFACTURING, unlike the occupation types described previously, is a secondary form of production. Through it the products of the first six broad types, called "raw materials," are processed into more usable form. Flour is milled from wheat; furniture is made from lumber; iron and steel from ore, coal, and limestone (FIG. 2.11); cotton and other fibers are woven into cloth; metals are refined and fashioned into implements.

FIGURE 2.10. *A silver and lead mine in the mountains of northern Mexico. The mine buildings and the workers' houses are perched on the edge of a canyon, spanned by the bridge. Workings are to be seen at several levels.*

FIGURE 2.11. *The steel mill is part of the Ford Rouge Plant at Dearborn, Michigan. Coal, iron ore, and limestone are assembled here to be processed by blast furnaces (center of view), converters, and rolling mills into steel. One of the characteristics of manufacturing is the concentration of productive activity in a small space. From Ford Motor Company.*

Indeed, most household goods are more or less "processed" before they reach the consumer. This means that manufacturing in the broad sense is very widely distributed and that every community, however small, has some manufacturing. But complex manufacturing is largely concentrated in a few localities, such as the northeastern United States, parts of western Europe, Russia, China, and Japan. In addition, there are hundreds of smaller manufacturing districts associated with large cities in all parts of the world. Manufacturing is largely confined to cities or their immediate vicinity, a fact which justifies the superposing of the manufacturing regions over the other production regions on a world production map. In the United States we have overlapped the Corn Belt, the Dairy Belt, and the Appalachian Coalfield with the main manufacturing region.

THE STUDY OF PRODUCTION REGIONS

In the following chapters where individual regions are studied, the first step is to delineate the region on a map. Although the name of the dominant type of production is given to the region, other forms of production are usually present. Parts of the Commercial Grazing Region of North America, for example, could be called the "Commercial Grazing-Oasis-Wheat Belt-Mining Region." Finally, it should be kept in mind that the regions as outlined in this book are generalized, and most boundary lines on maps represent transitions from one category to another. The border between the Corn Belt and Dairy Belt, for example, does not mean that no milk is produced to the south and no corn to the north. The border merely indicates where the dominance of one type disappears and the other begins.

The study of production types should, if possible, begin at home. Not only is one's information concerning one's own country likely to be more specific and complete, but by means of the geographic patterns of the homeland one is provided with a framework around which knowledge of distant lands can be built. Yet it is a mistake to assume, as some do, that one knows everything about one's own country. Above all, frequent comparisons should be made between various regions and countries, noting what products are exchanged.

To this end the production regions of North America are studied first, and this study is followed by a discussion of the other regions of the world belonging to the same type. Chapter 5, for example, describes the fishing regions of North America, followed by a discussion of similar banks in various parts of the world.

It is evident that the geography of production is not to be understood by the study of products alone. Only by a study of all the significant geographic elements within the production region is it possible to understand the devious pattern of production. Therefore material on the background of production in the Americas and in the other continents is introduced in the next chapters.

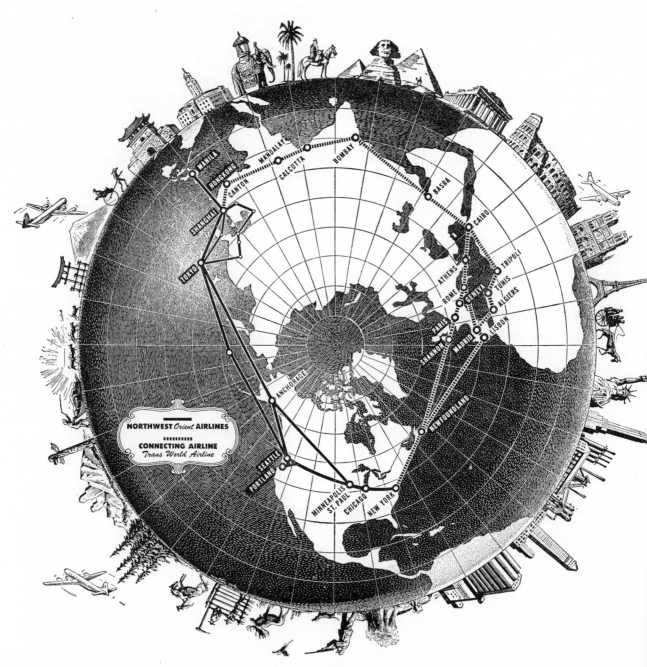

FIGURE 3.1. *Position of North America. Relatively short routes around or across the North Pole connect North America, western Europe, Russia, and eastern Asia. Why are these routes significant? From Northwest Airlines.*

3

The Geographic Background of Production
in the Americas

North America

FOR more than three centuries many people looked upon North America as a barrier between Europe and Asia. Columbus and his contemporary explorers were not looking *for* North America; they were seeking an easy all-ocean route from western Europe to eastern Asia. To them it was a disappointing fact that the Americas, particularly North America, lay across their course. Today it is highly significant that North America is fairly close to both western Europe and eastern Asia. Far from being a barrier North America has become an important link in northern hemisphere communications. If one were able to look down on North America from above the North Pole the strategic location of the continent, with respect to other important areas in the Northern Hemisphere, would be clearly seen. See FIGURE 3.1. The routes across the north Atlantic between eastern North America and western Europe are well established. Likewise, the north Pacific routes to Asia are fixed. With the coming of the Air Age, however, the routes across the Arctic are of great significance. From a point in the interior of the continent, such as Chicago, an airplane following the great circle course to western Europe would travel across Greenland. To get to Moscow an airplane would follow a course almost over the North Pole. To reach Japan the flight would go over the heart of Alaska.

It should be pointed out that the position of North America is no better from the standpoint of communication than that of northern Europe; but North America does have equal access, along with western Europe, Russia, and Japan, to the great human agglomerations of the Northern Hemisphere. In addition, North America has equal or better access to important areas in the Southern Hemisphere; to South America; to the west coast of Africa, which is destined for rapid development; to the south Pacific, which is far away but the inhabitants of which are *inclined* more and more to trade with and adopt the culture of North Americans. By its very position in the world, as well as its resources and its people, this continent is destined to play a much greater part in the affairs of the world in the future than it has ever played in the past.

Of the six continents North America is the third largest in size. It contains more than $8\frac{1}{2}$ million square miles. It is smaller than Asia and Africa and slightly larger than South America. In population North America with almost 200 million people is third among the continents. It is large enough to have a great variety of surface, broad plains, plateaus, and lofty mountains. The climate ranges from arctic cold to moist tropic heat. It is sufficiently extensive to have a great abundance of natural resources, soils, forests, and minerals.

Perhaps the most significant fact about North America is its youth, so far as the development of resources is concerned. Unlike western Europe and eastern Asia, North America has been effectively occupied by men for little more than a century and a half. To be sure, there are few or no productive areas on the continent which have not been occupied, and some of the natural wealth such as the forests has been depleted. On the other hand, many resources have not been fully utilized. North America is capable of much greater development, is capable of supporting more people, or is capable of supporting the present population at a higher standard of living than it has in the past.

SURFACE FEATURES

In the North American continent, from the Arctic to Panama, is included a wide variety of surface features, by means of which, together with the climate, mineral resources, soils, character of the peoples, and other factors, opportunities for many kinds of productive activity are afforded. Parts of the continent, however, are by their very nature unproductive. These various factors of the environment (using the term in the broad sense to include man and man-made features) belong to a complex pattern which functions as a unit. It is advisable, before studying the production of North America, to examine some of these factors individually.

The *Continental Shelf* is the margin of the continent which lies beneath the shallow seas (FIG. 3.2). This region has a definite place in the production pattern because of the importance of commercial fisheries and because of the character of coastal features through which easy access to the land is allowed or impeded. On the eastern border of the continent, the continental shelf extends as a broad band from Labrador to Panama. On the western side, the shelf is much less conspicuous, but broad shallow areas exist in a few localities. The depth of water over the continental shelf is rarely over 600 feet, and in many places there are shallow areas, known as "banks," which are favorable for commercial fishing.

The Atlantic-Gulf *Coastal Lowland* extends from Cape Cod, Massachusetts, to Yucatán, Mexico, as a low, gently sloping belt of varying width (FIG. 3.2). In general, it is a smooth plain with no surface features which might interfere with the production or movement of goods. However, there are many swamps, unproductive sandy areas, and, in the Mexican portion, a few low mountains rising above the general level. Because of the wide latitudinal extent, considerable variety of climate, natural vegetation, and production is found in the lowlands. The driest parts are in southern Texas and northwestern Yucatán.

The *Appalachian Highland* reaches from Newfoundland to central Alabama (FIG. 3.2) as a moderately high range of mountains with associated plateaus, uplands, and hill country. The maximum elevation is about 6700 feet. The general trend is northeast-southwest, almost parallel to the coastline for a distance of nearly 2000 miles.

The easternmost division of the southern Appalachians is the Piedmont, with low, rounded hills and residual soils over hard rock. To the west is the Blue Ridge, mostly forested, over 6000 feet high in the south and declining gradually to the north. This area is used widely for recreation and as a source of water supply. Farther to the west is the Ridge and Valley Region, a corridor running the length of the mountains. The rolling valley floors are good farming land, and the northern parts were settled at an early date by thrifty farmers who are commonly known as Pennsylvania Dutch. The Appalachian Plateau, a dissected region with deep V-shaped valleys and some smooth land on the uplands, is the western subdivision of the Appalachian Mountains. More high-grade bituminous coal is produced in this region than in any other region in the world.

The northern Appalachians in New England and the Canadian Maritime provinces are made up of many small ranges, such as the Green Mountains, and intervening rough glaciated uplands. All in all, the Appalachians constitute a weak barrier between the Coastal Plain and the Interior Lowland.

The *Laurentian Upland and the Tundra* (FIG. 3.2) to the north include the greater portion of eastern and northern Canada and smaller parts of the United States. It is a rough but not a mountainous region except in the eastern part. Forested in the south and dotted with numerous lakes, streams, and waterfalls, much of the region was scoured by the great ice sheet which covered a large part of North America (FIG. 3.3). Much bare, hard rock is exposed. No part of the region is densely populated, and, on the whole, it has fewest persons per square mile of any region on the continent.

The *Central Plain* of North America lies west of the Appalachians, south of the Laurentian Upland, east of the Rocky Mountains, and north of the Atlantic-Gulf Coastal Lowland. The Central Plain resembles the Coastal Lowland in many respects, but much of it lies at greater elevation. Indeed, some of it could be described

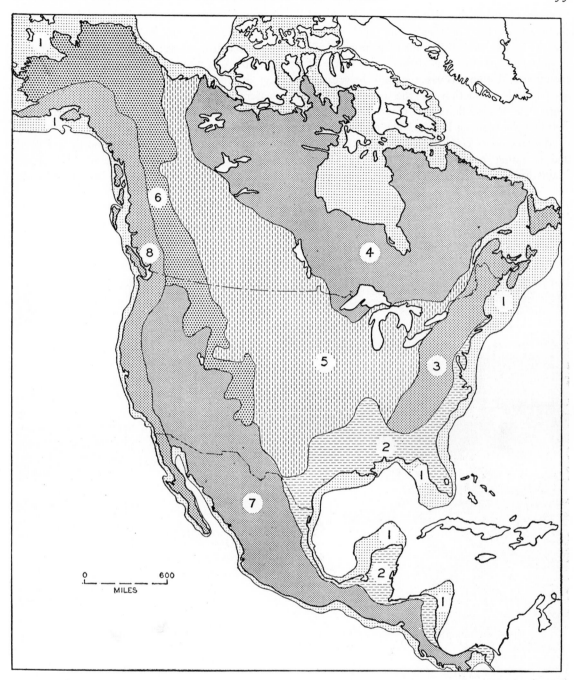

FIGURE 3.2. *The major physical regions of North America:* 1. *The Continental Shelf.* 2. *The At-lantic-Gulf Coastal Lowland.* 3. *The Appalachian Highland.* 4. *The Laurentian Upland (including the Hudson Bay Plain and the Tundra).* 5. *The Central Plain (including the Great Plains).* 6. *The Rocky Mountains.* 7. *The Intermontane Plateaus (including Central American Plateaus).* 8. *The Pacific Borderlands. The islands north of the Laurentian Shield together with those of the West Indies do not belong specifically to any of the eight regions listed above.*

as a low plateau rather than as a plain. Here and there are districts of rough land, such as the Ozarks or the central plateaus of Kentucky and Tennessee, but no areas deserve the name of mountains. Within this vast region is the greatest agricultural production of the continent—the Corn Belt, Wheat Belts, and parts of the Dairy Belt and the Grazing Region. The northern part of this region is covered with glacial deposits and is rather rough in character. The Great Plains are often described as a separate region because of greater elevation, the higher parts surpassing some of the higher summits of the Appalachians. There, because of dryness rather than the elevation, production is limited to grazing, dry farming, and irrigation agriculture where water is available.

The *Rocky Mountains* extend from Alaska to New Mexico (FIG. 3.2) and consist of many different ranges, usually trending north and south with narrow intervening valleys. The highest peaks are more than 14,000 feet high in Colorado.

FIGURE 3.3. *A view of the Laurentian Upland along the Gatineau River in Quebec. "Sacks"* (*rafts*) *of pulpwood all but cover the stream; thin forests cover the rocky hills. From National Film Board of Canada.*

The Rockies are forested except for the higher elevations and some lumber is obtained. Above timberline there is grass for summer grazing. Minerals, such as gold, copper, lead, and zinc, occur in many places. Many valleys and mountain basins within the Rockies are also irrigated. Abundant water is obtained from the Rockies to irrigate the plains below, which otherwise could not be intensively cultivated.

The *Intermontane Plateaus* lie between the two great mountain ranges of western North America (FIG. 3.2), the Cascade-Sierra Nevada on the west and the Rocky Mountains on the east (FIG. 3.2). In Mexico the bordering ranges are, respectively, the Sierra Madre Occidental and the Sierra Madre Oriental; these, however, are not continuations of the northern ranges. The uplands range in appearance from the Colorado Plateau with its even skyline and its Grand Canyon to the Basin Range region, in which broad basins alternate with narrow sharp-crested ridges. To the north is the Columbia Plateau, almost entirely covered with lava flows. On the southern margin the Central Plateau of Mexico is high enough to have snow-covered peaks and some basins even too cool to grow crops. A large proportion of the Intermontane Plateaus (FIG. 3.4) is arid or semiarid, but water is obtained from the nearby mountains to irrigate certain districts.

The *Pacific Borderlands* (FIG. 3.2) stretch along the west coast of North America from the Aleutian Islands to Central America, a region of lofty mountain ranges such as the Sierra Nevada, Cascade, and the Sierra Madre Occidental of Mexico. Between the mountains there are many valleys, some wide like the Great Valley of California, and many narrow such as the Fraser River Valley of British Columbia. Mt. McKinley in Alaska is the loftiest peak in North America, 20,300 feet above sea level. On the Pacific Coast,

FIGURE 3.4. *Contrasting views of the Intermontane Plateaus. The upper view shows a part of the Henry Mountains which rise above the level of the Colorado Plateau. The middle picture illustrates the deep dissection and even skyline of the Grand Canyon country. The lower view shows the angular character of the mountains in the Basin Range region of northern Mexico.*

unlike the Atlantic Coast, only small isolated bits of coastal plain are found.

Central America, bordered by fragments of the Atlantic-Gulf Coastal Plain, is essentially a continuation of the mountains and plateaus of Mexico. Although the coastal lowland seems to end in Yucatán and northern Guatemala, eastern Honduras, Nicaragua, Costa Rica, and Panama have small marginal plains. On the Pacific side the lowlands are even less extensive. The interior of Central America consists of highland, plateaulike or mountainous in character. Most of the people live in the more comfortable highlands while the hot humid plains are sparsely populated, except for a few small plantation districts.

DRAINAGE

Once the major relief features are delineated, the drainage pattern of North America is more easily studied. The continent is well drained, having only comparatively small intermontane areas with interior drainage. A few great rivers—the Rio Grande, Mississippi, St. Lawrence, Mackenzie, Yukon, Columbia, and the Colorado —together with their tributaries, drain a large portion of the continent. They also provide natural routes for communication, not only by water, but by rail and highway lines along their valleys. It is noteworthy that each of the rivers mentioned above drains more than one country and that most of them drain parts of several regions. The Mississippi River system, for example, is more than 4200 miles long (to the upper Missouri), and drains part of Canada as well as a very large part of the United States. It draws water from most of the Central Lowland, parts of the Rocky Mountains, the Appalachians, and the Coastal Lowland.

Many smaller streams are important also. Rivers, such as the Hudson, Mohawk, Susquehanna, or the James, flow all or part of the way through the Appalachians and provide travel routes much more important than the size of the streams would indicate. Some of the western rivers like the Colorado, which are not so significant as lines of communication, are nevertheless very important as sources of water power and water for irrigation.

No drainage features in North America are more used than the Great Lakes and their connecting rivers—the St. Marys, St. Clair, Detroit,

Niagara, and St. Lawrence. Indeed, this system forms the most valuable inland waterway in the world. From the head of the lakes at Duluth, the waterway extends more than 2600 miles to the sea. Many large cities owe much of their importance to this waterway—Milwaukee, Chicago, Detroit, Toledo, Cleveland, Buffalo, Toronto, and Montreal. The people of New York State profited by a connection to this waterway via the Erie Canal, a route paralleled today by the New York State Barge Canal. So important is this waterway that a plan, known as the Great Lakes–St. Lawrence Seaway Project, has been drawn up to enable ocean freighters to use the Great Lakes. Large quantities of iron ore, coal, grain, petroleum, and package freight are carried on this waterway (FIG. 3.5). The greatest handicap is the winter freeze-up, which closes the channels from five to six months every year.

CLIMATIC REGIONS

Although North America extends from about 8° North latitude to more than 80° North, most of the continent lies in the middle and northern latitudes. As a result, there are large areas in the interior with the continental climate, which is marked by strong seasonal contrasts in temperature. In Fort Yukon, for example, a January average of −21° F. has been recorded, and a July average of 61° F., a range of 82° F. There are colder places in North America but not many with a greater range. The very highest temperature recorded in Alaska is 100° F., the lowest −81° F. In southern Mexico, Central America, and the West Indies, the temperature conditions are subtropical and tropical, except in the higher altitudes. At Belize, British Honduras, near sea level, the January average is 76° F., the July average, 82° F., a range of only 6° F.

Precipitation is also highly variable. From the Aleutians to northern California along the west coast and from Newfoundland to Texas on the east coast, as well as in most parts of the West Indies and Central America, the rainfall is over 40 inches. The rainfall exceeds 100 inches in several small areas in Alaska, British Columbia, northwestern Washington, Mexico, and Central America. On the other hand, parts of the southwest desert have less than five inches of rain.

Along the northern fringe of the continent (FIG. 3.6) from Labrador to Alaska is the Tundra

FIGURE 3.5. *Great Lakes steamers in the Rouge docks at Dearborn, Michigan. The Great Lakes and their connecting waterways are among the most significant natural features of North America. From Ford Motor Company.*

FIGURE 3.6. *Climatic Regions of North America From "Geographical Review." Jan., 1941.*
See Appendix A for definitions of symbols.

climate (ET) which may be described as a polar climate with summers too cool and too short for trees or crops to grow. The average temperature of the warmest month is below 50° F. There is little production in this region, but it should be noted that grasses, mosses, lichens, and other forms of vegetation provide pasturage for reindeer in places, although the natives of the region, mostly Eskimos, live largely on products of the sea. (Definitions of the climatic symbols are given in Appendix A.)

South of the Tundra (FIG. 3.6) is the Taiga climate (Dc) with less than four months having an average temperature over 50° F. "Taiga" is a Russian word which may be freely translated as "northern forest." The growing season is longer than in the Tundra but is still too short for crops except on the southern margin. Furs, pulpwood, and minerals are the chief products. Both coniferous and deciduous trees grow rather well on the southern edge of the Taiga but are dwarfed on the northern margin.

South of the Taiga in eastern North America the growing season becomes longer, the summers warmer, and the winters milder. Rainfall also increases to the south. This cool-summer continental climate (Db) extends almost across the continent from British Columbia to New England and the Maritime Provinces of Canada. The growing season varies from 90 to 160 days, the summers are short and rainy, the winters long and, near the middle of the continent, severe. The summers are long enough, however, to grow many crops, of which the most important is hay. Dairying is the principal agricultural type, but on the southern margin from South Dakota to Pennsylvania, large quantities of grain are grown. It will be noted from the map (FIG. 3.6) that a long finger of this climate reaches southward along the Appalachians.

The hot-summer continental type (Da), a region which corresponds in part with the Corn Belt, extends from eastern Kansas to New Jersey. The summers are comparatively short, especially on the northern margin, but hot and rainy, a condition favorable for many crops such as corn, wheat, hay, and soybeans. The winters are severe, with snow. The average temperature of the coldest month, usually January, is less than 32° F. and the warmest month, July, is above 72° F. Precipitation occurs largely in summer and is

adequate for most crops, but the region is rather dry on its western margin.

The humid subtropical climate with hot summers (Cfa) occurs in the southeastern part of the United States, from eastern Texas to Virginia. See FIGURE 3.7. The summers are hot; the average temperature of the warmest month is above 72° F., in many places several degrees above. The winters are mild, but in all parts there is a distinct cool season and frosts. The northern part of the region has snow in the winter, but it does not remain on the ground for any length of time. In the southern section the rain is generally heavier than in the regions to the north, ranging from about 25 inches in Texas to more than 60 inches in southern Mississippi. Most of the rain comes in the hot season, but there is precipitation in every month and in the southern part, especially in the peninsula of Florida, both temperatures and precipitation are favorable for the growth of crops in the winter season. Corn is very important in the north and is grown throughout the region. The principal cash crop in the south is cotton.

The Mediterranean climate (Cs) with its winter rain and summer drought borders the Pacific from southern California to the Columbia River. The winters are mild enough for many crops to grow. Frosts occur during the winter, but there are no protracted periods of freezing. During the summer dry period uninterrupted sunshine is the rule, and abundant water for irrigation comes from the adjacent mountains. Precipitation increases northward. Los Angeles receives only 15 inches of rain; San Francisco, 20 inches; Eureka, 43 inches; Coos Bay (Marshfield) in western Oregon, 54 inches.

North of Oregon along the western part of Washington and British Columbia (FIG. 3.6), the climate is called the Rainy Temperate Type (Cfb). The winters are very rainy and while there is summer rainfall, it is not abundant. The summers are quite cool, too cool for many crops to mature. The heaviest rainfall in the United States, perhaps the heaviest in North America, occurs in this region.

The Steppe (BS) climate is intermediate between the humid regions and the desert. The western part of North America from Canada to the vicinity of Mexico City (FIG. 3.6) is arid or semiarid, with the exception of the higher moun-

FIGURE 3.7. *A farm in the humid climate* (Cfa) *near Spartanburg, South Carolina. Strip crop-ping, terracing, and other methods reduce soil erosion in a region of heavy rains and mild winters. From Soil Conservation Service.*

tains and a strip along the Pacific Coast. No exact definition can be given in terms of rainfall alone because both temperatures and evaporation rates must be considered, but, in general, the rainfall on the humid margin of the Steppe ranges from 20 to 30 inches annually and on the desert side from 10 to 20 inches. The western border lies just to the east of the Sierra-Cascade Mountains. The eastern margin of the Steppe follows approximately the 100th meridian from the Canadian border to central Mexico. Not all of this vast region is Steppe; humid mountains and, in

the southwest, desert occupy large areas. The season in which the maximum precipitation occurs is most significant since evaporation is much higher during the summer than in the winter.

The Desert (BW) regions of North America stretch from central Nevada to almost the tip of Lower California and to the Tropic of Cancer in Central Mexico (FIG. 3.6). This climate is defined in terms of little rain and high evaporation. In general, there is not enough precipitation for grass to grow or for any kind of crops without irrigation. See FIGURE 3.8. Intensive cultivation in

FIGURE 3.8. *The All-American Canal in the Imperial Valley of California. Water from the Colorado River is used to irrigate the level floor of the valley in the distance. Notice the arid aspect of the sandy land in the foreground. From Bureau of Reclamation.*

small areas such as the Imperial Valley on the border of California and Mexico and in other similar districts is possible because of local supplies of water. This region is the hottest in North America in the summer season with July averages above 90° F. for many stations in California, Arizona, and Mexico. In Death Valley, California, an absolute maximum of 134° F., the highest temperature in North America, has been recorded.

The Rainforest (Af) of North America is limited to a fringe of eastern Central America, a portion of the West Indies, and southern Florida (FIG. 3.6). In few places is there a typical development of the climate similar to Amazonia or the Congo of Africa. From British Honduras to eastern Panama this climatic zone corresponds to the coastal plain. There is great variation in rainfall and vegetation (FIG. 3.9), especially with reference to exposure to the trade winds, variation not only in the amount of rainfall but in the length of the dry season. The data below for Belize in British Honduras and for Colon in the Canal Zone give the range of conditions fairly well along the east coast of Central America. It will be noted that more rain has been recorded for Colon than for Belize, but because of less favorable exposure to the trade winds the dry season in Colon is more marked. The differences in temperature are slight.

CLIMATIC DATA FOR BELIZE, BRITISH HONDURAS AND COLON, CANAL ZONE		Belize	Colon
Average Temperature (degrees Fahrenheit)	Jan.	76.1	75.2
	Jul.	82.4	80.2
Average Rainfall (inches)	Dry month Mar.	2.33	1.58
	Wet month Nov.	13.29	20.70
Average Annual Rainfall (inches)		84.53	127.35

In the Tropical Savanna (Aw) the dry season is long enough to discourage the growth of trees except along stream courses or other favorable places. Coarse grasses are abundant but are not so well suited for grazing animals as those in the middle latitudes. On the west coast of Middle America, the Savanna extends from Panama to the tip of Lower California and, on the east coast, from Tampico to the peninsula of Yucatán (FIG. 3.6). The leeward shores of the West Indies are also of this type, while the windward coasts belong to the Tropical Rainforest. The Savanna climate is favorable for agriculture, especially for sugar. The hot humid season is excellent for rapid growth and the dry season increases the sugar content of the cane. Rice, corn, coffee, cotton, cassava, and many other crops are important.

SOILS

Soil, the thin layer of weathered material on the surface of the earth, is composed mainly of minerals, organic material, water, and air. Soil is a most valuable resource, the productivity of which depends on the texture, and mineral and organic content, as well as other qualities. Soils good for one crop are not suitable for another. A light sandy soil may be quite satisfactory for horticulture where the value of the crop permits the use of large quantities of mineral fertilizers,

but the same soil may be very poor for grain. The quality of soil varies with the nature of the underlying rock, the climate, natural vegetation, and other factors. Three horizons or "layers" of soil are generally recognized. See FIGURE 3.10. The "A" horizon at the top is a zone from which the soluble minerals and the finer particles are slowly being removed. This horizon varies in color, but under natural conditions is gray, black, or brown depending partly on the amount of the partially decayed organic material (humus). The "B" horizon, often called the subsoil, is the zone of deposition, in which some of the material removed from "A" is accumulating. The "C" horizon is the parent material, the bed rock or other substances from which the soil is being formed. The thickness of the "A" and "B" horizons varies widely.

Two broad types of soils occur in North America—the *pedocals* or lime-accumulating soils in drier regions and the *pedalfers*, nonlime-accumulating but with accumulations of aluminum and iron compounds. Since most of the grains have been domesticated from wild grasses which grew in the steppe lands, the soils of the steppes are especially well suited for many crops. Rainfall in the steppes, however, is not sufficient for good yields, so that on the whole the grains grow better in the regions of the forest soils, the pedalfers.

In the pedocals of North America are included four soil types—the chernozem, chestnut, brown desert, and gray desert. Of these, the chernozem is best known, in both North America and other parts of the world, having a rather close relation to the wheat belts. A belt of chernozem can be traced from the plains of Canada in southern Alberta, Saskatchewan, and Manitoba, through the Dakotas, Nebraska, Kansas, Oklahoma, and Texas into northeastern Mexico, associated throughout with the Steppe (BS) climate and grasslands. The "A" horizon is dark gray to black accounting for the common and rather indefinite name "black earth" (other types of soils are black also). The "B" horizon is generally an accumulation of lime carbonate and other soluble minerals which make for fertility. The structure is nutlike, the horizons thick, and the soil is easily cultivated for many years with little loss of fertility.

To the west of the chernozem region, in the

FIGURE 3.9. *Rubber trees in southern Mexico. North America possesses some small areas of rain-forest suitable for the growth of rubber but does not have everywhere the skilled labor to tap the trees, as the crude hacking on these trees suggests.*

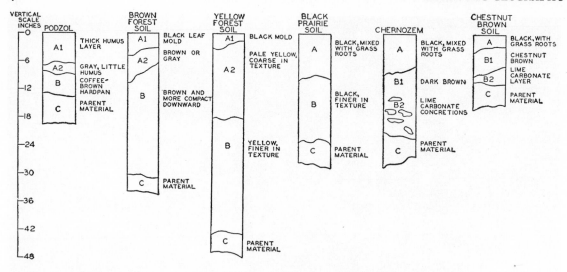

FIGURE 3.10. *Profiles of six representative kinds of soil. Podzol is found in high latitude coniferous forests, the brown and yellow forest soils in the middle latitudes, black prairie in the humid grasslands, and the chernozems and chestnut brown soils are characteristic of the arid lands. From "Syllabus for Economic Geography," Hartshorne and Dicken.*

drier part of the steppe, are the chestnut soils. Less humus in the "A" horizon means that the soil is lighter in color, dark brown rather than gray or black. The "B" horizon has a well-developed layer of carbonate; the structure is rather tight. The soil is excellent, however, if rainfall is sufficient or if water is available for irrigation.

The brown desert soils are in even drier locations (BW climate) than the chestnut soils. Humus is almost entirely lacking, and the carbonate layer is very close to the surface, often in the form of a "hardpan." The soil is shallow. The gray desert soil in the driest portion of the desert is very thin, has no humus, and the carbonate layer is often at the surface in the form of a crust, known as alkali flats.

In the moist climates the pedalfers include the humid prairie soils, the red and yellow forest soils, the gray-brown forest soils, the podzols, and the laterites. In these types the soluble minerals have been largely dissolved and removed, and careful cultivation and the use of commercial fertilizers or manure are necessary to maintain productivity. The climates, however, are generally favorable for many crops.

The humid prairie soils are to be found in the humid grasslands on the eastern border of the chernozems. The superficial resemblance of the humid prairie soils to the chernozems often leads

to confusion. The "A" horizon is dark brown to black; the "B" horizon is brown. Unlike the chernozems, the humid prairie soils are nonlime-accumulating but are generally high in fertility.

The red and yellow forest soils are found chiefly in the areas of Cfa, Cw, and Cs climates. The largest area in North America corresponds to the middle and eastern portions of the Cotton Belt. There is a thin gray humus layer which may disappear after long cultivation. The lower part of the "A" horizon is light yellow, and the "B" layer is yellow or red depending on the nature of the parent material. In many cultivated districts the "A" horizon has been entirely removed by erosion and the red subsoil exposed. These soils are low in minerals and need constant fertilizing to maintain yields.

The gray-brown forest soils occur in the middle latitude forest areas of Cfb and Db climates, mainly in the northeastern part of the United States. In part of this area, the soils are frozen during the winter, the humus layer is thicker than in most forest soils, and the mineral content is higher. There is, of course, great variation in quality depending on the parent material. On the sandy soils and the glaciated areas the humus is low; the soils are leached and tend to be more like the podzols described below. On the other hand, the areas of limestone tend to resemble the red and yellow forest soils, although the "A" horizon is often very low in lime.

The podzols develop in the coniferous forests of the higher latitudes, in the Db, Dc, or cooler parts of the Cfb climates. The surface layer is usually raw humus, consisting of the needles from the coniferous trees. The "A" horizon is so leached that it is white or ash colored, giving the name *podzol* (Russian term for "ashes") to the soil. The "B" horizon is dark brown and richer in minerals. Although this soil tends to be rather thin, some parts, are fertile and may be improved by careful cultivation.

The laterites, limited to the more humid tropical locations (Af), have a very limited occurrence in North America; only small districts in southern Mexico and in the coastal margins of Central America being represented. The humus layer is very thin in spite of the heavy forest conditions under which the soils develop, since any organic material decays rapidly. In neither the "A" nor "B" horizons is there much soluble mineral, but these layers consist largely of insoluble compounds of iron and aluminum. The soil is quite infertile without the addition of mineral fertilizers, which are retained poorly.

PRODUCTION REGIONS OF NORTH AMERICA

Out of the complex of land, climate, soils, forests, grasslands, and useful minerals, the peoples of North America have developed the existing production pattern. Its evolution is still in progress. From the lands of their ancestors, the peoples brought their various ways of life, their ways of making a living, and of living together. Some things they learned from the native Indians to supplement this old world "bank" of useful knowledge. In certain places, such as Mexico, the contribution of the Indian was of enormous consequence; in other regions the quick elimination of the red man allowed little chance for the absorption of his culture. It is not to be assumed that we have reached the acme of production or even achieved the types of production best suited to special areas. The role of environment, passive as a limiting factor, sometimes active in the opportunities suggested to resourceful people, is reasonably clear. We have a pretty fair knowledge of the available resources, and the varied cultural patterns of the people are reasonably well known.

Every production region (see END PAPER I) is related to some of the environmental factors—the position, surface, climate, soil, drainage, mineral deposits, communication lines, population density and quality. For example, the significance of the *Commercial Fisheries* (1) is dependent in part on the latitudinal position of North America as well as on the character of the coastline. The *Tropical Hardwood Forest* (2h) is found in one of the warmest and rainiest parts of the continent, on the east side of Central America and parts of Mexico, while the *Softwood Forests* (2s) are in higher latitudes, in lands often too cool in summer or too rough for agriculture. *Commercial Grazing* (3c) is limited mostly to the dry western part of the United States and northern Mexico. Three *Wheat Belts* (4w) are to be noted, centering around Kansas, North Dakota, and the middle Columbia Basin. *Mediterranean Agriculture* (4m) is confined to California. In this type the long dry season in summer and the accompanying sunshine help produce crops which will not grow so well in the humid summer climates. The *Corn Belt* (4c) stretches from eastern Nebraska to the Atlantic Coast. *Dairying* (4d) is of greatest importance immediately south of the Great Lakes, in New England, and eastern Canada, but a smaller area is found in the Pacific Northwest. *Horticulture* (4h) is the dominant type in Florida and the Gulf Coast and occurs in many smaller areas not shown on the map. Many *Oases* (4o) are located in the dry lands, while *Plantations* (4p) are found in the Cotton Belt and in various parts of Middle America. *Subsistence Agriculture* of the extensive type (5e) is best developed on the uplands of Mexico and Central America. *Mining* (x) is widely scattered and almost independent of climate, but certain types of mining are associated with remote mountains, and position with respect to lines of communication may aid or restrict mineral production. *Manufacturing* (·) is also widely scattered, except for the concentration in northeastern United States. The production regions of North America and the other continents can be explained if all the natural and human factors can be evaluated. Description and analysis of statistical data should come first, and explanations should be stated only after careful consideration of alternative hypotheses. The coincidence of wheat farming and chernozem soil, for example, may or may not be significant.

South America

South America is similar, superficially at least, to North America. The high mountain barrier of the Andes, the central lowland extending from Venezuela to southern Argentina, and the highlands of Guiana and eastern Brazil correspond respectively to the western mountains, the central lowland, and the Appalachians. But the Andes are far higher than the Sierra Nevada and a much more serious barrier to communications; the Amazon Lowland has no counterpart in North America, and the Brazilian Highland differs structurally from the Appalachians.

The position of South America, mainly south of the equator but with the bulk of the continent lying between the tropics, means that the lowlands are mostly tropical or subtropical, although the highlands may have more temperate climates. Most of the people, with the notable exception of the Argentines, live in the highlands. The tropical lowlands are just beginning to be developed. In another respect position is significant: South America lies well to the east of North America. The westernmost limit reaches only to the 81st meridian, approximately the longitude of Cleveland, Ohio. The easternmost point near Recife, Brazil, is near the 35th meridian and farther east than Labrador. This easterly position of South America has some distinct advantages. It makes the east coast almost as close to western Europe as is the east coast of North America. For the same reason, however, South America is much farther removed from eastern Asia and Australia.

SURFACE FEATURES

The main physical regions of South America (FIG. 3.11) are: the Andes, the Orinoco Plain of Venezuela and Colombia, the Guiana Highland, the Amazon Lowland, the Brazilian Highland, the southern plains and plateaus, especially the Chaco, the Pampa, and the plateaus of Patagonia.

The *Andes Range* is the most striking feature of South America. It stretches 4000 miles from northern Venezuela and Colombia to the southern tip of Argentina and Chile, reaching a maximum height in the middle portion of over 22,835 feet (Mt. Aconcagua) above sea level. In the north, in Venezuela and Colombia, there are three distinct ranges or ridges with intervening valleys. In

Ecuador these ridges are joined together in the form of a knot. In southern Peru and Bolivia a plateau is bordered by two distinct ranges with lesser ridges. In middle and southern Chile the Andes take the form of one dominant ridge again. Along the entire length of the Andes few easy passes are to be found; so the great Cordillera imposes a barrier not only to human communication but to the movement of air masses since most of the passes lie above 10,000 feet. Furthermore, the trend of the Andes determines the coastline of western South America.

The Andean Range, including the bordering foothills, has a much denser population than the lowlands to the east. Nearly all of the people of Colombia, for example, live in or very near to the Andes, and the low eastern part of the country is very sparsely populated. People are attracted to the Andes by the minerals, and mining has played a very important part in the settlement and development of the country. But they are also attracted by the temperate climate of the middle altitudes of this very significant mountain range.

The *Orinoco Plain* (often called the *Llanos*) is an alluvial basin bordering the Orinoco River and its tributaries in Venezuela and Colombia. The savanna climate has a severe dry season in winter but fairly heavy rains in summer. The vegetation is dominantly coarse grasses, but there are also areas of rather stunted trees with some larger trees growing along the stream courses. It has been traditionally an area of cattle raising but is now being settled by agricultural peoples.

To the east of the Orinoco Plain is the *Guiana Highland*, a massive upland, underlain partly by hard crystalline rock worn down and dissected by streams and other agencies. The highest elevation reaches only 11,000 feet. This region is mostly covered with jungle and is very sparsely populated.

Southward is the great *Amazon Lowland*, a tremendous basin which lies between the Andes, the Brazilian Highland, and the Guiana Highland. For the most part this is an alluvial plain built up by the river and its tributaries as they have meandered and changed their courses through the centuries. But it is by no means entirely flat. There are low uplands which are well above flood stage as well as the lower plains which are flooded annually at the time of the heaviest rains. A very large part of the Amazon Lowland is forested,

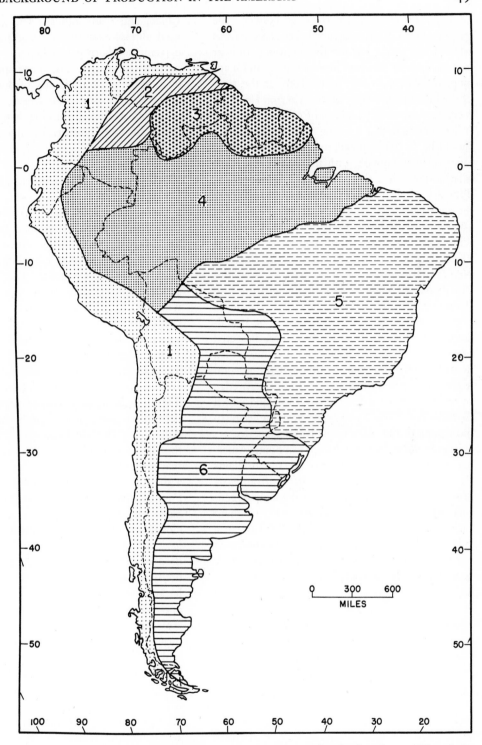

FIGURE 3.11. *The major physical regions of South America: 1. The Andes. 2. The Orinoco Plain. 3. The Guiana Highland. 4. Amazonia. 5. The Brazilian Highland. 6. The Southern Plain.*

but large areas of savannas occur between the streams. Some of these savannas are remote from streams and roads, but the Brazilian government is making great progress in exploration and mapping. Rainfall is heavy, particularly at the time of the highest sun. Most of the Amazon Lowland receives more than 80 inches of rainfall per year. It is remarkable that a region with these qualities should be so thinly populated, but the disadvantages of high rainfall, with the consequent high relative humidity, the presence of diseases, the difficulty of clearing the forest and maintaining the clearings have caused most people to stay away from Amazonia. Perhaps the next century will see great changes in this region.

To the south of the Amazon is the *Brazilian Highland*, occupying a large part of southern Brazil and extending in some slight measure into Paraguay also. This is a region of fairly dense population especially near the coast. The Brazilian Highland is mostly in the form of a dissected plateau which reaches an elevation of more than 8000 feet in a few places, although the general level is under 5000 feet. Along the eastern edge of the plateau is a narrow coastal lowland which extends from Cape São Roque, near the easternmost point of Brazil, as far as Rio de Janeiro.

The *Southern Plain* (or Pampa) in South America resembles in some respects the Great Plains Region of North America. It extends from eastern Bolivia and Paraguay down through Argentina and southern Uruguay almost to the southern tip of South America. In the north the plain has a subtropical aspect, and this portion is known as the Gran Chaco, or great hunting ground. This is still sparsely populated but is important for its reserves of petroleum and also as a potential agricultural region. To the south of the Gran Chaco lies the Pampa, a temperate grassland comparable on the west to the Great Plains but on the east, in the vicinity of Buenos Aires, more comparable perhaps to the prairies of Iowa and Illinois. The Southern Plain is a grazing region with arid grazing in the west and humid grazing and farming in the east. Livestock move from the dry regions to the humid just as they do in North America. Farther south this plain takes on some of the aspects of a plateau, which extends eastward from the Andean chain and is divided by the valleys of various rivers, such as the Rio Colorado, the Rio Negro, the Rio Chubut, the Rio

Chico, and many others. The southern part is used almost exclusively for grazing, and in the extreme southern part sheep are much more important than cattle. The more humid part of the plain in the general vicinity of Buenos Aires produces large quantities of wheat, corn, and other crops, as well as furnishing humid pasture and forage for large quantities of livestock.

DRAINAGE

The divide between Atlantic and Pacific drainage lies near the crest of the Andes, and all the important rivers drain to the Atlantic. Five great river systems drain a large share of the continent: the Magdalena, Orinoco, Amazon, São Francisco, and the Paraná–La Plata. Furthermore, these rivers are navigable. The Magdalena has several rapids and its lower course tends to fill with silt, but this river and its connecting railroads carry large quantities of freight. The navigation of the Orinoco is limited by low water stage during the dry season. The Amazon with its tributaries has 20,000 miles of navigable water, and river steamers ascend as far as Iquitos, Peru. Traffic is light, however, because of the sparse population and limited production throughout Amazonia. The São Francisco, draining a part of the Brazilian Highland, has rapids in the lower reaches, but the middle portion is navigable, and a short rail line affords an outlet to the sea. The Paraná is navigable for ocean freighters up to Santa Fé and for river steamers as far as Asunción. Parts of the Rio de la Plata estuary are shallow, and the harbor of Buenos Aires must be dredged. The west coast rivers are short and generally not navigable; nor do their outlets provide harbors for ocean ships. Most ships anchor in open roadsteads at ports, such as Valparaiso, Antofagasta, and Iquique, and transfer goods by means of lighters and other small boats. Guayaquil in Ecuador has a protected harbor on the Gulf of Guayaquil.

CLIMATIC REGIONS

The general climatic pattern of South America (see APPENDIX A) depends mostly on the latitude, elevation, and configuration of the coast. Even on the equator the highlands have temperate and, at the highest altitudes, cold climates. The tropical climates of South America are more extensive, and the temperate belt smaller than the corresponding areas of North America. In a general way the climate of Middle Chile is like that of California, eastern Argentina is like the Carolina coast, and the Brazilian Plateau resembles the plateau of Mexico.

The *Tropical Rainforest* (Af) of South America lies mostly in Amazonia together with smaller spots along the coasts of the Guianas, Venezuela, Colombia, and eastern Brazil. The climate does not differ markedly from that of the east coast of Central America, described on page 43. Rainfall and temperatures for Belém are similar to those of Belize, British Honduras. Rainfall is heavy in the South American rainforest most of the year, excepting only a short, almost insignificant dry season. About half of the region averages 80 inches or above annually. Temperatures are uniformly high but not extremely high. Much of this region is still covered with a variety of forest types, including thorny jungle and dense rainforest, but savanna grasslands are also common.

The *Savanna Climate* (Aw) is found to the north and south of the Rainforest, in parts of the Orinoco Plain, in the Guiana Highland, in southern Amazonia, and in the Brazilian Highland. Smaller areas occur in Colombia and Ecuador. The dry season, of varying length, limits the growth of trees but is generally favorable for the ripening and harvesting of many crops. Similar climates prove favorable for sugar cultivation in Cuba and Java, for rice and small grains in India and China, but the Savannas of South America are not widely cultivated at present. The coarse grasses provide forage for cattle and horses, more rarely for sheep and goats.

The *Steppe* (BS) and *Desert* (BW) climates are found in narrow strips along the west coast from Ecuador to Middle Chile and immediately east of the Andes from Bolivia to Patagonia. The desert reaches the Atlantic Coast in latitudes corresponding to New England and Newfoundland, 42° to 52° S. Such is the barrier effect of the Andes to the masses of warm, moist air from the southern Pacific.

The *Humid Temperate Climate* (Cfa) includes eastern Argentina, Uruguay, and the extreme southern part of Brazil. The climate is similar to that of the Carolina coast, except for cooler summers. Buenos Aires is a homoclime (is similar in climate) for Charleston, South Carolina. South of Buenos Aires, however, the differences, lati-

tude for latitude, are more noticeable. Bahia Blanca (lat. 39° S.) is warmer in winter and much drier than Washington, D. C. (lat. 39° N.). The narrow southern tip of the South American continent is obviously less subject to extremes in temperature than northern North America.

The *Mediterranean Climate* (Cs) in South America is limited to Middle Chile. Santiago has a climate similar to that of Los Angeles. Winter rains and summer drought are the rule. Wheat, corn, grapes, and citrus fruits are cultivated.

The southern part of the Brazilian Highland belongs to the *Winter Dry Temperate Climate* (Cw) as does part of the Andean Highland. Sometimes called the "coffee climate," the rainy, warm, summers are favorable for the growth of coffee, and the dry, mild winters aid in the ripening, harvesting, and drying. This is essentially a temperate savanna similar to the Aw climate, except for the colder winters. In the highlands, temperatures and rainfall vary locally with elevation and exposure. Frost is fairly common in winter, except on favored slopes.

In the Andes and other highland regions of South America the people think of climate in terms of altitude rather than latitude. The low country, below 3000 feet, is the *tierra caliente* (hot land). The intermediate lands, from 3000 to 6000 feet approximately, represent the *tierra templada* (temperate land). Above 6000 feet is the *tierra fria* (cold land). Of course, at the very highest elevations the snow-capped peaks are in a climate of perpetual frost (FIG. 3.12). See APPENDIX A for description of ET and EF climates.

SOILS

The soils of South America (see APPENDIX B) follow the climatic pattern, but with many local exceptions associated with varying landforms, vegetation, and rock types. East of the Andes and north of the Tropic of Capricorn is a vast area of tropical lateritic soils. This includes all of Amazonia, the Guiana Highland, the Brazilian Highland, and parts of northwestern Colombia. In Amazonia most of the soils are leached and lacking in soluble minerals. Along the river flood plains the soils are poorly drained and in many places flooded for a part of the year. On the higher ground drainage is better, but here too soluble minerals and humus are deficient. Once the forest cover is removed, even gentle slopes

FIGURE 3.12. *Misti Volcano in southern Peru is over 19,000 feet in elevation. The lofty, snow-covered peaks of the Andes supply water for irrigation on the adjacent plateaus and lowlands. From USAF.*

are subject to erosion, as the Ford Motor Company found in establishing rubber plantations at Fordlandia on a tributary of the Amazon. The soils of Amazonia can be made productive but will require artificial drainage, skillful handling, and large quantities of mineral fertilizer. The generally poor quality of the soils, together with the dense vegetation, has been the greatest deterrent to effective settlement.

In the southern part of the Brazilian Highland, the special quality of the soils depends on the rock material even more than on the climate. The best known of these soils is the *terra roxa* (reddish earth), sometimes called the "coffee soil." Derived from the weathering of basic igneous rock (diabase) this soil is well suited to coffee because of its mineral content, which gives flavor to the coffee, and because of its porosity, which allows the roots of the coffee plant to penetrate deeply. The *terra roxa* is not well suited to cotton or corn, however, and erodes rapidly when improperly cultivated. Small areas of chernozem and chestnut brown soils occur in the dry region of northeastern Brazil.

In northern Argentina the soil map resembles that of north central United States, with the "humid" soils on the east. Belts of humid prairie, chernozem, chestnut brown, and desert soils occur in succession from east to west, correlated with corn belt agriculture and humid grazing in the east, wheat farming in the middle, and semiarid grazing and irrigation in the west. Of special interest are the chernozem soils of the Argentine Pampa, because of their fertility and excellent yields of corn and wheat grown on these soils. In part these soils are derived from wind-blown deposits (loess), similar to those of the Mississippi Valley and the Columbia River Plateau. The soils are thick, porous, and well supplied with humus and soluble minerals. To the west of the chernozem a hardpan is found in the soils, making cultivation difficult even where water is available for irrigation.

On the west coast, in southern Chile, a small area of gray-brown podzols is associated with the mixed and coniferous forests. These soils are of fair fertility but need mineral fertilizers. Fortunately, there are large quantities of nitrate in the northern Chile deserts, which is one of the deficient minerals in the southern forest. In the coastal districts of northern Chile and Peru, desert soils are characteristic. These soils are rich in minerals and produce well under irrigation with careful handling.

PEOPLES

The population pattern of South America is distinctly different from that of Anglo-America. Most of the people live in the highlands rather than in the lowlands; isolated clusters of population are common, rather than large agglomerations; the native Indian element is important in all countries except Argentina.

Two belts of fairly dense population contain most of the people of South America. One of these, the Andes Range, with its associated lowlands, supports numerous clusters of dense population. Most of the people of Venezuela, Colombia, Ecuador, Peru, Bolivia, and Chile live in the Andes or on its fringes. The other belt of moderately dense population lies on and near the east coast, from the eastern tip of Brazil to Buenos Aires. Most of the people of Brazil, Uruguay, and Argentina live in this belt.

The people of South America include Indians, Europeans, Mestizos, and, in addition, various minority groups, such as Negroes, Japanese, and Chinese. The Indians predominate in the Andean Highland and in most of the sparsely settled areas; the Europeans are most numerous in Argentina, Uruguay, and southern Brazil; the Mestizos, usually of mixed Indian and European blood, have a wide distribution.

PRODUCTION REGIONS

In South America the pattern of production regions, such as plantations, tropical forests, Mediterranean agriculture, and corn and wheat belts (see END PAPER 2), is related to such factors as climate, elevation, distance from the sea, and stage of settlement. Most of the people of South America live in the highlands of the tropical belt or in the lowlands of the temperate belt. They are oriented toward the temperate climates and have until recently shown very little interest in the resources of the tropical lowlands. Another important factor is the position of South America, eastward of North America. This, together with the fact that most of the rivers and the land slope from the crest of the Andes eastward, means that nearly all of South America is oriented toward the Atlantic. Ecuador, Peru, and Chile are oriented more toward the west, but they are handicapped by having no outlets for their goods in the immediate vicinity. This is in spite of the fact that the Panama Canal made the west coast of South America much nearer to the markets of eastern North America and western Europe.

Another important feature of South America is the difficulty of inland communication. Only three areas are well served by railroads—in the vicinity of Buenos Aires, southeastern Brazil, and the middle portion of Chile. Most of the rail lines are short. Otherwise land communications in the form of both railroads and roads are rather lacking, although several new routes are under construction. To a certain extent the airways make up for this deficiency, but airplanes are not yet able to carry heavy goods cheaply.

Once the outline of the geographic features of South America has been studied, the pattern of production regions falls into a fairly logical system (see END PAPER 2). *Fisheries* (1), mostly along the southern coasts, are poorly developed, perhaps because beef has been so easy to produce on the land. The *Tropical Hardwood Forests* (2h) of Amazonia are much more extensive than those of Central America, because of the equatorial lo-

cation. On the other hand, the *Softwood Forests* (2s) are small, limited mostly to one area in Brazil and another in the southern Andes. *Commercial Grazing* (3c) covers a large area, but except for the humid parts of Argentina, Uruguay, and the extreme southern part of Brazil, the animal population is quite sparse. The *Wheat Belt* (4w) of Argentina is smaller than the Winter Wheat Belt of the United States. The region of *Mediterranean Agriculture* (4m) in Chile, handicapped by the scarcity of water, is much less productive than that of California. Other types of commercial agriculture, the *Corn Belt* (4c), *Dairying* (4d), *Small-Grain and Livestock* (4s), *Horticulture* (4h), and *Oases* (4o), are generally represented by small regions, many of which are too small to be shown on END PAPER 2. *Plantations* (4p) have a moderate development and *Subsistence Agriculture* (5e) covers a large part of the highlands. Although *Mining* (x) is important in many parts of South America, the poor communications and the scarcity of coal are handicaps to production. *Manufacturing* (•) is increasing, but South America still depends on North America and western Europe for a large share of its industrial needs.

4

The Geographic Background of Production in Other Continents

Consciously or unconsciously one compares features of other lands with those of his own. The Alps are rather like the Rocky Mountains or the Sierra Nevada; lower Egypt is similar to the Imperial Valley; and parts of the Argentine Pampa resemble the Great Plains. A keen observer or a careful reader is more aware of the contrasts between different lands, especially with respect to cultural features, but, nevertheless, a familiarity with one continent is an excellent beginning for a study of the others. South America, Africa, Europe, the Soviet Union, Asia, and Oceania have a variety of landforms, climates, vegetation, drainage patterns, soils, peoples, and products. Although one region may resemble another in one respect, other qualities usually show considerable variation. The climate of Shanghai resembles that of Charleston, South Carolina, but the landforms, people, and products are quite different. New Zealand is like England in many ways—climate, people, crops, even religion and accent, but the difference in location with respect to large centers of population sets up contrasting patterns of production.

Africa

The "dark continent" is essentially a vast plateau straddling the equator, twice the area of South America. Africa was the last of the continents to be explored and developed, perhaps because of the few harbors, the rapid rivers, vast deserts, and disease-infested jungles. The plateau varies in elevation from a few hundred feet in the

western Sahara to more than 5000 feet in Ethiopia, usually presenting an abrupt scarp to the sea. Here and there a portion is upturned to form mountains, such as the Atlas in the north, or the Drakensberg in the south. A few higher mountains, of igneous origin, rise above the plateau. Mt. Kilimanjaro, east of Lake Victoria, is a volcanic cone rising above 19,000 feet. Low plains are not extensive as compared with those of South America and occur mostly in the dry lands, as in Libya and Mauritania. A noteworthy exception is the lowland of Mozambique.

The interior of Africa is no longer isolated, thanks largely to the airplane and a few modern roads, but for centuries the forbidding plateau scarp, the scarcity of navigable rivers, and the broad deserts made exploration difficult and offered little attraction to settlers from other continents. Even today with greatly improved transportation and health conditions, Africa does not appeal greatly to the peoples of overcrowded western Europe. Less than five million of Africa's 175,000,000 are of European origin.

Africa reaches about 37° north of the Equator and nearly 35° to the south. This makes for a symmetrical development of climates, natural vegetation, and even land use. Significantly, the greater part of the continent (and its deserts) lies in the northern hemisphere. Here the desert extends entirely across the continent from the Atlantic to the Red Sea and forms a serious but not an impassable barrier to movements of people and goods. Because of its latitudinal symmetry and comparatively even surface, Africa is almost

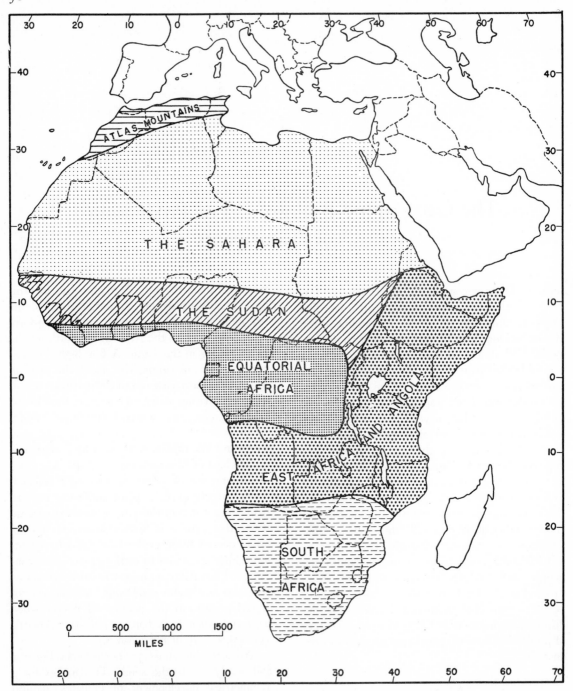

FIGURE 4.1. *The major physical regions of Africa.*

the "ideal" continent for the study of climates. On the north one encounters, in turn, Mediterranean climate—Steppe—Desert—Steppe—Savanna, and Rainforest at the Equator. Approached from the south (via the west coast) the sequence is the same. On the east coast the climatic sequence is somewhat different (see APPENDIX A).

SURFACE FEATURES AND CLIMATE

Since the broad regional subdivisions of Africa (FIG. 4.1) are usually based on both climate and landforms, it is desirable to discuss these two subjects under one heading, in order to avoid repetition. The Atlas in the northwest and the East African Highland are landform regions but have distinct climatic characteristics. The boundaries of the Sahara, the Sudan, and Equatorial Africa are based primarily on climate and vegetation. South Africa is essentially a political division with a variety of landforms and climates.

The *Atlas Region* of northwest Africa is a long, complex mountain system, which collects enough rainfall from the air masses to support 20 million people. From the eastern shores of Tunisia to the coast of Rio de Oro, the Atlas extends nearly 1400 miles in a straight line; the breadth varies from 100 to 200 miles. The region is important out of all proportion to its size, however, because of its moderate annual rainfall (12 to 40 inches) and its nearness to western Europe.

The Atlas Range has considerable diversity from east to west. On the west four distinct ranges can be recognized with valleys or basins between them. Toward the east these ranges merge into two, between which lies a narrow plateau. Nearly all of the region is either mountainous or hilly, excepting a few rather large basins in Morocco and in eastern Tunisia. Along the Mediterranean and Atlantic coasts there is a hilly lowland known as the *Tell*. This is the most densely populated part and includes the most important cities, such as Oran, Algiers, and Tunis. Toward the interior, on the higher slopes of the Atlas, forests of oak and pine occur.

The *Sahara*, the greatest of all deserts, is a vast, almost empty barrier, preventing profitable land communications with the Mediterranean to all of Africa, except the Atlas Region and lower Egypt. The very size of the region and its low productivity, rather than its relief features, discourages the movement of people and goods. It is 3500 miles

from Port-Étienne in Mauritania to the Red Sea; 1500 miles from Tunis to Kano in Nigeria. To be sure, the Sahara is crossed by caravan routes, airlines, and automobile roads, as well as by the Nile, with its portage railroads, but the volume of transport is small.

Not all of this area is strictly desert, however. The borderlands on the south slope of the Atlas and the margins of the Sudan are semiarid rather than arid. But most of the interior is arid desert with very light rainfall averaging at many places less than five inches annually. The Sahara is generally sparsely populated except in the oases. Nomadic herders roam parts of the area wherever grass and water for their flocks are available, but most of the people are concentrated in a few areas where there is water for irrigation. The most important of these areas is lower Egypt, where the Nile with its enormous supply of water coming from the highlands of Equatorial Africa supports 20 million people in a very small space. Otherwise the Sahara and its borderlands is a region of sparse population and low productivity, and many thousands of square miles are without people (FIG. 4.2).

The *Sudan Region* of Africa represents a transition from the dryness of the Sahara to the rainy, tropical region of the equator. In the summer season, when the sun is in the northern hemisphere, the Sudan receives torrential rains. The winter season is very dry. This alternation of rainy and dry seasons, characteristic of the Savanna climate (sometimes called the "Sudan" climate), extends all the way from Dakar on the Atlantic Coast to Ethiopia and the Red Sea on the east. Because of the rainfall in summer, the region is able to support a moderately dense population, especially along the upper Niger River and in northern Nigeria, where some districts have more than 100 persons per square mile. Pasturage is distinctly better than in the Sahara for cattle, sheep, and goats, but even so the coarse grasses are better suited to big game animals than domesticated livestock. Crops include millet, corn, cotton, rice, and root crops, such as cassava and peanuts. Both grazing and agriculture are being extended, especially where water is available for irrigation, as in the upper Niger Valley and near Khartoum on the Nile.

The *East African Highland* is a temperate region, most of which ranges in elevation from

2000 to 5000 feet. It includes Ethiopia on the north, Tanganyika Territory on the south and, in between, parts of Uganda, Kenya, and the Belgian Congo. The surface is much like an elevated plateau broken by faults in places into different levels. Above the plateau, particularly near the lakes, are rather lofty mountains, such as Kilimanjaro. The lakes are large, deep, and used considerably for local transportation. Because of its equatorial location this region receives moderate to heavy rainfall. Because of elevation of this region the temperature is somewhat more moderate but no less uniform and monotonous than that of the lowlands. Europeans have moved into this region in considerable numbers. They have become generally cultivators of export crops, such as coffee, tea, and sisal. East Africa provides more attractions to settlers from the temperate belt than any other portion of Africa, excepting only the extreme north and the extreme south. The interior of the eastern highland still suffers from lack of transportation, but railroads have been constructed from Lake Victoria and from Lake Tanganyika to the coast at Mombasa and Dar es Salaam, respectively.

Equatorial Africa lies south of the Sudan, west of the lake district, and north of the Portuguese territory of Angola. This is a low part of the African Plateau rising only slightly above 1000 feet, on the average. The Congo country of Equatorial Africa has often been compared to Amazonia. It is in the same latitude and has somewhat the same climate, but the differences perhaps are more important than the similarities. Equatorial Africa, because of its elevation, has somewhat lower temperatures than Amazonia and definitely less rainfall. This may help to explain the fact that millions of people live in Equatorial Africa while only a few thousands are scattered through Amazonia. The peoples of Equatorial Africa are generally agricultural, and many of them are on a subsistence basis, but plantations have been developed in many localities and Europeans are now moving into this region which was formerly considered unfit for white habitation. In the early days Equatorial Africa produced some quantities of wild rubber, ivory from elephant tusks, slaves, and smaller amounts of gold, pepper, and other products. It now seems well established that Equatorial Africa can be a suitable home for Europeans once the disease hazard has been reduced.

South Africa includes the Union of South Africa, plus Southern Rhodesia, southern Portuguese Mozambique, and French Madagascar. A series of plateaus, culminating with the upturned Drakensberg on the east, sets the pattern for production. On the west is the Namib Desert, almost wholly unoccupied. Further east is the Kalahari, ranging from desert to steppe, a land of poor grazing. On the west border of the Drakensberg the land is higher, cooler, and rainier, 20 to 35 inches per year. Corn, wheat, hay, and citrus fruits are grown, as the workers in the gold mines are a good market for food crops. On the lowland east of the Drakensberg, in Natal and Mozambique, the annual rainfall averages from 30 to 40 inches, favoring the production of sugarcane, cotton, sisal, and corn. Finally, the Cape District with its Mediterranean climate grows grapes, citrus fruits, wheat, and tobacco. Madagascar, an outlier of the south African plateau, is similar to the adjacent mainland, the important crops including rice, sugar, cassava, and corn.

DRAINAGE

The character of the plateaus and the climates set the pattern of drainage in Africa. Large parts of the continent send no water to the sea (FIG. 4.2), while most of the great rivers reach the ocean only after following circuitous courses, often interrupted by rapids and falls. Four great rivers, the Nile, Niger, Congo, and Zambezi, drain most of Africa. Compared to them the smaller rivers, the Senegal, the Orange, and the Limpopo, have quite small watersheds.

The Nile is the only river in Africa which flows entirely across the Sahara and reaches the Mediterranean. From its headwaters in the lake district of East Africa, the upper tributaries of the Nile flow from lake to lake and from rapid to rapid down to the flat, swampy region of southern Anglo-Egyptian Sudan. Almost immediately the desert portion of the river begins, and below the confluence with the Blue Nile at Khartoum no important tributaries enter the river. The volume of the river diminishes steadily as a result of evaporation and seepage. Six cataracts block the even flow of the river below Khartoum, but portage railroads by-pass them. The headwaters, 4000 miles above the Nile Delta, receive the heaviest precipitation in spring and early summer,

FIGURE 4.2. *A view of the Sahara on the margin of the Atlas Mountains in southern Morocco. Erosion of the dipping beds has produced a rugged terrain. The stream courses have water only at rare intervals and do not reach the sea.*

but the flood crest does not reach lower Egypt until late summer. Dams for storage of the flood-waters are planned for the lake outlets and for some of the cataracts. The Aswân dam at the first cataract, originally constructed in 1903 but later increased in height, was the first step in regulating floods and providing more water for the 20 million people of lower Egypt.

The Congo River also has its chief headwaters in the East African Highland. Shorter than the Nile, it nevertheless drains a larger watershed. From Lake Tanganyika, via the tributary Lualaba, the water tumbles over many falls and rapids. Portage railroads carry people and goods around the worst of these obstructions to the long stretches of navigable water between. The lowest falls in the Congo are above Matadi, only a short distance from tidewater, limiting the use of the lower river by ocean ships. The large volume and steep gradient of the Congo provide an enormous hydroelectric potential.

The headwaters of the Niger River are in the plateau of French Guinea, near the Atlantic Coast. The river flows northeastward into the Sudan, thence in a southeasterly direction to the delta on the coast of Nigeria. The Niger is generally navigable by small boats only, but it is linked by rail with the Senegal River to Dakar on the Atlantic and to Lagos on the Gulf of Guinea. A left bank tributary of the Niger, the Benue, is also navigable by small craft. The Zambezi River drains southern Angola and Northern Rhodesia, as well as the Lake Nyasa region. The south bank tributaries of the Zambezi, from Southwest Africa and Bechuanaland, drain dry lands and are therefore generally low in volume. The Zambezi is of little use for navigation nor does its mouth provide a shelter for ocean ships, but the numerous rapids and falls, such as Victoria Falls near Livingstone, Northern Rhodesia, offer excellent water power sites.

SOILS

The soils of Africa have not been studied in detail, and any brief treatment must be limited to generalizations. However, the broad regional distribution of soil types is fairly well known (AP-PENDIX B). In the rainforest zone where the rainfall is heavy during most of the year, the soils range from true laterites, which are thoroughly leached and generally infertile, to the immature

upland soils which give good yields without the addition of fertilizers. The amount of rainfall is a very important index to soil character; more than 80 inches is usually an indication of poor soil; less than 50 inches suggests that the soils may be fairly productive. The soils of the African rainforest are generally light in the A horizon and heavy in the B horizon, are readily cultivated, and hold water well. Large quantities of corn, bananas, cacao, palm oil, cassava, and other crops are grown on these soils, but large areas remain uncultivated.

Both to the north and south of the tropical soils are the chernozems, one belt extending across the Sudan, the other across South Africa. Dark in color, rich in lime, these soils are similar to those of the eastern parts of the Winter Wheat Belt and the Spring Wheat Belt in North America. Although the annual rainfall is comparatively light, about 15 to 25 inches, and insufficient for many crops, these soils produce wheat, barley, millet, and peanuts. With irrigation, high yields of these and other crops are obtained.

On the margins of the Sahara and in the Kalahari, where the rainfall is lighter, the chestnut brown soils are common. With less humus than the chernozems, these soils are lighter in color and have higher mineral content. They produce little except under irrigation. In the hot deserts the soils are even lighter in color and higher in mineral content, but produce well with irrigation, if the accumulation of alkali can be controlled. The irrigated crops include barley, wheat, beans, millet, cotton, and dates.

In the more temperate parts of Africa, especially in the Cape and Atlas regions with Mediterranean climate, the gray and brown soils are found, similar in character to those of southern Europe and parts of southern California. The African brown soils, however, are deficient in soluble minerals, especially phosphate, potash, and nitrogen. In spite of fairly good water supply from the rain and mountain streams, cultivation is somewhat restricted. In the cultivated areas, barley, wheat, the vine, olive, and citrus fruits are important crops, both with and without irrigation.

PEOPLES

The parallel of ten degrees north latitude (approximately) divides Africa into two broad cul-

tural divisions. In the north are white peoples—
Arabs, Berbers, Egyptians, and Europeans—who
have their own particular way of life which includes the use of livestock for grazing purposes
and also as draft animals. South of this line is
Negro Africa with its emphasis on subsistence
agriculture, the only important exceptions being
the parts of South Africa settled by Europeans.
Most of the five million or more Europeans who
live in Africa, out of a total population of 175
million, are found either in the Atlas region of
the northwest or in southeastern Africa in the
region from Capetown to Johannesburg.

The peoples of South Africa, approximately 25
million in number, include less than three million of European origin. Boers of Dutch descent,
Huguenots of French origin, and British colonists
make up most of the European element, which is
concentrated in the larger cities, Capetown, Port
Elizabeth, East London, Durban, Johannesburg,
and Pretoria. Europeans do not perform manual
labor in South Africa, as a rule. A comparatively
small number of Asiatics, 200,000 or more, live
on or near the east coast, where they are mostly
traders and merchants. The largest element in the
native population, the Bantu Negroes (locally
called Kaffirs), supplies labor for the farms and
mines. Some live on their own farms in the native
reserves, which are closed to colonization by
Europeans. In Madagascar, the native population
is largely negroid in the physical sense, but the
culture has strong Malayan characteristics, a
notable item of which is the cultivation of rice.

PRODUCTION REGIONS

The production pattern of Africa (END PAPER 3)
is the simplest of all the continents. Production
types include the *Tropical Hardwood Forest* (2h),
Nomadic Herding (3n), *Commercial Grazing* (3c),
Mediterranean Agriculture (4m), *Corn Belt* (4c),
Plantations (4p), *Oases* (4o), *Subsistence Agriculture* (5e), *Mining* (x), and *Manufacturing* too
small in amount to be shown in END PAPER 3. In
the north, south, and extreme east, the dryness
limits the people largely to pastoral pursuits, except in small districts which can be irrigated, such
as the lower Nile, the Atlas, and Drakensberg. In
the intermediate lands, the Sudan and its southern
hemisphere counterpart in Angola, as well as in
East Africa, subsistence agriculture is the rule.
Exceptions include small districts of plantations

or other commercial types, encouraged in some
instances by mining. In parts of the tropical region native farms and plantations have been established, although most of the land is still in
forest.

The production pattern of Africa is changing
rapidly. The extension of roads, railways, and
airlines is encouraging commercial agriculture
and mining in remote localities where formerly
only subsistence agriculture and grazing were
found. In recent years, the most rapid growth has
occurred in the Belgian Congo, Anglo-Egyptian
Sudan, and East Africa.

Europe

Europe, a peninsula of Asia rather than a continent, is the smallest of the land masses considered in this chapter and, also in many ways, the
most influential. In recent years the concept of
Europe as a unit has changed. The old limits were
considered to be the Mediterranean, Black, and
Caspian seas, and the Ural Mountains. Today the
Soviet Union is listed as a separate unit, and new
"Europe" is limited by a line drawn immediately
east of Finland, Poland, and Romania. This makes
the area of Europe small indeed compared with
other "continents."

SURFACE FEATURES

Europe is a "peninsula of peninsulas." This fact,
together with the character of the land surface
and the marginal seas, is of greatest significance in
the development of the region. No part of the
land is very distant from the sea, and numerous
good harbors are found, associated with the minor
indentations of the coastline. Four broad physical
regions are to be noted (FIG. 4.3): the Northwest
Highland, the Central Plain, the Massives, and
the Alpine Mountains.

The *Northwest Highland* includes Brittany in
northwestern France, all of the British Isles except southern and eastern England, Norway, most
of Sweden, and all of Finland. It is a region of
rugged hills, low mountains, and dissected plateaus. Interspersed here and there are small,
hilly lowlands. The coastline is highly irregular
with a great many fjords on the coasts of Scandinavia and the British Isles. Good harbors are
numerous, and the peoples of the Northwest
Highland look to the sea for their livelihood,

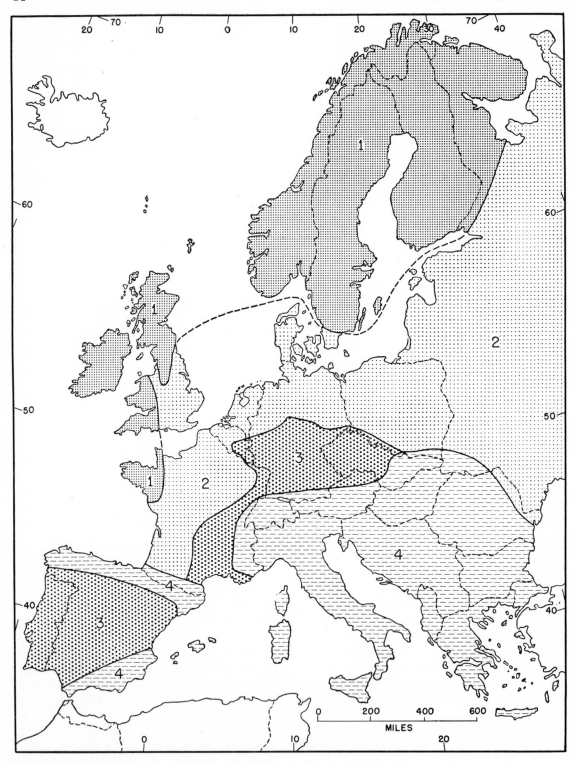

FIGURE 4.3. *The major physical regions of Europe:* 1. *The Northwest Highland.* 2. *The Central Plain.* 3. *The Massives.* 4. *The Alpine Mountains and associated lowlands.*

partly because of the favorable harbors and partly because of the limitations of the land.

The northwestern part of France, called Brittany, is a low, worn-down portion of the Northwest Highland. Elevations scarcely reach above a thousand feet, but this is a rough, hilly region, nonetheless. Much of the rock is hard and very resistant. The soils are poor, so that the people of Brittany, more than those of any other part of France, have seafaring occupations. Across the channel to the north is Cornwall, the southwestern peninsula of England. This peninsula, together with Wales, forms a part of the Northwest Highland. This is hill country, rugged in places, with steep slopes leading down to the sea. But the region provides harbors, and the people are noted for their interest in the sea. The most daring pirates of years gone by came out of the small harbors of Cornwall.

In northern England a single, long, rather narrow range of hills, called the Pennine Chain, is the dominant feature in the landscape. This chain is cut by numerous passes so that communication between the east coast of northern England and the west coast is not difficult. But the Pennine Range itself is used mostly for grazing purposes. The slopes are too steep and the climate too moist and cool for agriculture. The coalfields on the margins of the Pennines are the most important in England.

Three subdivisions of Scotland are usually recognized: the southern upland, a low plateau used mostly for grazing; the central lowland, in which most of the people live; and the northern highland, the most rugged portion of the country and very sparsely populated. The central lowland is by no means a plain. Here and there many low hills rise above the agricultural zone. Even at moderate elevations the summers are too cool for crops. The most important resource of the lowland is coal, which provides power and raw material for the industries, iron and steel, shipbuilding, and textiles, among others. Agriculture is restricted to the crops, such as rye, oats, and hay, that will grow well in a humid, cool climate. The fjords, called "firths" in Scotland, are used as water routes into the heart of the lowland partly for the importation of raw materials for the factories. A typical location for a town or city is at the head of a firth, where the stream is easy to bridge.

Scandinavia is, in effect, more like an island than a peninsula since the northern part is tied to the mainland across an isolated, sparsely populated region where Norway borders the Soviet Union. The dominant feature in the peninsula is the Norwegian Highland, running from the southern tip of Norway to the Arctic Ocean. The highland is dissected on the margins in the form of fjords and glacial valleys, but somewhat smooth and rounded on the top. The upper treeless (tundra) surfaces are pasture lands utilized for a short time in summer but far too high and cool for forestry or agriculture. Most of the people live on the margins of this highland, either on the Norwegian fjords on the west and south or in the valleys on the Swedish side of the highland. Sweden is somewhat lower in elevation but most of it is rugged also. Many finger lakes occur in the upper valleys, corresponding to the fjords on the Norwegian side. The Swedish Highland is for the most part forested, and this constitutes a major resource for the country. Sweden has long been important in the production of lumber, paper, matches, and other wood products. Finland is a low, rough, rocky land with many lakes of glacial origin. Finland too depends upon its forests for its principal resource and is an important exporter of lumber and pulp.

The Northwest Highland of Europe is definitely a region of limited opportunities because of the surface and climate, but it must be noted that the peoples have made the most of its resources and it supports a fairly dense population, at least as compared with other similar areas in the same latitude. The more favorable features include the mineral wealth, coal in the British Isles and a limited amount in southern Sweden, iron ore and limestone. Water power is abundant and relatively dependable because of the fairly high relief, as well as the heavy precipitation especially on the western side. All of the Northwest Highland was covered by the continental ice sheet, and this has left its mark on the land. The highest hills and peaks have been rounded by erosion; the ice has gouged out lake basins sometimes in solid rock and removed the soil in some districts. It has covered the lower areas with deposits of glacial material, including rocky moraines and fine clays.

The *Central Plain* of Europe is the heart of Europe. It extends from southwestern France northeastward through the Low Countries, eastern England, northern Germany, Denmark, and on into Poland and the Soviet Union. This plain lies between the Northwest Highland and the plateaulike massives farther to the south and east. The plain is by no means flat. It has many low hills, ridges, plateaus, and in many places rivers have cut rather sharp channels. The Central Plain is the most important region in Europe for agriculture and manufacturing. It is densely populated and includes a great many large cities. Excellent harbors and a close network of rivers, canals, and railroads provide good transportation.

In France, especially in the Paris Basin, many low hills or ridges rise above the general level. These ridges are often forested, but on the adjoining lowlands grains, grapes, and various other field crops, such as hay, sugar beets, and potatoes, are produced. In the Low Countries, especially along the coast of the Netherlands, the land has been reclaimed by the construction of dikes and used for hay, pasture, potatoes, and flowers. This reclamation has gone on for centuries and is still being extended. Farther to the east the plain was glaciated, and a great moraine extends from Denmark across northern Germany. Here the land is relatively poor with scattered lakes and rocky areas, but by dint of much labor and much fertilizer this area also has been brought under cultivation. A little farther south, in the vicinity of Hanover and Berlin, the soils are much better, and excellent crops are produced. In some places the plain is interspersed with marshes or flat lowlands, requiring artificial drainage.

South of the Central Plain are the rather numerous and isolated highland areas called *Massives*, dissected and irregular but rather compact in outline as contrasted to the Alpine Mountains. One of the best examples is the Central Massive of southern France rising above the plain and above the lowland of the Rhone River. One of the largest of the massives is the Meseta of Spain and Portugal. This is an upland sometimes described as a plateau but consists of a series of rather high basins separated from each other by low mountain ranges. In southern Germany and eastern France, the massives take various forms. Some are small and isolated; others are grouped together in a series. One of the latter is represented by the mountains of western Germany and northeastern France, including the Ardennes,

Eifel, Taurus, and Westerwald. The massives of central Europe are usually too high for favorable cultivation even where there is a little level land on their summits. The climate of central Europe is such that a very little elevation takes the land out of the zone favorable for cultivation. In Spain, which lies much farther to the south, dryness, rather than elevation and coolness, limits cultivation. In general the massives are rather sparsely populated compared to the adjacent plains, but nevertheless they contain many millions of people.

The *Alpine Mountains* of Europe, exemplified by the Alps, extend over a rather large area and with them are associated lowlands. The Alps proper extend from southeastern France northward through Switzerland and thence eastward through Austria to Vienna. It is a long, rather narrow, curving range, reaching heights above 15,000 feet in the core and having very rugged ranges on the margins. Other Alpine Ranges include the Pyrenees between France and Spain, the Appenines in Italy, the Dinaric Alps of Yugoslavia, and the Carpathians of Czechoslovakia and Romania. All of these mountains are long, narrow, and rather rugged. Water from the mountains is used for power and irrigation in the adjacent plains. The actual occupational use of the mountains is limited mostly to dairying, grazing, forestry, and recreation. Of special note is the summer season grazing on pastures above timberline.

The lowlands associated with the Alpine Ranges, such as the Portuguese Lowland and the Po Plain of Italy, are comparatively densely populated. The lowlands take advantage of water from the mountains, the level land, and more favorable climate for intensive cultivation. Particularly in southern Europe, where the summers are dry, the favorable location is near a lofty mountain range, from which there is a supply of water during the dry season from the melting snows on the higher peaks.

DRAINAGE

The drainage of Europe is conditioned by the moderate to heavy precipitation, the surface features, and the fact that no part of the land is very far from the sea. The rivers of Europe are comparatively short, closely spaced, and even flowing. Disastrous floods are rather rare, and only in the Mediterranean lands is extremely low water in the rivers likely to occur. A few small areas, at or below sea level, in the Netherlands, Belgium, eastern England, and near the lower Po River in Italy, require artificial drainage; otherwise the natural drainage is generally adequate.

Most of the important navigable rivers of Europe flow northward to the Bay of Biscay, the North Sea, or the Baltic Sea. A system of connecting canals facilitates exchange of goods between the various rivers. For example, canal boats can be taken from the Garonne River of southwestern France to various parts of the Low Countries, Germany, Poland, Czechoslovakia, Austria, and Hungary, via the Rhone, Rhine, Elbe, Oder, Wisla, and Danube rivers and their connecting canals. The competition of rail and truck transport, plus the ravages of war, have reduced the use of some of the canals, but many of the rivers still carry heavy traffic, especially in the bulky commodities, such as coal, iron ore, and cement. The lower reaches of the large rivers also provide good harbor for ocean shipping, a very important factor for a region so dependent on overseas trade. Many estuaries are so important as to have separate names, the *Gironde* for the lower Garonne and *London River* for the lower Thames.

Of all the rivers in Europe, the Rhine is by far the most important. It drains parts of France, Belgium, the Netherlands, Germany, Switzerland, and a small portion of Austria, passes through the heart of the European Manufacturing Belt, and taps the most important coalfields and iron mines. The even distribution of precipitation and the melting of the snowfields in the Alps give the Rhine a fairly regular flow. Floods are rare, and so are periods of extremely low water. The river is navigable below Basel on the north border of Switzerland, and a canal paralleling the river above Strasbourg makes upstream traffic much easier. Important industrial and commercial cities are located along the navigable stream, usually at the junction with an important tributary or canal. Strasbourg marks the eastern terminus of the Marne-Rhine Canal, Mannheim marks the confluence with the Neckar River, Mainz with the Main River, and Koblenz with the Moselle River. Rotterdam is the chief ocean port for the Rhine, but many other ports, such as Amsterdam and Anvers (Antwerp), share the ocean trade via connecting waterways.

Next in importance in northern Europe is the Elbe, navigable to Praha (Prague) in Czechoslovakia and connecting with the Baltic Sea via the Kiel Ship Canal and by barge canal to Lübeck. In addition to its great seaport, Hamburg, the Elbe serves Berlin, Magdeburg, Leipzig, and Dresden. In addition to the rivers mentioned above, the following are important mostly for their ocean ports: Mersey for Liverpool; Clyde for Glasgow; Forth for Edinburgh.

The Danube, largest river in Europe, is navigable to Ulm in southern Germany, but international trade restrictions along its course, the lack of a good harbor at the outlet, and the limited heavy industries in its hinterland have restricted traffic. In spite of these difficulties it carries quantities of petroleum and grain; and Wien (Vienna) and Budapest on the Danube, and Beograd (Belgrade) and Bucuresti (Bucharest) near it, owe much of their importance to the river.

The rivers of southern Europe are less important because of the long, dry summers and low water, the latter partly due to limited watersheds. Of these rivers, the Rhone is the greatest with its headwaters in humid Europe, but its delta cannot be used as an ocean harbor, and Marseille is located several miles to the east. The Po is little used for navigation because of heavy silting and excessive meandering. The Po Delta is too shallow for ocean ships and, as a result, the port for the Po Plain is Genova (Genoa), which has a small but adequate harbor. The lower reaches of such rivers as the Tejo for Lisboa and the Doura for Porto provide ocean harbors and limited navigation for small boats a few miles inland.

CLIMATIC REGIONS

Except for the absence of rainforest, savanna, and desert, the climates of Europe resemble those of North America (APPENDIX A). The cool summer, rainy, temperate climate of northwestern Europe is similar to that of the Pacific Northwest; the Mediterranean climate of the south compares with that of California; eastern Germany may be compared with northeastern United States. Studied in detail, however, the climates of the two lands show significant differences, especially in the amount and distribution of the rainfall. The following homoclimes (localities with similar climates) show both striking similarities and important differences.

A Comparison of Climatic Data for Selected Stations in Europe and the United States					
Station	Latitude	Average Temperature (degrees Fahrenheit)		Average Rainfall (inches)		Average Annual Rainfall (inches)
		Jan.	Jul.	Jan.	Jul.	
Dublin	53	40	58	2.0	2.0	27
Seattle	47	39	63	4.0	5.0	31
Rome	43	45	76	3.6	0.8	35
Sacramento	38	45	73	3.3	0.1	15
Berlin	52	31	65	1.5	3.1	22
Boston	42	29	72	4.0	3.0	38

The *Rainy Temperate Climate* (Cfb) with its mild winters, cool summers, and adequate rain at all seasons includes the British Isles, the coast of Norway, southern Sweden, northern Spain, most of France, the Low Countries, Germany, and Poland with parts of adjacent countries. In the west the rainfall maximum comes in winter, while in the east a summer maximum prevails. Rain is heaviest on the west coast of Scotland and Norway. It is lighter to the south and east, except where mountain slopes are able to extract more moisture from the air masses. Rainfall is generally sufficient for agriculture, and at certain places sometimes excessive, the more so because of the cool summers. In England the east coast is most favorable for crops because of the light rains and consequent higher temperatures and more sunshine. The most severe handicap in the Cfb climate, perhaps, is the coolness of the summers, which makes it difficult to grow many crops, such as corn and cotton. In many places the climate is not favorable even for the small grains.

Northern Europe, Scandinavia, and Finland belong largely to the cold winter climate, or *Humid Microthermal Climate* (Dfb). The winters are severe and snowy, the summers cool and comparatively short. In much of the region crops will not grow, and in the highest altitudes and latitudes (Tundra Climate ET) trees will not grow.

The *Mediterranean Climate* (Cs) of Europe extends from Portugal to Turkey and includes southern Spain, the southern coast of France, the peninsula of Italy (but not the Po Plain), the coasts of Yugoslavia, Albania, Greece, and Turkey. The winters are rainy and mild, the summers dry and warm, except for a few localities on the Atlantic where the summers are cool. The limited rainfall is partially offset by the nearness of high mountains, such as the Pyrenees and Alps, which provide water from melting snows for summer irrigation.

SOILS

The soils of Europe have been cultivated and modified for so many centuries that in many places the original quality has been lost. Lands which in North America would be considered difficult or impossible to cultivate have been patiently treated, worked, and fertilized until now they produce excellent crops. In other words, the character of the European soils today depends not only on the natural factors, such as slope, climate, and parent material, but also on the modifications made by man. The soils of the Dutch polders are quite different from those of the original salt marshes from which they were derived; the heavy clays of Flanders have been lightened by draining, plowing, and fertilizing; the soils of the French vineyards have been developed almost by formula in order to produce special qualities of grapes. These modified aspects of the soils should be considered in connection with the brief descriptions of the major soil regions.

Northern Europe, including most of Scandinavia, Finland, western British Isles, and parts of northern Germany, is dominated by the podzols. Developed mostly, but not entirely, in the zone of coniferous forests (past and present) the podzols are strongly acid and have a gray-white color in the topsoil (A horizon) and a brown subsoil, high in iron and clay. The moderate to heavy rainfall

FIGURE 4.4. *A view of the French Alps. In the foreground are neat stacks of hay and a village perched on a bench, well above the valley floor. The steep slope beyond the village produces hay also. In the higher elevations remnants of glaciers occupy the cirques between the horn-like peaks. From French Embassy, Information Division.*

results in leaching, and the lands under cultivation require liming to correct the acidity. They are improved further by the addition of other mineral fertilizers and humus. The gray-brown forest soils, with some podzolic qualities, lie in the middle zone from France to Poland. The A horizon is leached but less so than the true podzols, and the humus content is higher. The best soils of this region are found where the rainfall is comparatively light, as in eastern England, southern Sweden, and in Denmark. With the addition of fertilizer and humus, plus careful cultivation, the soils of the region produce excellent crops and, on the whole, represent the best agricultural land in Europe.

The soils of Mediterranean Europe are highly diverse but, under favorable conditions, produce well. Because of the light rainfall, leaching is not rapid and many of the soils are alkaline. Where the soils are derived from limestone, the color is often reddish, especially in the B horizon. These soils are sometimes called *terra rosa*, not to be confused, however, with the *terra roxa* of Brazil. In many of the areas of recent volcanic deposits, such as southern Italy, the soils are very fertile, encouraging the farmers to move into fresh lava flows, almost, it would seem, before the lava has cooled. Alluvial soils are extensively cultivated. However, an observer traveling through southern Europe is struck by the large areas of uncultivated land, where water is lacking, the slope too steep, or the altitude too great (FIG. 4.4).

PEOPLES

Although Europe has been invaded many times by peoples from Asia and Africa and these invasions have left their imprint on race and culture, the population is remarkably homogeneous. Three broad cultural regions may be described: the Nordic in the north and west; the Mediterranean on the south; and the Shatter Belt on the east. In northern Europe are the Nordics, generally tall, blond, and often with curly hair and blue eyes. They are seafaring people, with a strong inclination toward fishing, exploration, invention, industry, and trade. This leads to the saying, only partly true, "the blue-eyed people rule the world." Many of the Nordics are farmers, producing small grains, hay, and livestock and dairy products. The Nordic culture is more extensive than the racial characteristics. Brittany, Wales, western Ireland, and western Scotland, for example, are Celtic in race but essentially Nordic in culture.

In southern Europe, from Portugal to Greece, the Mediterranean people have dark hair, dark eyes, and are shorter than the Nordics. Less interested in the sea, the Mediterranean peoples have developed their own type of farming with emphasis on tree and bush crops, such as the olive, and with a decidedly limited development of livestock. Grapes for wine represent an important element in the culture. The cultivation is largely in small plots, often called "garden culture."

To the east, in Finland, the Baltic States, Poland, Czechoslovakia, Hungary, Yugoslavia, Romania, and Bulgaria, is the Shatter Belt, a zone of mixed culture. Slavs, Nordics, Mediterranean, and other peoples have interpenetrated but have not amalgamated. In general the culture pattern is more like that of the Nordics, but with a few exceptions, such as the Finns, the Shatter Belt peoples are not oriented toward the sea. Extensive farming is the rule, with rye, hay, and potatoes the leading crops. Industrial development is limited largely because of the lack of raw materials.

Nearly 400 million people live in Europe, excluding the Soviet Union. This represents the densest population of any large region except parts of Monsoon Asia. By most standards this represents overpopulation, especially considering the loss in trade which Europe has experienced in recent years. Formerly Europe's surplus people migrated to other lands in large numbers, but many of these lands are now closed or severely restricted. Some of the stresses of overpopulation have been temporarily relieved by loans and outright grants of billions of dollars through Lend-Lease, the Marshall Plan, and other agencies, but this apparently only postpones the day of reckoning. Only an increase in production and trade or a sharp decrease in population will bring a real solution. The alternative seems to be a lower standard of living for most Europeans for many years to come.

PRODUCTION REGIONS

The production regions of Europe correspond in a general way to the physical regions. The continental shelf, that part of the continent covered by shallow seas, supports most of the *Fisheries* (1), which are the most important in the world.

See END PAPER 3. The northern part of the highland is in *Softwood Forest* (2s), the remainder is used largely for *Dairying* (4d) and *Small-Grain and Livestock* (4s). The last mentioned also covers the Central Plain and the Massives Region. On the higher alpine mountains, especially the Alps and the Pyrenees, dairying is important, while production in the basins of the Po and Danube is classed as *Corn Belt* (4c), although differing in some respects from the North American Corn Belt. The fringe of the Mediterranean is the original home of the *Mediterranean Agriculture* (4m). *Mining* (x) is widely distributed, but most of the *Manufacturing* (•) is concentrated in a comparatively small belt, extending from central Britain through northern France and the Low Countries to northern Switzerland and central Germany.

The Soviet Union

The Soviet Union is the most continental of all regions because of its great size, high latitude, and limited access to the warm seas. A large part of its shoreline lies along the Arctic and north Pacific oceans where the harbors are closed by ice for several months of each year. To be sure, the Black Sea provides a rather roundabout outlet to the Atlantic by way of the Mediterranean, but this is of significance to only a small part of the Soviet land. The continental character of the Soviet Union is partly responsible for the limited trade with other countries and perhaps for its political isolation as well. In size the Soviet Union is very much a continent. With more than eight million square miles of territory, it is almost as large as North America and is larger by far than any other country in the world. Large parts of this vast territory are relatively unproductive because of light precipitation or long severe winters. The population, approximately 200 millions, is concentrated largely in the west, between the Carpathians and the southern Ural Mountains.

SURFACE FEATURES AND DRAINAGE

The surface features of the Soviet Union are on a larger scale and generally less complicated than those of other large regions. Of primary importance is the vast plain or lowland, reaching from the Arctic Ocean to the Black and Caspian seas (FIG. 4.5) and, except for the low range of the Ural Mountains, from Poland to the middle Yeni-

sei River. This plain is nearly 3000 miles long and from 1200 to 1500 miles in width and has an area greater than that of the United States. In this plain most of the people of the Soviet Union live, and here most of the production occurs. To the southeast and east of this plain is a series of lofty mountains, the Caucasus, the Pamirs, Tien Shan, Altai, and many lesser ones. So far as the territory of the Soviet Union is concerned, this mountainous belt is rather narrow along the borders of Turkey, Iran, Afghanistan, and Pakistan. Farther east it is wider but also much lower in elevation, with the aspect of rough hill land rather than mountains.

In a country with comparatively few railroads, the rivers, lakes, and seas take on added importance. Most of the Soviet Union's large rivers are used to transport heavy goods, coal, oil, and timber; some are used for power and irrigation. The low gradients of the rivers in the great plain, however, limit power development to a few favorable sites, and most of the mountain power sites are far from population centers. The important rivers of the Soviet Union can be grouped according to their outlets, the Black Sea, the Caspian and Aral seas, the Arctic Ocean, and the Pacific.

The Ukrainian rivers, the Dnestr, Bug, Dnepr, and the Don, drain to the Black Sea through rich farming lands, past coal mines and steel mills. These rivers flow gently in a southeasterly direction, the Dnepr and the Don turning to the southwest in their lower courses. Navigable only in their lower courses, these rivers are most important for water supply. The Dnepr at Dnepropetrovsk also furnishes large amounts of hydroelectric energy. The Don, although a rather small river, serves the very important Donbas industrial region. The Volga and Ural rivers flow into the Caspian Sea, which is 85 feet below sea level, and the Amu Darya and Sir Darya flow into the Aral Sea, also in a closed basin. In more humid times, the Aral Sea had an outlet to the Caspian, and the Caspian drained into the Black Sea. Only the Volga carries large quantities of freight, nearly half the tonnage of the nation. The Amu and Sir are used extensively for irrigation.

The chief Arctic rivers, the northern Dvina, the Pechora, Ob, Yenisei, Lena, and Kolyma, are frozen for a large part of the year. Since they also flow through sparsely populated regions, their usefulness is limited. However, in the open season the Dvina, Pechora, and Ob carry large quantities of timber to the Arctic ports. A proposal has been made to divert the upper tributaries of the Ob southward toward Turkestan where the longer summers are more favorable for irrigation agriculture. The only large river in the Pacific drainage is the Amur, which forms the boundary for many hundreds of miles between the Soviet Union and Manchuria. It will be noted that the headwaters of the Lena and Kolyma reach almost to the Pacific in several places and as a consequence no large rivers drain to the Pacific north of the Amur. The Amur has its headwaters to the east of Lake Baikal and flows through a broad plain which has seen great growth in agricultural and mineral production in recent years. The river and its tributaries, the Sungari and Zeya, are navigable by river steamers and are important in this pioneer belt, supplementing the Trans-Siberian Railway, which roughly parallels the Amur.

CLIMATIC REGIONS

The climate of the Soviet Union can be described as one with severe winters, rather cool summers, and light precipitation, excepting only some of the higher mountain areas (see APPENDIX A). Precipitation is so light in parts of the Soviet Union as to impose a severe handicap upon the utilization of the land for agriculture, grazing, or forestry. Only the lands along the Black Sea and the southern Caspian can be described in any sense as mild in climate, and these areas are quite small.

In the Great Plain of Russia landforms are so monotonous that geographic subdivisions are based upon vegetation and climate rather than on hill, plateau, and plain. On the northern fringe, extending from the Kola Peninsula all the way to the Pacific, is a belt of treeless country known as the tundra (FIG. 4.5). The tundra has severe winters and short summers, too short for trees to grow. It is covered with shrubs, grasses, flowers, mosses, and lichens. The rivers which flow through it to the Arctic are frozen most of the year. This country is still peopled in part by nomads who support themselves with herds of reindeer and by hunting and fishing. South of the tundra is the great northern forest, extending from Leningrad again all the way to the Pacific. This is a belt of coniferous trees mixed with hardwoods on the southern margin. It constitutes one of the greatest resources of temperate belt timber left on the earth. However, some of it is at present inaccessible because of the lack of transportation. This forest belt, in general, is too cool in summer for agriculture, and the agricultural peoples have penetrated only part of its southern margin. To the south of the forest is the great agricultural belt of Russia where most of the people live and where most of them work. This belt extends from the Carpathian Mountains across the southern Urals, across the middle part of western Siberia, and interrupted in places by hills and mountains, extends all the way to the Pacific. It is a region of light rainfall, severe winters, and rather cool summers, but it is favorable, in general, for the growth of wheat, rye, oats, barley, and hay. A part of this agricultural belt is often referred to as the Black Earth Belt of Russia because of the dark nature of the soils (chernozem).

The mountains and basins of eastern Siberia have the coldest winters found on the earth, so far as present records indicate. These winters are almost without precipitation, and the rainfall of summer comes at the most favorable time for the crops. Efforts made by the Soviet government to settle this region have met with considerable success. The valleys between the mountains can be cultivated during the short summer. The forests and the minerals are also being exploited. Production of furs is especially important.

SOILS

In the great plain of the Soviet Union the soil-forming factors, climate and vegetation acting on rock material, are not complicated by the great variety of landforms and rock material found in many other lands. The soils map is, therefore, comparatively simple, and this has made it possible for Russian soil scientists to make some very valuable generalizations concerning soils.

In the north, along the fringe of the Arctic, are the tundra soils, the subsoil continuously frozen, the topsoil consisting largely of slowly decaying vegetation. Even if the summers were long enough, the tundra soils would be difficult to cultivate. In the northern forest belt the podzols are dominant. Under the thin cover of organic material, consisting largely of coniferous needles, is a sandy layer of ash-colored material. The subsoil is generally brown, heavy with clay. The southern part of the podzol belt is cultivated.

The most productive soil in the Soviet Union is the "black earth," or chernozem. This soil occurs south of the forest belt, mainly on grassland. It is rich in soluble minerals and will stand up under cultivation for many years without the addition of fertilizer. This is the great "wheat" soil of the Soviet Union, but like other similar areas, the yield is limited by low rainfall. In the dry lands to the south of the chernozem are the brown desert soils, which are high in soluble mineral and can be cultivated only with the aid of irrigation. Even so they are likely to suffer from the accumulation of salt at the surface.

PEOPLES

Three fourths of the 200 million people of the Soviet Union are Slavs and the remainder are mostly of Mongoloid, Iranian, or Turkic origin. The original home of the Slavs appears to have been near the Carpathian Mountains, from which migrations led northeastward into what became European Russia, and southward into the Balkan Peninsula. Invasions of Mongoloid peoples brought Asiatic elements, both racial and cultural, into western Russia, but an old saying, "scratch a Russian and you find a Tartar," is an exaggeration. Invasions of Nordic peoples also left their mark, especially on the "White Russians," who are taller and fairer than their neighbors to the south and east. Customs were influenced more than complexion, however, and such cultural traits as house types and industrial organization have been borrowed from the west.

The population of the Soviet Union is predominantly rural, although the urban population is increasing very rapidly as the country is industrialized. The center of population lies west of the Volga, but as new industrial centers are developed in the Urals and in Siberia, it is shifting to the east. The pattern of settlement varies with the environment. In the extreme north, nomadic hunters and herders are widely scattered. Isolated lumber towns occupy clearings in the forest near the rivers. In the agricultural sections many of the farmers live in "street villages," all the farmhouses strung together in a line along a single road. In Turkestan many of the people are nomadic, although the increase in irrigation and commercial crops, such as cotton, has caused many herders to become sedentary farmers. The population of the Soviet Union has increased rapidly in recent decades, and as a consequence it is a nation of young people.

PRODUCTION REGIONS

The production regions of the Soviet Union are comparatively simple. On the north is the *Softwood Forest* (2s), with its great reserve of coniferous trees and lesser amounts of hardwood. (See END PAPERS 3 and 4.) In the west, European Russia, as it was formerly called, is the *Small-Grain and Livestock Region* (4s), a triangular region with Leningrad, Kiev, and Sverdlovsk (in the Urals) at the corners. The great *Russian Wheat Belt* (4w) reaches from Odessa and Kiev on the west to the southern Urals and thence into Siberia. This is by far the most extensive wheat belt in the world, but production in recent years has been less than that of the United States. In addition to the large regions mentioned above, the Soviet Union has a large area of *Nomadic Herding* (3n), a small section of *Corn Belt* (4c) on the lower Danube, and numerous irrigated *Oases* (4o). *Mining* (x) is widely scattered while most of the *Manufacturing* (·) is located in the west.

Asia

Even without Siberia, Asia is a large continental mass, stretching from the eastern Mediterranean around the fringes of the Indian Ocean and far north on the Pacific Coast. It contains many millions of square miles and includes more than a billion people. It is important to note that all the countries of Asia, from Turkey on the west to China and Japan on the east, have access to the sea, and yet with a few exceptions the peoples of Asia are not maritime in their interests or character.

Asia, as defined above, has two distinct broad regional divisions (FIG. 4.5). These might be characterized as Dry Asia and Monsoon Asia. More particularly, the dry part of Asia includes the southwestern part, Turkey, Arabia, Iraq, Iran, Afghanistan, and part of Pakistan. It also includes the high plateaus, interior basins, and mountain ranges of Tibet and western China. Humid Asia is more properly described as Monsoon Asia. India, Burma, Indochina, Siam, Indonesia, eastern China, and Japan are all profoundly affected by the monsoon, especially the summer monsoon.

DRY ASIA

Dry Asia is a land of plateaus, comparatively small mountain ranges on the west, larger plateaus and more lofty ranges on the east. There are a few basins, such as Mesopotamia or the basin of the Indus River or the Tarim Basin to the north of the Himalayas. Some of these basins are capable of intensive irrigation and have, therefore, a fairly dense population; but others are limited by their water supply and thus support only a few people. In general, southwestern Asia is sparsely populated. Many of the people are nomads, or at least herders, and live by their flocks alone. Irrigated oases are few and far between. The only large ones are those of the Tigris and Euphrates and of the Indus River. These support a rather large population on the basis of the cultivation of grains, fruits, cotton, and other crops.

The great handicap of this region is the lack of water. The plateaus of the mountains do not intercept enough rain or snow to supply the needs of the adjacent basins. The interior parts of Dry Asia, the plateau of Tibet and western China, are, therefore, very sparsely populated. Here, in addition to the dryness is the handicap of high altitude, altitude too high for crops to grow. Many of the people are nomadic herders; others, like the Tibetans, are sedentary herders and are able to find enough forage and water for their animals, so that it is not necessary to move about from place to place. Yaks, horses, and sheep are the principal animals of the nomadic herders, this region being generally too cold for camels. The region does have great mineral wealth, especially petroleum. In recent years the development and exploitation of petroleum in Iran, Iraq, and Arabia have brought great changes in the life of the people.

MONSOON ASIA

More than half the people of the world live in "Monsoon Asia," a region of intensive subsistence agriculture in southeastern Asia which embraces India, China, Japan, and Indonesia (FIG. 4.5). Monsoon Asia is distinguished by its monsoon climate, dense population, and intensive subsistence agriculture. The alternating seasonal winds, from the ocean in summer and from the land in winter, correspond with the rainy season in summer and the dry season in winter. There are many local variations, especially in the amount of rainfall. The summers are generally hot but the length of the growing season varies; the winters near the equator are imperceptible except in terms of the dry season, but farther north, in Manchuria, the cold season is long and severe. On the deltas and flood plains of the great rivers, the peoples of Monsoon Asia have taken advantage of the humid climate and the fertile soils to develop an intensive agriculture almost unique in its application of enormous quantities of hand labor to small plots of land. Concurrently with the development of this intensive farming, the population has increased up to and at times even beyond the available food supply until this part of the world supports more than 1200 million people. The outstanding food is rice, but it is by no means the only crop. In some areas where rice does not yield well because of inadequate rainfall or short season, other food crops—millet, sorghum, wheat, barley, and soybeans—take its place. There are also important industrial crops like cotton, jute, and rubber. Monsoon Asia is rich in minerals, coal, iron ore, and petroleum, and although it has been and still is predominantly agricultural, industrial production has made substantial progress.

SURFACE FEATURES AND DRAINAGE

From western India through China to Japan, alluvial plains, plateaus, and mountains alternate in a varied pattern. Most of the people live in the plains, but the mountains and plateaus are very important in supplying water for irrigation of the plains. The plains are of various sizes and shapes. The Plain of the Ganges, the Hwang Ho, and the Manchurian Plain are large; those of the lower Yangtze, Irrawaddy, and Mekong are intermediate in area. Hundreds of smaller plains are found throughout Monsoon Asia, and most of them are under intensive cultivation. Small plains are especially characteristic of Japan.

The plateaus are less intensively cultivated, but even here many places are populous. The Deccan of India, an old lava plateau, presents a steep front to the west but slopes generally to the east, most of the rivers flowing to the Bay of Bengal. Only a small part of the Deccan can be irrigated, but rainfall is sufficient in most parts for cultivation of cotton, millet, and other crops. The great plateaus of China, especially in Yünnan, Sze-

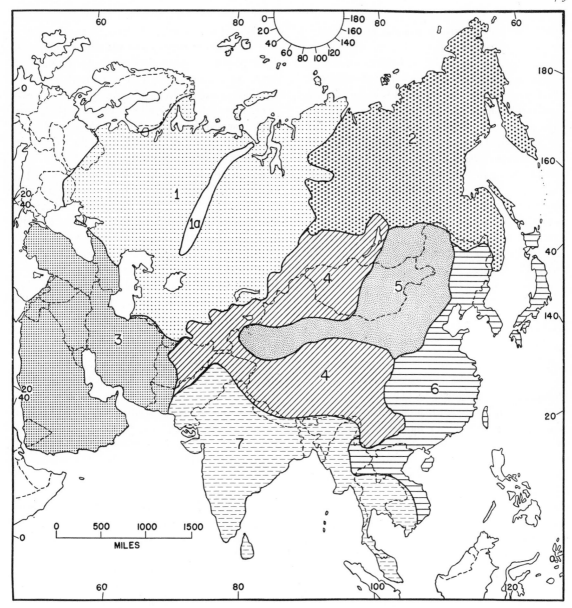

FIGURE 4.5. *A generalized map of the physical regions of the U.S.S.R. and Asia. 1. The Great Plain of Russia, interrupted but not completely divided by the low Ural Mountains (1a). 2. The hill, plateau, and mountain land of eastern Siberia. 3. The basins, plateaus, and mountains of southwestern Asia. 4. The lofty mountains of Russia, India, and China. 5. The arid interior plateaus. 6. The alluvial plains, hills, and small mountain ranges of eastern China, Korea, and Japan. 7. The plains and plateaus of India and southeastern Asia. (For more detailed map of surface features see Cressey, George B., Asia's Lands and Peoples.)*

chwan, and Shansi, are likewise moderately populated. The valley bottoms and the lower slopes are often intensively cultivated, using the waters derived from the upper slopes. In Shansi much of the plateau is covered with loess, a wind-deposited silt of great fertility, but subject to severe erosion if improperly handled.

To the north, Monsoon Asia is fringed by mountains, the Himalayas, the Tsinling Shan, the Great Khingan ranges, and many lesser ones. The Himalayas, capped by Mt. Everest, the highest point on the earth, present an almost unbroken front to the Ganges and Brahmaputra plains. The ranges provide water for irrigation, and the headwaters of many great rivers are located either in the Himalayas or in the Tibetan Plateau to the north. The Ganges, Yangtze, and Hwang Ho are all large rivers. The Irrawaddy, Menam, and Mekong bring quantities of water to the lowlands.

CLIMATIC REGIONS

All of southeastern Asia, from India to Manchuria and from the heart of China to Java, is more or less under the influence of the monsoon wind. During the summer the wind blows from the sea to the land bringing with it abundant moisture which is so necessary for intensive agriculture. In winter the winds blow from the land to the sea to the accompaniment of light rainfall or even drought. The explanation of this phenomenon is fundamentally as simple as the movement of air above a heated stove. In summer the great continent of Asia becomes heated by the intense rays of the high sun, the air expands, and the pressure falls. The moisture-laden air from the Indian and Pacific oceans moves toward the heart of Asia, the center of low pressure. In western India the winds blow from the southwest, in Burma from the south, in China and Japan from the southeast and east. When the moist air masses strike the land heavy precipitation is the result, especially where mountains or hills force the air upward. This is the "bursting" of the monsoon, the yearly salvation of millions who depend so completely on soil and weather. An early monsoon means good crops and plenty. A poor or delayed monsoon brings famine, misery, and death. Forecasts of the approach of the summer monsoon come from the islands in the Indian and Pacific oceans. From these reports the people on the continent know when to expect the first heavy rains.

In winter the conditions are reversed. The land is cold and the pressure is high. Air masses move from the land to the sea, but the cold air contains little moisture. As a result the precipitation is light in winter throughout southeastern Asia. Rainfall is heavy enough in many places, however, to enable the people to grow small grains such as wheat, barley, and millet. Where the winter monsoon strikes elevated areas the rainfall is greater than in the lowlands.

In all these Oriental Lands—India, China, Japan, and the East Indies—the summer season is rainy, and the winter has light rains or no rain at all. The length of the wet season varies greatly with location. On the west coast of India, the Malabar Coast, the rainy season is eight months long, and the short rainless period is mitigated by the magnitude of the total precipitation. Although rainfall is of primary importance in the Orient, temperature plays a very significant role in the distribution of crops and in the distribution of population, which is so intimately related to the crop pattern. The similarity of climate for the region as a whole should be kept in mind, especially with reference to the summer maximum of rain and the prevailing high temperatures of that season. The climate varies from the Rainforest (Af) of the low latitudes to the Humid Microthermal (Dwa) of Manchuria.

SOILS

Although the soils of Monsoon Asia are highly complex and variegated, especially if the mountain and marsh soils are included, the six major types described below characterize the major agricultural regions (APPENDIX B). Although the major qualities of the soils depend on climate, parent material, and natural vegetation, centuries of cultivation, irrigation, drainage, and fertilization have modified the original character.

In the rainiest parts of Monsoon Asia, southern and eastern India, eastern Pakistan, Burma, Thailand, Indochina, and Indonesia, lateritic soils are found. Heavy rains, high temperatures, and the humus acids from the tropical forests have produced a highly leached soil, very low in soluble minerals and often partially cemented. The subsoil is often hard enough to be carved into bricks and used for building purposes. The Hindu word "later," from which the soil name is de-

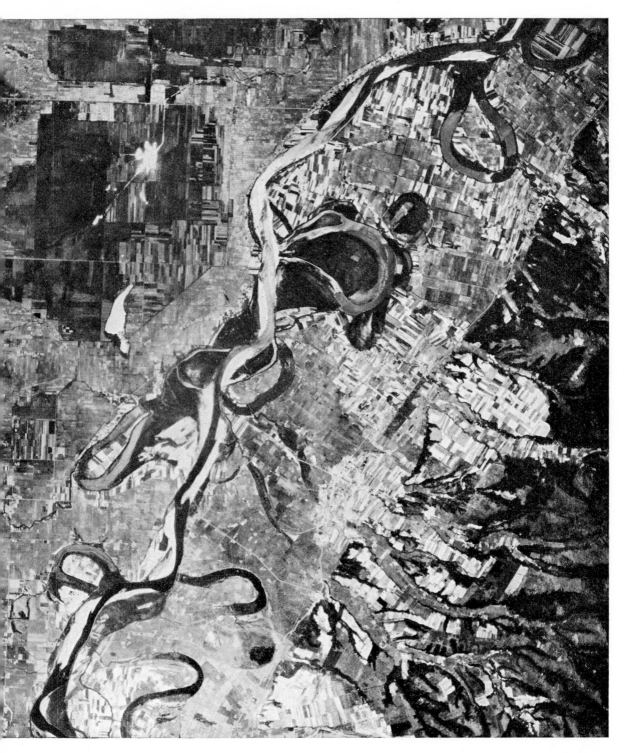

FIGURE 4.6. *Vertical view of rice paddies and other cultivated fields in southwestern Hokkaido, Japan. Notice the meandering stream with cutoffs and the small size of the fields, some of which appear on the sides of the hills. From USAF.*

rived, means "brick." In climax form the lateritic soils are infertile and difficult to cultivate. Fortunately the soils of the most humid parts of Monsoon Asia are often developed on recent alluvium (FIG. 4.6) or on recent deposits of volcanic materials.

The red and yellow soils are found in the savanna climates which have a distinct dry season, such as northern India and southern China. Leaching is less evident, and lime and magnesium salts are present. The topsoil varies from brown to black; the subsoil is generally reddish or yellow. These subtropical forest soils, easier to cultivate and more fertile than the laterites, produce large quantities of rice, also wheat, barley, sugarcane, and many other crops.

Two large areas of chernozem soils occur in Monsoon Asia, one in the Deccan Plateau of India and the other in Manchuria. Both are regions of moderate rainfall, but the temperature conditions are widely divergent. The Deccan might be considered as a tropical chernozem, while the Manchurian regions may be compared with the Red River region of North Dakota as far as soils are concerned. In India the chernozem (locally called "regur") is from three to six feet thick and has enough clay in the subsoil to hold water well. This is an important quality if the soil is to be irrigated. The soluble mineral content is adequate and so is the humus. Cotton and millet are grown on this soil often without irrigation; if irrigation is possible, rice yields well. The chernozem of Manchuria is perhaps the most fertile soil of China. Rainfall ranges from 15 to 25 inches annually in the "zone" of the chernozem. The freezing of the soil in winter minimizes the leaching of the soluble minerals. Wheat, barley, and soybeans are the principal crops, since the summers are not long enough to grow rice. Bordering the chernozem soil belts of India and Manchuria on the dry side are the chestnut brown soils, somewhat similar to the chernozems, except for higher soluble mineral content and lower humus content.

In the North China Plain and part of Japan, the gray-brown forest soils reflect the temperate climate and moderate rainfall. The soils are largely derived from recent alluvium and are not always mature. They are well supplied with soluble minerals and are easy to cultivate. In Japan most of the crops are grown on small alluvial plains and deltas without mature soil profiles.

The more recent the deposit of alluvium, the better the Japanese farmers like it. Older alluvium on the upper terraces and some of the volcanic deposits are not fertile, and most of the surface is too steep for cultivation. On the favored land, rice, barley, wheat, sweet potatoes, fruits, and vegetables are grown by intensive methods.

The podzols of Monsoon Asia are limited largely to northern Japan, northern Manchuria, and the island of Sakhalin. These highly leached soils of the coniferous forests are not extensively cultivated. Most of the crops are grown on the flood plains and deltas.

PEOPLES

It is estimated that more than 1200 million people live in Monsoon Asia. No accurate enumeration has ever been made; so this figure may be in error by 100 million or more. Yet parts of Monsoon Asia are sparsely populated, particularly the high mountains and the drier regions.

The people of India and Pakistan are partly of Mongoloid extraction, but Caucasoid elements are strong in the north and Negroid influences are notable in the south and in Ceylon. These three groups, Mongoloid, Caucasoid, and Negroid, have mingled in Pakistan and India to produce a more complicated racial and cultural pattern than that in any other part of Asia. Religious differences are marked. Of the 425 million people (more or less) in India and Pakistan, 250 million practice Hinduism, 100 million are Mohammedans, six million are Christians, and the remainder belong to various sects or are without religious affiliation. Religion plays a very important part in the culture. Hindus, for example, raise cattle but do not eat beef.

The peoples of Burma, Malaya, Siam, South Indochina, and Indonesia are largely Mongoloid in character, most of them related to the Chinese. Some Caucasoid and Negroid characteristics are to be found. Burma and Siam have approximately 17 million total population each, Malaya five million, Indochina 27 million, Indonesia about 80 million, a total of nearly 150 million for southeastern Asia.

Estimates of China's population based on sample counts of small areas range from 325 to 460 million. The total area is over 3,850,000 square miles, but only a small part supports a dense population. However, in some rural areas the population reaches more than 800 per square mile. Most of the people of China are farmers, concentrating large amounts of hand labor on small plots of land, less than one half acre per person. Famines caused usually by floods or drought are common and have probably caused the death of 100 million or more in the last century. Famine, war, disease, and migration tend to keep the population fairly stable. Millions of Chinese migrated to Manchuria, Malaya, Indonesia, and other lands in the last centuries.

Japan's area and population were reduced, following World War II, to approximately 142,000 square miles and 80 million people. The average density is over 500 per square mile and over 3000 per square mile of cultivated land. The Japanese are Mongoloids, with short, thick-set bodies and large heads. Most of the people are farmers, but fishing is quite important, and Japan is the most industrialized nation of Monsoon Asia.

PRODUCTION REGIONS

In Monsoon Asia, the dominant type of production is classed as *Oriental Agriculture* (50). See END PAPER 4. If more space were available, it would be desirable to indicate several subdivisions. Obviously there is great variety, from the cottonfields of the Deccan to the rice paddies of eastern Pakistan, Java, and Kwangtung, to the millet and soybean fields of Manchuria. In Chapter 26 three broad subdivisions are suggested, the Rice and Plantation Crops type, the Rice and Small Grains type, and the Millet type. Small areas of *Plantation* (4p) and *Tropical Forest* (2h) are also present. In addition to agriculture, which is of prime importance, *Mining* (x), *Fisheries* (1), and *Manufacturing* (·) are significant in the economy of Monsoon Asia.

Oceania

Oceania includes Australia, New Zealand, Papua, and various islands of the southern Pacific, which are usually divided into the categories of Micronesia, Melanesia, and Polynesia. It is an extensive area, but the land surface is not great except for Australia, which is almost as large as the United States.

Perhaps the most important quality of Oceania is its remoteness from centers of dense population. It is a great distance by land or sea from eastern Australia or New Zealand to eastern North America or to western Europe. The distance to the densely populated areas of Asia is

not so great, but then the associations for trade and communication are by no means so urgent.

The climates of Oceania (see APPENDIX A) include the tropical rainforest on some of the islands near the equator, the temperate climates of eastern Australia and New Zealand, and also the arid desert of central and western Australia. Actually a very large proportion of the total land surface is dry, although most of the smaller islands are humid.

Australia, the largest unit in Oceania, is of continental size. A compact continent with very little indented coastline, it has a few good harbors on the east and south, but not so many on the west. Australia has three rather broad surface regions (FIG. 4.7), a western plateau, an interior basin, and an eastern mountain range. The western plateau of hard rock including granite rises to elevations of 2000 feet or more. It is notable mostly for its mineral content, especially gold and uranium. In the southwest there is a small subhumid area in the vicinity of Perth, in which wheat is the chief crop. The interior lowland, a part of which is referred to as the Artesian Basin, is an alluvial plain for the most part, similar to the Great Plains of the United States or the Argentine Pampa. However, the rainfall is light, less than 10 inches annually in the west, and only a small portion on the south and east is suitable for cultivation without irrigation. In general, the wells of the Artesian Basin have been used to supply water for livestock and for domestic purposes rather than for extensive irrigation. Irrigation is practiced along the Murray and Darling rivers but is not very extensive. Eastern Australia is characterized by a low, plateaulike mountain range known as the Great Dividing Range. Its highest elevation scarcely reaches 7000 feet, and it is broken by passes which provide access from the east coast to the interior. It is a region of moderate rainfall. Humid grazing, dairying, and lumbering are of some importance. Tasmania is but an isolated southern extension of this mountainous district. It is a hilly island with very little level land, cooler and wetter than the mainland.

The two islands of New Zealand plus many smaller islands represent about 100,000 square miles of territory and support about two million people. In general, New Zealand is humid and temperate but with a distinct dry season in the north and with heavier rainfall in the south.

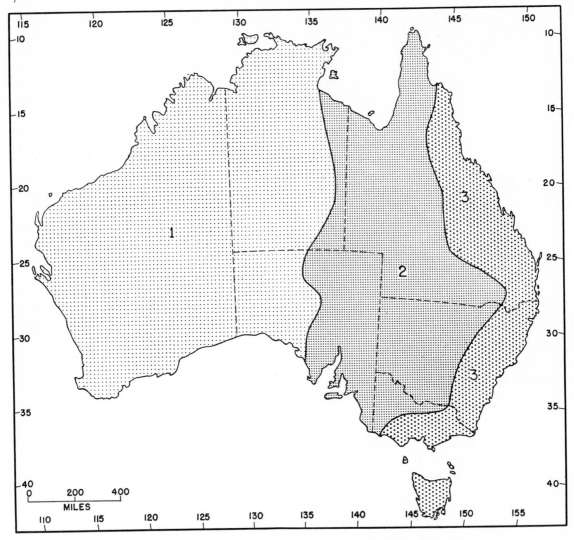

FIGURE 4.7. *Map of the major physical regions of Australia. 1. Western Plateau, underlain in part by hard, crystalline rocks. Dunes and dry lake beds are common. 2. Central Lowland, including a large artesian basin. 3. Eastern Highland, which includes Tasmania. The southern part of this highland is called the Great Dividing Range.*

Settled by people from Britain, New Zealand is in many ways a counterpart of the British Isles, except for the limited industrial development. Grains are grown in the most favorable places. Grazing of sheep and cattle is very extensive. Dairy farms are common, and the exports include wool, butter, and meat.

In the Pacific Islands from the Solomons to Hawaii to Tahiti conditions are quite different from those of Australia and New Zealand. Most of the islands are more tropical in character, with-

out a cool season and with only a short dry season. Many of the islands rise only a few feet above sea level and have very little soil on the coral rock. Other islands, partially of volcanic origin, rise several hundred or even thousands of feet above sea level and present a much greater variety of surface (FIG. 4.8). In general the people have depended upon fishing, the coconut, and cultivation of food crops, such as taro, for their livelihood. In recent years plantations have been established in many of the islands to produce

FIGURE 4.8. *A view of the northeast margin of the island of Hawaii. The dissected lower slopes with steep sea cliffs and cultivated land is typical of many volcanic islands in the Pacific. From USAF.*

copra, sugar, pineapples, and other crops, and there has been some immigration to the islands from the mainland of Asia.

The production types of Oceania include the following: *Commercial Fishing* (1), around most of the islands, especially Tasmania; *Hardwood Forest* (2h), interior of the larger islands, such as Papua, and uncleared portions of southeast Australia; *Commercial Grazing* (3c), Australia and New Zealand; *Dairying* (4d), southeast Australia and New Zealand; *Plantations* (4p), northeast Australia, various islands; *Wheat Belt* (4w), southeast Australia (west of mountains), a small area in southwest Australia; *Small-Grain and Livestock* (4s), South Island, New Zealand; also *Mining* (x) and *Manufacturing* (•).

SUMMARY

From a study of this chapter and the preceding one it will be noted that the background of production is distinct for every region on the earth. The differences in specific qualities, such as climate, may appear negligible when some regions are compared, but a study of all the elements is certain to bring out significant contrasts. To a variable extent these differences are related to the great variety of production. Some elements merely limit production, as the frost on the slopes of the Colombian Andes limits the distribution of coffee plantations. Some elements suggest new forms of production. The wild groves of the sour orange in Florida suggested to some that the sweet orange could be grown commercially. Certainly many elements in the physical and cultural background influence the character, amount, and distribution of production. But man is a clever worker, and he frequently overcomes or modifies "influences." Study of the background is indispensable for the understanding of production, but careful examination of all the possibilities is necessary before a satisfactory conclusion can be reached. In many cases the major part of the explanation lies in the cultural heritage of the people who produce.

5

Products of the Seas

NEARLY three fourths of the earth's surface is ocean. There are 140 million square miles of ocean, 45 times the area of the United States. The chief function of the oceans, from the standpoint of mankind, is to supply moisture to the lands. A secondary, although significant, use is for transportation. Man, accustomed to land production, gets little in the way of food or other materials from the seas. Yet almost all the surface waters of the oceans, especially close to the shore, contain potential food. The total amount of vegetation of the oceans is greater than that of the land. The tallest plants (kelps) and the largest animals (whales) live in the sea.

The oceans of the world produce more than a billion dollars worth of marine products annually, which is a very small amount when compared with agricultural production. In addition to the common food fishes, large quantities of crustaceans, mollusks, and seaweed are used for food. Whaling has declined, partly as a result of overexploitation, but whale oil is still an important source of fat for some countries. A good market is found for pearls and shell in spite of the production of the "culture" pearls. Fertilizer and glue are made from the scrap material of the food fish. Magnesium, the lighest commercial metal, is extracted from sea water, as is a large proportion of the world's common salt. The variety of potential products is enormous, but the very nature of the oceans makes it difficult for man to advance from the "gathering" stage to more intensive kinds of exploitation as he has on the lands. It will not be easy to "farm" the seas or domesticate the sea animals, although much progress has been made in the planting of oysters in Japanese, French, and United States waters.

North America

North Americans, as a whole, are not large consumers of fish. The per capita consumption in the United States is about 20 pounds per year, as compared with 48 pounds in Great Britain, 70 pounds in Sweden, and more than 80 pounds in Japan (1950). Until recently it has been difficult to obtain fresh sea foods in the great interior of the continent; but with improved methods of freezing and marketing fresh fish, however, no place in North America need lack for the fresh and tasty products of the sea. Refer to FIGURE 5.1.

Changes in the productive economy of the continent will probably encourage increased production of fish. As the population increases, and as the soils wear out, the per capita meat supply declines and prices rise. Even before World War II, beef was a luxury to millions of Americans. Under these circumstances it is natural to turn to the marginal seas for additional protein food. Production, of many species at least, can be increased, but a certain amount of "education" is necessary before many people will eat more fish. Increased consumption of fish began in earnest during World War II when beef, pork, and lamb were scarce.

The great fishing grounds of the world lie in the shallow waters of the Northern Hemisphere, off the coasts of middle and northern North America, northwestern Europe, and eastern Asia (FIGS. 5.1 and 5.8). In all these areas the conditions are favorable for fishing: large areas of shallow, "hard" bottom; abundant fish food derived from the rivers flowing into the seas; nearby areas of dense population with limited supplies of land-produced meat. North America is the poorest market in the Northern Hemisphere for fish, since the continent receives a relatively good supply of meat. Europe is a good market, and the hungry millions of eastern Asia will eat more fish if they can get them.

In the tropical regions there are many fish of numerous varieties, but because of the rocky uneven bottom large-scale fishing is difficult. Marketing is made difficult by reason of the great variety of fish; and the peoples of many of the tropical lands, such as Brazil, are so well supplied with beef that they have little interest in fish. Thus it is that the resources of the sea, unlike those of the land, have not yet been thoroughly

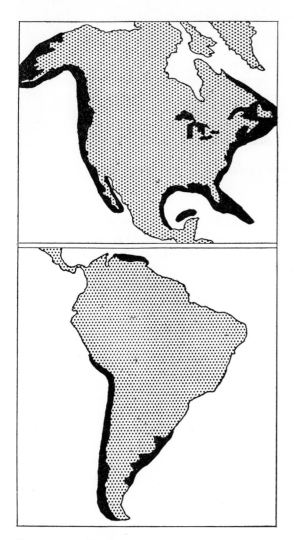

FIGURE 5.1. *Chief fishing banks of the Americas are indicated by black areas.*

exploited. Several times the present catch could easily be supplied from many of the fishing grounds of the world if the demand for fish increased. With population growing in many parts of the world, it is likely that fishing will play a greater role in the future than in the past.

THE ENVIRONMENT OF THE FISHERIES

The production of fish in large quantities depends upon a number of factors. First in importance is shallow water, with a depth not greater than 600 feet, preferably less. The bottom should be firm and smooth. Food for the fishes, the *plankton,* must be abundant, for even the carnivorous fishes are dependent ultimately on this conglomeration of minute organisms. The basic food of the fish, *plankton,* is made up of minute organisms, such as algae, protozoa, and rotifers, which thrive by virtue of the abundant light in the water over the banks, water which contains soluble minerals and other material brought from the land by streams. Currents which stir up the minerals from the floors of the banks are also helpful in maintaining the supply of *plankton;* thus the stormy area of the cyclonic winds, especially in latitudes 40° to 60°, provides the best fishing.

Requirements of water temperature, salinity, and current vary with different kinds of fish, but the shallow waters of the middle latitudes are more favorable for the common varieties. Good harbors are needed as bases for the fishing fleets, and an irregular coastline affords more shoreline for inshore fisheries. Because of unproductive land area near the fishing banks, as in Newfoundland, the people usually turn to the sea and fishing, but in order for them to produce large quantities of fish and make a profit, areas of considerable population must be near by as a market for at least part of the catch. Such a combination of conditions limits the large-scale production of fish to a few regions.

On the continental shelf of North America, off the coasts of New England, Canada, and Newfoundland, and off the coasts of British Columbia and Alaska are the principal fishing banks (FIG. 5.1), where a very large share of the commercial fishing is done. The water above these banks is less than 300 feet deep and in some locations much less. The depth is especially significant for catching the bottom-feeding fishes, such as the cod. The quantity of light which reaches the bot-

FIGURE 5.2. *A deck load of tuna taken off the coast of New England. From Fish and Wildlife Service.*

tom and the character of the bottom, whether sandy, rocky, muddy, rough or smooth, also control the abundance of fish. A smooth bottom is favorable for the use of dragnets in fishing for the bottom-feeding varieties. It is a highly significant factor that the land masses adjacent to the fishing banks of North America were glaciated, thus large quantities of sediment were supplied to the nearby shallow seas and the bottoms were made smooth. The effects of the continental glacier are

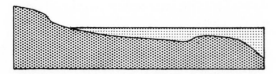

FIGURE 5.3. *Diagram of a fishing bank on the submerged margin of a continent. Ocean water (light shading) encroaches on the margin of the continents where fish food is more abundant. Depth of water over the bank is rarely over 500 feet, usually less than 200 feet.*

helpful to the fisherman in another way, since an irregular coastline with many good harbors as ports for the fishing boats is a result. The fjords of Labrador and Newfoundland and the bays of Nova Scotia, New Brunswick, and New England provide an abundance of protected harbors; but only those harbors which have good access to the markets receive large quantities of fish.

NEW ENGLAND AND CANADIAN MARITIME FISHERIES

The oldest commercial fishing region in North America lies off the coast of New England and eastern Canada, from Cape Cod to Newfoundland. See FIGURE 5.4. Numerous banks, large and small, comprise a fishing region 1000 miles long and contain nearly 70,000 square miles of fishing ground. Large banks include Georges, Sable, Banquereau, St. Pierre, and Grand. Depths vary from 20 to 500 feet. The first exports from the New World to Europe came from this region.

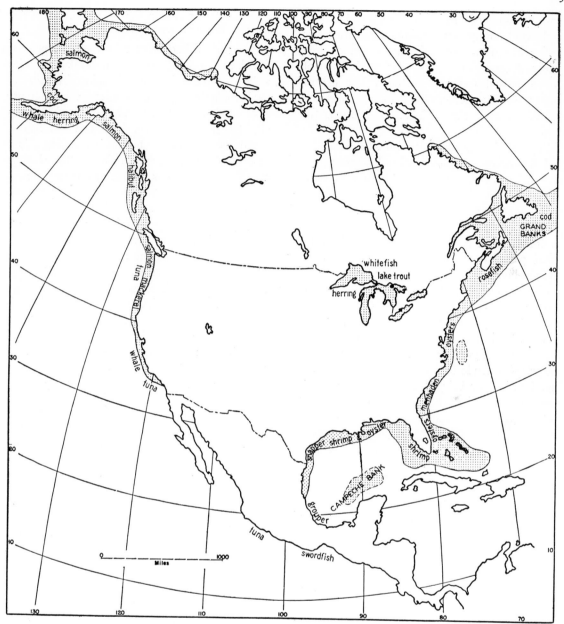

FIGURE 5.4. *The fisheries of North America. This map is a modification of one by the U. S. Bureau of Fisheries.*

Along the coast of Labrador and Newfoundland, the chief thought of the people for generations has been fish. Inland from the numerous small rocky harbors, the land is not inviting. The glacier scoured it and the soil is thin. The climate, with the short cool summers, frequent frosts, and fog, makes agriculture almost impossible. The cold Labrador current hugs the shore, with ice in winter and early summer, and very cold water the rest of the year—unpleasant conditions for fishing but favorable for fish. Newfoundland was "discovered" in 1497 by John Cabot, but fishermen from France and other countries had been frequenting this coast for years. After 1500 the number of ships was increased rapidly, and Europeans still vie with Canadians, Newfoundlanders, and New Englanders for the fish in these waters. Fishing conditions have changed,

however, and not all the hazards are to be found
in the cold stormy seas. At times the industry has
suffered from overproduction and extremely low
prices. At one time almost all the fishermen of
Newfoundland were on the dole. The use of
modern efficient methods has put many fishermen
out of work in spite of increased demands for
fish.

Some of the old methods with all the dangers
and discomforts still remain. Small schooners are
rare, but small power trawlers "put out" for the
banks. Upon arrival dories (rowboats) are used
to "shoot" the long lines with baited hooks.
These hooks sink to the bottom where the cod
or other fish are feeding. Later the lines must be
lifted, passed over each dory, the fish removed,
and the hooks rebaited. The fish are then taken
to the mother ship, cleaned, and iced. Most of
the work is cold, wet, often dangerous. The
landlubber may wonder why the fisherman elects
to continue in an occupation where there is so
little chance of great return (if the catch is large
the price is often low), and always to risk drown-
ing, freezing, or being run down by an ocean
liner in a fog. The fishermen wonder, too. One
commercial fisherman after refusing payment for
passage told the author, "Just tell your students
not to take up fishing as a profession."

The fisheries of New England are similar to
those of Newfoundland. There is, however, more
variety in New England fisheries, although more
opportunities are offered in the use of the land.
Edward Ackerman summarizes the beginnings of
the fisheries in *New England's Fishing Industry*
(University of Chicago Press, p. 2, 1941):

New England's fortune lay in the sea, but it was no
bonanza. In the early days, as on land, nothing in the
sea was to be had for the asking. Long days and nights
of work and hardship, weeks of fog and frost and icy
decks, were the lot of the fishermen, then as now.
The rise of the industry, therefore, was slow. But in
time nearly all of the many little harbors along the
coast sheltered a fishing fleet. As the fleet grew, so did
the fish surplus, and in turn the fish trade. With local
experience in building fishing vessels, a huge timber
supply, and a cargo that needed bottoms the construction of ocean-going vessels was only a logical development—especially after the Revolution. Shipping companies followed, and the famous 'triangular trade'
arose: fish to Europe; Mediterranean products to the
Spanish West Indies; and sugar, molasses, and rum
back to New England. When there was occasion for
direct trade with the West Indies (fish and barrel
staves in exchange for tropical products), New England

companies took that over, and New England was well
along on the path that codfish had started it on.

The early fisherman of New England operated
for the most part close to shore; large dories
were used to fish the waters within a few miles of
the home port. The fish were landed a few hours
after catching, and then salted or dried. Gradually larger vessels were built and the fishing
range was increased, but it was many years
before men in the fishing industry shifted their
attention to the banks. When this occurred, new
methods of preserving became necessary; at first,
the fish were salted on board ship; later, icing
and freezing methods became popular. Some fish
are still dried, smoked, and pickled.

The methods of taking fish have undergone an
evolution as complete as the methods of preservation. From the hook and line fishing inshore
the "gear" has gradually been improved, culminating in the "factory ship" and the modern
trawls. The modern "factory ship" is equipped
to catch, clean, and freeze fish on a large scale,
and power machinery is used for many operations. Fishermen in some of the larger ships make
long voyages of many months' duration and over
thousands of miles of ocean, before the huge
holds are filled with fish. In a large measure this
improvement in fishing techniques was related to
the keen competition between the fishermen and
the producers of meat on the farms. The results
are improved quality of fish on the markets,
wider range of market, as well as some unemployment of fishermen who still use older methods.

The most important fishes in the waters off
New England are the haddock, which surpassed
the cod in value many years ago, and the rosefish
which has come into large-scale production recently. The haddock is very abundant from
Georges Bank off Cape Cod to Banquereau off
Cape Breton Island at depths of 150 to 300
feet; inshore and on the more distant banks this
fish is less plentiful. Because of the restricted occurrence, both as to depth and area, and the small
size, five to eight pounds, the haddock is well
suited to the fresh fish market. The cod has a
wider range on the banks and is better suited to
salting and smoking. Other members of the cod
family—hake, cusk, and pollock—are less important. All members of the cod family are taken
mostly with trawls—open conical bags dragged
slowly along the floor of the banks. The rosefish

was long neglected because of its small size, one to three pounds, large head, and bony character. As the catch of other fish declined and as the marketing of fillets rather than whole fish became the fashion, fishermen began to seek out the rosefish and bring in large catches. The habitat is much like that of the cod, and most catches are taken from depths of 300 feet or more.

The halibut, a member of the flatfish family, is also a bottom-feeder, and because of its great size (up to several hundred pounds), fine flavor, and firm flesh, is much sought after on the New England Banks and in the waters of Iceland and Greenland. Overfishing has reduced the take of halibut and the greater supply now comes from the Pacific waters. Other flatfish, called flounders, are also taken in the New England waters. The halibut, flounders, and the cod family are caught the year round. Most of the other important fish are available only in the summer season.

The majority of mackerel are caught in the immediate vicinity of Cape Cod. Like the herring, they are surface-feeders and are caught in quantities only when they come to the surface. The season is from May to September in the waters off New England. The amount of the catch is difficult to predict; the results of a few days' fishing by means of the mackerel boats may be very great with a consequent decline in price; a few days later no fish may be taken. The catch also varies widely from year to year. Herring, an abundant fish on the banks of New England and eastern Canada, is not very popular in the markets, and the catch is, therefore, rather small and variable. The largest number are taken close inshore with gill nets and are canned as sardines, for which purpose only the smaller fish are used.

Along the inshore coast of New England and Canada, the most sought after and highest priced marine food is the lobster, a bottom-feeding crustacean found on both rocky and muddy bottoms, in cold and warm water. Lobster fishing is restricted to the summer season by the habits of the animal and to certain periods of the summer by law. Lobsters are caught mainly in "pots," baited traps made of wood slats. The pots are baited, weighted, and lowered to the bottom and left for a day or two before "hauling." The lobster fisherman faces many hazards—increasing scarcity of lobsters, high cost of bait, damage of pots by storms, and in times of the best catches, fluctuating prices. More and more of the lobster supply of New England is brought from distant shores, especially from Newfoundland.

Oyster fishing off the coast of New England is limited largely to Narragansett Bay and Long Island Sound, and even there the supply of oysters has declined rapidly in recent years because of overfishing and severe storms. Thus the oystermen of New England tend to become more like farmers than conventional fishermen; young oysters are transplanted to more favorable bottoms and are fed with shell to give them firm anchorage in plots carefully staked out by means of buoys. Special beds are selected for spawning, setting, maturing, and fattening of the oysters, all inshore.

In addition to haddock, rosefish, cod, lobsters, mackerel, flatfish, and oysters, the fisheries of New England and Maritime Canada produce many other varieties. Herring, swordfish, tuna, smelt, salmon, clams, scallops, and crabs are all of some commercial importance.

MIDDLE ATLANTIC AND GULF REGION

In the middle Atlantic fishing region, from Cape Cod to Cape Hatteras, there are no large offshore "banks" as in the northern region. Instead there is a succession of bays, estuaries, coves, tidal marshes, and shallow, comparatively warm water. There the fishing is frequently close to the shore and the most important catch is shellfish. From Cape Cod to Hatteras the oyster is abundant, reaching its greatest importance in Chesapeake Bay where conditions are nearly ideal. The water in this bay is just salty enough, the tide is weak, and the bottom is nearly free of mud and shifting sands. Furthermore, the large cities near by— New York, Philadelphia, and many others—are large markets. The oysters are dredged from the bottom of the bay. In former days the oyster beds were nearly exhausted by means of heavy dredging, but today the catch is regulated and oyster "farming" is widely practiced. This consists mainly of "planting" young oysters in sites favorable for their development. When young oysters are dropped they attach themselves to any solid object, such as an old oyster shell, and remain fixed, pumping sea water through the gills and thus obtaining food and oxygen. Oysters are not usually marketed from May through August, since at this time they either are full of

FIGURE 5.5. *A catch of shrimp taken in the Gulf of Mexico off the Louisiana coast. From Fish and Wildlife Service.*

spawn, or, having just spawned, are stringy and tasteless.

The shrimp also is of some importance in the middle Atlantic district but is produced in the greatest amount in the Gulf of Mexico, off the delta of the Mississippi. See FIGURE 5.5. Clams, scallops, sea trout, shad, and menhaden are also numerous in the middle Atlantic. The menhaden occurs in great schools and is taken in quantities, to be used as a source of oil and fertilizer, since this fish is not edible until the oil is removed.

Off the coast of Florida and in the Gulf of Mexico, fishing is less intensive than in the regions just discussed, but shrimps, oysters, red snappers, pompanos, and other varieties of excellent food fish are to be found. In most of the bays and lagoons along the coast oysters are produced; Biloxi, Mississippi, is an important packing center. Shrimps are taken much like oysters, by dredging along the bottom with net bags. Unlike the oysters, the shrimp are not attached. Most of the shrimp are iced to be shipped inland fresh, or they are canned. Some are dried.

The most important sponge region of North America is off the west coast of Florida, with a base at Tarpon Springs. The sponges grow on the bottom at depths of more than 100 feet. They are taken by divers or by hooking. The industry is operated largely by Greeks whose ancestors for generations had experience in sponge fishing in the waters of the eastern Mediterranean. After being pressed and dried, the sponge is ready for market.

PACIFIC COAST FISHERIES

The Pacific Coast fisheries have been commercially important for little more than a century. The first fishing was in the rivers and bays, and the greatest catch was salmon, as it is today. Halibut, tuna, cod, and pilchard (sardine) are caught offshore, some in Bering Sea.

Salmon range from the north coast of California to Bering Strait, and most of the salmon are caught in the rivers and in the sea near the outlet of the rivers, as the fish are migrating upstream. The use of nets and seines accounts for the greatest number, and the seines are pulled by horses in the shallow river water. The salmon is so easy to catch that there is a serious threat of depletion, and in many localities the catch has declined. Contributing factors besides overfishing

have been the pollution of streams and the construction of dams for power, navigation, and irrigation purposes. In many places fish ladders have been constructed so that fish may avoid the dams, and at the Grand Coulee Dam a fish elevator enables the salmon to reach their traditional spawning ground in the upper reaches of the river. When the young fingerlings descend the stream, however, many of them pass through the power turbines, and are killed as they strike the blades with great force. Pending a solution of this problem, the salmon are being transplanted from the upper Columbia River to more accessible streams.

From northern California to Alaska the coast is dotted with salmon canneries, located on the sea where there is good salmon fishing, fresh water derived from streams for cleaning, and deep water for the ships. Most of the canneries are in Alaskan waters and are operated only in the summer season. The fish are caught nearby (FIG. 2.1), rushed immediately to the cannery, washed and then cleaned, and scaled and sliced by machinery. By means of a machine the cans are filled, and then are sealed and heated. Most of the canned salmon is moved to Seattle, Oakland, or other Pacific ports. There the cans are labeled and shipped to markets in North America or Europe.

Many other kinds of fish, such as tuna, herring, and halibut, are caught off the west coast of North America. Halibut are second in importance to salmon. They are caught by hook and line, as in the Atlantic, and marketed fresh or frozen. Tuna (albacore) were formerly important off the coast of southern California, but they migrated to the waters off the Oregon coast, causing a migration of canneries also, and now a large part of the catch is canned at Astoria, Oregon.

The whaling industry, which was important in the development of fisheries, continues on a small scale in the North Pacific. Men on whaling ships set out in the early summer from Seattle, from Victoria, and from bases on the Queen Charlotte Islands. Several hundred whales are harpooned annually, towed into the nearest whaling port, and processed. Whale oil, canned "beef," and fertilizer are the chief products. The number of whales is decreasing rapidly and these huge mammals may be very near extinction.

88

Oysters are becoming more important on the west coast especially at Willapa Bay, Coos Bay, Grays Harbor in Washington, and in San Francisco Bay. Most of the product is canned. It is worth noting that a very large part of Pacific Coast fish is canned, reflecting the limited market for fresh fish in this region.

INLAND FISHERIES

Inland fisheries have flourished in the Great Lakes, in some smaller lakes, and in the Mississippi River for more than a century. Whitefish, lake trout, lake herring, perch, and many varieties of rough fish are taken. In recent years the catch has declined because of overfishing and because the lakes have become polluted by sewage and industrial refuse. Most of the fish are caught in the summer months by means of gill nets and traps and are marketed in the immediate vicinity. The demand for lake trout far exceeds the supply.

LATIN AMERICA

As already indicated, the fisheries in the tropical waters are restricted by the great variety of fish, the rough, rocky bottom, and the difficulty of preserving and marketing fish. It might be supposed that the people of a country like Mexico with a low per capita production of land-pro-

duced meat would turn to fishing on a large scale. But the coasts of Mexico, Central America, northern South America, and many of the islands of the West Indies are not favorable for fishing. Much of the coastal margin is sparsely occupied; most of the peoples live inland in the higher elevations and are not oriented toward the sea. During the conquest of Mexico, however, Cortez observed that fish were rushed from the coast to the Central Plateau by relays of runners, in order to supply the royal tables. A swampy coastline, however, with few harbors and few people is not encouraging to large-scale commercial fishing. The supply of fish is good; red snappers and groupers are found along most of the coast from Texas southward, and great numbers are found in the banks of Campeche. Swordfish, tuna, and many varieties of smaller fish are found in most of the shallow waters of the Gulf and Caribbean as well as on the west coast of Mexico and Central America. Because of the large numbers of tourists who visit many of the good harbors, sport fishing rather than the usual type of commercial fishing is the rule, yet the catch makes a sizable contribution to the food supply.

For various reasons the fisheries of the Caribbean do not supply enough fish to meet the demand, and about 50 per cent of the fish consumed

FIGURE 5.6. *Graph of Columbia River landings of Chinook salmon, 1865–1950. Note the general decline since 1910.*

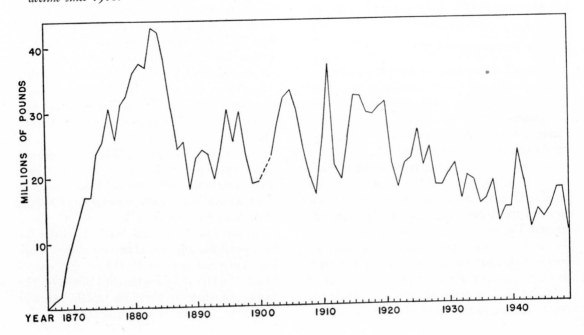

are imported. Careful surveys by the Caribbean Fishery Mission show that production can be increased in certain areas without overexploitation. The best possibilities are to be found in the migratory fish such as the tuna, Spanish mackerel, swordfish, and shark (FIG. 5.7). More boats, equipment, and fishing crews are needed to catch the large fish; a single tuna often weighs as much as 400 pounds. "Open bottom" fishing such as is practiced in higher latitudes is not particularly attractive to the commercial fisherman, since the sea floor is often too rough for trawling or netting.

Because of the production of vitamin A from shark liver oil, the fisheries off the coast of Argentina, long neglected because of the cheapness of beef and mutton in that country, have been stimulated to greater activity. The sharks are caught with hook and line and are brought to factories on the La Plata for processing. Argentina ranks second to the United States in the production of vitamin A. The shark meat can be sold also and the leather brings a high price.

In Peru the continental shelf varies in width from two to five miles in the extreme north and south. In latitude 5° to 10° S. the width reaches as much as 70 miles. The Peru (or Humboldt) current carries large concentrations of *plankton*, and is often red, yellow, or brown because of this animal and vegetable matter. Along the margins of the current are many tongues of warmer water so that the Peruvian fisheries include both cold and warm water types (resembling in this respect the fisheries off California and Lower California). The large numbers of fish-eating birds, as well as the enormous deposits of guano (bird dung) on the islands, have long testified to the abundance of fish in Peruvian waters.

Commercial fishing is carried on from numerous small ports all along the Peruvian coast from Pizzaro on the north to Ilo near the Chilean boundary. Few of the harbors are satisfactory, and at many places it is necessary for the fishing boats to be hauled through the surf to the beaches. Since, in addition, little protection from storms is afforded, the development of the Peruvian fisheries has been retarded. More than 200 varieties of fish are taken, however. The bonito, mackerel, shark, sea bass, and drumfish make up more than half of the catch. Fish eggs, shellfish, sea lions, and anchovies add to the variety. Food fish are available in all months of

FIGURE 5.7. *Shark fishermen off the coast of Costa Rica. The liver of this shark weighed 134 pounds and was worth several hundred dollars. From CIAA.*

the year along the coast of Peru, and the total catch exceeds 30 million pounds. The per capita consumption, however, is less than five pounds per year because of poor transportation to the highlands of Peru where most of the people live. The Incas delivered fresh fish to the royal tables at Cuzco by relay runners. Today, a number of insulated trucks carry iced fish to the interior.

In Chile, in addition to food fish similar to those taken in Peruvian waters, whales are caught in coastal waters in increasing numbers. One of the most modern whaling stations and conversion plants is located at Quintay Cove, near Valparaiso. Because of the proximity of Quintay Cove to some of the best whaling-grounds in the world, all processing can be done on shore, instead of aboard ship. The capacity and potential catch of the little whaling-ships are increased accordingly.

COMPARATIVE PRODUCTION

It has been shown that North America and South America are favorably situated for commercial fishing. The prospect is at least equal to that of Europe or Asia, where the people have easy access to only one ocean; North Americans have access to two. But North America ranks a poor third in the production of fish and South American production is small indeed. This disparity of production is associated mainly with the eating habits of the various peoples and not with the supply of fish.

A considerable part of the fish products listed in the production reports of Europe and Asia are derived from North American waters. The people of European countries fish the North Atlantic grounds; Japanese and Russians fish the North Pacific. Exports of fish from Canada and Newfoundland go largely to Europe.

Fisheries of Other Continents

THE fishing banks of the other continents—Europe, Asia, Africa, and Oceania (FIG. 5.8) are only slightly more extensive than those of the Americas, but the annual catch is much larger, partly because the land adjacent to some of the banks is so densely populated and partly because of the low per capita production of meat. In the Americas there is a large fishing industry in only two countries, the United States and Canada; while in Europe the industry is large in nearly a score of nations. The Russians and Japanese are leading producers in Asia, but in China and Siam there are also fishing industries. In Africa, Australia, and New Zealand, fishing is about on a par with that in Latin America. The per capita catch is small, but the fisheries are being expanded as this resource is brought to the attention of the people.

The best fishing grounds of western Europe are in the shallow seas extending from the Bay of Biscay to the northern part of Norway. The North Sea, the Baltic, the waters around the British Isles, the Shetlands, and a narrow strip along the Norwegian coast are all shallow enough to be fished. The banks around Iceland, Spitsbergen, and Novaya Zemlya are also used by the European fisheries. The total annual catch of Europe is approximately four million metric tons, greater than that of all the Americas, and is rivaled only by the amount taken from banks of eastern Asia. Europeans also take some fish from the Mediterranean.

In Asiatic waters commercial fishing extends from Siam to the Bering Sea. Most of the fish, however, are caught near the banks around the main islands of Japan, near the coast of Siberia around the peninsula of Kamchatka, and in the sea of Okhotsk. Only a part of these banks are bordered by lands with dense population. On the other hand, the production of fish by Japan, China, and the Soviet Union combined, compares favorably with that of northwestern Europe. See FIGURE 5.9.

FIGURE 5.8. *The chief fishing banks of Europe and Asia are indicated by solid black areas.*

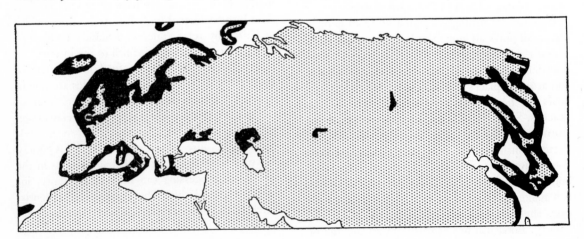

In Africa, Australia, and New Zealand the fisheries, like those of Latin America, have been neglected. Since the pressure of population is not great, and the production of beef and mutton is heavy, there has been less interest in the products of the seas. Because of World War II with its disruption of trade and food scarcities, the attention of the people of these districts has turned to fishing. Off Africa there is only a narrow continental shelf at best, but in the waters off Australia and New Zealand there are excellent possibilities for commercial fishing.

WESTERN EUROPE

The fishermen of Great Britain, of all the countries of western Europe, have the best access to the fishing banks. There are numerous harbors in the islands within easy reach of the North Sea, the Channel, and the banks around the Shetland Islands and the Faeroes. In addition, Britain has a fairly dense population, an indifferent environment for agriculture, and the British have a flair for the sea. To be sure, British interest in the sea is a result of fishing activities, rather than a cause. At any rate there are more fishermen employed in Britain than in any other country of Europe. The British catch is nearly as large as that of any country in the world, exceeded only by that of the United States, Japan, and Russia.

The waters on all sides of Britain (FIG. 5.10) are favorable for fishing, but because of the exceptionally good location of the North Sea the growth of fishing ports on the east side of England and Scotland, and on the English Channel was encouraged and only a few ports on the west side were built. About fifty of the smaller ports are engaged chiefly in fishing. In Scotland, Wick, Aberdeen, Montrose, and Leith, all on the east coast, are best known. In eastern England, Hartlepool, Whitby, Hull, Grimsby, Yarmouth, Lowes-

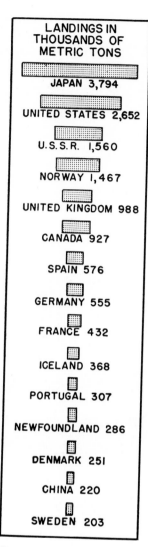

LANDINGS IN
THOUSANDS OF
METRIC TONS

JAPAN 3,794

UNITED STATES 2,652

U.S.S.R. 1,560

NORWAY 1,467

UNITED KINGDOM 988

CANADA 927

SPAIN 576

GERMANY 555

FRANCE 432

ICELAND 368

PORTUGAL 307

NEWFOUNDLAND 286

DENMARK 251

CHINA 220

SWEDEN 203

FIGURE 5.9. *Graph of fish landings by leading countries according to tonnage. From F. A. O. Yearbook of Fisheries Statistics.*

toft, and Whitsable are representative of many others. On the Channel, Folkestone, Hastings, Brighton, and Plymouth are less used as fishing ports, becoming more important as seaside resorts. On the west coast only a few harbors like Milford Haven in Wales and Fleetwood near Liverpool are dominant fishing ports.

Of all the fishing banks in the world, Dogger Bank in the midst of the North Sea is the most productive. Lying approximately halfway between northern England and Denmark it is about 150 miles long by 70 miles wide and the depth ranges from 60 to 120 feet. This submerged plateau is dissected on its margins and in it are a series of "pits" or channels which are excellent sources of cod. The Dogger is supplied with fish food from the great deltas to the south, including that of the Rhine, which pour into the sea quantities of fine mud, together with small organisms which make good feed for young fish. The British have no monopoly, of course, on Dogger Bank. Fishermen from many other countries come there for both herring and cod. Since the decline of the Netherlands as a great sea power, however, the British have taken a greater share of the Dogger fish than the fishermen of any other country.

The fishing industry of Britain, like that of most countries, is usually divided into three classes: inshore, in which various methods are used; gill net fishing for surface varieties; and trawling for bottom-feeding varieties. The inshore fisheries along the coast of Britain have been depleted, partly because of the increased catches by the trawlers in distant waters, partly because the fishermen find it more lucrative and pleasant to cater to the seaside resorters than to fish. Overfishing and pollution of inshore waters are contributing factors to the decline of inshore fishing, but the variety of such fishing remains.

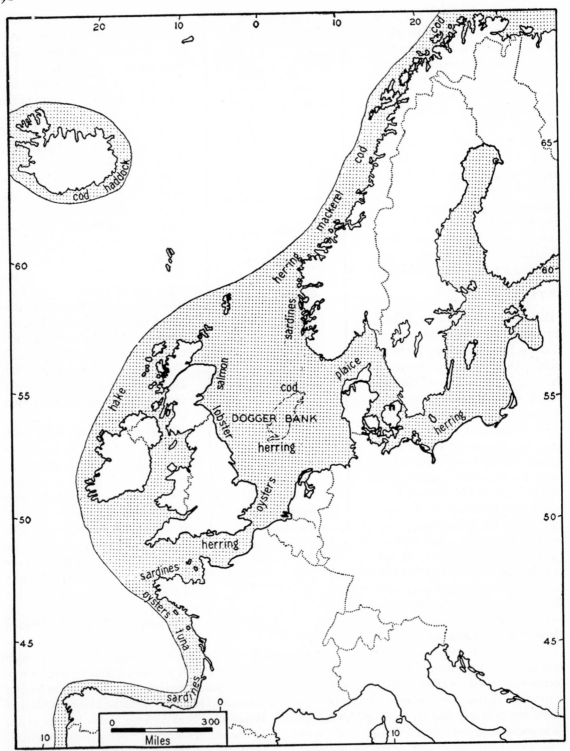

FIGURE 5.10. *Fisheries of northwestern Europe.*

FIGURE 5.11. *Fishing for herring with gill nets on Dogger Bank, North Sea. Notice the float (left) which keeps the nets near the surface. Weights keep the bottom of the net down. From the London "Times."*

Whitsable on the Thames Estuary is the chief oyster dredging port, but the production of oysters, shrimp, and shellfish, in general, has declined. Only a few lobsters and salmon are taken from the north coast of England and Scotland. Inshore fishermen go only a mile or so from shore at most and use small boats. They use a variety of equipment—seines, nets, trawls, baited lines, and traps. The catch varies with the season. At one time, these fishermen may use gill nets for mackerel inshore. Later they may build lobster "pots" (see page 85) and "shoot" them close to shore. Inshore fishing is still a small-scale individual business in contrast to fishing by means of drifters and trawlers.

The herring fishermen, chief users of the gill net method, are associated with Great Yarmouth and neighboring ports on the east coast of southern England. For more than six centuries this industry has been on a commercial basis. Defoe describes the industry in 1724 (*British Sea*

Fisherman, by Peter F. Anson. William Collins of London, p. 30, 1944):

. . . during the Fishing Fair, as they call it, one sees the land covered with people and the river with barks and boats, busy day and night, landing and carrying off the herrings, taken the night before; and this, over and above what was brought on shore . . . by open boats. . . . The barks come from the coast of Kent and Sussex and let themselves out to fish for the merchants at the said Fair, . . .

Herring fishing is very different from trawl fishing. The vessels or drifters, as they are called, are rarely away from the home port for more than 24 hours. Herring, mackerel, and other surface-feeding fish are taken in gill nets (FIG. 5.11) which are hung like walls in the water, with floats at the top and light weights at the bottom to keep the net in a vertical position. These nets, two or three miles in length, drift along with the current. The fish feeding near the surface become enmeshed in the net and are unable to free themselves. The herring and mackerel are rushed to the market, since they are very perishable. A large proportion of the catch is marketed fresh, but, as in the past, a part is smoked, pickled in brine, or both pickled and smoked. The herring season is rather short, lasting from midsummer to October or November. During the season in Yarmouth alone 8000 women are employed in cleaning and curing the fish. For many years, however, the market for herring has been poor.

Trawling is the most highly organized form of commercial fishing in Britain. The ports of Hull and Grimsby on the east coast and Milford Haven and Fleetwood on the west coast are reception points for a large proportion of the cod, hake, haddock, halibut, skate, sole, whiting, and turbot. The modern trawler is a far cry from the old sail schooners used to fish the distant banks. The best ones today are fast steam-powered or Diesel-motored vessels with the most modern equipment for finding, catching, and handling the fish. By use of radio direction finders fishermen are helped to locate the pits or reefs where the cod are to be found. By means of fathometers the exact depth which brings the location down to pin-point accuracy is given. If the fishermen in a vessel miss the pit by a few yards, no fish at all may be obtained. The ships are built with an eye to the comfort of the fishermen too. The arctic trawlers, in general, are built with steam heat, bathrooms, and comfortable quarters for the dozen men who make up the average crew. The trawlers are usually taken out about two or three weeks, are brought back to port for 36 hours, and then are taken off again on another voyage. It is a tough life for a fisherman, even with the best of modern equipment. He starts at the bottom as a "decky-learner," cleaning up the mess which follows the hauling and cleaning of a trawl full of fish. In a few years, if he combines seamanship, skill, cunning, and perseverance, he may be promoted to mate, and eventually to skipper, after which he receives a larger share in the profits. A skipper works under great tension, however, for it is his responsibility to find the fish and get them to market in good condition. And fish, as many a fisherman knows, are unpredictable.

Fishermen in a modern trawler take most of their fish in a purselike net, a trawl, which is dragged along the bottom, sometimes for several hours before being hauled to the surface. It is

obvious that a fairly smooth bottom is favorable to this method. However, metal bobbins attached to the trawl roll along the bottom and protect the mesh of the trawl from small irregularities. When the skipper has maneuvered the vessel into a likely position, the trawl is "shot" (heaved overboard). The ship tows the trawl slowly along the shallow area where the fish are feeding. Most trawls have a large open end, followed by a restriction and then the "cod" end where the fish accumulate. When the run is ended, the trawl is hauled on deck by use of a steam winch. This is the time the fishermen have been waiting for, as the following description from L. Luard's *Conquering Seas* (Longmans, Green and Co., Inc., pp. 205-209, copyright 1935 by L. Luard) graphically illustrates:

At ten o'clock they hauled. The warning ring of the telegraph sent Jack running up the engine room ladder to call all hands. . . . In the wheel-house John [the Skipper] switched on the group lamps. A torrent of light blazed over the deck, rolling back the darkness, which stood heaped beyond in solid flood . . . John moved to a window. "Knock out, aft!" Hearing the order, Alf jerked the pin from the towing block, . . . At once Henry swung the winch valves open. They banged and thudded; steam hissed and roared; the warps coiled round the drums with a crunching grind, as if about to part. One by one the marks came home —five, four, three, two. . . . The quarters of the net came inboard. Twenty yards distant the waters bubbled and stirred. They rose in a heaving mound, eddying and seething; they parted with a sullen splash. A moment later the cod end appeared, a distended globe. . . . It rolled sluggishly, sagged and spread—pulsing with hidden life. . . . The catch surged forward, rising slowly, topped the rail, and steadied against the bag lines by the fore rigging . . . Henry ran forward and scrouched underneath, jerking at the securing knot. He sprang back to avoid the sudden gush of fish that poured into the pounds. . . . "Hundred baskets, Skipper," Henry cried, . . . "Golden cod—all rock-hard, and a sprinkling of ducks, coalies, and soldiers.". . . He [the Skipper] searched the horizon and breathed freely. "Overhaul cod ends, Henry. Play lively. If another ship sights us, she'll call the lot."

The fish net is emptied, "shot" again, and the crew goes to work cleaning and icing the first haul. Trawling has been more successful than other methods of fishing because through it vast quantities of fish can be delivered to a single market. All phases of the business are highly organized, so that coarse or low-grade fish can be marketed in competition with the more delectable fish produced in small quantities by inshore or drift fishing.

The fishermen of Britain, accustomed to a hard life, have had an unusually difficult time in recent years. In World War II the industry was severely set back. Fishing boats were destroyed, many fishermen were lost with them, and many fishermen shifted to other occupations. Furthermore, the increasing dominance of the large companies means that the individual is now merely a cog in a highly organized industry. As a consequence, fishing is less attractive to the younger men. Then, too, the export market for fish has decreased. The people of Mediterranean countries who formerly took a good part of the herring catch are now too impoverished to purchase large quantities of fish from abroad. And the British people at home have shown a decided preference for canned fish, salmon, sardines, lobster, and crab, most of which comes from abroad.

The Scandinavians have always been associated with commercial fishing, and many people suppose that Norwegians produce more fish than any other people. The fact is that the people of Norway get more of their national income from fisheries than from any other source. The reasons for this are twofold: there are excellent fishing grounds near at hand in Norway and there are many good harbors for fishing ports; when the resources of the land are limited the people turn toward the sea. Most of the people live on the fringe of the country between the mountains and the sea. The settlements are usually located at the head of the fjords where small patches of gently sloping land can be farmed. The season is cool and the steep valley sides limit the amount of sunshine. The typical fjord is so narrow even at the sea end that a net can be placed across it, and the walls are so steep that "one has to lie on his back to see the sky." The water is deep enough so that large ships can be brought near the head of the fjord, but not deep enough to allow the cold water of the ocean depths to penetrate. The islands fringing the outlets of the fjords, the "skerry guard," are additional protection to the harbors, thus forming many ideal sites for fishing ports.

Cod and herring are the important fish in the home waters; the cod in the north, the herring in the south. Most of the herring are caught south of Bergen, a city founded to facilitate the trade in fish. Unlike most settlements along this coast, Bergen is located just inside the "skerry guard" and not at the fjord head. By this location quicker access is given to the sea. For centuries the people of Bergen have been shipping herring in various forms to southern Europe and taking in return olive oil, salt, and wine. Much of the herring catch is packed as sardines in olive or cottonseed oil.

Cod fishing has two chief centers, one in the Lofoten Islands, the other in Finmark on the north coast of Norway. Since there is no permanent settlement of any size in either of these islands, the cod fishermen are away from home for long periods. The cod are salted or canned in the northern waters and the crude cod liver oil is rendered from the fish livers. The common methods of fishing are similar to those used by British fishermen (see pages 91–94). Norwegian fishermen are usually to be found on all the fishing banks of the world. The whalers range from the Arctic to the Antarctic, sending the whale oil to Norway or to other countries. Some of the whalers are absent from the home port for two or three years.

Swedish people, with better resources on the land than the Norwegians have, look less to the sea. Agriculture, lumbering, and mining are each more important than fishing, but from the Baltic and North seas the fishermen of Sweden take enough fish to supply their own people.

In Iceland there are excellent fishing banks and a small population, and Icelandic people lead the world in per capita fish production. Cod fishing goes on the year round, but the best time is the spring and the best banks are to the south and west of the island. The cod migrate over long distances and many of them reach the waters south of Iceland as they approach maturity. The chief herring season is in summer and the most frequented banks are to the north of Iceland. In addition to the Icelandic fishermen, Norwegians, Swedes, and Finns fish heavily in these waters.

Although cod and herring are the chief fish in all the banks of northwestern Europe, many other varieties are of commercial significance. Danes lead in flatfish, especially plaice, and also in oysters. The fishermen of Norway, Sweden, and Denmark all take lobsters, shrimp, and crabs.

The fisheries of other countries in northwestern Europe follow the same general pattern as in Britain and Scandinavia. Fishing and the process-

FIGURE 5.12. *View of the fishing port of St. Jean de Luz in southwestern France. This port specializes in sardines (cannery on left) and tuna. From "Yvon."*

ing of fish is normally a large industry in Germany, the Netherlands, Belgium, and France. If space permitted it would be worth while to trace the trends and individual differences in these countries in recent years. The people of these countries have been hard hit by World War II, and the catch of fish at present is far below the demand. Many fishing vessels were lost in the war; crews were also lost and replacements are hard to find. The methods of fishing and the varieties of fish in the various ports, however, are still the same as before the war.

Along the west coast of France (FIG. 5.12), the numerous harbors make good fishing ports, and the hinterland is not very productive agriculturally compared to other parts of France. The Breton fishermen range from Iceland to Newfoundland and southward along the coast of Spain. In the summer months coastal fishing for herring, mackerel, flatfish, tuna, and sardines is

dominant. Some lobsters and oysters are also taken. Many of the fishermen are part time farmers also, for, in spite of the unfavorable soil and climate, the people of Brittany produce early vegetables and fruits. Oyster farming has become a major business, not only along the coast of Brittany but farther south.

In the Mediterranean fishing banks are extensive, but heavy exploitation for many centuries has all but exhausted certain species. The original sardines were caught from the waters around Sardinia. Greeks formerly produced most of the world's sponges. Today a number of kinds of food fish including tuna are caught in rather small numbers. However, fish is still imported from northern Europe to the Mediterranean countries.

RUSSIA

Russia has always been a continental land with little access to the sea, and the fisheries have been

FIGURE 5.13. *Sturgeon fishing in the lower Volga River, Russia. From "Sovfoto."*

is the chief catch. Kaliningrad (Königsberg) and Riga are useful ports in this connection. In the Caspian Sea and in the lower Volga, sturgeon and caviar have long been important and valuable products. The Caspian, with its fresh water to the north where the mighty Volga enters and with the higher concentration of salt farther south, is a varied environment for fisheries. Gray mullet have been transplanted from the Black Sea to the Caspian and fishing is now on a production basis in the Caspian Sea.

The greatest prospect for Russia lies in the Maritime Territory of eastern Siberia (FIG. 5.14). This region extends from northern Korea to Alaska, a coastline distance of 2800 miles. In the western part of the Sea of Japan, in the waters between Sakhalin and the mainland, and on the margins of the Sea of Okhotsk, fish are abundant and many fishing collectives have been organized. Herring, cod, mackerel, and salmon are standard fish and canneries for crabmeat have been established on the west coast of Kamchatka. Whaling is carried on in the same general area. In the south many of the fishermen also are part time farmers. Increased Russian exploitation of the Siberian fisheries is favored by the sharp decline of Japanese fisheries, improved communication with western Russia, and general increase in world demand for fish.

JAPAN

In the home islands of Japan, the fisheries play a more important part in feeding the people than in any other country in the world. Before World War II more than 2 per cent of the population was engaged in fishing. The tonnage production was roughly twice that of the United States. The Japanese produced more than 100 pounds and consumed 70 pounds of fish per capita per year. The wartime production slumped sharply but with the return of peace to Japan the fisheries recovered rapidly, aided by the United States. The population of Japan is so dense and the arable land is so limited that most of the crops must be grown for food. It is impossible to feed any large numbers of livestock. The long coastline with many small harbors approximates the conditions of the British Isles, but there is much less competition from neighboring nations. Japan also exports canned and dried fish, including tuna and salmon to various

largely of the inland variety, in the Caspian and Black seas and in the Volga and other large rivers. See FIGURE 5.13. The arctic fishers off the coast of Murmansk and the fisheries of Siberia have been too remote to mean much to the bulk of the Russian population. Today conditions have changed. Russia has access to the Baltic at several points, some of which are almost ice free. Improved rail transportation to the Arctic and to Siberia has made it possible to ship canned and preserved fish to the heart of the country. According to many reports, Russia has skyrocketed from a minor fish producer to a rank rivaling that of the United States and Japan. Recent quantitative data on Russian fish production, however, are not available.

The nature of some of the Russian fisheries has already been suggested by previous descriptions (page 87). Off Murmansk in the Arctic, cod is the chief product. The Russian fishermen also work the banks around Spitsbergen and Novaya Zemlya. Canneries at Murmansk preserve most of the catch. In the Baltic and North seas herring countries. All these factors contribute to the great emphasis on fisheries.

In view of the pressure on the fisheries and the range in latitude of the Japanese fishermen, it is not surprising that their catch is even more varied than that of the fishermen of other countries. A large part of the Japanese catch consists of familiar fish, small herring for sardines, larger herring, cod, salmon, tuna, swordfish, lobsters, crabs, and oysters. In addition, large quantities of cuttlefish, squid, and seaweed are consumed. Fish farms, especially for carp, are common in the inland waters. The Japanese use every device to extract from all available waters any edible or salable material. Large quantities of fish not suitable for food are used for fertilizer.

As in other countries the fisheries of Japan are divided into inland, inshore, and deep-sea types. In the deep-sea type is included all fishing from ships which remain at sea for more than two or three weeks, as well as oversea fisheries in Russian, United States, and Chinese waters. By use of the inshore fisheries the greater tonnage is produced, but before World War II the deep-sea products were the more valuable.

In the inshore fisheries are produced several million tons of food fish, which in order of value are the sardine, salmon, bream, yellowtail, mackerel, herring, tuna, bonito, and flounder. Shellfish and seaweed are also important. The fish and other products are taken in all sorts of nets, seines, traps, and other devices served by many kinds of small craft. The coastal and inland fisheries are carefully regulated by the government, and special licenses are issued for certain classes of marine products and for certain areas.

Licenses are also issued for "fish farming." Marine cultivation of seaweed, known as *laver*, occurs most frequently and *laver* is the most valuable product, but eels and carp are close seconds. Many Japanese farmers have small fish ponds of carp and eels for their own use. The most spectacular form of marine cultivation in Japan is pearl culture. For centuries the Chinese had been placing small statuettes of Buddha inside shells of oysters so that the figurines would become plated with mother of pearl. It remained for the Japanese experimenter Mikimoto to put the operation on a commercial basis. After much experimentation backed by the Japanese government, a factory was established near Tokyo. Diving girls

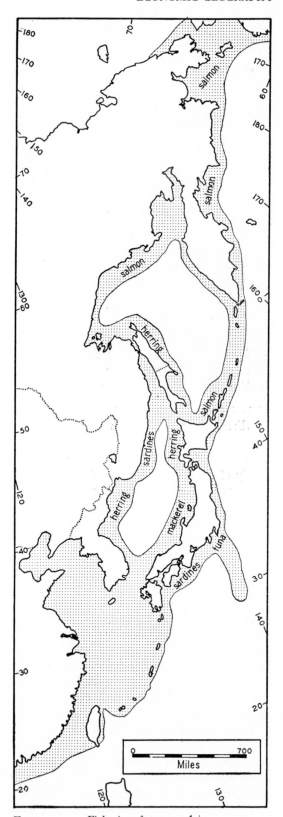

FIGURE 5.14. *Fisheries of eastern Asia.*

obtain the oysters from specially restricted beds. A small fragment of fresh water mussel is inserted into the body of each oyster. The oysters, suspended in iron baskets, are then returned to the ocean. After six or seven years the oysters are again opened and a small proportion produce pearls of commercial value. From this discussion one would think that "pearl farming" is an unprofitable business. The total value of the culture pearls, however, reaches over two million dollars annually and has apparently lowered the prices of pearls of all kinds on the world market.

Deep-sea fishing is a somewhat misleading term as applied to the Japanese fisheries. It simply means that the fishing vessels are absent from their home ports for two weeks or more at one time and does not imply that the fish are taken in deep water; in fact, most of the catch is taken in shallow waters at some distance from the home islands. This sort of fishing is of rather recent origin. During World War I the Japanese were called upon to furnish food for the warring nations, part of which was in the form of canned fish. This demand greatly stimulated large-scale deep-sea fishing, especially on the part of the large corporations which were able to obtain larger ships and the more elaborate equipment needed. Fast freighters were constructed to act as mother ships for the fleet of smaller boats working the salmon and crab areas off the Siberian coasts or in Alaskan waters. Some of the mother ships were floating canneries which were anchored in favorable places, and which received the catch of the small boats. The cans were sent by fast steamers to the larger ports of Japan. The king crab, more abundant in Russian waters than elsewhere in the world, was exploited by these huge floating canneries. In one cannery with the small boats for the actual fishing operations, more than 2000 people were employed. Most of the 300,000 cases packed annually were sent to the United States. The pack of salmon was also very large, including several varieties. With some ships in Alaskan waters, the Japanese exported more than 500,000 cases annually.

Long before the end of World War II the Japanese deep-sea fisheries had suffered severely from shipping losses, including ships taken over by the Japanese Government. Then too, by use of embargoes on Japanese fishing in foreign waters, the greater part of deep-sea fishing was ended.

By 1948 Japan had resumed her place as the largest (tonnage) producer of fish in the world.

AFRICA, AUSTRALIA, AND NEW ZEALAND

A study of a relief map of Africa shows how limited are the fishing banks of that continent. On the Mediterranean the banks are narrow and overfished, but tuna and sardines are produced for canning and export, as well as for local consumption. Lobsters, crabs, and small amounts of sponge are also obtained in these waters. The fishing town of Port Étienne on the southern tip of Cape Blanco on the west coast of Africa is unique in that all the water to supply the town is brought in by tankers. The banks around the Canary Islands are heavily fished and several thousand fishermen are supported by fishing there. The best fishing bank in all Africa is the Agulhas on the southern tip of the continent east of Capetown.

As already indicated, the fisheries of Australia and New Zealand are relatively unimportant. The meat supply is large, and the people are not accustomed to eating much fish. The continental shelf is extensive around both countries, but a part of it is not favorable to commercial fisheries on account of rough coral reefs. The best banks are south of Sydney and around Tasmania in the colder waters. Coastal fishing is the rule, and the barracuda, flathead, jewfish, bream, mullet, and trumpeter are the chief varieties. Herring and anchovy are available but until World War II were scarcely touched. When Australians were cut off from their normal supply of imported canned fish during World War II, interest in the local fisheries increased. In the waters around Australia are produced many large and valuable pearls, in addition to quantities of shell. Hundreds of small pearling luggers with polyglot crews of Japanese, East Indians, and even a few Americans ply the waters all along the northern coast. Broome, a port on the northern coast of Western Australia, is the chief pearling center. Fishermen on most of the luggers use fairly modern diving equipment and make more from the steady take of shell than from the pearls. The total value of the shell is from 20 to 100 times the value of the pearls. Some 2000 men are ordinarily engaged in pearl fishing. A "mother" ship is used in pearling as living quarters, while the diving is done from small boats. The season lasts from April to September.

6

The North American Forest Region

FROM Newfoundland to Alaska, and from the Mackenzie River Delta to the Rocky and Sierra Nevada mountains, stretches the great coniferous forest belt of North America, much of it a land of Indians, muskeg (swamps), lakes, snow, and winter cold (FIGS. 6.1 and 6.2). In this varied land of plains, hills, and mountains grows the second largest expanse of relatively undisturbed forest in the world, rivaled only by the vast forest of northern Eurasia. Most of this great forest is in Canada, but large and highly significant portions lie in the United States, including parts of New England, Michigan, Wisconsin, Minnesota, Montana, Idaho, Washington, Oregon, and California, and lesser portions of other states. On the warmer southern margin mature trees are generally of saw timber size; farther north and at higher altitudes they are stunted by the short, cool summers.

On the whole, this is an empty region, and the sparse population depends on the lumber, pulpwood, furs, and minerals which can be shipped from the more accessible localities. Comparatively few people are needed to exploit the forest and mineral resources. The summers are too cool and short for agriculture, and, except in a few favorable spots, the soil is too thin and rocky, and the terrain too rough.

The first product to be obtained from the North American Forest was fur, a commodity which could be transported over great distances and still be sold at a profit. This region is well suited to the production of fine furs. The cold climate promotes the growth of excellent pelts, the animals are protected in the forest, and feed is relatively abundant. Native Indians, wise in the ways of the fox, beaver, mink, and muskrat,

do the trapping. Long before there was any thought of exploiting the forest products, eager fur traders had penetrated most of the eastern part of this great forest and had established trading posts in order to purchase the pelts from the Indians at best advantage. In so doing, the early traders established the main lines of transportation and did an excellent job of exploring the forest.

Winter is the trapping season in the North American Forest. The trapper, leaving the trading post at which he has spent the summer in idleness, establishes himself on some remote body of water, sets out a string of traps, and obtains additional pelts by hunting. By the time the spring thaw comes, a good supply of pelts will have been accumulated, and he sets out for the post to trade in his furs and to get supplies. In recent years the trappers have had to go into more remote regions to obtain a good catch; furthermore, the scarcity of furs together with the high prices has encouraged fur farming.

Fur farms for fox, mink, and muskrat have been developed very rapidly in Canada, Alaska, and the northern part of the United States. The cold climate is favorable, the land is cheap, and the abundant fish in the nearby lakes can be used to feed the animals. A trapper, finding the wild animals scarce in his district, decides to go into the business of fur farming. He selects a convenient site, usually near a lake or river and not too remote from transportation. Pens and cages are constructed, and arrangement is made for animal feed. Rough fish can often be purchased from commercial fishermen at a low price. Breeding stock must be obtained. In the days of rapid expansion high-grade animals were rare and the price very high. In 1925 a pair of live, high-quality silver foxes would often sell for $20,000 or more. Prices for breeding stock fell sharply as the supply increased, but special varieties of fur animals still bring a fancy price.

Although silver fox farming has been of greatest importance in Canada, many other kinds of animals—mink, racoons, rabbits, and skunks—are found on fur farms. Apparently the fur farming industry is in the North American Forest to stay, since this region is as favorable for the animals on the "farms" or "ranches" as for the wild ones.

In spite of the fact that the best timber has already been cut in the northern part of the United States and the southern part of Canada, the production of lumber and pulpwood continues to be the dominant industry in the North American Forest. See FIGURE 6.4. Wood is the major resource, especially along the streams and lakes. The quality of the trees and the factors affecting transportation are highly varied. Production can best be described if comparatively small representative subregions are examined separately. Newfoundland, northern New England and the Canadian Maritime Provinces, the Laurentian Shield, the Upper Lakes Region, western North America, and Alaska are all primarily forested regions. Some of them are remote from centers of population and lines of transportation. In some regions there are agricultural possibilities in favored spots. In all there are mineral resources, potential water power in addition to that now developed, and vast facilities for recreation.

NEWFOUNDLAND

Newfoundland, at the eastern end of the great forest, is a glaciated, low, rocky island with an irregular, fjorded coastline. It is little wonder that the people shun the bleak interior and live on the coasts with good harbors and nearby fishing grounds. The forest resource is limited. Cold, short summers and strong winds limit the size of trees, and pulpwood is more important than saw timber. But for the fact that the coasts of Newfoundland are accessible to freighters, it is unlikely that even the pulp industry would exist. In Corner Brook, a town on the west coast, there is a paper mill, and with the present shortage of paper it is likely that production will be expanded. The iron ore of Newfoundland will probably

turn out to be more valuable than the forests. At Bell Island in Conception Bay there is an enormous reserve of high-grade hematite ore which averages about 55 per cent iron. At present no coal for smelting is available nearer than Cape Breton Island and so far production of iron ore has been limited to a few million tons per year. But the impending exhaustion of iron ore in the Upper Lakes Region (see page 106) suggests that production in Newfoundland will be increased. At present most of this iron ore is sent to Nova Scotia, where there is good coal, and to the eastern seaboard of the United States.

NORTHERN NEW ENGLAND AND THE CANADIAN MARITIME DISTRICT

The first settlers coming to Nova Scotia, New Brunswick, and New England found before them an unbroken forest of pine, spruce, hemlock, maple, oak, and hickory—a forest which had to be cleared before farms could be established. As in other parts of North America, much of the forest was destroyed by ax and fire to make way for crops, but soon the shipbuilders began to take their toll, even in the areas where no agricultural settlements were contemplated. This was the first area in North America to have a heavy cut of timber. Logs were floated down the rivers, the Penobscot and the Kennebec among others, to the seaboard where they could be converted into ships' timbers and lumber for various purposes. Today the timber is mostly gone from New England, but quantities of pulp are still produced in this region, partly because of the nearness of a good market, partly because of the old, established paper industry in southern New England. In New Brunswick and Nova Scotia, about 70 per cent of the land is still in forest, and woodland makes up a large percentage of the farmland. In many districts hardwoods—birch, maple, and others—are abundant. These woods are used for flooring, furniture, veneer, implement handles, and for fuel. Most of the forest, however, is of the softwood varieties—pine, spruce, fir, cedar, and tamarack—which are suitable for pulpwood. The lumbermen take advantage of the snow and frozen ground in winter to transport the logs to the nearest stream. When the spring thaw comes, the logs are "driven" downstream to the mills, which are usually located on or near tidewater. This method of transporting saw logs and pulp-

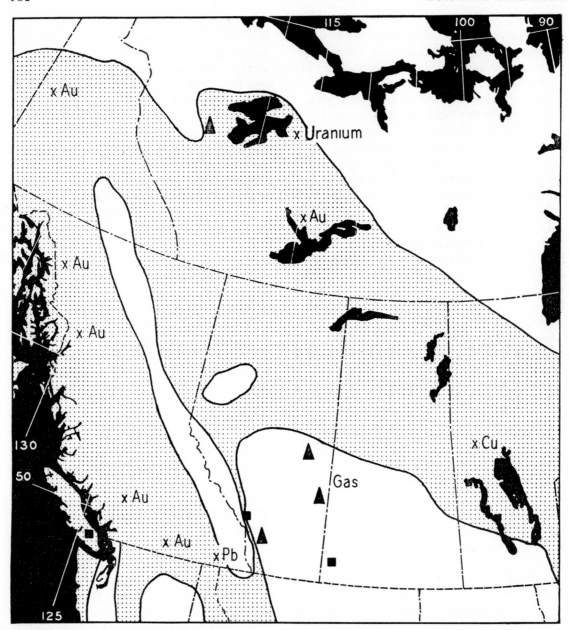

FIGURE 6.1. *Regional map of the Great Northern Forest (west half). The forest region is shaded.*
Abbreviations: gold, Au; copper, Cu; iron, Fe; nickel, Ni; lead, Pb. Petroleum production
is shown by black triangles, coal by black squares.

wood is so cheap that the use of tractors and other heavy machinery has been introduced very slowly.

Although potatoes and hay are grown in various parts of this district, only the Aroostook potato district in northeastern Maine is of commercial importance. There in a small, smooth, silty lowland more than 10 per cent of all the potatoes

of the United States are produced, including most of the seed potatoes. The season is short but sufficient for potatoes, and with highly mechanized production and the generous use of fertilizer high yields are obtained. Most of the farmers rotate potatoes with oats and hay, thus helping to maintain the fertility of the soil.

Pulpwood is produced in the rougher and more

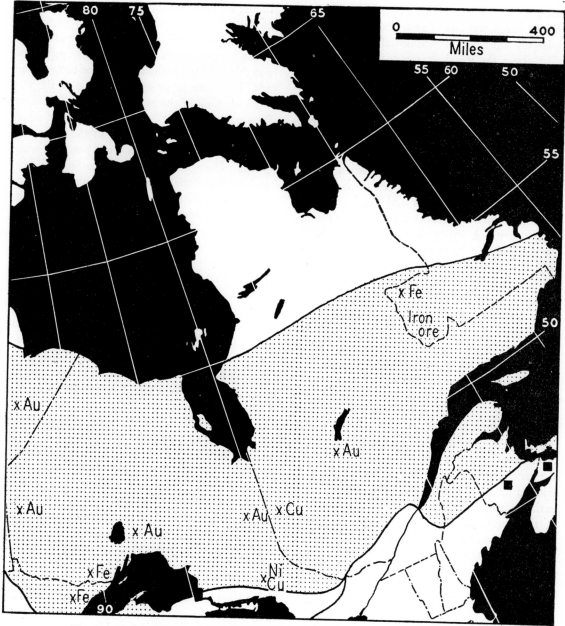

FIGURE 6.2. *Regional map of the Great Northern Forest (east half). The forest region is shaded. Abbreviations: gold, Au; copper, Cu; iron, Fe; nickel, Ni; lead, Pb. Coal production is shown by black squares.*

remote sections of this district, which have in addition all the qualities of a good recreational district accessible to large numbers of people. The forests, hills, rivers, and lakes attract many thousands of summer visitors. Like its counterpart in Minnesota and western Ontario, this district is canoe country. There are also trails for hikers, hunting and fishing, and resort hotels.

Even in winter many thousands are attracted, making recreation a well-paying business.

THE LAURENTIAN SHIELD NORTH OF THE ST. LAWRENCE

North of the St. Lawrence the forest stretches all the way to Hudson Bay. This area is called the Laurentian Shield, a worn-down mountainous mass, a land of lakes, swamps, rushing rivers, forests, scrub, and bits of grassland. The surface is largely a product of continental glaciation. In most places the ice sheet scoured the land, removed soil and loose rock, and left behind bare expanses which today are covered by thin soil. In a few places the continental ice sheet deposited a part of its load of clay, sand, gravel, and boulders. Some of these areas are suitable for cultivation. The fact that agriculture stops rather abruptly at the southern margin of the Laurentian Shield indicates that the lack of suitable soil is an important factor in the limited land use. In most of the eastern half of the Shield, the country is rough but not very high; many lakes and swamps occur, but there are no large areas of level land. Immediately west of Hudson Bay and to the north of the Canadian Plains, the country is smoother. Because of the terrain the lumbermen have certain difficulties in getting the forest products out to the market. Road building is difficult. There are some advantages, however; the frozen ground and lakes make good roadbeds in winter and the streams and lakes are good for transportation along certain routes in the summer. Refer to FIGURE 6.3.

The climate is a handicap as serious in its limiting effects on agriculture as the rough, rocky surface. Even in such a large region as the Shield the variation in climate is small. Everywhere the winters are long and severe; the only marked variation in climate is the length and temperatures of the summers. On the southern margin the average summer temperature is above 50° F. for three or four months. Farther north the season is shorter. There is a rather long lag in the seasons with reference to the sun. Some lakes do not thaw until July but remain open until November. The subsoil of the northern part of the Shield is permanently frozen in many districts north of the 54th parallel. Precipitation is light, 10 inches or less in some parts, but evaporation is so low that the humidity is high in summer.

In spite of its handicaps the Shield has important potential resources. The forests, which have been exploited only on the southern margin, the fur-bearing animals of the forest, the water power, the minerals, and the opportunities for recreation are the most valuable resources.

Lumbering followed fur trapping as the most important industry in the region. Much of the saw

timber has been cut in the more accessible parts of the south, but the more remote regions with smaller trees remain to be cut. The smaller trees of this region are an excellent source of pulpwood, and this industry is the chief one of eastern Canada. There are paper and pulp mills all the way from the Gulf of the St. Lawrence to Winnipeg. The paper industry is of greatest value where there are spruce and balsam. In the region are large quantities of developed and potential water power. The streams, such as the St. Lawrence and its tributaries, the Ottawa and Saguenay, as well as many lakes and rivers farther west, are used for the transportation of pulpwood.

Although the production of lumber in the Laurentian Shield has declined in recent years, owing to competition from the Pacific Northwest and from northern Europe, especially Russia, paper manufacturing is still the major industry. The spruce-balsam forests are best suited for paper making, and the best stands reach as far north as the "height of land" (divide) between the St. Lawrence and Hudson Bay. Much of this forest has not been exploited, and forest products should be produced continuously for many years even at the present heavy rate of consumption.

The old rocks of the Laurentian Shield contain a great variety of minerals—especially iron, gold, silver, nickel, copper, platinum, cobalt, zinc, and arsenic. Some of the minerals are in locations too remote for profitable exploitation, but as transportation is improved, partly for other purposes, they will become usable. For example, by means of the Hudson Bay Railway, constructed mainly to transport wheat, some mineral areas were made accessible and workable.

A mineral of great strategic value in the Shield is nickel, used widely as an alloy. The greatest quantity of nickel is produced in Canada, and most of this mineral is found in the Sudbury district, north of Lake Huron. Copper and platinum are taken from the same district. North of Sudbury is the Kirkland Lakes district in which a large share of Canada's gold is mined. In the Laurentian Shield proper there is probably no oil, but there may be some possibilities of oil production in the marginal sedimentary areas. Oil seepages along the Mackenzie River were reported in the early days, and the Indians used the accumulations to waterproof their canoes. The most workable deposits are in the vicinity of

FIGURE 6.3. *The Laurentian Shield at Shawinigan Falls on the St. Maurice River, Quebec. Much of the Shield is an unbroken expanse of forest. Notice the huge accumulation of pulp-wood in the river above the dam.*

Great Slave Lake where during World War II many wells were driven to supply petroleum to the Alcan Highway. This was known as the Canol Project. Since this oil is very remote from a market and cheap transportation is not possible, the project was abandoned as soon as war activities in Alaska declined.

The deposits of uranium on the shores of Great Bear Lake, mined for many years as a source of radium, became of world-shaking importance with the development of atomic energy. Mining is carried on under very difficult conditions. The region is remote from all transportation except by plane, and air transportation of ore is very costly. The lake is frozen for a large part of the year and the soil is permanently frozen to a considerable depth; nevertheless, water seeps into the mines during the summer and has to be pumped out. The ore can be moved out via the Great Bear River to the Mackenzie, and then upstream via the Great Slave Lake to the railhead at McMurray on the Athabasca River. Altogether Canada's richest resources of minerals are found in the Shield.

Manufacturing in the Shield is important because of the abundance of water power. Paper and pulp mills, sawmills, and the processing of ores are widespread, but the most important form of manufacturing is the refining of aluminum. The chief plants are at Arvida and Shawinigan Falls in Quebec. At Arvida on the Saguenay River is a very large plant in which before World War II about half of the aluminum in North America was refined. In recent years aluminum refining shifted toward western North America, but the Shield continues as the leading Canadian area.

THE UPPER LAKE DISTRICT

After the peak of lumber production in New England, the lumbermen moved on to Michigan, Wisconsin, Minnesota, and Ontario, a region in which the timber and the conditions of lumbering were not unlike those in the east. Large stands of white pine, mixed with other conifers and some hardwoods, were readily cut on the smooth plains and transported on frozen ground, or in the streams and lakes, to the mills. Many of the mills were on large rivers or lakes, whence rafts of logs or lumber could be transported to Minneapolis, St. Louis, New Orleans, and other cities. During the close of the last century and the beginning of the present one, most of the saw timber was cut over, leaving behind waste land, the majority of which was forfeited for taxes. In some of these districts, the land was suitable for agriculture and farms appeared; however, most of the despoiled areas grew up in brush including large areas of aspen. Lumbering pushed westward and northward until most of the good saw timber was cut. Then the industry declined but did not entirely disappear. The pulp and paper mills were established, and the smaller trees not suitable for lumber were utilized. Huge rafts of pulpwood were towed along the streams or across the lakes. Water transportation, so useful in the heyday of lumbering, is still a significant factor in the location of the forest industries.

The most valuable mineral of the North American Forest Region is iron ore. Most of it is mined in a few "iron ranges" at the upper end of the Great Lakes and in Newfoundland. Iron ore is heavy and bulky in proportion to its value, and to be mined profitably it must be near water transportation. The iron ore is moved to the northern Appalachian coalfields via the Great Lakes.

In the vicinity of Lake Superior the iron ore occurs in a series of "ranges," the Mesabi (FIG. 31.3), the Vermilion, and Cuyuna in Minnesota; the Gogebic, Marquette, Iron Mountain, and other ranges in Wisconsin and Michigan. Additional ore bodies are available in the adjacent parts of Canada but have not been extensively worked. In all this region relatively high-grade iron ore occurs either near the surface where it can be scooped up in huge shovels, or a few hundred feet beneath the surface where it can be reached by shaft mines. The ease with which the iron ore can be mined, the general high quality, the cheap shipment on the Great Lakes, make this the greatest iron ore producing region in the world. Unfortunately, the high-grade ores are being used rapidly and will probably disappear in the next quarter century or so. Recent investigations have revealed a huge deposit of high-grade iron ore on the border of Labrador and Quebec Province, near the headwaters of the Hamilton River, which may supplement the Mesabi ores. Indeed, with a railroad to bring the ore to the St.

Lawrence River and with further improvement of that waterway, this district may eventually become the most important source of iron ore in North America.

THE PACIFIC NORTHWEST, BRITISH COLUMBIA, AND ALASKA

Of all the parts of the North American Forest, the Pacific Coast from northern California to southern Alaska is the best fitted to produce large quantities of lumber. Three major subdivisions are to be noted—the Pacific Northwest, British Columbia, and Alaska. In the first, the mild winter, cool summer, and abundant rain are responsible for the thick growth of large trees, such as the Douglas fir, the western cedar, the western hemlock, the giant redwood, and many others. The Douglas fir is the most important tree because of its wide distribution, its great size, and the excellent quality of the wood. Modern large-scale logging began in this region after 1900 when the cut of lumber had already declined in the eastern areas (excepting only the southern pine region). It was apparent that the methods and techniques used in the eastern regions would have to be revised because of the giant trees and the closeness of the stand. Axes with longer handles and longer crosscut saws were only the beginning. Portable chain saws, powered by gasoline engines, speed up the operation of cutting down (felling) the huge trees, but at the same time introduce a new fire hazard, especially in the dry summer season. "Drag line logging" is on the decline but is still widely used. A tall tree is topped, trimmed, and fitted with a block and tackle. A steel cable and a winch are used to drag the logs from the felling point through the forest to the loading station. This method is very destructive of young growth along the "skid road" and often leads to gullying on hilly land. From time to time the outfit is moved. This method is efficient, but wasteful in the long run. In more recent times the large caterpillar tractor has been used successfully to drag the logs through the forest to highway, rail, or river transportation. Rivers are used whenever possible and in some places the logs are floated in water flumes (artificial streams) for many miles.

Unlike the practice of lumbermen in the eastern areas, logging and sawing of lumber are often two entirely different operations in the Northwest. Many operators in the Pacific region are engaged

FIGURE 6.4. *The Springfield, Oregon, branch of the Weyerhaeuser Timber Company produces lumber, plywood, paper, container board, and Prestologs. The plywood mill is on the extreme left. The sawmill is in the center with a conveyor leading from the pond. The power plant can be identified by the tall smokestack. The paper mill is immediately to the right. Other units may be identified by reference to the flow chart in Figure 6.5. From Valley Flying Service.*

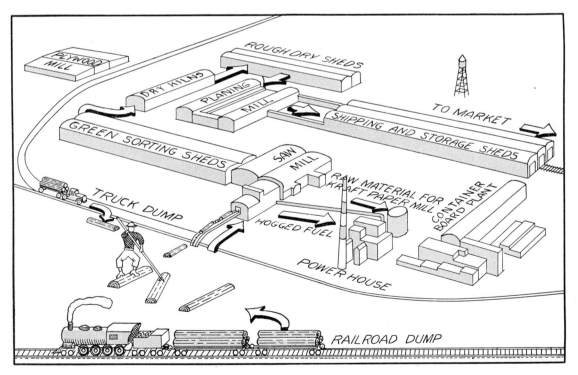

FIGURE 6.5. *Flow chart of the mill shown in Figure 6.4. From Weyerhaeuser Timber Company.*

FIGURE 6.6. *A lumber mill on the Willamette River at Portland, Oregon. Barges and freighters load from the docks. From U. S. Forest Service.*

primarily in the cutting and transporting of logs to a few key areas where the logs are sold to the lumber mills. There are four large collecting districts for the logs in the Pacific Northwest: the southern end of Puget Sound, Willapa Bay, Grays Harbor, and the lower Columbia River. In recent years the center of the lumber industry has moved southward, and production in the older areas has declined. Southwestern Oregon has shown the greatest increase in production. In all areas there is a strong tendency to produce more plywood, paper, and hardboard. See FIGURE 6.5.

For more than half a century there has been a wide market for the products of this region. Production was begun on a large scale after much of the best timber had been cut in eastern United States but while the population of the United States and the demand for houses were still rapidly increasing. The Pacific coastal areas such as southern California were just beginning to become populated. The nearness of the forest to the sea meant that lumber could be marketed cheaply in distant lands. Today seagoing rafts as well as the more usual types of freighters are used to reach distant ports, but little lumber is exported

from the United States. Quantities of wood products are hauled to the east by means of transcontinental rail lines. This region is destined to continue as the most important source of lumber and plywood for many years to come. If the cut can be regulated so as to reduce waste to a minimum, if forest fires can be reduced, a high rate of production can be maintained, for the rate of regrowth is relatively high.

The exploitation of the forests of British Columbia is much like that of the forests of the Pacific Northwest but is in an earlier stage of development. Douglas fir is the chief timber tree, growing widely on the west slopes of the mountains up to altitudes of 2000 feet. Western hemlock, western cedar for shingles and siding, and several varieties of spruce are also produced. The market for British Columbia forest products is mostly outside North America. At one time a good share of the products were sent to the treeless Canadian wheatlands and to the eastern seaboard of the United States. Still larger quantities, however, are normally exported to the markets of western Europe, Australia, South Africa, and Asia. In distant markets, where the lumber of

British Columbia meets stiff competition from other surplus lumber produced in regions such as Finland, Sweden, Russia, and Manchuria, the superior quality of the Douglas fir is a distinct advantage. In British Columbia plywood is produced from Douglas fir, and newsprint from various species. In view of the increasing scarcity of lumber in the United States, the timber reserves and forest production are of the utmost significance.

To most of the people of the United States, Alaska has meant very little. To be sure, most people know that we bought Alaska from Russia at a bargain price in 1867, that there was a gold rush or two, and that quantities of salmon are produced in Alaska. There the interest and knowledge often end. The attitude of the United States Government toward Alaska has varied from indifference to keen interest. The truth of the matter is that Alaska has not been worth a great deal to us in the past. The value of its products has scarcely justified the government expenditures for roads, railroads, mapping, and research. There are some valuable resources in Alaska, but because of its remoteness most of the resources are unexploitable.

The critical question concerning Alaska is how to get there and get back with the goods. As long as gold was produced in quantities, there was a readily exportable commodity. A man could afford to carry gold on his back, if necessary from the interior to the coast, and pay a high price for its transport by sea to the States. Salmon caught in or near the sea are not a serious problem, but heavy commodities such as lumber, coal, copper ore, or potatoes are not so readily exportable. As an example of Alaska's remoteness, it need only be said that before World War II it was cheaper for a person from the middle west to go to Europe than to Alaska. Formerly there was only one way to go—by ship from Seattle or some other port on the Pacific Coast. The usual trip is through the Inland Passage to the east of Vancouver Island, to the Alaskan ports of Wrangel, Sitka, Seward, and Anchorage. Of late years passengers, valuable freight, and mail have gone by plane.

If we study the events of World War II, the significance of Alaska as an important link on the way to Asia is apparent. Alaska is on the road to Japan and Russia and, for a time, many people,

including the Japanese, thought it was a one-way road leading from Japan to the United States. Today few people realize that Alaska's isolation is at an end. Now, thanks to the new lines of communication, Alaska's products are becoming more easily available to the outside world.

In Alaska furs, reindeer meat, coal, gold, copper, and various agricultural products are produced. The best agricultural areas are in the southern coastal valleys, but in the Yukon Valley forage crops and hay can be produced. No one will know how important agriculture can be in Alaska until cheaper transportation is available to the outside world. The Matanuska experiment in farming, located in southern Alaska, has shown that quantities of dairy products and vegetables can be produced. The problem is to find a market for these articles in large quantities.

Alaska with 128,000 people has often been compared unfavorably to Finland, in which nearly four million people are supported in a similar environment. It should be pointed out, however, that in Finland there is more rainfall, more forest to support most of the people, and far better access to markets than in Alaska.

MINING IN WESTERN NORTH AMERICA

Within the forest area of western North America, especially in and near the mountains, many communities depend solely on mining. Locally mining is often more significant than forestry. Mining communities, for the most part, have a brief existence. The minerals are exhausted and the miner moves on leaving behind a cutover forest, a tourist resort, or a ghost town. On the other hand, a few mining communities are still flourishing after many decades of activity. The mines vary widely both in minerals and in methods. Coal, petroleum, copper, silver, and gold are mined in many localities. Quantities of lead, zinc, tungsten, potash, borax, and magnesite are obtained. Many other mineral deposits are unworked because of remoteness and high transportation costs. By reason of an increase in the price of a mineral, however, production is often stimulated. Some years ago the author visited a silver mine in Colorado which had produced nothing for three years. There were apparently large quantities of high-grade ore in the mine and some of the ore contained metallic silver. It looked very rich indeed to an inexperienced eye. Asked why the mine was not in production the owner replied, "Why should we mine and sell all our good ore when the price of silver is low [then about 28¢ per ounce] and make only a small profit? We will wait until the price goes up, if it takes ten years." Before ten years had elapsed the price of silver had more than doubled, and the mine owner no doubt made a handsome profit.

Enormous reserves of coal are known to exist in the Rocky Mountain region but the production is small. The largest amounts of coal are mined in Colorado and Wyoming, from which more than 5,000,000 tons each were produced in 1950, and in Utah, which is in a position to supply the Pacific Coast. This relatively small production is the result of the limited market for coal in the vicinity and the competition of petroleum. The most important petroleum fields are in Wyoming, where (in many scattered districts) 46,000,000 barrels were produced in 1949. There is also some production in Colorado, New Mexico, and the Texas Panhandle, all within the area of Commercial Grazing. The Sierra Nevada and Coast ranges have little coal, but on the southern margin there are several important oilfields, the largest near Bakersfield, California. By use of large supplies of petroleum and huge water power development it is possible to run the trains and heat homes without coal. Water power, petroleum, and natural gas, however, do not quite make up for the lack of coal in the smelters or in the iron and steel mills.

One of the oldest copper districts is located in western Montana, in the vicinity of Butte and Anaconda. Butte takes its name from the rounded hill, honeycombed with shafts and tunnels, on which the town is built. In 70 years of operation more than two billion dollars in minerals, mostly copper, have been produced in the mines of Butte. The fumes of the smelters destroyed every shred of vegetation in and around the city until the citizens protested so strongly that the smelters were removed to Anaconda. Now trees, shrubs, grass, and flowers grow in the city, but large trees are notably lacking. The ores from the mines in this vicinity are converted into crude copper at Anaconda, and then shipped to Great Falls where cheap power is available for refining.

Many lesser mining areas are scattered through the forest region. Most of the old placers, sand and gravel deposits from which gold could be washed, are exhausted, but gold is produced along with other metals in many mines. In the Leadville district in the Colorado Rockies gold, silver, lead, copper, and molybdenum have been produced in turn, the last being of great strategic significance in an alloy of steel. Silver, lead, zinc, and smaller amounts of other minerals are mined in the Park City district of Utah and the Coeur d'Alene district in Idaho. The "mother lode," a mineralized zone in the western Sierra Nevadas of California, has been a major source of gold. By use of small placer mining, large hydraulic operations, and hard rock mining millions of dollars in gold are still produced every year.

Gold, lead, zinc, and silver are mined in many parts of British Columbia. At Trail, B.C., near the International Boundary, a huge smelter is used to serve many mines and a variety of metals is produced from the ores. Its capacity is approximately 450 tons of lead, 400 tons of zinc, 70 tons of copper, and 40 tons of cadmium per day. Gypsum, magnesium, bismuth, some petroleum, and natural gas are also produced in southern British Columbia. In the northern part of this province, gold and silver are the chief minerals. Remoteness from transportation and the heavy snows of winter are great handicaps to mining operations. There is an aerial tramway eleven miles long at one mine to avoid building and maintaining roads. At another there is an underground mill for extracting gold from the ore because of steep slopes, heavy snows, and landslides on the surface.

WATER POWER IN THE NORTH AMERICAN FOREST

The North American Forest is an appropriate region for the introduction of the study of hydroelectric energy because of the magnitude and variety of this resource, especially in the Laurentian Shield and in the forested mountains of western North America. In succeeding chapters water power resources of other regions will be studied since only in the flattest and driest of the occupied lands is it lacking.

Potential hydroelectric power depends fundamentally on two factors, precipitation and slope. The amount of energy obtained depends on the volume of water and the height from which it falls. See FIGURE 6.7. Development of the power hinges on these and additional factors. It is desirable to have an even flow of water throughout the

FIGURE 6.7. *Power plant at Queenston, Ontario, eight miles below Niagara Falls. Water is taken out of the river above the falls to run this plant.*

year, to have the fall concentrated within a short distance, either by a natural fall or by means of a dam, and to have a nearby market for the power. Thus, for the lack of a market the water power resources of northern British Columbia, northern Manitoba, and northern Quebec are undeveloped, while the best sites in southern Quebec, New England, Washington, and Oregon are used to produce power in large quantities.

Before any power site is developed, a careful study is usually made of factors which affect its efficiency and use. The stream is gauged for at least a year to determine the minimum flow of water at different seasons. Reservoirs above the site in the form of lakes, natural or artificial, tend to minimize the effect of a short low-water stage. If it is necessary to build a large dam at the site, a careful study of the underlying rock is made to insure a good foundation. Finally, a careful survey must be made of the demand for power within a few hundred miles of the site.

Hydroelectric Energy in the Shield

The potential hydroelectric energy of the Laurentian Shield is very great because of the fairly abundant precipitation, the rough nature of the terrain in which there are many natural waterfalls, the many lakes which can be used as reservoirs, and the hard rock which is an excellent foundation for dams. Ice on the streams and lakes in winter is a handicap but not a serious one. The greatest drawback, perhaps, is the remoteness of some of the power sites from any demand for hydroelectric energy. Were it not for the mines, paper mills, and aluminum refineries in the region, even less of the power would be developed.

From almost every point of view, the best sites for power development lie immediately to the north of the St. Lawrence River on the steep escarpment of the Shield. Here the gradient is steep and numerous lakes provide natural reservoirs. On a number of rivers such as the Saguenay, the St. Maurice, and the Ottawa there are excellent power sites close to the large cities of Montreal, Ottawa, and Quebec, and also near good transportation. The development of water power on the southern margin of the Shield, from Winnipeg to Quebec, is all the more significant since coal and petroleum, persistent rivals of water power, are lacking in the vicinity.

Hydroelectric Energy in the Western Mountains

From northern California to Alaska the potential water power is even greater than in the Shield since the precipitation is heavier and the mountains are higher. Development is limited sharply by the market, however. Furthermore, stream flow is irregular and few natural reservoirs in the form of lakes are present. Natural falls are not common, and expensive dams must be constructed in order to make the power available. In British Columbia and Alaska most of the power sites are untouched. The cost of constructing dams and installing turbines and generators is too high for the available market except near large mines or cities. As the agricultural population of these regions increases and as more mines are opened and forest industries are expanded, more power will gradually be developed but in all probability only a small proportion of the total available energy will be used during the present century.

In the Pacific Northwest Region, which includes Washington, Oregon, and Idaho, conditions for the development of water power are generally favorable, especially with respect to a market. This region has about 40 per cent of the potential water power of the United States and nearly 20 per cent of the developed power. Since agriculture is very important in this region (see Chapters 9 and 16) many of the power plants have been developed in connection with irrigation projects. Large projects, such as the Grand Coulee and Bonneville on the Columbia River and the Shasta Project on the Sacramento, have been constructed rather recently, but many smaller plants have been functioning for several decades.

The Grand Coulee Plant, Bonneville, and many lesser plants are linked together in a unified power system which can supply more than two million kilowatts of power to the industries of the Pacific Northwest. This cheap power has attracted aluminum refining industries, carbide manufacturing, and other electrochemical and electrometallurgical industries. Electric power is used in the woodworking industries and various other factories. About 20 per cent of the power consumed is residential, which represents a steady form of consumption, less subject to periods of inflation or depression than the industrial uses.

THE TOURIST INDUSTRY

Lofty mountains with snow-capped peaks, cool, forested slopes with rushing streams and many glacial lakes, old mining camps turned into resorts, dude ranches, plus good roads make the North American Forest attractive to tourists. Above all, there are "great open spaces" where one can hike, ride, fish, and camp, far from crowded cities and smoky factories. Tourism, developed largely with the aid of the automobile, is an important and permanent industry. Indeed, the people of some regions like the southern Rockies and the southern part of the Shield derive more income from tourists than from any other source. Twelve million tourists from the United States visit Canada every year; other millions visit the forested mountains of western United States, in spite of their great distance from areas of dense population.

AGRICULTURE

Because of the very nature of the North American Forest, any large-scale development of agriculture is precluded. The summers are too short and cool; the land is too rough and stony. Here and there in the most favorable places, however, some crops are produced in spite of difficulties. Technically, most of these small crop districts are outliers of the Dairy Belt or of Horticulture.

In the Laurentian Shield there are several small areas of agriculture, the largest of which is the Abitibi Clay Belt on the border of Ontario and Quebec and along the Canadian National Railway. Nearly 70 million acres of land are suitable for agriculture so far as surface and soil are concerned, but the climate is a handicap and only a small proportion is even cleared for farms. Even after the forest is cleared and the moss has been removed, the soils are difficult to till. The clay is heavy, and pockets of muck or rocky areas may interfere with cultivation. The chief crops are hay, root crops including the potato, berries, and various vegetables. Such crops as corn, wheat, and the tender vegetables will not grow. Some farmers in the Shield supplement their incomes from crops by the sale of pulpwood from other parts of the land. Trapping, guiding tourists, and working in the mines also furnish part-time employment.

FIGURE 6.8. *Apple orchards and forest in the Okanagan Valley, British Columbia. From the National Film Board of Canada.*

In the mountain valleys of western Canada, the winters are milder, the summers are longer, and the crops more varied. Hay and dairying are still important, but various tree fruits, such as apples, peaches, cherries, and apricots, are grown. See FIGURE 6.8. One of the best districts is the Okanagan Valley of British Columbia. The Okanagan River is a tributary of the Columbia. Rainfall is light, since the mountains on both sides shut out most of the moisture. In the Okanagan there is less than 15 inches of rainfall per year so that irrigation is necessary for all the cultivated crops. Several lakes which tend to moderate the extremes of temperature are located in the region. Both natural meadows and forest clearings are used for grazing. On the United States side of the International Boundary agriculture is represented by few cultivated patches in the forest. Instead, large areas of the lowlands have been cleared and are now devoted to large-scale agriculture along with drier areas, which did not require clearing. These districts will be studied in the succeeding chapters under the headings of the Dairy Belt, the Irrigated Oases, and the Wheat Belt.

THE NORTH AMERICAN TUNDRA

To the north of the Forest lies the Tundra, a treeless land with a short, cool summer. Much of this district is north of the 60th parallel, and there are long days in summer and very short periods of sunshine in winter. In the northern part, including Point Barrow in Alaska and the northern islands, such as Victoria Land and Baffin Land, there are several days to many weeks of continuous sunshine during the summer.

There are two schools of thought concerning the qualities of the Tundra. The older explorers called it a land of snow and ice, barren (of trees) and desolate. The newer school refers to the Tundra as "Arctic Pastures" or other more flattering terms. It is, in fact, a grassland with many kinds of grasses as well as varieties of mosses, lichens, sedges, and other plants, and with some trees in favorable places along the streams, such as the lower Mackenzie.

There are even fewer people in the Tundra than in the Laurentian Shield. A few Eskimos dwell along the coast, and a very few Indians and almost no permanent white residents live in the region. The Eskimos live mainly by hunting and fishing along the seaboard from Alaska to Labrador and on the coast of Greenland. The Tundra is good country for reindeer and several large herds have been developed, especially in the Alaskan Tundra. The reindeer were brought from the Tundra of Siberia. The reindeer require little care except for herding. They feed throughout the winter in spite of the snow. The greatest difficulties are getting the reindeer meat to market and educating the people to eat it.

Only limited resources for grazing are offered in the Tundra and almost none for agriculture, but there are large reserves of minerals. It is well known that workable deposits of coal and petroleum exist. Even more than in the Shield, the remoteness and lack of transportation are handicaps to the development of the mineral resources.

7

The Softwood Forests of Other Lands

THE coniferous forests outside North America are similar in character and production to those described in the preceding chapter. They grow mostly in the higher latitudes, in regions too cool for crops. On the warmer margins especially, several varieties of hardwoods are mixed with the softwoods. Specific products and methods of exploiting and preserving the forests, however, vary widely as does the accessibility. Until we learn to utilize the tropical forests more effectively, these softwood forests with their mixture of hardwoods are our major sources of lumber, pulp, and firewood.

The continents of Europe and Asia have long been occupied by man and large parts of the original forests have been cleared. In the far north, in Scandinavia and northern Russia, however, vast areas of timber are essentially intact. See FIGURE 7.1. The forests of Europe still cover more than 30 per cent of the total area, those of Asia more than 20 per cent. By far the largest parts of both Europe and Asia are in the northern coniferous belt. Because production is far below capacity in this northern forest, the people of western Europe starve for wood and must "cultivate" small forests to supply part of the heavy demand for lumber, fuel, and other wood products. Under the circumstances it would appear that better transportation is needed. The producers of the western portion—Norway, Sweden, and Finland—have fairly good access to the market, but those who live in the great stretches of the taiga of Russia in Asia are handicapped by frozen rivers and an icebound coast. Production is well established in the west, and when the Russian areas are fully exploited, more lumber and pulp may be produced in this whole region

than is possible in any other section of the world because of the vast timbered area.

The Eurasian forest belt reaches entirely across the two continents from Norway to Japan, ranging in latitude from 45° to 70° N. It should be noted that the Eurasian forests are farther north than those of North America, partly because of different distribution of the climatic belts, partly because of extensive clearing on the southern border in Europe. In general, the trees are similar to those of North America. The pine, spruce, fir, and larch are the chief needleleaf trees, while the

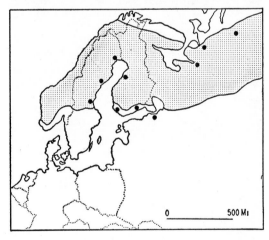

FIGURE 7.1. *The Softwood Forest Belt of Northern Europe. Four countries—Norway, Sweden, Finland, and Russia—account for most of the surplus forest products, although all European countries have some forest production. The black dots indicate some of the principal areas of forest production, including sawmills, pulp mills, and other processing plants.*

birch is the only hardwood occurring in extensive stands in the north. All of this forest zone, nearly 7000 miles in length, is under the control of five countries—Norway, Sweden, Finland, Russia, and Japan.

The surface of the Eurasian forest lands ranges from rough mountains in the west and east to low swampy plains between the mountains. The Scandinavian Shield includes most of Norway, Sweden, and Finland. It is an old mountainous region worn down and glaciated like the Laurentian Shield of North America. On the west in Norway, the slope is very abrupt to the Atlantic. Toward the east the slope is gentler, leading down to the Baltic in steps and continuing across Finland as a rough lowland. Some areas are almost devoid of soil. Numerous lakes and many streams are used for transportation for the forest products (FIG. 7.2). In the east, however, both streams and lakes are frozen for part of the year. Rainfall is moderate to abundant and hydroelec-

FIGURE 7.2. *Logs on the Baltic Coast of Sweden. These logs have been floated down a river and will be converted to lumber, pulp, and paper. From Swedish-International Press.*

tric development is advanced, often playing a part in the processing of the lumber and pulpwood. Furthermore, in the hard underlying rock are found a variety of minerals, especially iron, gold, and nickel, as in the Laurentian Shield of North America.

From Finland to the Yenisei River the forest lies on a low plain, excepting only the narrow band of the Ural Mountains. A number of long rivers—the Dvina, Pechora, and the Ob—are used to get forest products out to the Arctic. Excluding the outlet of the Dvina at Arkhangelsk (Archangel), the ice-free season is short in this area. Furthermore, the best forest trees are inland and at the southern margin of the forest belt. Eastward from the Yenisei River the land is more mountainous and even more remote from markets. This part of the Eurasian forest is least exploited, but as lumber becomes more expensive, it will be feasible to produce here in spite of the handicaps of remoteness and poor transportation.

The climate (mostly Dc in the Köppen system) of this region can be described as too cool in summer for most crops to grow year after year but warm enough for trees. In all parts the summers are short and cool, the temperature of the warmest month ranging from 50° to 68° F. On the extremities, in Norway and Japan, the winters are mild, but in the middle eastern portion, the Yakutsk district of Siberia, the lowest winter temperatures on the surface of the earth have been recorded. In many parts the winters are more severe in the forest belt than in the Tundra to the north. Data for stations near the 60th parallel represent conditions along the southern margin of the forest in Europe and in the middle portion in Asia. See table on next page.

It should be noted that the summers are warmer in the interior and the winters colder. Winters are mild on the west coast (Bergen) and severe on the east coast (Okhotsk).

Precipitation for the region varies from more than 80 inches on the west coast of Norway to less than 10 inches in the Lena Taiga. Except in the west, precipitation is light. In the extreme west the heaviest rain is in winter, but from Sweden eastward summer rain is the rule and the winters become progressively drier. Since the land is frozen in winter, the lack of precipitation is not very significant for vegetation.

From the standpoint of human comfort, the

Station	Average Temperature (degrees Fahrenheit)		Range of Temperature (degrees Fahrenheit)	Average Annual Rainfall (inches)
	Jan.	Jul.		
Bergen	34	58	24	81
Stockholm	26	62	36	18
Leningrad	18	63	45	20
Tobolsk	− 4	65	69	17
Yakutsk	−46	66	112	13
Okhotsk	−10	54	64	11

CLIMATIC DATA FOR STATIONS NEAR THE 60TH PARALLEL IN EUROPE AND ASIA

winters of Siberia are by no means as unpleasant as we might believe from records of thermometer readings. In winter the air is dry, bracing, and usually calm. Therefore, with adequate fur clothing it is possible to be comfortable in the open air. The air is so clear in winter that the heat of the low sun is felt distinctly. Snow will melt on a sloping roof with southern exposure when the air temperature is well below zero. From the standpoint of forest exploitation, the climate can scarcely be called a handicap, but crops are grown only with great risk and are restricted to the southern margin.

Excepting the North American Forest, more furs are taken from the Eurasian Forest than from any other region in the world. The major fur-bearing animals are the arctic fox, hare, lynx, bear, marten, weasel, and various members of the cat family. The quality of the fur varies widely with climate. In the colder areas to the north and east, the fur is thick but the hide underneath is thin because of the scarcity of food and the difficulty of attaining maximum growth. In the warmer regions the hide is thicker but the coat is thinner, and the long, undesirable guard hairs are most developed. The climate also affects the color of the fur, the lighter shades being produced in the colder regions. Most of this region has snow for all but a few months of the year, and most of the fur animals are white or nearly white. On the whole, the best furs are produced in the Lena River region but fur production is also important in the Ob Valley, the Lake Baikal district, the Yenisei River, and the Kamchatka district. On the southern margin of the forest, animals of the desert type furnish a limited number of furs.

NORTHERN EUROPE

Extensive forests are the most valuable resource of Norway, Sweden, Finland, and northern Russia. Because of the short cool summers and the long cold winters, the amount and variety of crops are limited. Forest products are exchanged for food and other necessities. The abundant water supply in the rivers which afford power and transportation, and the good harbors, many of which are open the year round with the aid of ice breakers, are advantages of first rank. Among the forest products exported from northern Europe are lumber, furniture, matches, pulp, cardboard, and paper.

In North America the wood industries were expanded from east to west. In northern Europe the opposite of this was true. The forests of Norway, limited in area, were nevertheless most accessible to the timber-starved people of western Europe, to those of Britain most of all. Thus today Norwegian forests are in a more advanced stage of exploitation than those of Sweden or Finland. The stage of lumbering in which the sawmill is dominant has passed. More attention is given to types of woodworking which require smaller amounts of wood, such as matchmaking, or to those types such as the pulp and paper industry, in which smaller trees are used. At the other end of the scale are Russian producers who place great emphasis on lumber and pulp but not on paper or other high-processed wood materials. The wood industries of Sweden and Finland are compromises between those of Norway and Russia as to type of production.

In view of the heavy demand for coniferous wood products in western Europe, it is a little surprising that in most of the northern forest belt the rate of growth exceeds the cut. In other words, the forests are not being exhausted as they are in North America. European foresters estimate that the annual growth in Sweden is nearly 20,000 million board feet, in Finland 17,000 million, in Norway 4000 million. It should be pointed out, however, that even where the annual growth exceeds the cut, a part of the growth may be in localities which cannot be readily exploited. In general, the cut of the north European forests is kept within the limits of the annual growth. In some areas and at certain times, overcutting may occur but, for the most part, the exploitation is well managed and there is no prospect of exhaustion of the forest resources.

The regulation of forest production is easier in Europe than in North America because of the type of ownership. In Europe large parts of the forest land are owned by the state. Other portions, owned by large lumber companies or by individuals, are subject to careful regulation.

The evolution of the woodworking industry in northern Europe began with the Hanseatic League which required large quantities of timber for its ships. At that time the timber was shipped out of the forest regions in the form of logs only. Sawmills, the first of which were driven by water power, were not used in the north country until the 16th century. Unlike the North Americans who thought that the forest was inexhaustible, the Scandinavians were afraid of early exploitation from the beginning. In Sweden, especially, the restrictions in the early days held down production and lumber was produced in the greatest quantity in Norway. At the beginning of the 19th century, the demand for timber in Britain, the Netherlands, and other countries of southern and western Europe became so great that import duties were reduced, and a great boom in forest products occurred. The sawmill industry was expanded rapidly along the shores of the Gulf of Bothnia in Sweden and Finland. There followed a rapid expansion of pulp, paper, and cellulose industries and development of the manufacture of boxes, plywood, matches, spools, furniture, millwork, and the thousands of other articles made from wood. Certain areas of the forest produce hardwoods, especially birch, which are important in the veneer, plywood, and furniture industries. In addition to the commercial uses, the use of wood for fuel accounts for one third of the cut in Finland and one fourth in Sweden. In this connection it should be noted that no coal is to be found in the northern forest region of Scandinavia.

Norway

Prior to the 19th century more timber was produced in Norway than in Sweden or Finland. The favorable position of Norway near the market on the western margin of its great coniferous forest was partly responsible. Because of the long fjords, penetrating far into the land, a large proportion of the forest is near the sea. Farther inland at higher elevations, trees do not

grow. In earlier days the chief forest products were ships' timbers, pine tar, and pitch. These items made up a considerable proportion of the trade goods of the Hanseatic League. But the forests of Norway are limited in area, largely by the terrain, to about 15 million acres as compared with 50 million for Sweden. On the west side of the country, the mountains break off steeply to the sea. The sides of the fjords rise like walls from the water's edge and such slopes do not support large trees. Above the fjords and the dissected western part of Norway is the "fjeld," rough to rolling upland too high for forest growth. This is essentially tundra, with grasses, mosses, lichens, and, in some places, dwarf trees. The "fjeld" is usable for grazing in the summer and as a source of water for power, but it is otherwise of little value.

The introduction of the water-driven sawmills in the 16th century gave Norwegian producers an additional advantage, for there are many possible water power sites on the steep slopes. For a long time Norwegians led in lumber exports, but eventually the large forest areas of Sweden and Finland began to be used, and Norwegians turned to more highly processed wood products, such as paper, cellulose, furniture, and plywood. In this regard the development of Norway and that of New England were similar. As local supplies of timber became scarcer, the people of both regions turned their attention to the production of goods which require more skill and less raw material.

Sweden

Nearly 60 per cent of the total area of Sweden is classed as productive forest land. Most of this is in the central and northern part of the country. Nearly all of Sweden's commercial trees are pine and spruce. A few hardwoods grow in the southern agricultural areas but are of local importance only. The Swedes are in an excellent position to export timber products to southern and western Europe. The Baltic and the Gulf of Bothnia are open from eight to ten months of the year; the logs are floated on numerous rivers out to the Gulf on which the sawmills are located. The melting of snows in the spring produces flooded streams, and conditions are then favorable to float the winter's cut out to the coast. A large part of the labor force is recruited from farming districts, where the people are not busy during the winter.

The products of the Swedish forests include lumber, rough-sawn, planed, or hewn. In the upper courses of the rivers plenty of power is furnished for the mills. The smaller trees are turned into pulp for the paper mills (FIG. 7.3), which are located mostly in south-central Sweden. Cellulose for the manufacture of rayon is also extracted. Swedish matches made from aspen, birch, or fir are perhaps the most widely distributed product of this district. Workers in the match industry can turn out 30,000 matches per second, and were it not for protective tariffs in some countries the export would be greater. Greatest competitors of the Swedes in the export of forest products are the Finns and the Russians.

Finland

The Finns depend more on their forests for national income than do the people of any other nation, since Finland is not well suited for agriculture and the mineral resources are limited. Even manufacturing is mostly woodwork, furniture, wood pulp, paper, matches, boxes, and plywood. Sawmills and factories are located on the coast and occasionally inland where water transportation is most favorable. The rough low Finnish Shield is interlaced with streams and lakes, which together with canals form a close transportation net (there are comparatively few railroads).

There is no important mineral production in Finland, but some small quantities of gold, copper, iron, and nickel are mined.

Minerals of Norway, Sweden, and Finland

The absence of coal in the forest belt of Scandinavia (FIG. 7.4) is only partially offset by the cheapness of wood fuel and the abundance of water power. The nearest coal is in southern Sweden and there the production is small and the quality poor. The miners of Norway dig some coal in Spitsbergen, but the fact remains that the Norwegian consumers import coal from Britain and the continent, mainly Germany and Poland. The lack of coal is felt chiefly with reference to the iron ores and other minerals which require smelting and refining.

The iron ores of Norway, Sweden, and Finland have been exploited on a large scale only in recent times. In central Sweden the first mines were opened in the Middle Ages, but large-scale operation in northern Sweden at Kiruna and Gällivare did not begin until the Bessemer process of steelmaking was introduced. This permitted the use of the phosphoric iron ores, which were not usable with the older methods. When the new methods were introduced into Britain and Germany, the export of iron ore from northern Sweden jumped rapidly. The ore contains 60 per cent

FIGURE 7.3. *A paper mill on the Baltic Coast of northern Sweden. In addition to pulp and paper, this mill produces a variety of chemical materials. From Swedish-International Press.*

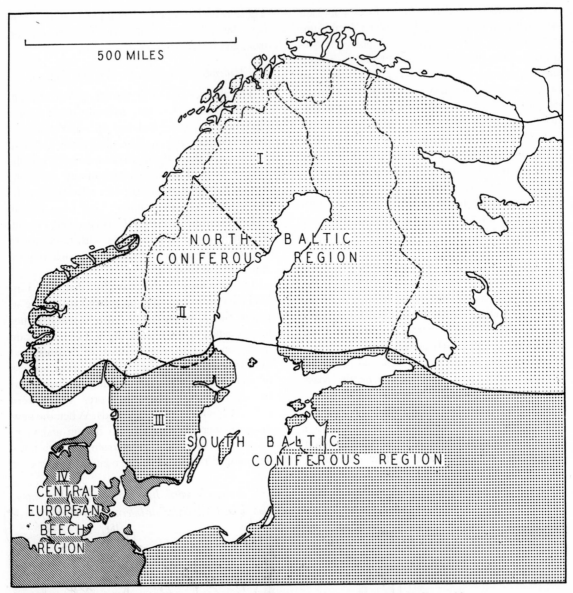

FIGURE 7.4. *Forests of Scandinavia and the Baltic. The northern forest is mostly virgin coniferous, the South Baltic is either managed or cultivated, while the Central European Beech region includes scattered patches of woodland surrounded by farm land. In Sweden four types of forests are indicated: I. virgin forest of upper Norrland; II. commercial forest of central Sweden; III. cultivated forests of southern Sweden; IV. the beech forest of Skane in the extreme south. From U. S. Department of Commerce.*

to 70 per cent of iron and can be used in the blast furnaces without processing. Some of the Norwegian ores must be concentrated before shipment is profitable. Sweden produces from 4 to 14 million tons per year, most of which is exported. Exports to the Atlantic coast of the United States

are increasing. In spite of the lack of coal there are in both Norway and Sweden small iron and steel industries, based partly on imported coal and partly on the use of various electrometallurgical processes.

Small quantities of gold, silver, copper, sulfur,

and other minerals are produced in the forest lands of Scandinavia and, in addition, ores of zinc, aluminum, manganese, and other metals are imported for refining. Some imports are in the form of crude metal rather than ore. Most of the refined product is exported.

Russia

In Russia there is more land in forest than in any other country in the world. Russian forests exceed 1½ billion acres, three times as much as those of the United States. Excepting only the extreme northern fringe of Tundra, approximately the entire northern third of Russia is forested. Many trees are too small, however, for saw timber, and others, which are large enough, are too remote to be cut profitably until better means of transportation are established. The usual trees in the northern forest of Russia are the pine, fir, larch, cedar and, in a few localities, some of the hardwoods—birch, aspen, and alder. The chief zone of exploitation is in the western or European part of Russia, especially in the watersheds of the Onega, northern Dvina, and

Mezen rivers. Even here the forest industries are in an early phase of development with emphasis on lumber and pulpwood.

In former times only the best trees were cut for lumber, and the rest were left standing. Now clear cutting, in which all the trees are cut, is practiced. Generally the smaller trees are used for pulp. New methods of cutting such as power-driven saws have been introduced from North America. Caterpillar tractors and trucks are used to get the logs to the nearest small stream, many of which have been improved to accommodate rafts. The rafts are moved down the rivers to the seaports, Arkhangelsk, Onega, and Mezen, where in modern factories the logs are converted into lumber, paper, plywood, alcohol and other by-products. A good share of the forest products also are moved out via Leningrad (FIG. 7.5) and the Neva River to the Baltic. In Leningrad there are large factories for woodworking. The Stalin Canal connecting Onega Bay on the White Sea with the Gulf of Finland is used to transport logs, lumber, and pulpwood. Most of the forested region is too cool in summer for agriculture, but

FIGURE 7.5. *Loading lumber from the docks of Leningrad. Notice the special equipment for handling the lumber. From "Sovfoto."*

a few reindeer and a smaller number of cattle are supported on the pastures. Forage crops and potatoes grow on the southern margin and some hardy farmers are pushing into the region. Mineral resources include nickel, copper, iron, and apatite, the last being a source of phosphorus for fertilizers and the match industry.

East of the Urals (FIG. 7.6) the forest products can be best described in terms of the river basins since river transportation plays such a critical role in production. The Trans-Siberian Railway skirts the southern margin of the forest, but would probably carry little lumber were it not for the rivers. The rivers flow at right angles to the railroad and reach all the way through the forest zone to the Arctic. The main rivers—the Ob, Yenisei, Lena, and the Kolyma—together with their tributaries, are frozen for a long period in winter, especially in their lower courses, but carry a good deal of traffic in the open season. Large steamers connecting with the railway are used on many of these rivers. Rafts and barges are also in use.

The first river basin to the east of the Urals is the Ob. Including its tributaries, a maximum of nearly 20,000 miles of navigable water is available at high water stage. In early summer the lower course is still blocked with ice and parts of the river are more like a lake than a normal stream. The Ob River basin is a typical northern forest region with good stands of fir, birch, and aspen. Rainfall is almost uniform over all the lowland varying from about 14 inches annually in the north near the Arctic to about 19 inches in the middle portion, then decreasing again to the south as the farming land of the Pioneer Agricultural Zone (wheat) is reached. Although this region may appear to be a land of little rain, because of the low temperatures little evaporation occurs and excessive seepage is prevented by reason of the frozen soil. Swamps and hordes of mosquitoes are among the handicaps.

Lumber is moved out from the middle Ob in both directions. The all-water route is used between the Gulf of Ob and Arkhangelsk, where raw timber products can be processed. This water route is open for part of the year in spite of sea ice. Icebreakers and airplanes, to spot the open passages, are used to make this route commercially feasible, if only on a small scale. The greatest amount of timber, however, is moved

upstream, via the Ob and its tributaries, the Irtysh and the Tobol. All three rivers cross the railway, the Tobol at Yalutorovsk, the Irysh at Omsk, and the Ob at Novo-Sibirsk. Thus large quantities of timber are brought to the Pioneer Agricultural Zone (discussed under Wheat Belts, page 190), where the people in agriculture and its associated industries are large consumers. Like the other districts east of the Urals, however, the Ob forest is in a very early stage of exploitation.

In the Yenisei River region, flanking the Central Siberian Highland on the west, there is a long stretch of summer-navigable water subject to the same general difficulties as the Ob. There are many hundred billion board feet of fir and pine, together with large areas of birch and aspen, in the vast forests of the Yenisei region. Sawmills are in operation at many points along the river and its tributaries, of which the Angara is the most important. Lumber is taken by steamer down river to Igarka, just north of the Arctic Circle. There it is loaded on ocean freighters for export, but the route is open in August and September only.

The Lena River portion of the great forest has been handicapped by two factors: the headwaters of the river are not near the railroad and the coldest winter weather in the world occurs in this district. But these disadvantages were offset by the early discovery and mining of gold, at first in the gravels of the river valley, later in the lodes of the bordering hills. Gold miners and their associates helped to develop transportation, and now steamers and launches are used to traverse the river from Bodaibo to the Arctic during the 150 days or less of the ice-free season. A spur of the Siberian railroad has been constructed north of Lake Baikal, thus making the products of the Lena Valley available to the outside world. Under the circumstances the forests have not been exploited on a large scale up to the present time.

East of the Lena is the "Far East," and it is, as far as the Russians are concerned, a district which extends from Bering Sea to Manchuria. Along the Amur River some progress has been made in agriculture, but most of the region is rather too cool in summer for successful farming. The forests include fir, spruce, Korean pine, tamarack, and some oak. It should be pointed out that the producers in this far eastern region are in an excellent position to export lumber and

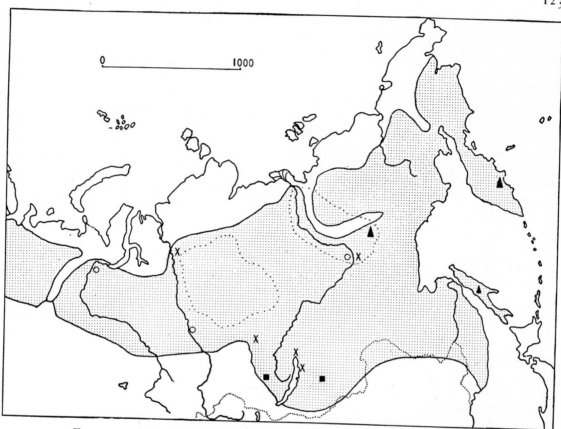

FIGURE 7.6. *From the Urals to the Pacific the great coniferous and deciduous forest of Russia covers a large portion of Asia. Along the southern margin broad-leaved trees are present, sometimes dominant. Like its counterpart in North America, this region is rich in minerals. The dotted lines indicate the approximate extent of the great coal basins of Siberia, as yet unexploited. The black squares show producing coal districts. Petroleum is found in the peninsula of Kamchatka, the island of Sakhalin, and near Yakutsk, while various metals (X), chiefly iron, gold, platinum, and tin, are mined in the more accessible localities.*

other forest products to the Pacific countries. Japanese and Australians were getting lumber from this district before World War II. It is likely that we in the United States will import lumber from this region as our own forest production declines. All things considered, the great northern forests of Eurasia constitute the most accessible source of forest products for timber-hungry consumers of western Europe and North America.

All along the southern fringe of the Russian coniferous forest from Leningrad to the Pacific is a belt of mixed hardwoods and softwoods. As in other countries, a part of this area has been cleared for agriculture, but large stands remain in Siberia. This district constitutes the largest re-

serve of mid-latitude hardwoods left in the world. The chief varieties are oak, maple, elm, linden, and hornbeam.

The mineral resources of the Russian Forest are immense but still largely unexploited. Coal is available in large quantities in the Pechora Basin west of the northern Urals, in the great Tunguska field of the Yenisei region, in the Lena field, and in the Chulym field to the west of Lake Baikal. Gold is widespread both in lodes and in placer deposits, from which large quantities have been produced in the Lena and Kolyma valleys. Platinum is found in the Urals, also copper, nickel, manganese, tin, lead, zinc, and iron. It should be emphasized that all the deposits of minerals are not of proved value nor are they all near transportation. By means of the symbols on the map on page 123, the more accessible areas in which production is already under way are indicated.

CHINA

In China, terrain and climate are favorable for forest growth, but most of the trees have been destroyed by forty centuries of farming. Every bit of level land available for agriculture has been cleared to feed nearly a half billion people. It is not correct, however, to say that all of China has been deforested. In the rougher land of the Mongolian Uplands, on the borders of Manchuria, and in the highlands of the southwest, some mixed forests remain. Altogether about 7 per cent of China's surface is forested. Refer to FIGURE 7.6.

In the original forest cover of the highlands bordering the middle Yangtze River, there were mixtures of coniferous trees—spruce, fir, and hemlock at the higher elevations, while oak, gum, and chestnut grew on the lower hills. Fairly large remnants of this forest still exist especially at the higher elevations. In the Szechwan Basin planted forests of pine, cypress, and bamboo indicate the scarcity of wood and other forest products in China. South of the Yangtze in the fir and pine forests there are broad-leaved evergreen trees, reflecting the more tropical location.

Except for the remote hills and mountains, most of the forests of China have been cleared again and again to furnish fuel for the neighboring farms. In many places the steeper slopes have been severely eroded and reforestation is difficult or impossible. In the more favorable spots, however, the forest tends to come back of its own accord. The exploitation of the Chinese forests is on a small scale since no accessible stands are sufficient to justify large-scale operations. Planted forests of bamboo and pine will have to be used to furnish most of the domestic supply in the near future, and if the Chinese are to build a modern industrial structure, lumber will have to be imported.

JAPAN

The coniferous forests of northern Japan correspond to the forests of New England and the Canadian Maritime Provinces of North America. Since only 16 per cent of the area of Japan proper is smooth enough to be cultivated, the forests cover a large area. The central and northern parts of Hokkaido together with the more elevated portion of Honshu are of the coniferous type although some deciduous trees are intermingled. This zone contains about 20,000 square miles of forest. The broadleaf zone is larger, 35,000 square miles, and the mixed forest about 20,000 square miles. In addition, small areas of bamboo forest and miscellaneous types are to be found in the southern part of the islands. Thus, more than half of the total area of Japan is in forest, and most of it is on rough land not suited to agriculture. Obviously, the forests play an important role in Japanese life, for they are used to supply lumber, pulp, fuel, and water power.

The coniferous forests of Japan, dominantly fir and spruce, are in a more humid environment than those of the Asiatic mainland. The annual rainfall of Hokkaido averages no more than 40 inches, but the summers are cool and the winters severe, so that evaporation is low. As a consequence, the forest growth is heavy and considerable undergrowth in the form of small deciduous trees constitutes a handicap to the exploitation of the forests. The undergrowth itself is of little value except for fuel. In many parts dead trees clutter the forest, further hindering operations. The terrain is rugged and lumbering is relatively expensive.

Most of the broadleaf deciduous forest of Japan is in the northern part of Honshu. The common varieties of hardwoods known in Europe and North America are to be found. The maple, oak, birch, beech, and poplar are most common along with mixtures of cedar, pine, fir, hemlock, cypress, and arbor vitae. This forest, because of greater accessibility as well as greater area, is more valuable than the coniferous forest to the north.

The study of the subtropical forest of southern Japan scarcely belongs with this discussion of the northern forests, but it probably fits into the production pattern here as readily as with the discussion of Japanese agriculture to follow. The original forest was made up of broad-leaved evergreen trees with both deciduous and evergreen oaks. As this part of Japan is the most densely populated, the exploitation of this forest for lumber and fuel has been very heavy. The second growth has tended more to broad-leaved deciduous types of oaks and to a variety of pines.

The bamboo, the camphor tree, and a few palms, tropical forms which are usually found only in much lower latitudes, grow in this subtropical forest.

Only a small part of the Japanese forests are virgin, and these are in the more remote districts. Most wooded areas are designated "cultivated," although little attention may be given other than careful cutting and following certain regulations in order that conditions may be favorable for self-seeding. On the whole the forests of Japan have been used wisely for many generations. This is to be explained by the ownership of the forests, the rough terrain, and the natural thrift of the Japanese people. The government owns about 20 million acres, and most of the privately owned forest is in the hands of large corporations which are easily regulated. Only the forests owned by the villages are difficult to manage. Here the demand for fuel is so great that the forests are over-exploited.

Every possible use is made of the forest products by the Japanese. The litter on the floor of the forest, even the leaves, is used for fuel. Most of the houses are made of wood although bamboo is a popular building material in the south. Houses in the north resemble those of northern Europe where wood frame houses are the rule. The vast fishing fleet of the Japanese, except for the larger ships, is made of wood. Furniture and various implements made in Japan are similar to those of Europe. A good share of the small trees and small fragments of wood are converted into charcoal for use as domestic fuel. The large charcoal industry reflects the scarcity of coal in Japan. The wood pulp industry has made rapid strides, and from this pulp Japanese make various kinds of paper, synthetic fibers, cellophane, and chemicals. Thus, the forests are the source of the raw materials for many Japanese factories.

Most of the rather small production of minerals is from the forest belt. Production is by no means sufficient to support large-scale heavy industry. Coal means more to the Japanese consumers than any other mineral because of its value and relative scarcity. Before the beginning of World War II for Japan in 1937, the production reached 40 million metric tons, about one tenth the amount we in the United States produced for the same year. This was a peak production for the Japanese and was brought about only in the fever of preparation for war. Under government pressure coal was mined at great expense under unfavorable conditions. Coal is widely distributed in Japan, but only the deposits in northern Kyushu and in Hokkaido are of good quality. The production in Kyushu is naturally much greater than in Hokkaido because of the nearness of Kyushu to heavy industries and to the industrial belt as a whole. The scarcity of petroleum in Japan proper is even more serious than that of coal. In spite of drastic efforts, the maximum average annual production has never been above $2\frac{1}{2}$ million barrels, about equal to one day's production in the United States. Most of the oilfields are on the west side of northern Honshu and in Hokkaido. More than 90 per cent of the Japanese production is from two fields, Akita and Niigata, on the west side of Honshu. The critical scarcity of coal and petroleum led to the Japanese conquest and exploitation of the coalfields of northern China and Manchuria and the oilfields of the East Indies.

Copper is found in all the main islands of Japan and, although of less value than coal, is nearer to supplying the nation's needs. Japanese domestic production reached a peak of 80,000 tons prior to World War II. Small quantities of gold, silver, lead, zinc, and aluminum are produced in Japan, but the greater part of the Japanese requirements of these metals must be purchased abroad.

SOUTH AMERICA

The temperate forests of South America are limited to two regions, the Paraná Forest of southern Brazil and the deciduous and coniferous forest of southern Chile. The Paraná Forest, including a small district in Argentina, is a mixture of pine and deciduous trees, interspersed with patches of grassland as in northern Florida. The pine trees often reach a diameter of seven feet and a height of 100 feet or more, and so far have proved to be the most valuable lumber tree in southern Brazil. Part of the forest is near the coast and the lumber is moved out by ship, mostly to Uruguay and Argentina. The more interior portions are near the Paraná River from which the forest takes its name, and the lumber can be moved down the river to Argentina. This forest district is the scene of a vigorous pioneer settlement, and some of the land is being cleared for agriculture. Although there are many more extensive forest areas in the tropical belt in Brazil, the Paraná Forest is more valuable than its extent and character might indicate. The pine is easy to saw, and the growth of such cities as Rio de Janeiro, São Paulo, Montevideo, Buenos Aires, and many others in the vicinity is responsible for a good market. With such demands it will be fortunate if the pine trees are not exhausted in a few years.

South of the 37th parallel, the deciduous and coniferous forest dominates the coastal fringe of Chile all the way to Tierra del Fuego. In the northern part, approximately between the 37th and 41st parallels, there is a mixed deciduous and coniferous forest. There, both beech and cedar are cut for lumber. Concepción and Valdivia are significant lumber ports, and from them products are shipped to northern Middle Chile and to the mining districts farther north. In this belt much land has been cleared for agricultural purposes, partly by German immigrants who find themselves very much at home in a forest of this sort. The Chileans are not in a good position to export much lumber, but all the inhabitants of neighboring countries—Argentina, Bolivia, and Peru— are potential customers. South of the 41st parallel, the forest is so wet that lumbering is difficult. The forest includes both broad-leaved evergreens and various coniferous trees of which the pine and larch are most valuable. Much of Chile's southern forest is untouched. Some of it is on difficult terrain and can be reached only by the sea, but even so it constitutes a valuable resource for the southern part of the continent.

CONIFEROUS FORESTS COMPARED

In this chapter and the previous one, the chief regions of softwood forest production of the world have been described. Many other small districts in Africa, Australia, and New Zealand, usually associated with the agricultural belts, will be discussed later along with other forms of production in the appropriate regions. The regions just described, however, are the source of most of the forest products of the world. Furthermore, they include regions in which forest production (FIG. 7.7) is dominant. Nine countries share in this production in varying amounts. Of these the United

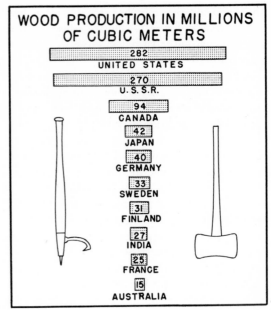

FIGURE 7.7. *Graph of wood production in leading countries. Which countries have the highest production per capita? Which are importers and which are exporters?*

States leads easily in production of lumber, but only by ruthless overexploitation. Russia leads in forest area, both of hardwoods and softwoods, and the Russians may soon lead in production and export also. The Finns rank first in per capita consumption of wood products. It is noteworthy that the first eight countries according to per capita consumption are in the coniferous belt. Russia is not among these since her population is large and the forest industries are still in an early stage of development.

There are indications that the consumers in most of the countries which have large areas of softwood forests are concerned about forest conservation. In Norway, Sweden, Finland, and Japan the growth is approximately as large as the cut. Increased "cultivation" of forest areas will add to the annual yields. Only in the United States is the cut far in excess of the growth. Apparently it will be necessary for the country to go through a real timber famine before production and growth are balanced. Perhaps the imminent large-scale exploitation of the vast tropical forests will mitigate this situation.

8

The Tropical Hardwood Forests

THE tropical hardwood forests contrast sharply with the coniferous forests of the higher latitudes. Most of the northern areas are too cool for agriculture; the tropical forests are too wet and, perhaps, too warm. In some areas, however, it has been proved that agriculture can be successful, and it is the belief of many people that the tropical forests will eventually be cleared and sown to crops. The difficulty of settlement in these humid lands is responsible, in a large measure, for the preservation of the forests. All the tropical forests (FIG. 8.1) lie near the Equator in irregular areas from Middle America and Amazonia through equatorial Africa to southeastern Asia. The largest areas are Amazonia and the Congo. All the tropical forests are sparsely populated as compared with the nearby regions, but population densities vary. Amazonia, because it is in an early stage of development, is occupied by the fewest people. In parts of the Congo the population is moderately dense, while in southeastern Asia the pressure of population has resulted in a determined invasion of the forests by agricultural

peoples. This chapter is concerned primarily with the forest products; later chapters will describe the impact of the plantations and the subsistence farms on the margins of these comparatively empty lands.

The tropical forests of the Americas occupy more than five million square miles of territory, nearly twice the area of the United States. There is an immense surplus of wood of many kinds—cabinet woods, lumber, dyewood, and tannin woods—but less than 5 per cent of the world's lumber is taken from the tropical forest. In the timber-starved temperate belts, where reconstruction following World War II will go on for years, many times the present production of tropical wood could be used. But the timber from these areas is not readily accessible to the people of the temperate belts. The tropical forests are remote from the centers of heavy production in eastern North America and western Europe. Lumbering is difficult because of poor transportation, the lack of pure stands, the shortage of labor (some people live in the rainforests, but no one wants to

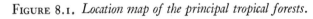

FIGURE 8.1. *Location map of the principal tropical forests.*

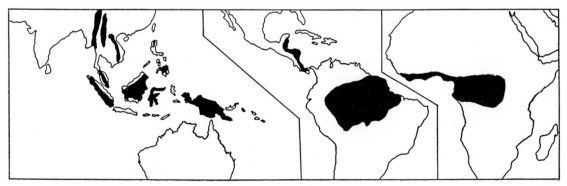

work there), and the prevalence of diseases which affect man and beast.

What products of the tropical forests are in general use in the middle latitudes today? The average person knows that some wild rubber comes from Amazonia and he is also familiar with mahogany. There is less knowledge of the other cabinet woods, such as lignum, teak, greenheart, ebony, brazilwood, and logwood. Other products of the tropical forests are widely used in the temperate belts—chicle for chewing gum, Brazil nuts, and palm oil for soap. Tagua nuts are being used more and more instead of ivory. From Babassu nuts an oil similar to palm oil is obtained. Dyewoods are no longer as important as formerly since good dyes are made from coal tar. Tannin for the leather industry is still brought from the tropical and subtropical forests. Many other products remain to be exploited.

MIDDLE AMERICA

The most extensive area of tropical forest in Middle America runs from southeastern Mexico, Quintana Roo, to Panama, along the eastern side of the Central American countries. Scores of smaller forest areas are to be found, mingled with agricultural districts, throughout Middle America. The list of forest products is a long one although only a few are of commercial value at the present time. At least 25 valuable tropical hardwoods, including mahogany, lignum vitae, balsa, dyewoods, and ceiba (kapok) are to be found in this region. In addition, many other timbers, medicinal products, fruits, and chicle are available.

Of all the products of this tropical forest, mahogany is probably the best known. Cortez used it to build ships and the Spanish Armada was built partly of mahogany from Middle America. Sir Walter Raleigh presented a table made of this wood to Queen Elizabeth. In the early days of New England, the Yankee traders carried mahogany to many lands. Numerous varieties are known and many other timbers are incorrectly called by the same name. All true mahogany belongs to the *Swietena* family, which ranges from southern Florida to Amazonia. The mahogany trees usually stand above the remainder of the tropical forest trees like sentinels, but scattered at varying intervals. The trees are symmetrical, often more than 100 feet in height, and may reach

a diameter of four feet near the ground. The distribution of the trees makes lumbering difficult and expensive. The axman usually climbs a tree before felling it in order to locate other trees in the vicinity. After the trees are felled, they are cut in convenient lengths and the logs are moved to the coast by water if possible and are exported without being sawed. Most mahogany is made into plywood or veneers.

Chewing gum is an international commodity with wide distribution, but its essential ingredient, chicle, is produced in a comparatively small area in southern Mexico and the adjacent sections of Guatemala and British Honduras. This district, with a population of less than 10,000, is one of the best examples of gathering economy in the world. The chicle trees do not thrive under cultivation but grow best, like mahogany trees, scattered through the forest. The harvesting is done mainly during the summer rainy season, from April to September, when the sap floats most freely.

Gathering chicle and harvesting wild rubber are similar. The worker (*chiclero*) having located a number of good trees in his area, makes herringbone incisions on the trunk of the tree near the ground. From these incisions the sap drains into a rubber bag or bucket. After a quantity of sap has been collected, it is mixed with water and cooked over a slow fire until it thickens. The chicle is then poured into wooden molds and solid blocks suitable for transport are formed. At this point chicle blocks are worth about $10 per hundred pounds. As it is moved slowly toward the chewing gum factory, the price increases rapidly. With the addition of local taxes, transport costs, transit toll through British Honduras, export taxes, and various other charges, the price is about $50 per hundredweight by the time it leaves Central America. Obviously, with such high overland transportation costs, air freighting of chicle can easily compete. As early as 1934, a Ford trimotor transport plane was used to carry two tons per trip to the coast. Today commercial transports move more than two million pounds of chicle per season.

The tropical forests of Middle America yield many other valuable products: timbers; drugs such as ipecac, belladonna, and quinine; oils for soaps; and various fibers. Some of these can be gathered from wild plants in the forest. Others will have to be cultivated in order to put production on a commercial basis. The plantation crops of Middle America, present and potential, are discussed in Chapter 23.

TROPICAL SOUTH AMERICA

About one third of South America is tropical lowland, one third is highland, while only the southern third is in the middle latitudes. This means that areas with humid tropical climates, which in North America are in the narrow part of the continent, are much more extensive in the southern continent. Likewise areas with temperate climates in South America are more restricted. South America, which is narrow in the higher latitudes, has no humid continental climate with both severe winters and warm summers. Otherwise the climates of the two Americas are similar in character, but the distribution pattern is quite different.

The rainforest climate (Af) is represented by four distinct areas in South America. The first region lies to the west of the Andes and covers the series of low coastal hills extending from Panama to northern Ecuador. In this region the lower slopes and valleys at the northern margin of the western range in the Andes are also included. The rainfall, in general, is more than 80 inches per year with no distinct dry season, although there is a period in December and January when the rainfall is comparatively light. It is to be noted that this district of the Andes is entirely north of the Equator, and there is no corresponding coastal area of rainforest climate to the south, where the winds and the configuration of the land do not favor heavy rains.

The second and largest area of rainforest lies east of the Andes in Amazonia; most of this district is south of the Equator in western Brazil but includes also parts of Venezuela, Colombia, Peru, and Bolivia. In the western part of this district on the lower slopes of the eastern Andes, the annual rainfall is the highest in the continent, more than 100 inches. The rainfall is almost uniform with the lightest rains generally occurring in the months of July and August. But even the driest months have abundant rain. The temperatures are uniformly high but by no means extreme, as is indicated in the following table of data for Manaus, Brazil. Manaus is in the eastern part of the heavy rainfall region and is slightly warmer and less rainy than the average.

It should be noted that the period from July through September has the least rain. Extremely high temperatures do not occur, and it is highly improbable that the maximum temperature has ever reached 100° F. The humidity is uniformly high, however, and people are uncomfortably warm in the middle of the day except in the driest months. Most of this region is sparsely settled. There is little cleared land and most of the country remains in dense forest.

CLIMATIC DATA FOR MANAUS, BRAZIL		
MONTH	Average Temperature (*degrees Fahrenheit*)	Average Rainfall (*inches*)
Jan.	80	9.2
Feb.	80	9.0
Mar.	80	9.6
Apr.	80	8.5
May	80	7.0
Jun.	80	3.6
Jul.	81	2.2
Aug.	82	1.4
Sep.	83	2.0
Oct.	83	4.1
Nov.	82	5.5
Dec.	81	7.7

Average Annual Temperature 81° Fahrenheit
Average Annual Rainfall 69.8 inches

A third area of rainforest extends along the northeast coast of South America from eastern Venezuela to the estuary of the Amazon. Most of this district is a low plain, but part of the interior portion lies in the foothills of the Guiana Highlands. Although the climate is very similar to that of the upper Amazon described previously, there is a more distinct period of light rain. Temperatures are much the same in both areas, although in some districts near the sea the temperatures are slightly lower.

The fourth area of rainforest climate lies along the eastern coast of Brazil from Salvador to the vicinity of Vitória, from latitude 12° S. to 20° S. This district is much farther from the Equator than the other rainforest areas and has a climate comparable to that along the east coast of Central America, as in Nicaragua. Type station is Recife (8° S. Lat.).

CLIMATIC DATA FOR RECIFE, BRAZIL		
MONTH	Average Temperature (*degrees Fahrenheit*)	Average Rainfall (*inches*)
Jan.	82	2.0
Feb.	82	3.5
Mar.	82	6.3
Apr.	82	8.6
May	80	10.8
Jun.	78	11.2
Jul.	77	10.3
Aug.	79	6.3
Sep.	80	2.7
Oct.	81	1.0
Nov.	81	1.1
Dec.	82	1.1

Average Annual Temperature 80° Fahrenheit
Average Annual Rainfall 65.0 inches

Amazonia

The dominating fact about Amazonia is that it is BIG. See FIGURE 8.2. The Amazon drains an area as large as the United States and includes parts of six countries—Brazil, Venezuela, Colombia, Ecuador, Peru, and Bolivia. The Amazon is navigable for 2000 miles and its tributaries for many thousands more. Since Amazonia is so large, it is unwise to speak of it in generalities. Most of the region is a tropical lowland, flooded during the rainy season, but parts of it are rough enough to suffer severe erosion if cleared for cultivation. Much of it is disease ridden, scarcely a fit place for man or beast; yet high quality beef cattle are produced on Marajó Island at the mouth of the great river. For the most part Amazonia is exploited by primitive gatherers and agriculturalists, but in some districts scientific agriculture is beginning. Here is the last great frontier of the Americas, capable of supporting millions of people and supplying the temperate belts with hundreds of products which are badly needed.

That Amazonia has not been developed in the past is, perhaps, an historical accident. The primitive peoples who have filtered into the region have had neither the will nor the weapons to conquer it. The Incas developed an advanced civilization on the Andean highlands to the west but left the low country very much alone. Europeans who visited both regions found the high-

lands more to their taste. To them the rainforest was a strange and terrible place, where weapons rusted, clothing rotted, and unfamiliar diseases threatened. In addition, the highlands contained gold. Since the first explorer, Orellana, crossed the Andes and descended the great river to the Atlantic, Amazonia has had a peculiar attraction to a few men. Soldiers, priests, naturalists, and many others have spent months or years in the region. Very few people, however, have elected to become permanent settlers. By 1940, the territory of Amazonas in Brazil had only 450,000 people in an area of more than 730,000 square miles, less than one person per square mile.

The utilization of Amazonia really began with the production of rubber. Commercial rubber development, in turn, depended on two factors, the vulcanization of rubber which made its widespread use possible, and the invention of the automobile which created a large demand. At the close of the last century when these two conditions had been met, most of the rubber in the world was in Amazonia. Outsiders found, somewhat to their surprise, that it was easy to penetrate Amazonia with river boats, that ocean-going freighters could go up hundreds of miles at high water stage. Manaus became the inland rubber center, easily reached by steamer. Belém (Pará) became the chief ocean port and gave its name to the crude rubber which originated in its hinterland. There was one serious difficulty, the poor labor supply. The natives could not or would not work for pay regularly. Then too, the tapping of the rubber trees requires a certain amount of skill, patience, and regularity. Rubber "stations," as they came to be called, have existed in Amazonia for more than a century and will continue to exist. A station is usually located on a navigable stream, assuring an outlet for the crude rubber and an inlet for the supplies of food and implements which must be brought in from outside. The manager of the station may be fortunate enough to have some well-trained agricultural workers from eastern Brazil, or he may have to depend on Indians. In any event a tapper is assigned to the wild rubber trees in a certain district. Each morning he makes the rounds, collecting the latex, and making additional incisions in the trees as needed. The collected latex is taken back to his hut where it is coagulated in the form of balls (FIG. 8.3) over a smoky fire. These round-

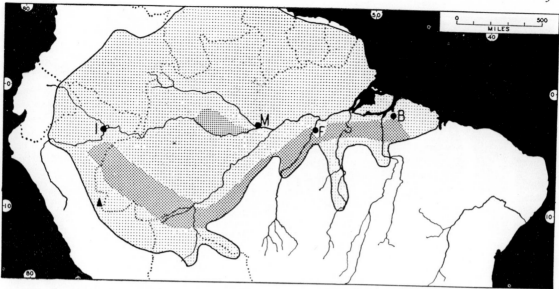

FIGURE 8.2. *The tropical forest area of Amazonia. This region covers parts of nine political divisions. It is little developed, with only a few small patches for agriculture and grazing. The chief areas of wild rubber are shown in the darker shade. Abbreviations: I, Iquitos; M, Manaus; F, Ford Rubber Plantation, now the property of Brazil; B, Belém, also called Pará. Although oil production (black triangle) in Amazonia is limited largely to eastern Peru, it is probable that all the eastern fringe of the Andes contains oil.*

ish balls, black with smoke (which does not injure the rubber), are called Pará "biscuits." They are then ready to be moved downstream to Manaus (FIG. 8.4) and to the world market. All this sounds simple, but the oppressive heat, the deterioration of equipment, the difficulty of keeping trails open, the irregularity of supplies from down river, dysentery, and malaria make life far from easy. These stations along with the few large plantations and the small native farms are envisaged as one way of getting rubber in production again in Amazonia.

With the rise of the rubber plantations in the East Indies and Malaya (where, unlike Amazonia, all the essential requirements of a plantation are met) the wild rubber industry in Amazonia declined, only to be revived during World War II. This time a great deal of help was provided from outside. A high wage scale and a drought in eastern Brazil brought thousands of eager workers to the wild rubber districts. Field hospitals and sanitary corps were sent in to check disease. The airplane counted heavily in the new attempt to conquer Amazonia. Amphibian planes landed on the broad rivers at many points, and the construction of landing fields was begun.

Rubber is by no means the only commercial product taken out of Amazonia today. Second only to rubber is the Brazil nut, growing widely on the higher ground in somewhat the same locations as the rubber trees. The nuts fall from the lofty tree crowns to the ground, are gathered, and are floated down the river to the nearest shipping point. If the world demand for Brazil nuts were to double, the additional amount could be easily harvested. Another product is the nut of the Babassu palm. It is about the size of a lemon and is rich in oil which can be used in the same manner as cottonseed oil or coconut oil in the preparation of margarine and soap.

It is impossible to mention all the cabinet woods to be found in Amazonia; only a few are produced in any quantity. There are more than a hundred species of cedar, usually named by the lumbermen after the dominant color of the wood —yellow, rose, and red. Brazilian teakwood is heavy and hard and is used in shipbuilding because of its resistance to salt water. Brazil was named after Brazilwood, a brilliant red, close-grained wood, satisfactory for furniture making. So the list goes on; many woods are useful for cabinetmaking and shipbuilding, some for paper

FIGURE 8.3. *An independent rubber worker in Amazonia is making a smoke ball. Notice the white latex and the shape of the rubber "biscuit." From CIAA.*

FIGURE 8.4. *Unloading rubber at Manaus on the Amazon in Brazil. These black "biscuits" were made by the method illustrated in Figure 8.3. From CIAA.*

making, some for excelsior, and some because of fibers with the quality of jute. Various kinds of mahoganies and rosewood are also found.

The difficulty, of course, is to get the tropical forest woods out to the market. Many of them grow widely dispersed, one tree here and another there, sometimes far from river transportation. Even if the logs are brought to the river, some of them will not float; rafts of lighter wood have to be built to carry these logs downstream.

Agriculture in Amazonia

Around the bend of a remote tributary of the Amazon is a small native village. The clearing in which it lies is scarcely large enough for a temperate belt farmyard, but it contains a dozen thatched huts grouped closely together. On all sides is the jungle wall, like a closely knit stockade, blocking exit from the village save by the stream and a few tunnel-like trails; only the natives know what lies back of that jungle wall. The houses are simply built; the support is four stout poles, one at each corner; a lighter framework forms the gabled roof. Over the main framework is a lighter pattern of small branches, and the roof is heavily thatched. An elevated floor of branches completes the house; for it is open on all sides for ventilation to catch whatever breeze may escape the impenetrable forest wall. Around the houses the little patches of land are cultivated in bananas, corn, cassava, and yams. On small plots these crops grow abundantly, if they grow at all. Few implements are needed to cultivate the small patches; a hoe, spade, or even a stick will do. The most difficult task is to clear the forest and maintain the clearing. The men of the village clear the land, hunt, fish, and fight with neighboring tribes; the women cultivate the land, plant, weed, and harvest the crops.

Most of the plants in the rainforest grow freely, hastily, even riotously. It is difficult enough to make a clearing in the forest just to grow a few subsistence crops such as corn, cassava, and beans. The forest, pushed back a tiny bit, seems to be waiting to recapture the little clearings. Shrubs and lianas appear almost overnight. Fungus diseases, root molds, and uncounted numbers of other small, invisible parasites attack the crops. If, in spite of all these difficulties, enough food can be raised to support a small community, and if in time some commercial crops can be added, the problem arises of getting the produce to a market. To be sure, there are the streams, but they are subject to flood and to low water and are not always dependable at the time needed. Even if the goods can be brought down to the coast, the producer must still face the export duties, the import tariffs, and perhaps difficult inspections before payment is received.

That is the primitive side of agriculture in the Amazon Basin. Along with the exploitation of the wild rubber and the growth of plantations, however, are the beginnings of a more modern farm pattern. The thousands of workers who rushed in during the period of World War II had to be fed, so thousands more were brought in to produce the food crops. Seeds, implements, and agricultural experts were sent from the United States and the Latin American countries to aid in the production of food. The government of Brazil particularly cooperated. Thousands of pounds of seed were imported and about 10,000 acres were planted to staple foods, rice, corn, beans, and cassava. At the same time the production of poultry and pork was substantially increased (chickens and pigs long ago were proved to be successful products in the rainforest). Vegetables and fruit grow well also, and the fact was established that Amazonia can be self-supporting so far as basic foods are concerned. Farm training centers were set up to train people in the special methods necessary in this humid tropical land.

What of the immediate future of Amazonia? The impact of World War II (which had an ef-

fect like a dose of benzedrine) has now faded, and Amazonia must stand or fall on its merits and the merits of the people who control its destiny. To most Brazilians, Peruvians, and Colombians, Amazonia is still remote and their energies are directed elsewhere. In Brazil especially, the trend of migration has been to the south, to the more temperate parts of the country. If any large part of Amazonia is to be put under cultivation, many, many thousands of laborers will be needed. Latin Americans are loath to move in except under special conditions. The door is closed to the millions of Oriental peoples who, perhaps more than any other group, are best fitted by inheritance and training to conquer the rainforest. The jungle will be pushed back slowly before the invaders: here and there a plantation will be established; transportation will be stimulated as the oilfields of the Andean margin are developed; eventually the pressure of population in the crowded areas of the world will force millions into the tropical rainforests. Then, and not until then, will the production of Amazonia begin to be brought to its full capacity.

Some indication of the nature of the plans for Amazonia is given in Bulletin A-1683 for the Office of the Coordinator of Inter-American Affairs:

Brazil's plan for colonization of the Amazon, for greater development of its resources, is a long-range program. . . . It aims to make the Amazon more attractive to man, by calling in the aid of science, the machine, improved agriculture. Doctors, nurses, airplane pilots, agricultural technicians, organizers are the vanguard of the colonization movement. The emergency migration after Pearl Harbor to obtain additional workers for wartime needs is an episode in the larger story of the trek to the Amazon. And, like the larger story, it illustrates how the Amazon-bound worker and colonist is receiving the benefits of progress in applying the principles of preventive and tropical medicine. The huge valley presents perhaps the greatest challenge to tropical medicine. Among those who have studied the Amazon region, there is wide difference of opinion as to its future for human habitation. But most of those who are wise in the ways of the Amazon country . . . would agree that the extended use of practical preventive and therapeutic measures can help greatly in making it more attractive to the colonist.

THE TROPICAL FOREST OF AFRICA

Africa is no longer the dark continent. The eleven million square miles from the Mediterranean to the southern ocean are now generally well known to the outside world. Production for world markets is, however, just beginning. It is remarkable that this continent, lying just to the south of overcrowded, resource-depleted Europe and not far from the poverty stricken millions of southeastern Asia, has undergone so little change in its production pattern in the last few centuries. The trend of world affairs suggests that Africa's time has come, and that the resources of this continent may experience accelerated exploitation in the years immediately ahead.

From the point of view of the geographer, Africa is an almost ideal continent. It lies astride the Equator but extends into the temperate belts both to the north and to the south. Most of the continent is a fairly uniform plateau with few mountain ranges or low plains. The coastline is regular and, therefore, short in proportion to the area. The position of Africa with respect to latitude gives it an approximate symmetry of climate and vegetation which is complicated only locally by elevation.

Although close to Europe, the bulk of Africa is separated from its northern neighbor by an extensive dry region. The Sahara and its borderlands have, until the present at least, played a significantly limiting role. It will be obvious, even from a brief study of Africa, that the great growth of the future will come in the tropical belt. In this respect Africa is like South America, which is also in the Southern Hemisphere.

The political geography of Africa has not favored an increasing production. Most of Africa is controlled by European nations which have not been able to persuade their people to emigrate to Africa in any great numbers, even when encouraged by subsidies. At the same time the immigration of Asiatics to Africa has been restricted or forbidden. South and North Americans were able to throw off the European yoke after sufficient numbers of Europeans had arrived. Africa has not yet experienced enough immigration to make any profound changes in the character of the people. The problems of African development are numerous and the pressure from inside and outside is increasing.

Since the Equator divides Africa approximately in two, it follows that the climates are arranged in a bisymmetrical pattern with respect to the middle of the continent. Also, since Africa is broader in the north, the desert, steppe, and

Mediterranean climates have greater areas there. The highland is somewhat more extensive in the Southern Hemisphere so that there the winter dry temperate climate (Cw) is larger. But from north to south the arrangement and sequence of the climates are similar. From Algiers to Capetown, either on a direct line or along the west coast, the following climates occur: Cs, BS, BW, BS, Aw, Af, Aw, BS, BW, BS, Cs. Wherever such a line is drawn across a highland, the climate is generally Cw.

All these climates have been described before in the study of North and South America. There are local variations in the African climates, however, which deserve special attention. The rainforest of Africa is smaller than that of South America. Three important areas of rainforest can be defined: one lies along the coast of Sierra Leone and Liberia, a second and the largest is in the Congo River drainage, and a third is on the east coast of Madagascar. In the western area of the Guinea Coast, near Freetown and Monrovia, the rainfall is very heavy, but there is a distinct dry period in the winter season of the Northern Hemisphere. The climatic data for Freetown, Sierra Leone, is typical.

Although December, January, and February are quite dry, the total rainfall for the year is high enough to make this a rainforest (Af) climate.

Climatic Data for Freetown, Sierra Leone		
Month	Average Temperature (degrees Fahrenheit)	Average Rainfall (inches)
Jan.	81	0.6
Feb.	82	0.5
Mar.	82	1.1
Apr.	82	5.4
May	81	14.8
Jun.	80	21.0
Jul.	79	36.0
Aug.	78	39.0
Sep.	80	32.0
Oct.	81	15.0
Nov.	81	5.3
Dec.	80	1.3

Average Annual Temperature 81° Fahrenheit
Average Annual Rainfall 174.0 inches

The climate of the Congo region is quite different from that of the Guinea Coast. In the first place, the region is for the most part a low plateau with sufficient elevation to modify the climate. Furthermore, the region lies astride the Equator, and most stations have a double maximum and a double minimum of rainfall. Banana, in the Belgian Congo and near the Equator, illustrates this type although it does not reflect the cooler temperatures of the plateau.

CLIMATIC DATA FOR BANANA, BELGIAN CONGO		
Month	Average Temperature (degrees Fahrenheit)	Average Rainfall (inches)
Jan.	80	3.5
Feb.	81	3.6
Mar.	81	4.0
Apr.	80	8.4
May	79	2.2
Jun.	75	0.0
Jul.	72	0.0
Aug.	72	0.2
Sep.	80	0.2
Oct.	77	1.9
Nov.	80	8.3
Dec.	80	4.6

Average Annual Temperature 78° Fahrenheit
Average Annual Rainfall 36.9 inches

In general, the interior of the Congo country is a few degrees cooler because of the altitude.

The east coast of Madagascar is comparable to the east coast of Brazil in the same latitude except that the rainfall is greater in Madagascar. At Tamatave the rainfall is heavy throughout the year (total 125 inches) with one maximum in January and another in July. There is a greater range in temperature than in the Congo because Madagascar is farther from the Equator. On the east coast of Africa there is no rainforest even on the Equator, because the monsoon winds blow parallel to the coastline or away from it.

The Congo and the Guinea Coast

The tropical forests of Africa along the Guinea Coast and in the Congo country are fundamentally like those of Amazonia, but there are a number of significant differences between these regions. The terrain in the Congo is plateaulike rather than like the lowland of Amazonia. River transportation on the Congo is more difficult than on the Amazon because of numerous rapids. Minerals are more abundant. Rainfall is lighter and temperatures are somewhat lower. The population is denser and the native peoples are better suited by nature and culture to live and work in the rainforest than are the natives of Amazonia. All these items add up to a greater variety of commercial production in the African forests.

The rainforest extends from Dakar in the Senegal to the outlet of the Congo, and to the eastern limits of the Belgian Congo. Interspersed with the forest areas are districts of subsistence agriculture and plantation cropping too complicated and extensive to be discussed here. (See Chapter 25.) Although known to the Portuguese since 1494, the African forests, like those of Amazonia, proved hard to penetrate, partly because of falls in the rivers, diseases (especially the sleeping sickness), and the very density of the forest itself. First to be exploited was the Guinea Coast, which became known according to its chief item of trade as the Grain Coast (on the west coast, "grain" meant pepper), the Ivory Coast, the Gold Coast, and the Slave Coast. The first and last of these terms are no longer used since the trade in the commodities they represent has either declined or disappeared.

The Congo produces some quantities of cabinet woods—mostly rosewood, ebony, and African mahogany. Wild rubber is taken from two plants, *Funtumia* which is a tree and *Landolphia* which is a vine. Elephant ivory is also a forest product, in a sense, although the elephant lives mostly in the savanna. The significant production of the region is from the small native farms where palm oil, cacao, and other commercial items are raised. Many of these crops are transplanted from the forest directly, but gathering of the wild products continues. Other introduced crops, such as cacao, can be grown here because of the cheap labor available.

By and large, palm oil is the chief product of the native farms. The oil palm grows throughout the entire area and even beyond, and with its many useful qualities had played an important part in native economy for centuries. The nut is edible, the oil extracted from it is edible, and the leaves make excellent thatching material for the houses and can even be processed into a kind of

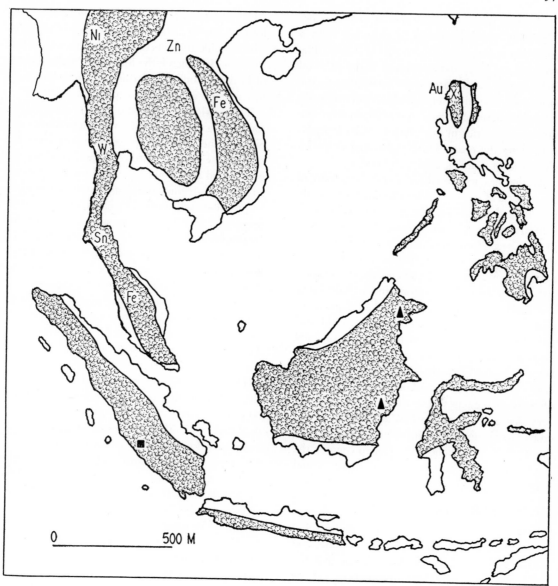

FIGURE 8.5. *The tropical forests of southeastern Asia have been invaded by agriculturists so that in general these areas should be classified as farm types. But large stands of forest remain. In Burma, Siam, and French Indochina teak is the most important lumber. Several varieties of hardwoods grow in the islands, including teak, bamboo, and Philippine mahogany. In addition to exports, the tropical forests of southeastern Asia furnish building materials and fuels for the adjacent areas of dense population. Abbreviations: Au, gold; Ni, nickel; Fe, iron ore; Sn, tin; W, tungsten; Zn, zinc. Petroleum production is indicated by triangles, coal by square.*

cloth. The wood is useful also in construction. Gradually the exploitation is changing from a gathering economy to a cultivated economy. The pressing, refining, and marketing of the palm oil is facilitated by the large mills established by the large concessionaires, one of which had originally 1,800,000 acres. See page 323. Cotton is grown in some quantities in the interior, cacao and peanuts along the coast. Other cultivated crops include rubber, vanilla, sugar, and coffee.

Mining has accounted for a very large part of the exports of equatorial Africa. The most highly mineralized zone is on the eastern margin, adjacent to the East African Plateau. Although a part of the Congo–Guinea Coast region is included in the area of subsistence agriculture, in the Congo portion quantities of gold, diamonds, tin, copper, and other minerals are mined. In the Kilo-Moto Goldfields to the northwest of Lake Albert more than 30,000 natives are employed. Additional thousands are employed in the copper, tin, and diamond mines, the last named being located largely on the Kasai River. In the mines especially, the demand for labor is very great and often is in regions where the population is not very dense. Thus, migrations are necessary and crops must be grown in the new locations to feed the workers. Throughout the Congo country the chief food crops are cassava, rice, bananas, and yams.

SOUTHEASTERN ASIA

The tropical forests of southeastern Asia (FIG. 8.5) extend from northern Burma to New Guinea and include the forests of the East Indies and the Philippines. In general, the environment and the resources of this great forest are similar to those of Amazonia and the Congo, but here the impact of man is more noticeable because of the constant pressure from the adjacent ricelands, the most densely populated regions in the world. The natural and cultural aspects of this region more closely resemble those of the Congo than those of Amazonia. The surface is generally mountainous (the valleys and gentler slopes have been cleared for cultivation). The monsoon climate dominates with variable amounts of rainfall and seasonal distribution. In general, the forests are in the regions of heaviest rainfall and roughest land, both factors making agricultural exploitation difficult.

The exploitation of the forest takes many forms. The cutting of teak in northern Burma and Siam is one of the simplest. In preparation for cutting, the trees are girdled a few feet above the ground and are allowed to stand for a few years so that, by drying, the density will be reduced and the logs will float. Elephants are often used to get the teak logs to the streams such as the Irrawaddy or the Mekong. From there the logs float down river to the ports of Rangoon, Bangkok, or Saigon. Teak is much prized for building ships; it is hard, strong, and resistant to salt water. Only because teak is valuable is it worthwhile to get this wood out to the coast since most of the trees are inland in rough country. The cutting of many other fairly good timber trees awaits better transportation.

The most widely distributed and the most valuable forest product of southeastern Asia is bamboo. With many varieties differing in height, thickness, and other qualities, the bamboo has many varied uses. It can be used as a solid wood, not very thick but hard and subject to little shrinkage. The large tubular bamboo is used to support houses; from bamboo in the split form screens can be made for the side walls. Roofs which are completely rainproof even in the wettest districts can be built with this product. Implements for fishing, hunting, and even for war are made from bamboo. The young shoots are excellent to eat, as any diner in a Chinese restaurant knows. Clothing, especially hats and shoes, can be made from the leaves; charcoal can be made from the stumps; water can be carried or piped in the hollow tubes. Bamboo is so valuable that it has become an important cultivated crop in those regions of southeastern Asia where it does not grow naturally.

9

Commercial Grazing and Oases in North America

South of the Great Northern Forest and west of the 100th meridian is the dry belt of North America. This is THE WEST. By many who have never seen it, this region is thought to be a land of romance, primitive Indians, colorful ranches, and daring cowboys who conquer prairie fires, blizzards, bucking broncos, and fair maidens with equal ease. Actually it is also a land of little rain, of parched pastures, dust bowls, and grasshoppers, and, for many settlers who have attempted to farm it, a land of monotony, misery, and defeat. Like the Great Northern Forest this is a vast region, more than 2000 miles long and 1000 miles wide, stretching from the Canadian border far into Mexico and from western Nebraska to California (FIG. 9.1). Some of the region is real desert, too dry for human occupation. On the other hand, humid mountains reach into the zone of coolness and moisture and provide excellent grass for summer grazing as well as water to irrigate the adjacent plains.

Of the three important grazing animals in the Great Plains—cattle, sheep, and goats—the cattle are more evenly distributed. There are some cattle in all districts; the variation in numbers is related in part to the "carrying" capacity of the range. In some of the more humid areas, less than 10 acres are needed for a cow; in other districts 25 acres or more are required.

In spite of difficulties, this commercial grazing region possesses certain advantages denied to its competitors in the Southern Hemisphere. To be sure, production costs are somewhat higher in western North America than in Argentina and Australia. But the excellent home market and the protection afforded by the tariff and other trade restrictions make it unnecessary for the producers of this region to enter into the world market to any considerable extent. Those parts of the commercial grazing region which lie in Canada and Mexico are outside the United States tariff wall and have a much more restricted home market.

The characteristic production unit of the commercial grazing regions is the ranch, which varies in size, quality of the grass, and water supply. All are large, some the equivalent of several square miles. Some are fenced, others are not. In many ranches are small areas of irrigated land which produce forage crops for winter feeding. Ranchers near the mountains have access to mountain pastures for their flocks and herds in the summer. Some of these mountain pastures are in the National Forests.

An example of the more isolated ranch is found in the Henry Mountains in southeastern Utah. Here the only rancher within fifty miles takes advantage of the humid slopes of a nearby mountain range for pasture, and a small valley is irrigated to furnish winter feed. This was formerly a cattle ranch but was changed to sheep, partly because of the poor quality of the grass and partly because of the isolated location. There are no fences, only the ranch house, corrals, the rough mesas and ridges of the mountains, and a tortuous road to the nearest rail town about 75 miles away. Under these circumstances wool and not meat is the commercial product of the ranch.

An example of a different type of sheep ranch lies on the eastern border of the Rocky Mountains in northern New Mexico. The ranch proper is in the plain, but near by are several mesas with flat tops and steep sides, and farther west are the foothills of the mountains. Irrigation is important

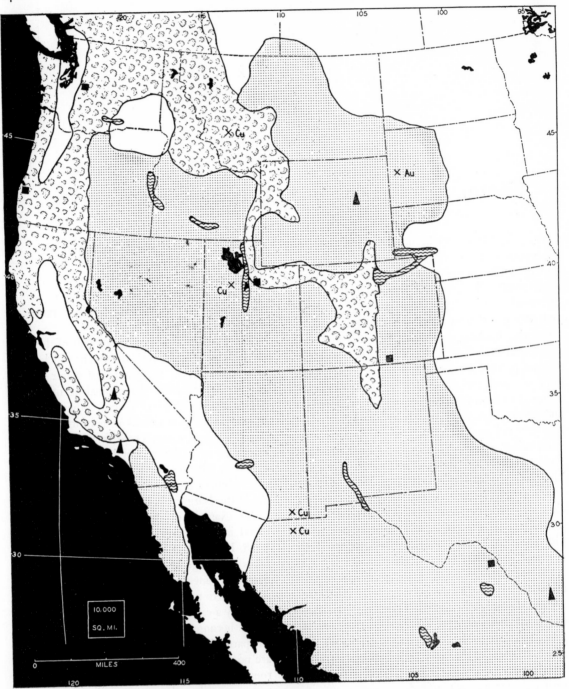

FIGURE 9.1. *Commercial Grazing, Forests, and Oases of western United States. Commercial grazing occupies most of the semiarid lands including the western part of the Great Plains and a large portion of the Intermontane Plateaus. The adjacent forested mountains furnish summer pasturage for sheep and cattle. The oases, indicated by wavy ruling, produce hay for winter feed along with small grain, sugar beets, and various other crops. Some of the outstanding mining regions are indicated. Abbreviations: Au, gold; Cu, copper. Petroleum is shown by solid black triangles, coal by solid black squares. Notice the isolated grazing area in southwestern California and the northwestern part of Lower California.*

and, in addition to alfalfa, some sugar beets and fruit trees are to be found. Ranching, however, is the principal use of the land. The sheep spend the winter in the corrals near the ranch house, and in the spring move up the mesas and later to the mountain pastures, only to return when the cold and snows appear at the high altitudes. This ranch is near the railroad and from it both wool and meat on the hoof are sold.

One of the best ranching areas of North America is the Llanos district of central Texas. This is a low plateau region with excellent grass, streams, and many well-fenced, carefully managed ranches. One of these is the "101 Ranch," bearing the same name as a more famous ranch in Oklahoma. A good-sized stream runs through the ranch, affording plenty of water for the purebred Hereford cattle, the principal breed in this region. The ranch is fenced, the ranch house is substantial, and the whole appearance suggests a large, well-managed farm, rather than the old-fashioned type of ranch.

THE GREAT PLAINS

In that part of the grazing region east of the Rockies, the Great Plains (FIG. 9.1), the cattle industry began in the south with the introduction of Spanish cattle from Mexico. Prior to 1870 the region had been looked upon as a roadway, a dry region to cross in order to reach the goldfields of Colorado and California. An old government report stated that "all land west of the Mississippi is little better than a desert." After the Civil War, however, the region began to assume some importance in its own right. C. W. Thornthwaite in *Migration and Economic Opportunity* (Univ. of Pennsylvania Press, 1936, pp. 207–208) tells of the advancing frontier in the Great Plains:

At the end of the Civil War the Great Plains were chiefly waste land occupied by roving herds of buffalo and scattered nomadic Indians. The few existing settlements were trading posts that had developed as a result of the Gold Rush. These found cattle raising profitable as a side line and furnished the nuclei for the subsequent development of the cattle industry. By 1870 two railroads had been extended across the Great Plains: one from Omaha across Nebraska to the Pacific and the other from Kansas City across Kansas to Denver. The original purpose of these was to tap the trade of the Far West. Incidentally, they facilitated and found profitable the activities of the buffalo hunters, and during the following decades the export of hides, horns, and bones was enormous and the animals were practically exterminated.

To the south lay Texas, a former Spanish colony, with a culture organized around cattle raising and a land system well adapted to the requirements of that culture and to the peculiarities of the semiarid climate. The Civil War had brought about a cattle shortage in the North but had left Texas fairly overflowing. The resulting price differential was so great that vast numbers (nearly six million before 1885) were driven over the trails to the railroads leading to the northern and eastern markets. Actual and prospective profits from the cattle drives caused a phenomenal extension of ranching over the entire Great Plains area. The boom which followed quickly overstocked the ranges, resulted in a devastating drop in prices, and left the ranchers helpless in the face of the inevitable droughts, blizzards, and plagues of grasshoppers.

The Great Plains slope gently from the foothills of the Rocky Mountains, where the elevation is nearly one mile, to the Mississippi Lowland and the Gulf Coastal Plain. The surface varies from very smooth, almost level country in the High Plains of eastern Colorado and the Staked Plains of Texas to rather rough, hilly land in the Missouri River region. The streams occupy deep valleys and the interstream areas are often heavily rolling or rough. In districts where the rock material is very weak and the vegetation sparse, "badlands" are likely to develop. In western South Dakota and North Dakota the badlands have the appearance of a desert with sharp ridges, vertical canyons, and very little vegetation.

Most of the surface of the Great Plains is covered with recent alluvial material washed down from the Rocky Mountains. This material is only slightly cemented; it is somewhat porous and, therefore, resistant to erosion especially if the original grass cover is intact.

Commercial grazing in the Great Plains is limited to those sections not suited to crops. The humid margins are devoted to wheat farming and the irrigable districts to the production of forage crops and sugar beets. In the grazing areas it takes from 15 to 40 acres to support one unit of livestock (one cow, one horse, or seven sheep); even so, the animals can live on the range only during part of the year. In winter they must be fed hay and forage produced in the irrigated oases. The distribution of sheep is different from that of cattle. The cattle are almost evenly distributed from northern Mexico to southern Canada, although some parts of the Great Plains have a higher carrying capacity than others. For instance, the Sand Hills of Nebraska are much better than the Bad Lands of South Dakota. But there are no decided concentrations of cattle in the Great Plains. Sheep are somewhat more restricted. They tend to be clustered near the mountains so that they can take advantage of the grass above timberline in the summer and yet be near the irrigated lands in the winter.

Goats are dominant in the brush country of south Texas, sheep second. This was formerly a cattle country, but the thorny vegetation is a handicap to cattle raising. The goat, and to a certain extent the sheep, is a browser. So the leaves and twigs of the brush, as well as the grass growing beneath the bushes, are good forage. Neither goats nor sheep are as conspicuous in this country as on the open range; they are hidden in the brush. But if the traveler will climb down from his automobile and stoop to a goat's level, he may see, under the upper branches of the brush, many goats munching the leaves, sometimes standing on their hind legs to reach a tender sprig. This goat region constitutes the largest source of mohair in North America. Some of the meat is eaten by the Mexicans who look after the flocks. Most North Americans will not eat goat meat at home; yet, when they enter a Mexican restaurant they frequently order *cabrito* (kid) and describe it as an exotic delicacy.

The most important products of the Great Plains Ranching Region are meat, wool, and mohair. The meat, beef and mutton, moves toward the market on the hoof. See FIGURE 9.2. The yearling beef cattle and lambs are shipped to the Corn Belt farms. There corn, oats, and hay are used to fatten them, improving the quality of the meat as well as increasing the weight of the animal. In this way a Corn Belt farmer makes a profit. Some of the meat animals are ready for slaughter when they leave the range, if they come from the best pasture areas and have had supplementary feeding. During World War II many animals were slaughtered as soon as they arrived from the plains whether they were ready or not. The product was marketed as "utility beef," but most of us were glad to sink our teeth into it (when that was possible). The wool and mohair are much easier to get to market than the meat. They are not perishable and the price per pound is much higher than meat on the hoof. That means that sheep for wool may be grown profitably in

the more remote places. However, a few places in the Great Plains are too far from a railroad to market mutton.

As indicated previously, the irrigated areas within the Commercial Grazing Region provide additional forage for the range animals. Along the foot of the Rocky Mountains and in some places well out into the plains, numerous oases are found. In many of them sugar beets, fruits, and wheat are produced, crops which have little relation to Commercial Grazing. In all of the oases, however, alfalfa is grown for the neighboring ranches. Let us study one of these oases, the South Platte River Valley in northeastern Colorado.

The South Platte River rises in the Front Range of the Rocky Mountains. Among the peaks which retain some of their snow until the middle of the summer are the headwaters of the river's tributaries. Numerous small lakes act as reservoirs, keeping the water up in the mountains until needed in the plains below. Many small dams and a few larger ones increase the capacity of these lakes. Very little interference with the natural course of the streams is made until the river emerges from the mountains. By means of huge diversion ditches, some of the water is taken from the river, called here the Big Thompson, and is carried along the contour at a level above the adjacent plains. Much of the water, however, continues down the river bed to irrigate the flood plain many miles from the mountains. Away from the mountains where the higher parts of the plains cannot be irrigated, the contrast between the irrigated valley floor and the uplands is striking. In summer the valley is lush and green, the uplands brown and dry. In the valley, sugar beets and alfalfa use up most of the water. The beets go to a refinery (for example, FIG. 9.3) to be converted into sugar which is becoming more and more like cane sugar as the processes are improved. The beet sugar advertisements of a few years ago boasted that not even a chemist could distinguish beet sugar from the cane product. In a few more years, perhaps, not even a housewife can tell the difference. Then cane sugar will no longer command a slightly higher price in the retail market. Alfalfa, and other hay, is taken mostly to the nearby ranches where it brings a good price. Almost any time during the summer, one can see from the rim of the valley hundreds of stacks of hay dotting the valley floor. Sugar beets are not

FIGURE 9.2. *Cattle from the Montana ranges are loaded at Cascade, Montana, bound for the eastern markets. From Great Northern Railway.*

produced in all of the irrigated districts, but hay is grown in even the smallest of them.

THE INTERMONTANE PLATEAUS

Between the Rocky and Sierra Nevada mountains are the Intermontane Plateaus, the Colorado and Columbia plateaus, and the Basin Range Region. Most of this is grazing country like the Great Plains but drier, rougher, and, on the whole, less intensively grazed. A part of it, in southern Nevada and southeastern California, is scarcely used at all except for an occasional oasis, an isolated mine, or as a backdrop for a western movie. On the other hand, parts of the Colorado

Plateau and some of the Basin Ranges are high and humid enough to support trees.

In most of this region the rainfall is so light (less than 10 inches annually for half the area), the land is so rough, vegetation so sparse, and local transportation so poor that ranches are operated only in the more favorable spots. The carrying capacity of the range is low, often requiring 75 acres to support one cow, so that a rancher with 10,000 acres does not necessarily have a large herd. Sheep thrive better than cattle in many districts since they can live on poorer grass and rougher land, but the slow-footed wool producers will not travel far for water and are thus ruled out of many areas. In northern Arizona, western Utah, southern Idaho, and Oregon there are at least five sheep per person as compared with one per person for the United States as a whole. The greatest density of sheep is in the Snake River Valley where irrigated areas supply large quantities of winter forage (see OASES on this page). Most of the sheep ranches are located near water holes or streams, and the herders drive their flocks to the nearby ranges in summer. Very few of the ranches are fenced. Cattle are only slightly less important than sheep, and horses are also numerous. In many parts of the region there are still droves of wild horses which are sometimes captured and sold for meat. The Navajo Indians on the southern margin of the Colorado Plateau have both horses and sheep in large numbers. Much of the wool is made into rugs by the Indians. The selling of rugs to tourists and the selling of horses make the life of the Navajo at least semicommercial. Goats thrive in New Mexico and Arizona, especially in the brushy regions not suited to cattle or horses.

Most of northern Mexico is a part of the Intermontane Grazing Region. Broad basins, many of them too dry for grass to grow, are flanked by low ranges. Near the United States boundary in the vicinity of El Paso, the land is dry indeed. Only a few ranches exist in favored places and many basins are covered with creosote bush not even suitable for goats. As one travels south toward the Laguna cotton district (FIG. 9.1), the moisture gradually increases. Cattle, sheep, goats, and a few horses appear on the scanty grasslands. Cattle were formerly exported from this region to the United States in spite of the tariff and rigid customs inspections, but the herds have declined in recent decades. The livestock density is very low except on the southern margin of the region and in the brushy coastal lowland on the east. Some pasture is available all the year round either in the low basins or in the open pine forests on the higher ranges. There are few alpine pastures, however, since the upper timberline here is above 12,000 feet.

THE MOUNTAIN PASTURES

The higher mountains rising above the commercial grazing lands belong to the Forest Belt, but they contain a large area of humid pasture land. In the various ranges of the Rocky Mountains, Sierra Nevadas, and in many smaller ranges in the Great Basin and on the plateaus, there is usually excellent grass on the gentler slopes above the timberline for a fairly short period in summer. Some of these areas are too isolated to be used, but many of them have their quota of sheep or cattle in the summer season. On the broad benches of the Front Range in Colorado, for example, between the cold timberline and the continental divide, there is excellent grass from July to September. See FIGURE 9.4. Small flocks of sheep in charge of a lonesome shepherd, with his chuck wagon and dog, can be seen on many an isolated mesa. In September snow begins to fall at this altitude and the animals must be driven down to the plains. This migration up and down the mountain with the seasons is a very ancient institution, still practiced in mountainous districts all over the world. The most valuable contribution of the mountains is the water used to irrigate the nearby portion of the plains. Without irrigated forage crops, the production of meat and wool would be cut in half.

THE OASES

As indicated at the beginning of this chapter, there are other types of land use in the western part of North America in addition to grazing: dry farming, irrigation, mining, and the tourist industry. Of dry farming little need be said at this point since the subject will be discussed with the wheat belts. The irrigated oases, however, merit considerable attention. Most of the large projects are in valleys of the rivers which emerge from the Rocky Mountains, such as the Bow and Saskatchewan in Canada and the Missouri, North and South Platte, Arkansas, Pecos, Rio Grande, and Colorado in the United States. The water is derived from melting snow and rain in the lofty Rockies, and at some places elaborate dams and ditches have been constructed to hold back the water and distribute it to the lowlands. The irrigated oases contrast sharply with the ranch lands. The farms are usually small and a large proportion of the land is in crops—alfalfa, sugar beets, wheat, barley, and oats. In the southern part of the region, cotton and some fruit trees are grown.

The Imperial Valley, lying athwart the United States–Mexican boundary, is in some respects like the lower Nile. The source of water in each

FIGURE 9.3. *A beet sugar factory at Spreckels, California. This factory has a capacity of 5400 tons of beets per day which is converted to 18,000 one-hundred-pound bags of refined sugar. From Research Foundation.*

district is in distant humid mountains; the rivers, the Nile and the Colorado, flow through the desert and form deltas on relatively quiet seas. The climate of each region is the same, hot desert (BWh).

Most of the Imperial Valley is gently sloping land below sea level. The Colorado does not flow through the valley but is marginal to it, making it necessary to divert the water by means of large canals. Water for irrigation was formerly taken out above Yuma, Arizona, and brought to the valley by a circuitous route to avoid sand hills. The All-American Canal carries the water along the International Boundary and provides more water at a higher level. The gentle slope of the valley floor toward the Salton Sea is just right for effective irrigation.

The crops on the two sides of the International Boundary are so different, because of the tariff barrier, that it is better to discuss them separately. On the United States side the principal crop by acreage is alfalfa, in keeping with the general pattern of the irrigated oases in the

grazing lands. This is true in spite of the fact that there is little grazing in the vicinity of the Imperial Valley, for there is demand for hay in the Los Angeles district in connection with the local dairy industry. Other important crops include barley, cantaloupes, lettuce, cotton, sorghum, grapefruit, dates, and various early vegetables.

On the Mexican side production is quite different in a number of ways. Three crops—corn, wheat, and cotton—occupy most of the cropped land. There is little market for vegetables or fruits. This region is cut off from the rest of Mexico by its position on the west side of the Gulf of California. There is no rail connection with the main body of Mexico. Even the cotton which is exported from the region goes through the United States in sealed cars. Some of the other conditions of production are indicated in the author's article, "Cotton Regions of Mexico" (Econ. Geog., Vol. 14: 364–365, 1938):

Until recently a large share of the land in the valley was held by the Colorado Land Company, which con-

FIGURE 9.4. *Sheep on summer pasture near Great Falls, Montana. From Great Northern Railway.*

trolled more than 600,000 acres, only a small part cultivated. Most of the remainder was held by smaller land companies and very little by small individual farmers. In 1926, when first visited by the writer, the largest holding was administered much like a large plantation. The agricultural workers, Mexican, Chinese, and Japanese, were share croppers or cash renters. . . . The company supervised carefully the planting, cultivation, and irrigation. In March and April, 1937, most of the privately controlled land was expropriated by the Mexican Government, . . . divided into *ejidos* (communal holdings) of approximately 5,000 acres each, with about 150 families per *ejido* . . . .

At least 400,000 acres could be cultivated in this district if there were sufficient water and demand for the products. But the region is decidedly handicapped by its position with respect to the main body of the nation. Cotton which is sent to the interior markets of the Republic passes through the United States either via Arizona and the Mexican Southern Pacific Railway, or through California, via San Diego and thence by boat to Veracruz. Wheat and flour are exported from San Diego or the Mexican port of Ensenada. It need scarcely be pointed out that export to the United States is curtailed by the tariff wall.

Far to the north of Mexico the Utah Oasis,

along the west front of the Wasatch Mountains, in the vicinity of Salt Lake City was settled by the Mormons in 1847. The oasis is supplied with water from the Wasatch Mountains by means of many creeks rather than by one large river. The west side of the mountains receives heavy snow in winter which provides water for irrigation well into the summer. The irrigated land lies on the floor of old Lake Bonneville, the fresh water predecessor of Great Salt Lake. The lake deposits weather into excellent soil, but water is necessary to grow many crops, although some of the grain is dry-farmed. Towns are located close to the mountains where small streams emerge and most of the farmers live near by. Crops are more diversified than in the Imperial Valley; consequently this district is more nearly self-sufficient. Most farms resemble gardens. The chief crops in acreage are alfalfa, wheat, and sugar beets. The alfalfa reflects the importance of the livestock industry, including commercial grazing in the vicinity. Wheat has been an important food crop of the people since settlement, and sugar beets are the cash crop, since for the most part they are exported from the region. Some of the winter wheat is dry-farmed on lands which cannot be irrigated because of the scarcity of water. In addition to the staple crops smaller amounts of corn, sorghum, deciduous fruits, potatoes, and a variety of vegetables are produced. On the southern margin of this oasis where water is very scarce, some of the settlements have failed. Because of too little water the "alkali" has come to the surface and has spoiled the land.

The Snake River Oasis probably bears a closer relation to Commercial Grazing than most other irrigated districts. Alfalfa is a major crop in an area of more than a million acres. The water from the upper Snake River is used to irrigate the plain above the deep canyon in southern Idaho and eastern Washington. This region supports half the people of Idaho and some of the people of Oregon and Utah. The chief crops after alfalfa are the small grains, the large baking potatoes known the country over as "Idaho potatoes," sugar beets, beans, various vegetables, and fruits. The chief use of the oasis, however, is to supply winter feed, mostly in the form of hay, to the livestock which graze on the mountain pastures in the summer. In Jerome County, Idaho, for example, in one year more than 75,000 tons of alfalfa hay, nearly two million bushels of potatoes (FIG. 9.5), 40,000 tons of sugar beets, 100,-000 bushels of oats, 400,000 bushels of wheat, and 130,000 bushels of rye, and smaller amounts of fruits and vegetables were produced. Sheep, for meat and wool, and dairy and beef cattle are the most important livestock.

MINING

The mines and minerals of the Commercial Grazing Region are much like those of the adjoining forest regions, described in Chapter 6. South of Great Salt Lake in Utah, around Bingham Canyon, Eureka, and Tintic, are some of the best copper mines in North America. The first mining claim was staked out here during the War between the States, and mining has been going on more or less continuously ever since. Only recently have large-scale operations been in effect. A good deal of the mining is by the strip method. Huge electric shovels are used to scoop up the low-grade ore which contains only about 1 per

FIGURE 9.5. *Irrigated potatoes in Fremont County, Idaho. Notice the curving contoured ditches which carry water to every row. The gentle slope of this field is well adapted to irrigation. From Soil Conservation Service.*

cent copper. Cheap mining methods make the exploitation of such ore profitable. The smelters are at Garfield near the southern end of Great Salt Lake.

Although in no one district in Arizona is as much copper produced as in the area just described, the state of Arizona as a whole leads in copper production. Most of the mines are in the southern and southeastern part near the Mexican border. Copper ore is found in the adjacent portion of Mexico also and constitutes the most important source of copper for that country. It is interesting to note that the part of Arizona in which most of the copper is found was purchased from Mexico after a railway survey had indicated mineral deposits. This is still known as the Gadsden Purchase on some maps. Bisbee, on the Southern Pacific Railroad, is in the richest and best-situated copper country. Prosperity fluctuates with the price of copper, but some of Bisbee's mines can show a profit even when the price is low. During World War II many Mexican miners were brought to this district to supplement the local labor force. Most of these migratory workers were from the silver mines of Mexico and were skilled in mining operations. Silver was plentiful everywhere, copper scarce; therefore, many of the Mexican silver miners could be spared to increase copper production in the United States.

Salt of good quality at low cost is produced from Great Salt Lake. The lake water is pumped into specially prepared basins and is allowed to evaporate in the desert sun. The hard salt layer on the margins of the lake is good for automobile race tracks and can also be plowed and "harvested" to produce salt. The crude salt thus obtained is readily marketed for livestock use on the ranches of the Commercial Grazing Region. Petroleum production in the grazing lands is discussed in Chapter 34.

10

Commercial Grazing in Other Lands

In the semiarid lands of the Southern Hemisphere, Commercial Grazing is the dominant form of production over vast areas, as it is in western North America. Western Argentina and parts of South Africa and Australia are similar, in general, to the Great Plains, although each has its own individual variations. The savanna lands of South America, like the *Llanos* of Venezuela, and the *Campos* of Brazil are used mainly for grazing in spite of the handicaps of remoteness and the tropical climate. In addition, in parts of the cool humid grasslands of Argentina, New Zealand, and Great Britain, which for a variety of reasons have not been cultivated, excellent pasture for sheep and cattle is furnished the year round.

Each of the grazing regions described in this chapter has an individual character of its own. Some are in an early stage of development; others have developed crop agriculture which is encroaching on the pasture land. Some have numerous oases to supply forage crops to the ranches; others are near humid regions where animals can be fattened for market. All the regions except those of Great Britain depend on external and distant markets, and in the past, most of the meat, wool, mohair, and hides have gone to western Europe, including Great Britain. In recent years more of the hides and wool have been imported by the United States.

THE TEMPERATE GRAZING LANDS OF SOUTH AMERICA

The Dry Pampa and Patagonia

The temperate grazing region of South America extends from the southern border of Paraguay to the Strait of Magellan, an airline distance of more than 2000 miles. In the north the width is over 500 miles, and although the region is narrow in the south, the area is roughly comparable to that of the Great Plains grazing land of western North America. In other ways the South American region may be compared with the Great Plains: there is a humid region on the east where livestock can be fattened; to the west rises a lofty mountain range, the Andes, which supplies water for irrigation. The region is unlike the Great Plains in that the market within the continent is limited and also in that the producers of this region have ready access to the sea.

The surface of western Argentina also resembles the Great Plains in its variety of land forms. On the east is the smooth Pampa, in the west plains, plateaus, and isolated mountains. Much of the grazing region has less than 10 inches of rain annually, which means that dry farming is almost impossible. Grazing is the all-important industry except for the oases; low-grade cattle, goats, sheep, and burros are the important animals. High-grade animals are found farther east in the Humid Pampa. The scarcity of forage leads to migrations similar to those on the western margin of the Great Plains; in the spring and early summer the flocks begin to move up the valleys and onto the slopes of the Andes for the summer season.

In the southern part, Patagonia, wool sheep reach their greatest relative importance. The cooler weather, more dependable water supply, and isolation make this district more suited to sheep than to cattle. Wool is exported, together with some quantities of frozen mutton, from Río Gallegos, Puerto San Julián, and Puerto Deseado.

The Humid Pampa Grazing Region

In the eastern part of the Argentine Pampa between La Plata and Bahia Blanca, is a rather unusual grazing region. The climate is suitable for agriculture, but crops with the exception of alfalfa have made little progress. Large ranches, established soon after European settlement, are so profitable and provide such an attractive way of life for the owners that the introduction of crops meets with considerable cultural resistance. Purebred stock, year-round pasture, and the excellent alfalfa contribute to the production of high-quality beef, mutton, pork, and wool. This region is more like the humid grazing regions of New Zealand and the British Isles, described on pages 161 and 162, than the semiarid types of Commercial Grazing.

The types of land use found on the margins of the Humid Pampa Grazing Region suggest the nature of the land use which is slowly replacing the ranches. To the south and west is the Wheat Belt of Argentina. It is a remarkable fact that wheat yields are better in the Humid Pampa than in the Wheat Belt, largely because of the heavier rainfall. To the northwest is the Corn Belt, in which quantities of flint corn are produced for feed and export. The small hard kernels of this variety are well suited to shipment and storage. Corn will grow well throughout the Humid Pampa. To the north in the vicinity of Buenos Aires is an embryo Dairy Belt which, if the demand for dairy products continues to increase, may occupy larger parts of the Humid Pampa. As the population of Argentina increases, it is extremely unlikely that this grazing region will continue to exist.

The temperate grazing lands of South America, steppe and humid, mostly in Argentina but including parts of Uruguay and southern Brazil, support about 40 million cattle, 50 million sheep, 10 million horses, and 8 million goats. The humid portion makes a great contribution to the number and quality of the animals. The lush pasture, good most of the year, and the vast fields of alfalfa are well situated near the coast. The range animals can move into the humid region for fattening before export. The chief product of this region is meat; wool, hides, and mohair are of lesser importance, although some parts of the region produce nothing but hides, others nothing but wool. The big problem is to get the meat to market in good condition. Packing plants, refrigerated warehouses, and deep-freezing plants are located in all the main ports from southern Brazil to the Strait of Magellan. Any disturbance of world economy is likely to be felt promptly in this region. During World War II the export of many commodities was curtailed, but every effort was made to keep Argentine meat moving to Britain. Many people, in both South and North America, would like to see the United States market opened to the meat of South America. For many years fresh Argentine beef has been denied entry on the ground that it might be contaminated with hoof and mouth disease. Britain,

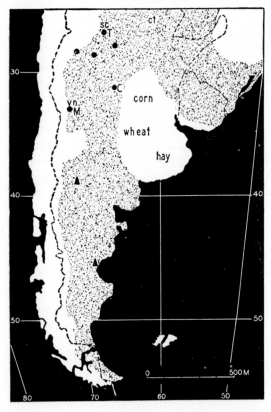

FIGURE 10.1. *The Temperate Grazing Lands of South America. The stippling indicates the areas of dominant commercial grazing, in which oases are shown by large dots and petroleum by black triangles. In the Humid Pampa corn, wheat, and hay are the dominant crops and much of the land is still in grass. Abbreviations: cotton, ct; sugarcane, sc; vine, vn; Córdoba, C; Mendoza, M; Tucumán, T.*

FIGURE 10.2. *A sugarcane oasis southwest of Tucumán in northwestern Argentina. Notice the fruit trees in the foreground, the refinery in the center, and the canefields beyond. From American Geographical Society.*

meanwhile, takes all the Argentine beef she can afford. The real reason for the embargo is the inability of United States producers to compete with those of Argentina and Uruguay. The South American grazing region with its cheap land and labor, seaboard location, and humid pastures can produce good beef at about one half the cost in the United States.

The Oases of Tucumán and Jujuy

In northwestern Argentina lies Tucumán, the most important sugar center of Argentina. See FIGURE 10.2. In some ways Tucumán is not a typical oasis, because some of the crops are grown without irrigation, but the cultivation of sugarcane depends largely on water from the Andes. Tucumán began its commercial life as a trading town on the road from La Plata to Bolivia and Peru. There were wagon and cart makers, tan-

neries, and harness shops for the mule drivers. In the grazing region near by, hides and meat were produced; the forest on the mountain slopes furnished wood. In the early period there was little irrigation.

With the coming of the railroad in 1878, the character of the community changed. Sugarcane was introduced and became the most important crop. Tucumán is probably not the best place in Argentina for the growth of sugarcane from the climatic point of view; farther north it is warmer and there is less danger from frost. However, the winds which blow from the dry plains of northern Argentina are forced up by the lower slopes of the Andes in the vicinity of Tucumán and the increased humidity which results is a factor of great importance in reducing the frost hazard. But the good labor supply around Tucumán offsets any small disadvantage in climate.

The sugar industry is organized around a group of independent cane producers, *caneros*, mostly small farmers, a rather unusual condition in the sugarcane lands. The *caneros* sell the cane to the factories where the cane is ground, the juice is evaporated, and some of the sugar is refined. The factory owners grow some cane on their own farms with paid labor, and occasionally tenant farmers grow cane on shares. Even in this area of fairly dense population there is likely to be a scarcity of labor in the harvest season. Beginning in June large numbers of workers migrate from all the towns in the vicinity and spend about five months near Tucumán. Some of these workers have settled in the Tucumán district; consequently the difficulties of obtaining migratory labor are not as acute as formerly.

Jujuy to the north of Tucumán also produces sugar, but in smaller amounts and with different methods. There are almost no small farms; the sugar is grown on large estates which are essentially plantations. Here, too, there is a scarcity of labor during the harvest period, and workers come from as far away as Bolivia. Large numbers of Indians from the Chaco work in the canefields in winter, taking their pay in meat, corn, and tobacco (preferably cigars). Most of the workers in Argentina are of European descent, including some Italians and Germans.

In normal years the sugar oases of northwestern Argentina produce enough for the domestic market and a small surplus for export. Total production in Argentina exceeds 500,000 tons, approximately one tenth of the production in Cuba. In addition, there are other oases like Mendoza, famous for its wine grapes; Córdoba, where alfalfa is grown at the foot of the isolated Córdoba Range; Catamarca and La Rioja, associated with silver mines; and the Rio Negro, where mostly alfalfa is produced.

The grazing regions of Argentina are not richly endowed with mineral wealth. Some oilfields, however, are in production in the northwestern piedmont, in the Gran Chaco, in the vicinity of Mendoza, and near Comodoro Rivadavia on the east coast. Of these, only in the last has there been a large production of oil.

THE CAMPOS OF BRAZIL

North of the temperate grazing region of South America is the *Campos*, a vast mixture of savanna and forest, reaching from Paraguay and Bolivia northeastward across Brazil to the Atlantic. This is a potential rather than an actual grazing region, if one considers the great area involved and the limited amount of grazing at present. Most of the *Campos* region is a rolling plateau covered with typical savanna vegetation, grass and shrubs. The dry and wet seasons are strongly marked, and at the time of low sun the land is dry and brown. The rivers are fringed with trees but in the dry season there may be little water in the stream beds.

In this thinly peopled land, grazing of cattle is easily the dominant occupation. As many as ten million head of cattle graze in this region with little supplementary crop feed. The cattle are large, bony, and of poor quality, but have the stamina to withstand the hot weather, the tropical diseases, and the coarse vegetation, at least to a greater extent than the purebred cattle of the temperate belt. Many perish from Texas fever and hoof and mouth disease, but many more survive. The cross-breeding of Zebu cattle from India with the native cattle has produced a breed which promises better meat while retaining a high resistance to heat and disease. The grazing industry finds a market in the towns and villages which have grown up in connection with the production of diamonds (FIG. 10.4) from the alluvial deposits in the streams. Only better transportation and greater pressure of population, however, will lead to large-scale settlement.

At present only the southern part of the region is served by railroad and highway. A railroad connects São Paulo with Corumbá on the Bolivian frontier. Under construction is a line to Santa Cruz at the foot of the Bolivian Andes. By means of both the railway and the highway, a better market for cattle and hides, as well as for agricultural products, will be opened. Progress is slow, but it should be kept in mind that in similar areas in Asia millions of people are supported.

THE LLANOS OF VENEZUELA

The *Llanos* of Venezuela, lying for the most part in the northern watershed of the Orinoco River, is a savanna grazing region like the *Campos*. The differences between these regions, however, are more striking than the similarities. The *Llanos* is a vast level plain rather than a plateau. It is near

FIGURE 10.3. *A view of the Rimac Valley oasis east of Lima, Peru. Notice the contrast between the irrigated alluvial terrace, the stream channel, and the dry mountain slopes. Cane sugar, cotton, and various food crops are produced in such oases. From American Geographical Society with permission of the Ministerio de Aeronautica, Direccion General de Aerofotographia.*

FIGURE 10.4. *Washing diamonds in southeastern Brazil. Most of the diamonds found in the river beds are suitable for industrial uses only. From Pan American Airways.*

the sea and has fairly good roads plus the river to get the products to the market. The grassland is extensive, while the forest areas are limited to the banks of the streams and to isolated groves. It is not, however, a good grazing country under present conditions. The rain is so heavy during the wet season, from April to October, that floods are common. The dry season during the other half of the year is so severe that the smaller streams run dry, and it is difficult to supply the cattle with drinking water. Diseases are fully as prevalent there as in the *Campos*.

In spite of the difficulties, about three million head of cattle are supported in the region and some are sent to market, partly in the form of salt beef. Hides and horns are also exported. Some of the cattle move to market via the valley of Valencia, pausing there for fattening on the better pastures. The *Llanos* has great possibilities for agriculture. Some crops grow well during the

rainy season, and during World War II corn was grown for shipment to the northern part of Venezuela, which formerly imported most of its food from abroad. Rice, sesame, beans, and various vegetables grow well, and by use of the recently constructed highways some of the produce is taken to the northern part of Venezuela where a market, as well as facilities for shipment, is available. The oilfields of Venezuela, described in Chapter 34, provide the best nearby market for the products of the *Llanos*.

SOUTH AFRICA

On a large blank base map of Africa, one can mark off "South Africa" as that part of the continent south of 18° S. latitude and west of the Mozambique Lowland (FIG. 10.5). Then, like the old cartographers, one can indicate the salient points of production, leaving vast empty spaces to be filled in, perhaps with mere decorations. At

Capetown on the southwest corner, one can mark a small spot of Mediterranean Agriculture, an area of vine, fruit, and wheat. Five hundred air-line miles to the northeast is Kimberley which means "diamonds" to people all over the world. Five hundred miles to the west of Kimberley one can mark "diamonds" again, for there the gems are found in the gravels of the lower Orange River. Three hundred miles northeast of Kimberley is the Johannesburg gold mining region, where by far the largest amount of gold in the world is produced. Southward for a hundred miles from Johannesburg is the "Maize Triangle," a

region of corn, wheat, good grazing, cattle, and sheep, as well as coal mines. Farther south goats are important also. In between the spots indicated, an airborne observer would see many open spaces, with few men and few animals, for South Africa has an area of nearly a million square miles and a population of only ten million.

South Africa consists of a series of plateaus at different levels with a few marginal mountains. On the southern margin are the Cape ranges with alternating ridges and valleys. Then come the Little Karroo and the Great Karroo, semiarid dissected plateaus. There the rain is too light for

FIGURE 10.5. *The Commercial Grazing Lands of South Africa. Most of the semiarid interior of South Africa is used for grazing. On the west is the coastal Namib Desert, on the south the region of Mediterranean crops, and on the east Subsistence Agriculture and Plantations. The Corn Triangle represents a region of subhumid agriculture within the grazing region. A few oases represented by wavy lines produce citrus fruits, grain, hay, and other crops. Large quantities of gold, copper, diamonds, and coal are mined.*

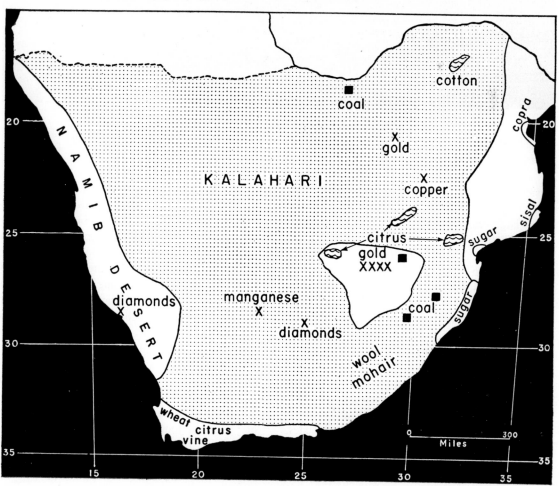

FIGURE 10.6. *A view of the Basuto Highland in South Africa. Notice the small patches of cultiva-*
tion and the larger areas of grassland. This territory is a Native Reserve, not open to European
settlement. From Mary Light and the American Geographical Society.

agriculture, and grazing is the most important use of the land. Sheep, cattle, and goats roam over large well-grassed and sparsely grassed areas. The first settlers in South Africa procured both sheep and cattle from the native Hottentots. Soon European cattle and sheep were introduced and were crossed with the native stock. Purebred European varieties also thrive in this area. Wool and mohair are the most important products in the plateau of the Great Karroo and to the east of the Drakensberg. Another plateau is the High Veld with a range in elevation of from 4000 to 6000 feet. There the rains are greater, it is somewhat cooler, and there is more agriculture. The Basuto Highland (FIG. 10.6) in the headwaters of the Orange River is rough country with altitudes ranging up to 10,000 feet. Native Basuto farmers grow quantities of corn, also kaffir (grain sorghum), and have more than 2,000,000 head of

sheep. On the western margin of South Africa is the Kalihari Desert, formerly the home of nomadic Bushmen and Hottentots but little used today since European colonization has greatly disturbed the lives of the native nomads.

The climate of most of the grazing land of South Africa is the hot Steppe (BSh) with a summer maximum of rain and severe winter drought. Rainfall is heaviest in the east, especially on the east slopes of the Drakensberg, and lightest on the west where the grazing land fades into the desert of the west coast. Although temperatures are modified slightly by altitude over all the region, the summers are quite hot below 5000 feet. In Kimberley at 4000 feet there is a January average of 77° F. In Johannesburg at 5700 feet, on the other hand, there is a cool temperature of 66° F. in the warmest month, January. In most of the High Veld, the lower temperatures and the heavier rainfall are responsible for a more humid climate, the winter dry temperate (Cw). This region includes the "Maize Triangle" to be discussed in Chapter 19.

Most of the cattle and sheep of South Africa are in the eastern part of the region between Johannesburg and Durban. Here the Merino wool sheep, some mutton sheep, and various breeds of beef cattle are the basis of a widespread pastoral industry. The lack of phosphorus in the grasses is a handicap, and the cattle are often given a daily ration of a small quantity of calcium phosphate, which greatly improves the market quality of the animals. This is merely one example of the difficulties of this region in comparison with the dry land grazing regions of other continents. From Durban large quantities of wool are exported; from Port Elizabeth, wool and mohair.

The oases in South Africa are limited to a few favorable spots. The heaviest precipitation is on the eastern flanks of the Drakensberg, whereas the western margins need irrigation. Two or three dams on the Vaal River make it possible to irrigate more than 100,000 acres, but on the whole, not more than one per cent of the land on the west flank of the Drakensberg can be irrigated at present. There are several small oases in Southern Rhodesia with a few thousand acres under ditch. The usual irrigated crops in South Africa are corn, cotton, tobacco, and various fruits. Another potential irrigated area is in the northern part of Southwest Africa. There, the Kunene River, with headwaters in the highlands of Portuguese Angola, sometimes overflows into the shallow lake known as the Etosha Pan. A dam on the river would make it possible to irrigate many thousands of acres. At present all the irrigated areas of South Africa are small scale. The ranges of lofty mountains with reservoirs of snow, which contribute so much to the oases of North and South America, are lacking here. Many small projects, however, can contribute to the stability of South African agriculture. The farmers of this region must depend less and less on the stimulus of mining and learn to stand on their own feet.

In the rainier parts of the Grazing Region, some crops are produced without irrigation. Of these, wheat, corn, kaffir, and alfalfa occupy the largest areas. South Africans could extend their acreage of wheat and develop a wheat belt if and when the world demand is brisk. Alfalfa acreage can also be increased, but the prospect for corn is not so favorable. The native farmers are satisfied with a low yield of inferior corn. The conditions for growing corn for feeding livestock or other commercial uses, however, are more favorable on the lowlands of the east coast than in the more humid parts of the grazing lands.

Mineral production in South Africa has been a great stimulus to the development of grazing and agriculture as well as a first rank industry in its own right. The diamond mines in the vicinity of Kimberley, now largely exhausted, brought farmers and ranchers, as well as miners, into that part of the country. The Rand mining district extends east and west from Johannesburg. A narrow belt 70 miles long accounts for more than half the annual gold production of the world. Copper mines are in production in the north, especially in the Rhodesias. Coal of medium and low quality is abundant, but only a small part of the product makes good coke. The prospects of great industrial growth, therefore, are not too bright. The coal, however, is useful for fuel, for power, and for smelting.

AUSTRALIA

Australia, the smallest of the continents, is sometimes called the "island continent." It is almost as large as the United States and has the lowest average elevation of all the continents. On the east is the Great Dividing Range, the water divide between the Pacific and the interior. The name belies its quality, for the district is better described as a dissected plateau than as a mountain range. The highest elevation is slightly over 6000 feet, and passage from the coast to the interior is easy via several valleys. One effect of the eastern highland is to concentrate the heaviest rain on the east coast and at the same time to throw the basins to the west partly into the "rain shadow." The Great Dividing Range provides forest products of importance where otherwise there would be only farming and grazing land. To the west of the Range are the interior basins, occupied in part by the Murray-Darling river system. Much of this region is flat with intermittent stream courses running through the monotonous plains of grass, saltbush, and acacia. In some districts artesian wells supply water for the sheep and cattle, but the quality of the water is not

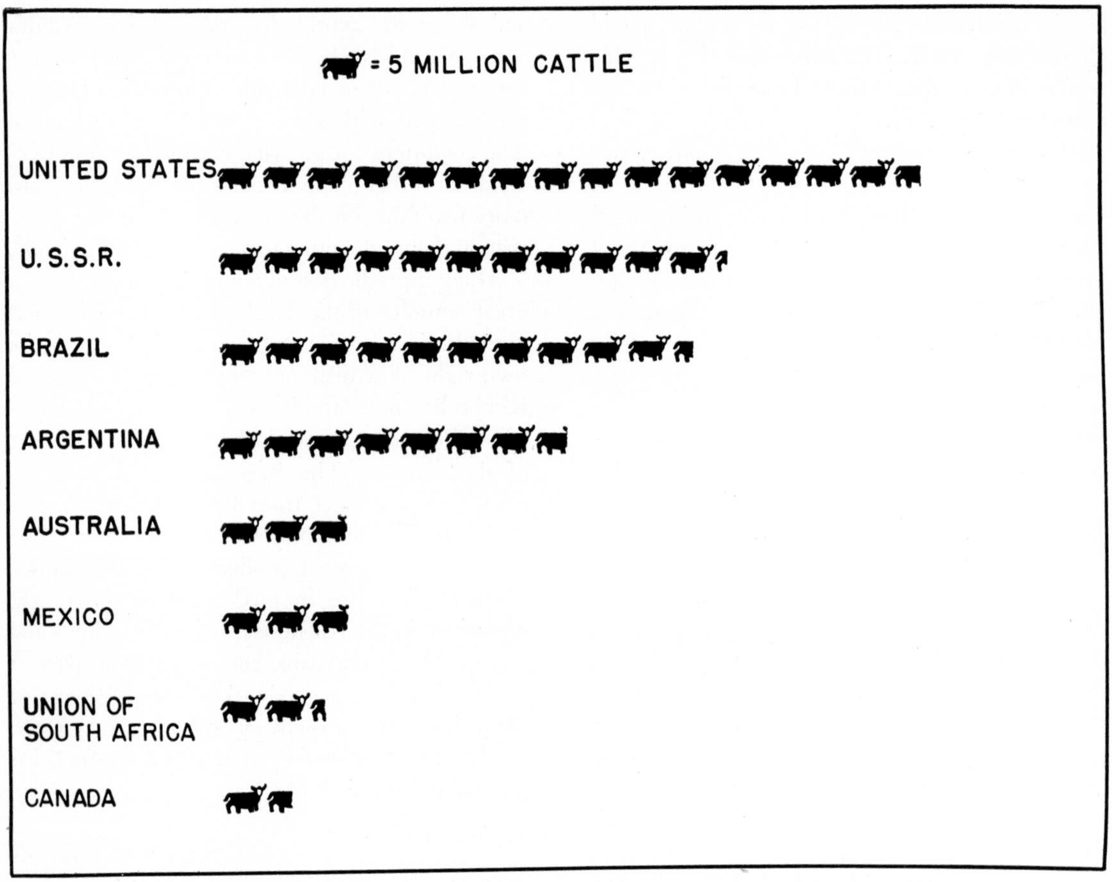

FIGURE 10.7. *Graph of cattle in various countries having semiarid grasslands. Only a part of the cattle represented here are found in areas of Commercial Grazing. See Table 17, Appendix C.*

everywhere equally good. Most of western Australia is a low shield, similar to the Laurentian Shield in surface material, but differing sharply in climate and vegetation. The rainfall is so light that much of the land has no drainage to the sea, and parts are too dry even for grazing.

Except for the humid eastern fringe of Australia, grazing occupies most of the settled part of the continent (FIG. 10.8); the vast interior is almost totally unused desert. The important animal is the sheep, and there are more than 100 million of them. The fifteen million cattle are of less significance, even allowing for the difference in value of cow and sheep. Most of the cattle and sheep are in New South Wales and Queensland to the west of the mountains. Cattle are also numerous on the humid east coast, but sheep are not; cattle are found in northern Queensland, but sheep do not thrive so well as cattle in the hottest parts of Australia.

The grazing industries of Australia developed rapidly. In 1788 five cows, one bull, and 29 sheep were imported (the natives had no cattle). By 1900 there were more than 100 million sheep and 12 million cattle. Goats, camels, and ostriches have also been introduced into the grazing lands but with little success. The conditions for semiarid grazing are favorable on the whole. The absence of severe winter and the scarcity of insects and animal diseases are favorable. On the other hand, rabbits are numerous and consume large quantities of forage. In some districts the water supply is insufficient.

Most sheep are grown on large ranches; formerly some single ranches had as many as 500,000 head of sheep, but most of the large units have been broken up and today there are many small outfits with only 500 head. See FIGURE 10.9. To reach a typical "station" or ranch one must travel from 25 to 50 miles from the nearest rail point, across a monotonous plain with very little sign of human life. Among some trees, which have been planted and irrigated to form a windbreak, is a neat white residence with wide verandas and a glistening metal roof. Near by are corrals for the sheep, a well, a windmill, and large tanks for the storage of water in times of little wind. In periods of drought the estate will suffer severely. It may even be necessary to send the sheep to the nearest railroad and ship them to a more humid region, for in times of drought both water and grass fail.

The grazing lands of Australia are comparatively free of livestock diseases except in the tropical north, but pests, including rabbits, wild dogs, and cactus, have caused great losses of animals and pastures in the past. The rabbit is easily the champion pest of Australia. Introduced into Victoria about 1860, the rabbits multiplied and spread rapidly over most of the southern half of the continent. Apparently rabbits found no natural enemies in the land, and the vast semiarid grassland was well suited to them. The threat to the pasture was soon realized, since 30 or 40 rabbits will eat as much grass as a sheep. Various methods have been used to confine or destroy them. Thousands of miles of rabbit-proof wire fence have been constructed. One fence in western Australia, from Condon on the north to Hope-

town on the south, is more than 1000 miles in length. In southern Queensland many more thousands of miles of fence restrict the northward advance of the rabbits. Fencing, poisoning, trapping, and shooting are all used to combat this menace and the number of rabbits is gradually being reduced. Rabbit skins and meat are exported, but the sales do not compensate for the losses of pasture.

Wild dogs, or dingos, natives of Australia, prey on both the rabbits and sheep, and on some ranches have killed 25,000 or more sheep in a single year. Fences are constructed against the dogs also, and a heavy bounty for their scalps has resulted in a marked reduction. Some ranches have shifted from sheep to cattle because of the wild dog menace.

The prickly pear, a variety of cactus introduced from North America, turned out to be a pest of great magnitude in eastern Queensland. It spread rapidly over the grassland, killing the grass as it went. No fence could stop the relentless spread of this worthless plant, but after much experiment a moth was imported from South America which feeds on the cactus, and thus most of the millions of acres covered by the prickly pear have been reclaimed for pasture.

Oases

In Australia the difficulty of irrigating a considerable part of the grazing land is similar to that in South Africa. Since the Great Dividing Range receives heavy precipitation on the east side, the coastal lowland below does not require extensive irrigation. On the west side, where millions of acres could profit by irrigation, the rains are light. Fortunately, the Great Dividing Range is plateaulike in character, and some of the rivers draining to the west tap the crest of the range, where rainfall is fairly heavy. The largest project of this kind is on the Murrumbidgee River where the Burrinjuck Dam provides water for the irrigation of nearly 200,000 acres. Before this area was irrigated, the land was occupied by a few sheep ranches with a very sparse population. Today fruit, grapes, rice, and hay and forage crops are produced on the oases for dairy farms. Such an oasis does little to improve the grazing industries, since little of the hay or forage crops is fed to the range animals, but the increased water supply is of some value to the marginal ranches.

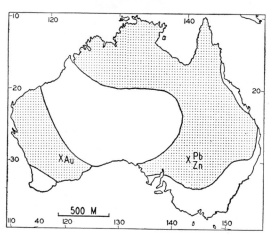

FIGURE 10.8. *The Commercial Grazing Region of Australia. Sheep and cattle produce meat, wool, and hides for export. The most important minerals are lead (Pb) and zinc (Zn) at Broken Hill and gold (Au) in western Australia. For production in other regions of Australia see Figure 13.2.*

FIGURE 10.9. *A sheep station in eastern Australia. The grass is very thin and even the forest has a dry appearance. From Keystone.*

The heaviest precipitation in Australia is along the coast of northern Queensland in the vicinity of Townsville. A proposed irrigation project would collect the heavy runoff in the region, and lead it by tunnel through the Great Dividing Range to the plains on the west. Such a scheme, though expensive, would provide water to irrigate hundreds of thousands of acres in what is now ranching country.

Mining

Throughout the arid lands of Australia, the mining industry takes an important place in production. Gold, silver, lead, zinc, copper, and iron are the leaders in value. The grazing regions have no coal, but mines on the east coast near Sydney supply most of the needs of the continent.

If total production to date is taken into account, gold is the most valuable mineral in Australia. The best goldfield is in Western Australia near the town of Kalgoorlie. Veins or lodes of gold-bearing rock occur near the surface in the form of vertical dikes. The gold ore is mined in surface workings or in shallow shafts, after which it is concentrated and the gold extracted. Many other gold deposits in Australia are in production, including some placer deposits.

The Broken Hill mining district, where silver,

lead, and zinc are produced, is located in the western part of New South Wales. See FIGURE 13.2. A long, narrow ore body outcrops and reaches a depth of 1000 feet or more, the shape of the ore being compared to an irregular sword blade, partially buried on edge. The ore yields about 15 per cent lead, 12 per cent zinc, and 8 per cent silver. Since no coal is available in the vicinity, the ores are taken to Port Pirie at the head of Spencer Gulf by rail. There water-borne coal from the Newcastle district near Sydney is available. On the west side of Spencer Gulf are the best iron mines in Australia. A short rail haul brings the ore to tidewater at Whyalla and Port Lincoln, from which shipments are made by sea to the Newcastle iron and steel district.

NEW ZEALAND

The grazing region of New Zealand represents a large portion of both islands, more than half the used land in North Island and more than three fourths in South Island. New Zealand, as a whole, is nearly 900 miles in length and averages more than 100 miles in width. It is a little larger than Italy and, like that country, has the rude outline of a boot. The closest comparison, however, is with Britain, which New Zealand resembles in climate, people, and livestock, and even to some extent in the kind of agriculture. A large part of the surface is mountainous; a lofty range, the Southern Alps, dominates South Island and there are smaller volcanic ranges in North Island. Numerous small plains near the sea are well suited for agriculture and grazing, and are readily accessible.

The grazing lands of New Zealand (FIG. 10.10), in contrast to those of Australia, are entirely in the humid climates; in this respect the grazing industries are more like those of the humid Argentine Pampa than of the Great Plains of the United States but there are many differences. New Zealand has many advantages for grazing, two of which are mild winters during which no shelter is needed and good pasture all the year. The most important animals are sheep, 27 million, and more than three million cattle. Most of the cattle are in North Island; the majority of the sheep are in South Island. There are also more than a million dairy cows, mostly in the dairying region of North Island, some horses, and a few swine.

Sheep have been important in New Zealand for

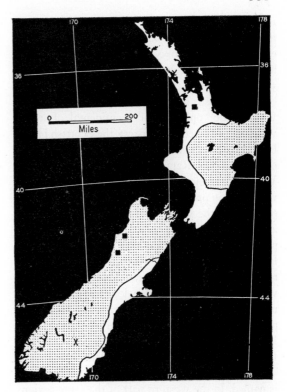

FIGURE 10.10. *Commercial grazing areas of New Zealand. Small-grain farming and dairying are also important. The black squares indicate coal-fields, while the x represents gold production. Compare the grazing areas of New Zealand with those of the British Isles, as to latitude, extent, and population.*

a long time, especially since the development of refrigeration in 1882 greatly increased the export of frozen mutton. Wool is the most valuable export, but the amount is rather variable, the average less than 400 million pounds. The beef cattle are represented by the best British breeds, and frozen beef makes up an increasing part of the meat export. Western Europe, Great Britain especially, has been New Zealand's best customer but in recent years has had to reduce imports. The wool trade has suffered less than that of meat and dairy products, but wool faces keen competition from synthetic fibers. New Zealand produces more wool and mutton, per capita, than any other country. Trade in these items is critical.

BRITISH ISLES

In the higher elevations of Scotland, England, Wales, and Ireland the dominant use of the land is still sheep herding, in spite of the pressure of neighboring dense population. The elevation of even 1000 feet above sea level places a severe handicap on agriculture at these high latitudes, 52° N. to 58° N., and the rough nature of some of the uplands is another limiting factor for crops. Unlike the uplands of continental Europe, which are covered with forest, the Scottish Highland, the Southern Uplands of Scotland, parts of the Pennine Range in England, and most of Wales are treeless except in the valleys. Grass is very good in many districts, supporting one sheep per acre all the year round in some places. Sheep are grown both for wool and for mutton, and the pattern of life and production in these lonely uplands has been fixed for centuries. Wool was the textile which started Britain in the business of weaving. Cotton later developed a greater volume, but wool and woolens continue to be important products of these humid pasture regions. It is the home of many famous woolen fabrics. In the Southern Uplands of Scotland is the river Tweed, for which a loosely woven woolen cloth is named. In the western part of the same region, the Paisley shawl is made. Not in all parts of the regions indicated are there good conditions for sheep. Some areas are almost entirely covered with heath and bracken, affording only indifferent forage for the sheep.

GRAZING VERSUS HUMID FARMING

The regions of commercial grazing described in this chapter and the preceding one cover large parts of the earth's surface. They are mainly in the climates too dry or too cool in summer for agriculture and as a consequence represent extensive use of the land. Little change in the boundaries of these regions is likely to be observed for many years. In the Humid Pampa agriculture will probably make some advances at the expense of the grazing lands. New irrigation projects will preempt some of the pasture land, but this is likely to permit an increase in livestock by supplying additional forage.

The commercial grazing regions account for most of the wool and mohair produced in the world and a substantial proportion of the hides and meat. A study of production data, however, indicates that producers in the humid farming regions with the aid of abundant forage crops compete successfully with ranchers in the cheaper grazing lands in the production of meat, wool, and hides. The greatest meat production in the United States is in the Corn Belt. In general, the cost of production in the grazing lands is lower than in the humid farming regions, a fact which offsets in many districts the greater distance from market and the poorer quality of the product.

CHAPTER

11

Nomadic Herding and the Oases

FROM the Atlantic shores of northern Africa, the dry lands extend eastward almost without interruption for 12,000 miles to western China, including within the deserts and their semiarid borderlands the Sahara, Arabia, Iraq, Iran, Afghanistan, Russian Turkestan, Sinkiang, and Mongolia. These dry lands occupy an area more than four times as large as the United States, but the rainfall is too scanty for agriculture without irrigation, and the people must depend on the grass-eating animals for food, clothing, and shelter, or they must cultivate the small irrigated oases. For centuries millions of nomads—Berbers, Arabs, Turks, Jews, Kurds, Afghans, Khirgiz, and Mongols—have practiced the wandering pastoral life in many lands, some of which are now occupied by settled peoples. See FIGURE 11.1. More millions are sedentary dwellers of the oases, some in tiny spots where there is a mere trickle of water, others in larger areas with modern irrigation methods like the lower Nile. In a few districts—parts of Russia, Iran, Iraq, Arabia, and Egypt—there is some mineral production, mostly petroleum, but the majority of the producers are either herders or oasis cultivators.

The life of the nomad is simple but hazardous; dependence on the herd is absolute. It is almost the only source of food, clothing, and shelter. Clothing is largely wool and leather; tents and many utensils are made from leather and wool. The flocks and herds must have grass and water and, in a land where both are limited, the people must move from time to time. This necessity for migration is described by Merian C. Cooper in *Grass* (G. P. Putnam's Sons, pp. 185–190, 1925). The following account, quoted by permission of the publisher, is a description of a nomadic migration from the vicinity of the Persian Gulf to the summer pastures. It applies as well to the nomads of Africa.

Yes, hundreds of thousands of tribesmen and vast herds, uncountable, will be astir. On horseback, afoot, women carrying cradles on their backs and driving beasts loaded with all their possessions, men, children, animals, will struggle onward. Up over hill and mountain, on through desert and forest, beaten by storm and rain, sweating under a burning sun, shivering in glacial snows—over thousands of miles of wilderness the migratory tribes of Persia will be on the move. . . . Now let there be no mistake as to the reason for this great migration. Let me state it as clearly and simply as I can. It is all caused by a cruel trick of Nature. First she makes the tribes dependent on grass for life (in all this rugged country, there is not nearly enough fertile land on which to grow sufficient grain to feed its people), they must live off grazing animals . . . ; even their shelters—goatskin tents—come from their animals. Nature thus first makes Grass the vital thing of life, and then she doesn't grow grass in any one part of the tribal country the year round. Here to the west of the mountains it is low and hot. Therefore there is plenty of vegetation here in winter; but that vegetation is withered up in the summer. Now, on the other side of the mountains—the eastern side—it is high and cool. Therefore there is plenty of grass there in the summer; but that grass is killed by snow and ice in the winter.

Like the tribe described by Cooper, most nomads migrate between summer and winter grazing grounds on the moist margin of the desert. In the northern part of the Sahara, the people spend the winter on the desert at low altitudes; in the summer they move to the slopes of the Atlas Mountains. On the south side of the desert, the seasonal pattern of migration is reversed; the tribes move northward into the desert margins in summer and southward into the Sudan in winter. Wherever possible the summer migration is to-

FIGURE 11.1. *The grassy slopes of this collective farm on the margins of the Caucasus Mountains were formerly used by nomads. They are now used as summer pastures for herds which spend the winter in the lowlands. From "Sovfoto."*

ward higher elevations where the weather is cooler and where there is a greater likelihood of rain.

In spite of the fundamental similarity of the Old World arid lands there are differences in relief, climate, location, the cultural background of the people, and the relationship between the nomads and the oases. A few major regions will be discussed—the Algerian Sahara, the lower Nile, southern Arabia, Iraq, Iran, Russian Turkestan, and the Mongolian Gobi.

THE DESERT CLIMATE

In the lands of little rain, the amount and seasonal distribution of the precipitation are of the greatest significance; the people are interested in the slightest trace of rain or snow. The Sahara is, in many respects, the best example of an area with desert climate (BW). It is almost regular in shape

(FIG. 11.2) and the climate is not unduly complicated by high relief. The Sahara is, however, a land of startling contrasts and, for those unfamiliar with the desert, a region of fascinating surprises and grim hardships. It is a symbol of aridity the world over, but an occasional torrential rain will destroy a mud town, the houses crumbling and dissolving like sugar lumps. Like all deserts the driest part is usually in the middle, the wettest on the margins. A few mountains within the general area are cool and humid and, therefore, are not a part of the desert.

The nature of the rainfall in the Sahara is indicated by data for the following stations: Algiers on the Mediterranean, representing the humid climate north of the Sahara; Ghardaïa, representing the poleward margin of the desert; Timbuktu, 1000 miles farther south, representing the equatorward margin.

CLIMATIC DATA FOR ALGIERS, GHARDAÏA, AND TIMBUKTU			
RAINFALL	Algiers	Ghardaïa	Timbuktu
Average Annual Rainfall (*inches*)	27	4	8
Average Rainfall Wet Month (*inches*)	Jan. 4.0	Jan. 0.8	Jul. 4.0
Average Rainfall Dry Month (*inches*)	Jul. 0.1	Jul. 0.0	Jan. 0.0
CLIMATE	Humid	Desert	Desert
Average Temperature Warm Month (*degrees Fahrenheit*)	77	93	95
Average Temperature Cool Month (*degrees Fahrenheit*)	53	47	70

If the stations are located on a map, it will be inferred that the rainfall decreases from Algiers southward to (and probably beyond) Ghardaïa and at some point in the middle of the Sahara begins to increase toward Timbuktu. Furthermore, in the north the rain falls mostly in winter, in the south mostly in summer.

In the desert the dryness of the air hastens the evaporation of the little rain that falls; the relative humidity (per cent of saturation) often ranges from 5 to 20 per cent, compared with 65 to 72 per cent for a middle latitude station such as New York City. The low humidity contributes to a great range in temperature. For example, although snow and ice are not unknown in the Sahara, the highest surface temperature on the earth, 136° F., has been recorded there. When thermometers were buried in the sand of this desert, a temperature of 158° F. was recorded. Day and night temperatures there show the greatest contrast on earth, sometimes below freezing at night and more than 100° F. in the hottest time of the day.

This description applies especially to the Sahara, but it is applicable with some modifica-

FIGURE 11.2. *The Nomadic Herding Region and the Oases of north Africa. The large dots and circles indicate oases, either in districts (the lower Nile and the upper Niger), or as isolated spots of irrigation (Algeria, Libya, and Egypt). The white areas in the Sahara are virtually unused except for a very few small oases.*

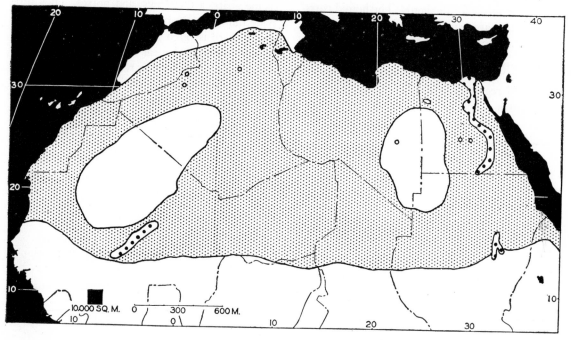

tions to most low latitude deserts—Arabia, the Thar (India), Kalahari, Atacama, and the Australian Desert. If allowance is made for greater annual ranges in temperature, the deserts of higher latitudes can be included—Russian Turkestan, the North American Desert, and the Patagonian Desert.

THE STEPPE CLIMATE

On the margins of all deserts is the steppe, which is a transition to the humid lands. The steppe resembles the desert in that the precipitation is deficient and variable, but there is sufficient rain to support a grass cover, scattered bunch grass on the dry margin and a close grass cover on the humid side (much of which has been plowed under). As with the desert, there is no simple definition of the steppe in terms of rainfall, but some representative stations in the Old World lands of Nomadic Herding compared with similar stations in the New World will indicate the amount and seasonal variation of rain in the Steppe Climate. See the table on this page.

One station (Tripoli) gets most of its rain in winter and many of the other stations receive maximum rain in summer. Evidently, there is wide variation in the annual temperature of the stations, indicating different rates of evaporation.

The nomadic herders usually are found on the dry margins of the steppes, where from their point of view the grass is adequate and there is more likely to be water for the herds. The humid parts of the steppe are usually occupied by sedentary agricultural peoples, but there are exceptions.

THE ALGERIAN SAHARA

In the arid region of northwest Africa, the sedentary oases people cultivate their date gardens

with persistent intensity; the nomads drive their hungry and thirsty flocks with even greater perseverance. One group is docile, industrious, and loves law and order; the other is restless, wandering, alert, and often lawless. In northwest Africa the nomads are often the white masters; the Negroid farmers are leaseholders of the oases. Most nomads trade with the oases, raid occasionally, and sometimes conquer but do not usually dominate the settled peoples.

The life of the nomads is centered around the group of tents which comprises the temporary village; nearly all nomads live in tents, but not all tent dwellers are nomads; some are sedentary steppe peoples and agriculturists as well. Nomads usually live in large groups or tribes, composed of at least several families in order to have protection from the dangers and difficulties of desert life. A *douar*, or tent village, to the south of the Atlas Mountains may be taken as an example of a nomad settlement. Fifteen black tents, each large enough for a family, are arranged in a rude circle with the openings of the tents toward the center. This forms an enclosure into which the livestock can be driven at night. The camp is on a level stretch of land surrounded by hilly land with thin grass failing to conceal the rocky soil. In the distance there is a higher ridge with a scraggly growth of brush which is relished only by the goats and donkeys. The grazing animals include several hundred sheep, some goats, a few cows, and horses. They provide milk, cheese, meat, wool, hides, and skins. Since there is often a surplus, the tribe can exchange cheese and meat with the oases peoples, taking grain and dates in return, or they can sell some of their hides, wool, and skins to a more distant town for transport by auto road and rail

CLIMATIC DATA FOR REPRESENTATIVE STATIONS IN LANDS OF NOMADIC HERDING				
STATION	Average Annual Rainfall (inches)	Average Rainfall Wet Month (inches)	Average Rainfall Dry Month (inches)	Average Annual Temperature (degrees Fahrenheit)
Tripoli, Libya	16	Dec. 5.0	Aug. 0.0	67
Tashkent, U.S.S.R.	15	Mar. 3.0	Aug. 0.0	56
Omsk, U.S.S.R.	13	Jun. 6.0	Feb. 0.4	32
Laramie, Wyoming	11	Jul. 1.7	Dec. 0.4	40
San Luis, Argentina	20	Jan. 5.1	Aug. 0.1	69
Cloncurry, Australia	22	Dec. 4.0	Jul. 1.0	62

to the outside world, getting in return guns, knives, and other metal implements.

For centuries the nomads of the Algerian Sahara have lived in the same manner, but many times they have been threatened with change. A million and a half Europeans have migrated to north Africa in recent years. Most of these peoples—French, Spaniards, and Italians—settled near the coast and have had little direct contact with the nomads, but some of the best grazing land has been taken over by these agriculturists. Many times in the past the region has been conquered by foreigners—Phoenicians, Romans, Arabs, and the French—but none have had a very lasting effect on the life of the nomads. Farther to the east, in Russian Turkestan, the effect of modern agriculture on the nomads has been more pronounced.

The Saharan Oases

The Saharan oases are small, dependent as they are on limited supplies of water. Most oases have running water at the surface even if it has to be lifted by pump or beast of burden. Some obtain water from artesian wells, others from horizontal tunnels in the hills, and still others merely use the moisture of the sands by means of a sunken garden, which must be frequently re-excavated to keep it free of the drifting sands. The outstanding product of the oases is the date, of which the variety known as the "daglat nur" is the finest in the world. Dates are valuable enough to allow for rather costly transportation and are exported in some quantities. Other crops include barley, beans, various fruits and vegetables, most of which are consumed locally. Some of the larger oases south of the Atlas Mountains such as Colomb-Béchar and Touggourt have rail connections with the Mediterranean coast; others are connected to railheads by automobile roads. Altogether the population of the Saharan oases is not more than 200,000. Thus, they are of minor importance compared with the great oasis of the Nile.

EGYPT, "GIFT OF THE NILE"

The lower Nile is a classic example of a large oasis not only because its irrigation is very old but also because it is absolutely dependent on irrigation; rainfall is so light (the annual rainfall of Cairo is 1½ inches) as to be of little conse-

FIGURE 11.3. *Irrigation on the flat delta of the Nile. Cotton, sugar, corn, and small grain are produced in this farming area. From Keystone.*

quence. A large volume of water from the equatorial highlands of Africa flows for 3000 miles to irrigate this comparatively small strip of land, shaped like a wine glass with a long curving stem. This is the flood plain and delta of the river, a narrow ribbon of cultivated land 600 miles long from Aswân to Cairo. The cultivated land is on a monotonous plain (FIG. 11.3) slightly above sea level and is bordered by abrupt desert cliffs. A little more than 7,000,000 acres support 20,000,000 people.

Formerly irrigation depended on the natural flooding of the Nile. The floods did not reach lower Egypt until late summer, and although at that time the plain could be given a good soaking, it was too late for certain crops, cotton, sugarcane, and maize, to be grown to best advantage. Gradually the system has been modernized; the greatest step was the construction of a dam at Aswân, which holds back some of the flood

FIGURE 11.4. *The town of Laban lies on the Nile Delta about four miles west of Cairo. All the land in this picture except that occupied by roads and buildings is under irrigation. From Mary Light and the American Geographical Society.*

waters to be used the following season. With auxiliary dams at other points and a system of canals, year-round irrigation has been brought to four fifths of the cultivated land, and the water is used much more efficiently. Irrigation does not hinder the use of the Nile as a waterway; boats go up to Aswân with no difficulty and farther with some interruptions owing to rapids.

There are two principal crop seasons in Egypt, winter and summer. The winter crops are wheat, barley, alfalfa, beans, and peas. Most of these crops are sown in September or October after the period of maximum irrigation. The grains and beans are harvested in early spring, the alfalfa is cut several times, and the harvested fields are grazed until time to sow the summer crops. The summer crops include cotton, corn, rice, and, for

the period of major growth, sugarcane. In addition, there are small areas of vegetables and fruits —onions, tomatoes, artichokes, raisins, and dates. Part of the summer and winter crops are grown on the same land.

Cotton is the most important crop and the chief export of Egypt. Most of it grows in the delta where about 40 per cent of the arable land is sown in cotton in the summer. There are two unusual qualities of Egyptian cotton, its long fiber and the high yield. A premium price is paid for long-fibered Egyptian cotton on the world market, which includes the United States and other countries which have more than adequate supplies of the standard fibers at home. As for yield, Egypt produces 7 per cent of the world total on $2\frac{1}{2}$ per cent of the cotton land; the yields are the highest in the world. Most of the cotton is grown on small holdings and by somewhat primitive methods which make the high yields more surprising, but the cultivation is regulated and guarded by government agents. The remarkably small plots (FIG. 11.4) make the cultivation the more intensive; 90 per cent of the holdings are five acres or less; very few are above 50 acres.

Egypt is not endowed with great mineral wealth, but there is some production of petroleum on the Red Sea coast, and there are mines of phosphate, salt, nitrate, and manganese iron ores. The phosphate and nitrate deposits are of importance because of the increased use of mineral fertilizers. Industry is only slightly developed. There is some manufacture of cotton goods and, curiously, the manufacture of cigarettes with tobacco imported from Turkey.

Egyptians have some pressing problems, the most fundamental of which is overpopulation. In a little over half a century, the population has more than doubled and the present rate of increase is more than 1 per cent annually—170,000 people added every year. Never before in the long history of the Nile has the population been so great. The irrigable land is limited and is, in fact, nearly all in cultivation at present. The second problem, a shortage of water, is related to the first, because in recent years there has been great expansion of cotton production in the Anglo-Egyptian Sudan. This has tended to decrease the water available to the lower Nile, and

FIGURE 11.5. *The Oases and Nomadic Herding of southwestern Asia. The oases of Iraq and Azerbaidzhan are shown by heavier shading while smaller oases are indicated by the letter* O. *Petroleum (indicated by black triangles) is the chief mineral product. The oases of Russian Turkestan are shown in Figure 11.6.*

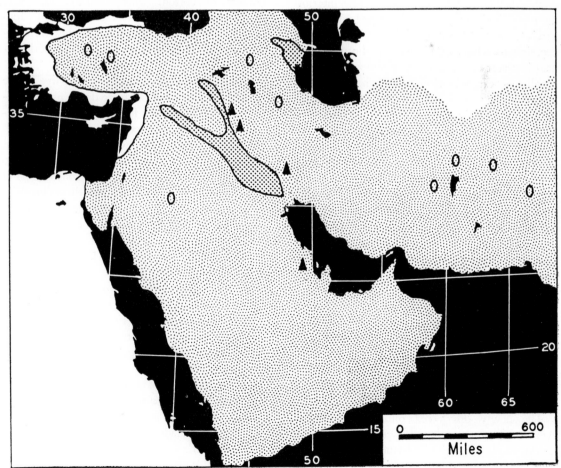

if expansion continues, this problem may assume serious proportions. Egyptians, with long-time priority, consider all the water of the Nile their property; in the future more and more land in the middle reaches of the river will be used.

ARABIA, IRAQ, AND IRAN

Nomadic Herding (FIG. 11.5) continues to be the most widely distributed human activity over the plateaus of southwest Asia, although in the numerous oases, large and small, more goods are produced. Minerals, especially petroleum, have greater economic and political significance in some districts than the products of agriculture and grazing combined.

Arabia, like the Sahara, is a land of contrasts. Most of it is a barren waste of moving sands or rocky plateaus, but grassy steppes and even forested mountains are to be found on the margins. Except in the subhumid southern part of the peninsula, the life of the nomad is even harder in Arabia than in the Sahara. In the southern interior the camel is the only domestic animal which can survive. There the rearing of the camel is the occupation to which every Arab is born. There man is a sort of parasite, since almost all of his supplies—meat, milk, clothing and shelter—come from this one animal. Every effort must be made to utilize the scanty pastures and the scantier water most efficiently. In winter, pasture is of first importance, for the camels do not require frequent watering at this season. If the grass is moistened with dew or light rain daily, the camel may survive for two months without water. Meanwhile the herders live on camel milk and meat and never touch water. In summer, however, when the excessive heat speeds up evaporation, the herds need water every other day. The camel supplies almost all of the needs of the herders—milk, meat, leather, camel hair for clothing, ropes, saddle girths, and miscellaneous articles. In the more humid margins of Arabia, the horse, sheep, and other domestic animals add to the variety of nomad life. In the southern corner of the country, near Aden, crops are grown either with or without irrigation. Of these coffee and the date are most valuable.

The newly discovered oilfields in eastern Arabia are of great importance to the outside world. Wells on Bahrein Island in the Persian Gulf have produced many millions of barrels as have other wells on the adjacent mainland. It seems probable that the Persian Gulf Coast of Arabia will develop into a great oil producer comparable to the combined Iraq and Iran fields. Various oil companies including some from the United States are competing for the fields. Many large concessions have been established, and it has even been proposed that a pipeline to the Mediterranean would facilitate delivery to western Europe. Most of the region is within easy reach of tankers which come into the Persian Gulf, and it is unlikely that the pipeline will be constructed unless production exceeds present expectations.

Iraq, or Mesopotamia, the northern edge of the Arab realm, was once a large-scale oasis like the lower Nile with two great rivers, the Euphrates and the Tigris, furnishing water for extensive irrigation. In the 12th century there were many low dams and a carefully prepared system of ditches. As a consequence there was large production of cotton, wheat, barley, rice, and fruits. Partly as a result of the invasion of Mongols and Tartars, the dams and ditches were destroyed, and they have never been properly rebuilt.

Today most of the people of Iraq live in the alluvial lowlands and cultivate dates, grains, millet, cotton, and various food crops. Irrigation depends on the natural flooding of the rivers, which fortunately comes in late winter and early spring, and on modern irrigation works. A plan drawn up by a British engineer calls for the construction of many more dams, reservoirs, and diversion channels. This would prevent floods and utilize the water to greater advantage. Provision can be made for the irrigation of about 6,500,000 acres in winter and early spring and about 3,000,000 acres in summer. For the most part the waters of the Tigris would irrigate the land east of that river, while the Euphrates would supply water for the land between the rivers.

Iraq produces about one third of all the dates in the world, and the export value of this crop is second only to that of oil. The chief producing area is in the lower part of the valley in the vicinity of Basra. This district exports about three fourths of the dates which enter the world market. The grains include wheat, barley, rice, millet, and corn. Barley is the chief winter crop, since it grows well with little rain and in a short season.

The quality of the cotton is good, but the production is small. As much cotton could grow in Iraq as in Egypt if the irrigation systems were improved. The poppy is grown both for the oil and for opium. Only on the upland margin of Iraq do the people depend mostly on pastoral pursuits. Here good quality wool is produced, part of it for sale.

The development of petroleum in Iraq has been very rapid, especially since World War I. For centuries it has been known that oil existed in Mesopotamia. Bituminous material for mortar was utilized in the construction of the Tower of Babel; nomads used the seepages of petroleum to treat the mange on their camels; burning springs were visited by ancient fire worshipers. There was some modern exploration of the petroleum resources before 1914, and the Germans had a concession on all mineral deposits in connection with the Berlin to Bagdad Railway project. After the war several oil companies, mainly British, French, Dutch, and American, became interested in the deposits of Iraq, along with those of Iran; exploration was intensified and production began. Wells were put down in the vicinity of Mosul and Kirkuk, and there were few dry holes. Production became significant in 1927 when a well near Kirkuk came in as a gusher, flowing 90,000 barrels a day. Production gradually increased to about 30,000,000 barrels annually in the period 1936–1949 for all of Iraq. The increasing production raised the problem of transportation. As there were no railroads, a pipeline was constructed from the oilfields to the Mediterranean. The line, sponsored jointly by the French and British, branched on the west side of the Euphrates, one part going to Haifa in Palestine (then British Mandate), the other going to Tripoli in Syria (then French Mandate).

Whatever the future political complexion of Iraq, which is coveted by Turkey and Arabia as well as by several European powers, the prosperity of its 4,500,000 people will hinge on the development of irrigation and petroleum. In connection with the agricultural development, it will be necessary to construct more roads, airports, and railway lines (since the development of irrigation will interfere with the use of the rivers for transportation). Pastoral peoples will continue to occupy most of the area away from the rivers.

Iran, formerly called Persia, is an upland with lofty mountain ranges and broad basins. It resembles the Basin Range country of western United States and Mexico rather than the Sahara. Here, there is a combination of nomadism and oasis culture in which the relations between the two are a little more intimate than in most of the dry lands. Irrigation of the basins is dependent on a large number of underground tunnels similar to those constructed in the Algerian Sahara. Sixty of these canals converge on the town of Yezd. The principal crops grown in the oases include wheat, barley, cotton, millet, rice, opium, and in the warmer zones, maize and the mulberry. The principal exports are carpets, cotton, petroleum, dates, opium, silk, and horses. Most of the exports ordinarily go to Russia, since the easiest transportation is in this direction. Even so, the isolation of Iran from centers of dense population imposes a great handicap to trade. The products of Iran must compete in the Russian markets with similar products from south Russia.

The nomads who occupy the land between the oases furnish wool for the rug industry and also camels and donkeys for the principal transportation of the country. Until recently there was only one railroad of importance, a short line from Tabriz in the northwest to the Russian city of Tiflis, but in 1941 a line was completed from the Caspian via Tehran to the Persian Gulf at Bandar Shapur. Oil is the chief commercial product of Iran, and the production is nearly three times that of Iraq. The most important fields are near the head of the Persian Gulf from which pipelines take the oil to Bandar Shapur. Other fields are located near the Iraq fields of Kirkuk and Mosul.

RUSSIAN TURKESTAN (CENTRAL ASIATIC RUSSIA)

From the Caspian Sea a thousand miles eastward and from the Ural Mountains a thousand miles southward stretches Russian Turkestan (FIG. 11.6), a vast desert land of nomads and large-scale irrigated oases. It is a dry land with from 5 to 20 inches of rain, but it contains many important oases and scattered settlements, including both nomads and sedentary peoples. There are several fundamental facts about this vast region. In the first place, it is a land of interior drainage, no surface water reaching the sea. Instead the drainage is into the Caspian and Aral seas, which are salt. Another important fact is that large parts of the region are covered with wind-blown soil, or loess, a very fertile soil if water is available. The third fundamental quality is that the eastern part of the country is mountainous and the lofty mountains furnish water for irrigation. Most of the irrigation is on the borders of the two great rivers, the Sir and the Amu, which flow from the mountains to the Aral Sea. Furthermore, the climate of this region is desert (BW); in very few parts is there more than ten inches of rain annually. Secondly, the winters of all but the southern portion are severe, even in the south cold periods occur, and there are occasional light snows. The summers are hot; temperatures over 100° F. are very common. The average for July in the central part of the region is above 80° F., comparable to Arabia, the Sahara, and the great desert of Australia.

The soils show great variety; there are the salt flats, with accumulation of various kinds of salts on the surface. Clay plains with sparse vegetation alternate with areas of loess, a yellow wind-blown material which is cultivated wherever there is available water. The loess is a fine silty sediment, easy to cultivate. It holds water well and resists erosion on steep slopes, on the banks of streams, or along road cuts.

The nomads have many sheep, especially the fat-tailed Khirgiz sheep and the Karakul, from which the Persian lambskins are obtained. There are also horses, goats, cattle, and camels. Great losses of livestock occur in the severe winters, especially when there are ice storms. The nomadic population is decreasing, owing largely to the increased cultivation of the oases.

Agriculture in Turkestan is determined largely by irrigation. Considering the hot summers and

FIGURE 11.6. *The Oases of Russian Turkestan. East of the Caspian Sea (solid black) the irrigated areas (dotted) along the Amu and Sir rivers produce large quantities of cotton, millet, and small-grain. Mineral production includes coal, salt, petroleum (black triangle), and gold (Au). Cities include Bukhara (B), Krasnovodsk (K), Samarkand (S), and Tashkent (T). Railroads connect the region with the Caspian Sea, with European Russia to the northwest, and with the Trans-Siberian Railroad to the northeast.*

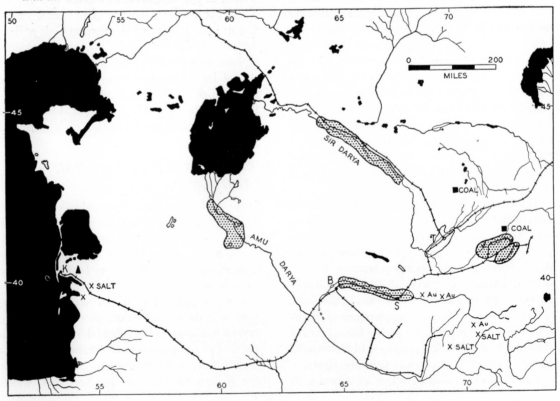

the fact that most of the precipitation comes in winter, there is little opportunity for dry farming. The most important commercial crop is cotton (FIG. 11.7), which has increased enormously in acreage in the last decade, placing the Russians in third rank of world production and making them nearly independent of foreign cotton. The increase in cotton production has been accomplished by improvement and extension in irrigation and by the importation of new American varieties of cotton, in some places at the expense of the food crops—wheat, barley, rice, potatoes, sorghum, and maize.

The irrigated areas are largely along the Amu and Sir rivers and their tributaries. The oasis of Khiva, for example, is along the delta of the Amu. Here most of the irrigated land lies along the left bank because the right bank is high and covered with shifting sand. The flood plain of the river is about 60 miles wide at this point and is covered with loess, reworked by the river. Here, as usual, the chief crop is cotton, with some rice, wheat, and barley. Aside from the pastoral and agricultural resources, in Russian Turkestan some oil is produced near Krasnovodsk, coal mostly in the vicinity of Tashkent, gold in the same district, and various salts and sulfur. The chief oil production of Russia is described in Chapter 34.

THE MONGOLIAN GOBI

The easternmost unit of the Old World arid region is the Gobi, which is not a desert like the Sahara but is a gravelly steppe. Since the days of Genghis Khan the way of life has changed little. There, as in the other desert borderlands, the people depend on their herds, sheep, goats, cattle, horses, camels, and yaks. As with the Khirgiz, the horse merits special attention; it is the most esteemed animal. The Mongolian horse is short, wiry, and has remarkable powers of endurance, easily carrying a rider fifty miles per day. The horse was probably domesticated near the Caucasus Mountains, from which it was brought to the Gobi by men who had to travel fast and far.

In Mongolia each tribe has its own special grazing land, and the seasonal migrations are over short distances. Many groups of nomads travel not more than one hundred miles between their summer and their winter pasturage. Like the Arabs, Berbers, and Khirgiz, they live in tents,

FIGURE 11.7. *Cotton picker in Russian Turkestan. The irrigated oases of this region provide most of the raw cotton for Russian factories. From Keystone.*

and their tents are large, comfortable structures with a framework of light wood covered with thick felt. The standard of living is not substantially higher than that of other nomads. A visitor estimated that the possessions of a Mongolian prince were worth not more than one hundred dollars. This estimate, however, did not include the value of the livestock which is the principal form of wealth. Since cattle are rarely sold by the nomads, their value in money is difficult to determine.

Aside from the care of livestock, the principal occupation of the Mongols is transportation. They equip and look after caravans; they are available as guides; and they carry the mail. The men are inveterate wanderers and visitors; they attend numerous fairs and sporting events and visit friendly tribes all the way from Tibet to the southern confines of Siberia. During such pilgrimages the women are left at home to look after the livestock.

THE TUNDRA

On the northern fringe of Europe and Asia, the land is little used. A few nomadic peoples—the Lapps, Samoyeds, Tungus, and the Yakuts—manage to exist with the aid of the reindeer, an animal which can browse on the mosses, lichens, and other forage plants even when the ground is covered with snow. The Lapps, numbering about 25,000, live in northern Scandinavia and the adjacent parts of Finland and Russia. These people migrate with their herds of reindeer according to the seasons. In summer the open tundra furnishes good grazing for a short period. In winter the herds are driven into the taiga, which is the northern edge of the forest. The trees offer some protection from the rigors of winter, and where the snow cover is light the reindeer are able to expose the browse plants by scraping with their feet. The hazards are many, however. Wolves prey on the reindeer, diseases take their toll of the herd, and although few animals are better prepared to withstand the severe winters, losses from blizzards are often high. In addition to supplying meat, milk, hides, and horn, the reindeer makes a good pack animal, superior to the horse in the tundra.

In North America the tundra is occupied mostly by Eskimos who live by hunting and fishing rather than by herding. They had no domesticated animals until the reindeer was imported from northern Europe and Siberia, and even since that time herding has played a very minor role in their lives. In recent years, however, interest in the reindeer as a commercial animal has increased among the Indians of Alaska and northern Canada. Several large herds have been developed in the tundra of western Alaska, the total numbering more than a million.

Grazing of reindeer is possible over a large proportion of the tundra in spite of some difficulties. In summer the reindeer browse on the grasses, shrubs, and herbs which are abundant in the warm season. In winter the chief forage comes from the mosses and lichens, which grow very slowly and can be easily overgrazed. The abundant summer feed tempts the owners to de-velop larger herds, too large to be supported during the winter. In Canada the Third Deficiency Act of 1939 provided for the purchase of all reindeer from white owners, thus making the industry exclusively native. But the Eskimos and Indians are accustomed to hunting and fishing rather than pastoral pursuits, and they do not relish the less exciting and often less profitable life of the herder.

SUMMARY

From the Sahara to the Gobi the nomadic life is essentially the same. The differences lie in the details of climate, land surface, water supply, livestock, and the customs of the people. Generally speaking the sheep is the most important animal in the nomadic life, since it can thrive on sparse grass, needs little water (although sheep cannot travel far to get it), and supplies wool, meat, skins, and milk. Goats have about the same qualities and uses but are more suited to the brushy vegetation than the sheep. Cattle are widely distributed, except in the more arid parts of the Sahara and Arabia. The camel is most important in Arabia, parts of the Sahara, and in the Khirgiz Steppes; it is best suited to the hot lands and has some difficulty with the cold in Mongolia. In the coldest lands of higher altitudes, the yak and the reindeer are the most appropriate animals.

Since nomads wander only of necessity, many are temporarily sedentary when conditions permit. If grass and water hold out, the people do not move, often live in permanent houses, and use their tents for short temporary migrations. Although the nomad may sow and reap an occasional crop of grain, he is in no sense an agriculturist; indeed, he looks with contempt on the farmer and the prosaic life he leads.

In contrast with the nomad, who is little concerned with the world of trade and commerce, the average oasis farmer is quite concerned with the price of cotton, wheat, barley, and rice. There is some variation in crops but mostly a question of degree rather than kind. Commercial producers in the large oases, however, must have better transportation, water or rail, or both, if they are to succeed in reaching the world markets. All the large oases are, in fact, on railroads and some, notably the Nile Oasis, are near good water transportation also.

12

The Commercial Wheat Belts of North America

To AN overworked farmer in eastern United States or to a factory worker out of a job, the wheat belts on the dry fringe of agriculture have always had a peculiar attraction. Land is cheap; most of the work can be done with machinery; a substantial cash income is assured *if the crop matures*. It is the "if" which causes some prospective wheat farmers to pause, for on the dry margins of agriculture the risk of crop failure is great. The farmer must be prepared financially and mentally to endure two or three crop failures before a good harvest is obtained.

The wheat belts are not suited to the complex types of humid farming, as are the corn belts or dairy belts, because of the dryness. Feed crops for fattening cannot be produced on a large scale so that, in general, it is not feasible to finish meat animals for the market. Livestock is limited mostly to work animals, range animals, or it may be entirely lacking.

The modern commercial wheat belt is the end product of a sort of destructive evolution which was impressed upon the European farming types as they advanced into the subhumid and semiarid lands of the New World. The settlers on the Atlantic seaboard of the United States grew wheat, but it was rarely a dominant crop. In the east and the humid parts of the middle west, wheat found a definite but modest role in the farm economy. But as the settlers moved into the drier areas, corn, hay, and other forage and food crops were left behind. Only wheat and a few other crops, such as barley, rye, and flax, which grow under similar conditions, were produced. With one exception, the Ukraine in Russia, all the commercial wheat belts of the world were settled and developed less than a century ago. The greatest expan-

sion came in the last half century following the invention of heavy power machinery for the plowing, harrowing, seeding, and harvesting operations.

In most of the cultivated land of the earth, wheat is the outstanding grain food. Rice, corn, rye, barley, millet, and other grains are used for food in varying quantities, and in some regions one or more of these may rank above wheat. World production of wheat averages slightly more than six billion bushels; of this North America produces approximately one fourth, Russia one fifth, Europe one fourth, while the remainder comes from South America, Australia, Africa, and Asia.

Wheat is produced in most countries, but in only a few, like Canada, the United States, Argentina, and Australia, is there any considerable export surplus. In some years very little or none at all is exported from the United States. On the other hand, large quantities were exported from Russia for a few years prior to World War II, and the Russians are fast becoming exporters again. All the export surplus is from the semiarid wheat belts. Production of wheat in other agricultural areas does not satisfy local needs.

In the United States the consumption of wheat is about 137 pounds per capita compared with 30 pounds of corn, 5 pounds of rice, and 2 pounds of rye. The proportion in Canada is not substantially different.

More wheat is exported from Canada, which has a very large acreage and a small population, than from any other wheat-growing country in the world. See FIGURE 12.3. Large quantities of wheat are usually exported from the United States, although at the same time some wheat is imported from Canada. Wheat is also exported from Argentina and Australia, but increasing quantities are used in these countries for fuel, feed, and the manufacture of alcohol.

The typical wheat farm in any of the belts is on a gently rolling plain which was, before plowing, a semiarid to subhumid grassland. The farm is large, a section or 640 acres, half of which is cultivated in alternate years. The half which is left idle or fallow for one season is presumed to store up the moisture of two years to be used on one crop. During this period the soil is cultivated to maintain a fine mulch or dust at the surface. The improvements on the farm are very simple. A small residence and a shelter for the machinery make up the farmstead. A windmill for pumping water from a deep well is a conspicuous feature. There is a three-strand barbed wire fence around the whole farm to keep out wandering cattle. There is no orchard, no garden, and even at sowing or harvest time the farm has a solitary, almost deserted air. The farmer calls this his permanent home but, aside from the brief periods of feverish activity at sowing and harvesting, spends most of his time in town. There are long periods when there is nothing to do on the wheat farm, a feature which attracts many prospective farmers.

The farm described is what might be called a "pure" wheat farm. In many places there are additional elements on the farm: a small irrigated area for alfalfa, some cattle on the adjacent grasslands which feed on the stubble of the wheat after harvest. Where the rainfall is a little greater than average, other crops—flax, grain sorghum, rye, oats, or potatoes—may be grown.

In the United States wheat is one of the four most important crops because it is the national bread crop and because it makes up a large part of our agricultural exports. Wheat is usually the fourth crop in value after corn, hay, and cotton, but it is in many ways of primary importance in the commercial life of the nation. In Canada wheat is of even greater relative significance. Not only is it the chief food crop, but large quantities are used for feed for livestock (corn does not mature well in Canada) and for the production of alcohol. About three fourths of Canada's wheat crop is exported, making it the major item in Canada's foreign trade. Wheat is grown widely in North America, from the Great Northern Forest to the Central Plateau of Mexico. In almost every state in the United States, in all the southern provinces of Canada, and in all the middle and northern states of Mexico some wheat is grown. But in only three regions is it the dominant crop: the Winter Wheat Belt, the Spring Wheat Belt, and the Columbia Wheat Belt.

THE WINTER WHEAT BELT

The Winter Wheat Belt of the United States (FIG. 12.1) lies nearly in the center of the country including parts of Kansas, Nebraska, Colorado, northern Texas, and Oklahoma. The boundary fluctuates from year to year with the variations of rainfall and the price of wheat—higher prices tend to cause an extension in the area particularly on the drier western side. Most of the region is in the Great Plains, parts of which have

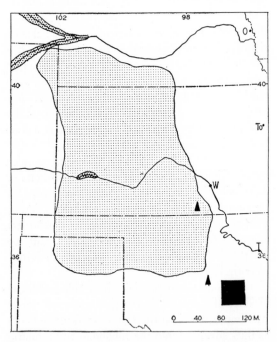

FIGURE 12.1. *The Winter Wheat Belt of the United States, including western Kansas and parts of Oklahoma, Texas, Colorado, and Nebraska. Boundaries are variable depending on amount of rainfall, the price of wheat, and other factors. Irrigated areas in the Platte and Arkansas river valleys are shown by heavier shading. On the southeast is the Mid-continent Oilfield (see Chap. 34). Most of the winter wheat is shipped out via Omaha (O), Topeka (To), Wichita (W), and Tulsa (T) to the Great Lakes, the eastern seaboard, and the Gulf. The black square represents 1600 square miles.*

FIGURE 12.2. *Wheat is an important crop in eastern Kansas where much of the land is terraced to reduce erosion and conserve moisture. The yield in this field was about 35 bushels per acre, much higher than the average for the Winter Wheat Belt. The trees in the background suggest that this is on the humid edge of the Wheat Belt. From Soil Conservation Service.*

been described in Chapter 9 on Commercial Grazing. The smooth, gently rolling land is suited to machine cultivation, the soils are generally fertile, and the chief handicap is the variability of the climate, especially with regard to rainfall. The rainfall in the western part is about 12 inches annually, increasing to 25 inches on the eastern margin, but the unpredictable variation from year to year makes the production of wheat on the western margin little better than a fifty-fifty gamble. Thus a town, such as Scott City in western Kansas, which has an average rainfall of nearly 20 inches may have only five or six inches in some years, 25 or 30 inches in others. Furthermore, one part of the Winter Wheat Belt may have a severe drought, and the rest have almost normal rainfall. Another climatic factor is frost. Most of the wheat is sown in the late autumn or early winter so that the seeds will sprout and the plants will attain a limited growth before the cold weather arrives. The seeding season is earliest in the northern part of the belt, in Nebraska, latest in the southern part, Texas. The danger is that a delay of cold weather will allow the growth to go too far, and winterkilling will result. A late frost in the spring, after the wheat has come into head, may seriously affect the yield. For example, at Colby, Kansas, the last frost in spring may vary from March 4 to May 26, and the earliest frost in the fall from September 12 to November 2. Consequently, the chief concern of the wheat farmers, next to the price of wheat, is the climate of the crop year, especially the rainfall.

Although wheat may occupy up to three fourths of the cultivated land, some corn, barley, grain sorghum, and hay (especially alfalfa) are also produced in the Winter Wheat Belt. Corn is limited to the eastern humid part of the region where much of it is grown for fodder rather than for grain. The grain sorghums are grown in rotation with wheat, especially in the southern part of the region, Oklahoma and Texas. Most of the alfalfa is produced in the irrigated valleys, such as the Arkansas Valley.

The farms in the Winter Wheat Belt are large. A farm of 160 acres, large enough in the humid corn belt for an average family, is far too small in this region. A farmer should have at least two sections of land (1280 acres) on the dry margin, one section (640 acres) on the wet margin. Land is cheap—a realtor once offered the writer two sections of land at $15 per acre, on easy payments! The prospect of 25 bushels of wheat to the acre even when wheat was only $1 per bushel, made the offer look very attractive indeed. Another inviting aspect of commercial grain growing is the machinery which does all the work and does it in a short time. The seeding season is a busy one, but it lasts only a few days on any one farm. If the land has been plowed before, the disking and seeding may be done in one operation. Then the farmer has only to wait for the harvest, hoping meanwhile for rain, which because of its scarcity is often referred to reverently as "moisture." The harvest takes very little time with large combines or with modern binders and threshers. See FIGURE 12.2. One man who farms several sections of land in this region has no house on his land. He lives in California, and "visits" his wheat farm in the seeding season. A week or ten days is enough; then he goes back to California. He comes back in early summer for the harvest; if there is a crop, the wheat is harvested and sold, and before the very hottest weather arrives he is back on the Pacific Coast. This case is exceptional, perhaps, but the fact remains that the wheat farmer is not "married" to the farm as is the dairy or corn belt farmer.

In the Winter Wheat Belt the wheat farms occupy the smoothest land on the uplands between the rather infrequent streams. The rougher land and the drier areas are used for ranching, while the floors of the river valleys are used for irrigated crops, alfalfa and sugar beets, if there is enough water. Thus the region has three types of land use with wheat raising dominant. As indicated before, the land use is variable, being most stable with irrigation and most risky with wheat raising. In times of heavier rainfall, ranch land may be sown in wheat; in drier periods some of the wheat land may revert to ranching or, because the native grasses have been destroyed, may stand idle. Between the wheat farms, ranches, and oases, there are rather definite relationships. Irrigation provides hay and winter forage for the ranches, and the cattle sometimes graze on the stubble of the wheat and for a brief period may even graze in the fields of young wheat in the early spring. This last practice is intended to increase the yield of wheat by encouraging a thicker growth, as well as supplying pasturage, but the animals must be kept moving in order not to have them graze too closely and thus injure the crop.

Winter wheat moves eastward to market. From the combine or thresher, trucks take the loose grain to the nearest railroad. Here, the grain is stored in a small grain elevator for a short time until a quantity is available for shipment. By rail the grain is moved into the local grain centers in, or on the margin of, the region: Omaha (Nebraska), Kansas City (Missouri), Hutchinson (Kansas), Enid (Oklahoma), or Amarillo (Texas). Flour mills in these cities turn some of the wheat into flour. Larger quantities of wheat are moved on to the larger cities farther east, such as Chicago, Buffalo, and New York, while some goes to the Gulf ports, Houston and New Orleans, a part of it for export.

The Winter Wheat Belt has few mineral resources, very little manufacturing, and no large cities. Petroleum and natural gas are produced in the Texas Panhandle and in central Kansas. Oil and gas wells interfere little with wheat growing, and once the wells are drilled only an inconspicuous pumping station here and there attests to the presence of this resource. Most of the oil and gas are marketed outside the region.

THE SPRING WHEAT BELT

The Spring Wheat Belt of North America (FIG. 12.3), nearly three times as large as the Winter Wheat Belt, extends from the Red River Valley of northwestern Minnesota westward and northward to the Canadian Rockies. It includes parts of four states—Minnesota, North Dakota, South Dakota, and Montana—and parts of three Canadian provinces—Manitoba, Saskatchewan, and Alberta. The region is limited on the east by the humid Dairy Belt and Corn Belt, on the north by the Great Northern Forest of the Laurentian Shield where neither climate nor soil is favorable for cultivation, on the south by grazing land, and on the west by the Rocky Mountains. The Spring Wheat Belt differs from the Winter Wheat Belt in the time of sowing, in the shortness of the growing season, and in the fact that it lies in the glaciated region. The population is less dense and precipitation is lighter, but this latter fact is offset by the cooler summers and the lower evaporation.

The most significant factor is the climate, especially the length of the growing season and the amount of precipitation. In the southeastern part the growing season is about 140 days, in the northern part less than 100 days. Since it is advisable to take the utmost advantage of the short season, the wheat is seeded as early in the spring as possible, and the young plants sprout before the

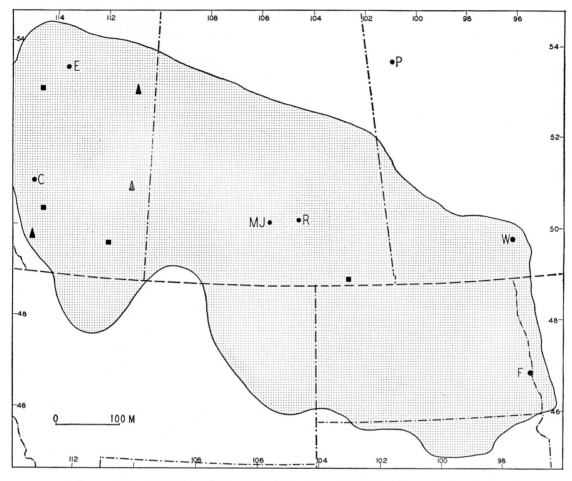

FIGURE 12.3. *The Spring Wheat Belt of Canada and the United States, the boundaries of which are variable. Parts of four states and three Canadian provinces are included. Although generally poor in minerals, the region produces coal (black squares) and petroleum (black triangles) mostly in the western portion. The chief cities are Edmonton (E), Calgary (C), Moose Jaw (MJ), Regina (R), Winnipeg (W), and Fargo (F). Most of the wheat is shipped out via Winnipeg and Fargo, but a small portion goes to Hudson Bay via The Pas (P).*

last frost, for wheat has a great tolerance for cold at this stage of growth. The early frost in the fall is to be more feared, since it can do serious damage. Although the severity of the winter makes it generally undesirable to seed in the fall, some winter wheat is grown in the Spring Wheat Region, particularly on the western margin of the region where the warm, dry chinook wind from the mountains often moderates the winter weather. The rainfall usually varies between 12 and 22 inches annually, most of it coming during the growth of the crop. The effect of the rain is greater because of the cool summers; for example, the July temperature averages from 60° F.

to 72° F. The coolness of the summers and the shortness of the growing season are offset somewhat by the long summer days, which are from 16 to 18 hours in length.

Although few parts of the Spring Wheat Belt are rough or rugged, the surface varies both in the form of the land and the nature of the soil. The eastern part, the Red River Valley, is the smoothest and best. During the Ice Age the natural drainage of this district toward Hudson Bay was blocked by the ice. This ice dam produced Lake Agassiz, with an area of more than 100,000 square miles, into which the finer sediments from the melting ice were washed. The bed of the lake,

exposed when normal drainage was resumed, includes northwestern Minnesota, eastern North
Dakota, and a large part of southern Manitoba.
The surface is smooth and so flat that artificial
drainage is required in many places. The soil is
fine textured, dark gray in color, and fertile. This
district has the highest yields and the greatest
variety of crops, owing to the excellent soils, the
heavy rainfall, and the earlier settlement, as compared with the remainder of the Spring Wheat
Belt. On most relief maps this district, the Red
River Valley, stands out since the 1000 foot contour line approximates the border.

To the west the surface is rolling and largely
morainic in character. Since it stands higher than
the Red River Valley, the streams have cut deeper
into its surface. But it is still smooth enough for
easy farming with heavy machinery. For the most
part, the land rises gradually to the west, but
there are also some abrupt changes. The Missouri
Couteau (ridge) runs diagonally through the middle of North Dakota and continues through southern Saskatchewan. Above and to the west of this
ridge the Canadian Plains are about 3000 feet
high, increasing to 4500 feet at the base of the
Rocky Mountains.

As in the Winter Wheat Belt, wheat is the
dominant but not the only crop. Some corn is
grown for grain in the extreme southeastern part;
it is, however, widely grown for forage. Flax,
oats, barley, rye, and alfalfa are also important.
More wheat is produced in the Spring Wheat Region than in any other region in North America.

Most of the Spring Wheat Belt is in Canada
where wheat is the only important food grain.
Rye and barley are grown, but these grains occupy rather small acreages. Canadians usually
harvest nearly 400 million bushels of wheat, but
at the beginning of World War II the disruption
of transportation left them with a large surplus of
wheat. As a result the acreage planted in the war
years was less than normal, and only after the
world shortage of wheat was felt at the close of
the war was the acreage expanded to the usual
figure.

The domestic consumption of wheat in Canada
is usually about one fourth of the production, leaving a larger amount for export than in any other
country. Both wheat and flour are exported to
western Europe in quantities; at the peak this included about 13 million barrels of flour and 150
million bushels of wheat. Most of the wheat and
flour is sent to the United Kingdom, to various
other countries of western Europe, and to the
United States. Since in the United States a surplus of wheat is produced, only the hard varieties
of wheat of special quality are imported. During
the acute shortage of wheat following World
War II, Canadian wheat was exported to Egypt,
Turkey, and even Russia.

Transportation of Spring Wheat

Since the Spring Wheat Belt is near the center
of the North American continent, it is both difficult and expensive to get the exportable surplus
to the seaboard. Because the belt is large, several
different routes are used, but the bulk of the crop
is transported via the Great Lakes for at least a
part of its journey to the Atlantic. The Canadian
surplus is moved by rail via Winnipeg to the Lake
Superior ports of Fort William and Port Arthur,
thence by lake steamer to Buffalo. Here, the
wheat is moved into the United States under bond
in order to avoid the payment of duty. A part is
converted to flour, and both wheat and flour are
then shipped overland by rail to New York, Philadelphia, Baltimore, Boston, or Portland (Maine)
for export. The harvest of spring wheat in Canada begins in late summer and early autumn. By
the time the bulk of the crop reaches the lower
Great Lakes, the St. Lawrence River may be
frozen. This explains the shipment of a large
part of Canada's export wheat across the United
States.

The Hudson Bay Railway from the Canadian
Spring Wheat Belt to Fort Churchill on Hudson
Bay has been mentioned in Chapter 6, The North
American Forest Region. This line was built
across the lonely wastes of the Laurentian Shield
of Canada for the express purpose of getting the
wheat out to sea with one rail haul. A part of the
line was built on frozen muskeg, which in summer
makes a very unsatisfactory railroad bed. Travelers across this section notice that the rails sink
several feet with the weight of the train so that
the engine is always climbing a slight grade while
the caboose appears to be running downhill. The
route has not been effective in getting wheat out
of Canada, but the fault does not lie with the railroad. Hudson Bay is open for several months, but
navigation is risky because of ice and fog. As a
result of these hazards, plus the fact that the Great

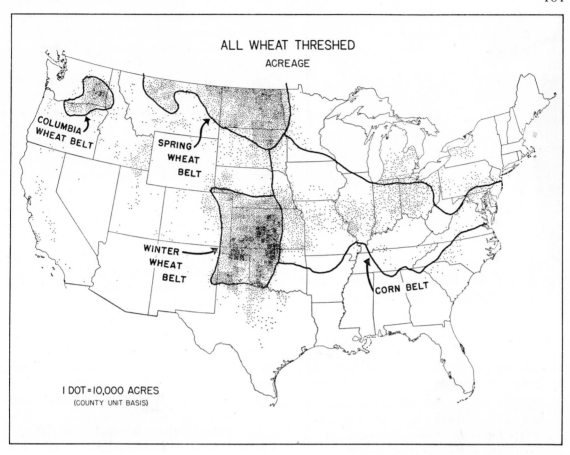

FIGURE 12.4. *Acreage of wheat threshed in the United States in 1949. Most of the acreage is in three major belts. From Bureau of Census.*

Lakes route was established much earlier, few ocean freighters come into Hudson Bay to pick up cargoes of grain.

Wheat from the United States side of the Spring Wheat Belt is also transported on the Great Lakes. At Duluth and Superior at the upper end of Lake Superior large amounts of wheat are handled in the same manner as at Port Arthur and Fort William. The wheat is shipped down the lakes somewhat earlier than the Canadian wheat, when the St. Lawrence is still ice free. In some years most of the United States export has even gone via Montreal. In both Canada and the United States, grain is shipped direct by rail from the wheat fields to the Atlantic seaboard, but the railroads can handle only a small portion of the crop. Particularly during bumper crop years, the combined facilities of rail and water transportation are unable to move all the crop. Wheat ac-

cumulates in elevators and sometimes in huge piles along the railroads where, exposed to the weather, it is often damaged by rain.

THE COLUMBIA WHEAT BELT

The Columbia Wheat Belt (FIG. 12.5) occupies a small area in eastern Washington, Oregon, and western Idaho. Although the production is much smaller than that in the other wheat belts, its position near the ocean makes export more easy. When there is a large surplus of wheat in the United States, a very large proportion of the crop is exported from this region via Portland (Oregon), Seattle, and the Panama Canal. Wheat farming is even more specialized here than in the Spring and Winter Wheat Belts. Wheat occupies the larger proportion of the cropped land and other crops, such as hay, barley, and oats, are less important. Around the margins of the Columbia

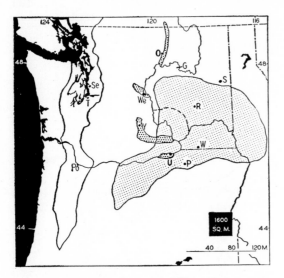

FIGURE 12.5. *The Columbia Wheat Belt occupies parts of Washington, Oregon, and Idaho. Irrigation of fruits and other crops is common on the margins. Okanagan (O), Wenatchee (We), Yakima (Y), and Umatilla (U) oases are shown. Completion of the dam at Grand Coulee (G) permits the irrigation of a million more acres. Important elevator and milling cities include Spokane (S), Ritzville (R), Walla Walla (W), and Pendleton (P). Much of the wheat moves out of the region to Portland (Po) in the Willamette Valley, while some goes to Seattle (Se) and Tacoma (T) in the Puget Sound Region.*

Wheat Belt, irrigated oases produce large quantities of hay and fruits, especially apples.

The size of the farms varies, since on some of them wheat is irrigated while on others in the drier parts irrigation is not possible. The irrigated farms average from 100 to 200 acres, but the nonirrigated farms range from 1000 to 5000 acres. Representative wheat farms include about one section of land, half of which is in crop and the other half fallow. In the Columbia Wheat Belt both winter and spring wheat are grown, but the greater acreage and generally the greater yield are in winter wheat. In general, the temperatures are favorable for both types and the variation in rainfall is the determining factor. According to the season one variety may be substituted for another. Spring wheat is substituted for winter when the autumn is dry or when winter planting fails to survive. This tends to reduce crop failures.

Harvesting is usually begun in early or mid-July and is completed during the last half of August. In some years the harvest may be begun in the southern part of the region in the last days of June. Nearly all the wheat is cut by combines, some of which cut, thresh, and sack the grain, but the bin type of combine from which the grain flows into trucks or wagons is increasingly used. Partly because of the irrigated wheat, average yields are higher here than in the other wheat belts. In general, in the more humid parts of the nonirrigated districts the yield is as much as 50 bushels per acre, but in the driest areas as little as five bushels per acre has been harvested.

In spite of the relatively small size of the Columbia Wheat Belt as compared with the Winter Wheat Belt and the Spring Wheat Belt, the conditions of crop production, climate, surface, and soil vary widely. In the north, exposures of bare lava occur, along with steep-walled canyons and isolated hills. To the west, directly south of the Grand Coulee Dam is the Big Bend country, part of which can be irrigated. In southeastern Washington north of the Snake River is the "Palouse" with its rolling, hilly surface and its thick, fertile, fine-grained soils.

The Palouse country is probably the best part of the Columbia Wheat Belt. The "Palouse" is a region of dark soil which was derived from volcanic ash and other deposits, and this region resembles the loess areas of the Mississippi Valley. The soil is fine in texture and rich in mineral plant foods. Settlement in this district began in the 1870's and the Snake River provided an outlet for the wheat to the Pacific Coast before the advent of the railroad. At first, cattle were important and large areas of the rougher land were used exclusively for pasture. The acreage of wheat was gradually extended with the introduction of the combine and other power machinery. Although some of the slopes are steep, the land is generally smooth enough for heavy combines. Frequent cultivation and the practice of burning the stubble have resulted in soil erosion and decreased yield especially on the steeper slopes. The highest yields are taken from the lower south-facing slopes, the lowest yields from the hilltops from which much of the soil has been washed.

Faced with decreased yield, many farmers have introduced conservation measures, although the average wheat farmer is reluctant to vary the traditional methods. Rotation of crops—clover hay, winter wheat, spring wheat, peas, winter wheat—is a common five-year plan which is increasingly practiced. More livestock are being introduced, thus interfering with the farmer's leisure but improving the quality of the farms.

From 6 per cent to 10 per cent of the wheat acreage of the United States is in the Columbia Wheat Belt. The production, ranging from 75 to 100 million bushels, is far more than is needed in the producing states. As a consequence, a larger proportion of the wheat is exported, either in the form of grain or flour, than from any other wheat belt of the country. The region is near the sea and much of the export is shipped via Portland (Oregon) and Seattle to California and the Orient, and to Europe via the Panama Canal. In general, most of the wheat is moved out via the Columbia River, but the larger proportion of flour is exported from Puget Sound. Flour mills are located at strategic points in and near the wheat belt. The chief centers are Seattle, Portland, Tacoma, and Spokane, and the lesser ones are Wenatchee, Cheney, Ritzville, Walla Walla, and Pendleton. Only the last three are within the boundaries of the Wheat Belt.

Oases

In many parts of the Columbia Wheat Belt and on its margins irrigation makes it possible not only to get higher yields of wheat but to grow fruit crops as well. In most of the larger oases such as the Okanagan, Wenatchee, Yakima, and Umatilla there is specialization in fruits and little or no attention is given to wheat. Apples are produced especially in the Wenatchee and Okanagan valleys, apples and pears in the Yakima Valley, while in other oases prunes, apricots, peaches, and cherries are produced in addition to apples. In the Yakima Valley there is a tendency for apples and pears to be concentrated in the upper valley where the summer nights are cool and the codling moth less prevalent. The lower valley is being planted in the "stone" fruits—peaches, plums, prunes, and cherries. Although most of the prunes of the Pacific Northwest come from the Willamette Valley, high-quality prunes, which are marketed either fresh or canned, are produced in the Walla Walla district. Smaller amounts are dried since the demand for dried prunes has declined.

The marketing of fruit is quite different from that of wheat, requiring the organization of many growers. Packing houses, cold storage plants, dehydrators, and canneries are located in the fruit districts, with the towns of Yakima, Wenatchee, and Walla Walla as outstanding examples.

THE UNITED STATES WHEAT SUPPLY

The United States is at the same time a large producer, an importer, and an exporter of wheat. All three of these items vary in amount and thus help to determine at any given time how much wheat is on hand in the country. In the first place, production varies widely, ranging from 630 to 1367 million bushels per year in recent years, grown on 50 to 80 million acres of land. Production depends on a number of circumstances such as the climate of the crop year and the acreage planted. Winter-killing or summer drought may cut the crop to half the expectations. Whether the crop is good or bad, hard wheat from Canada is imported to the United States for flour and, in some years, cheaper grades for stock feed. In any event, the import from Canada involves special qualities of wheat and does not indicate a general shortage in the United States. The total imports average about 10 millions of bushels, part of which is milled for export.

The consumption of wheat in the United States varies widely and depends on the supplies of other crops such as sugar and corn. The production of flour for domestic use, however, does not vary greatly. The per capita consumption of wheat for food, including flour, cereals, and other prepared foods, ranges from 150 to 160 pounds or about $2\frac{1}{2}$ bushels. As the population increases, a slight advance in gross consumption for food is to be noted. It is other uses, however, particularly for livestock feed and for the manufacture of alcohol, which vary. So long as sugar and corn are abundant, little wheat is used for feed or for alcohol unless the price is very low.

Exports depend on the size of the domestic crop, the amount of the carry-over, and the demand for wheat in the world market. Wheat is not produced in the United States at a low cost. When the world price of wheat is low, only subsidies will encourage the sale of much wheat abroad. In general, however, in the United States exports exceed imports by the amount of 300 million bushels or more.

13

The Wheat Belts of Argentina, Australia, and Russia

Oᴜᴛꜱɪᴅᴇ North America there are three countries —Argentina, Australia, and Russia—with sub- humid wheat belts and a surplus production of wheat. Wheat is exported from Argentina and Australia consistently, and these countries, to- gether with the United States and Canada, ac- count for most of the foreign trade in wheat. Rus- sian export is variable, partly as a result of wars and the aftermath of wars, partly because of the large home market for bread grains. Russians are potentially very large exporters, however, since their combined wheat belt in Europe and Asia is larger than that of any other country.

All the wheat belts are alike, fundamentally. The climate is subhumid, partly in the steppe (BS). The land is gently rolling or flat so that power machinery can be readily used, and the soil is fertile although less so than at the time of settlement. Farms are large and the population sparse. Each belt has distinctive qualities of its own. The Argentine Belt is similar to the Winter Wheat Belt of the United States except that the winters are milder and the wheat is nearer ocean transportation. The Australian Belt grows winter wheat also but under conditions more nearly com- parable to the Great Valley of California than to Kansas. The wheat grows continuously during the winter without a period of rest owing to cold weather. The Russian Wheat Belt resembles the Spring Wheat Belt of North America in some re- spects, but it is much older and has a more compli- cated production pattern. Crops are more diversi- fied, and the population is denser. Large deposits of coal, iron ore, and other minerals contribute to a substantial industrial economy within the con- fines of the wheat belt. This in turn reacts on the agriculture and in the Russian area many food crops, such as potatoes, sugar beets, and sunflow- ers, are produced in addition to wheat.

THE ARGENTINE WHEAT BELT

The Argentine Wheat Belt or Wheat Crescent (ꜰɪɢ. 13.1), as it is sometimes called, is an irregu- lar arc extending from southern Uruguay north- westward to Santa Fé, thence westward and southward to Bahia Blanca, and finally eastward along the southern margin of the Humid Pampa. On the western side the belt is limited by dryness, but on the eastern parts of the crescent, in south- ern Uruguay and eastern Argentina, the climate is humid. Inside the arc of the wheat belt is the compact Argentine Corn Belt and also a humid grazing region. The similarity to the Winter Wheat Belt of the United States is apparent. In both there are semiarid grazing regions to the west and mountains supplying water to irrigate some oases. In both there are humid corn belts to the east, and both are located on smooth plains.

The surface of the Argentine Pampa is well suited to the use of power machinery so necessary on the large wheat farm. The plain is uniformly level, sloping toward the east at about four feet per mile. This slope is too gentle to be perceived by the eye, and even the slight undulations of the surface are difficult to note. In a few places iso- lated mountains or ridges break the monotony of the plain, but such features are very rare in the wheat belt. The plain is covered with a thick de- posit of loose material which weathers into an excellent soil. Most of the surface material is fine sand, silt, or clay, which, in general, retains mois- ture well. Rocks and pebbles are not to be found in the Pampa soils as a rule. Some districts suffer from poor drainage, however. The surface is so

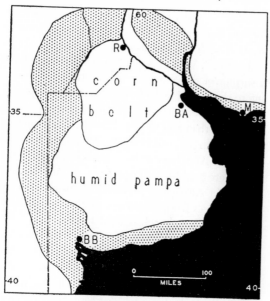

FIGURE 13.1. *Map of the Argentine Wheat Belt including a small part of Uruguay. The belt is in the form of a band bordering the Corn Belt and the Humid Pampa, in both of which wheat is also grown. Most of Argentina's export wheat moves out through four ports: Buenos Aires (BA); Bahia Blanca (BB); Montevideo (M); Rosario (R).*

smooth that few streams are to be found and most of the drainage is underground, except for a few large through-flowing streams like the Paraná and the Salado. During periods of heavy rains temporary lakes form in the shallow depressions, some of which are reed-filled and not suitable for farm land until drained. Because of the poor drainage and uneven rainfall, the soils of the Pampa are highly variable in character although generally of high quality.

The climate of the Argentine Wheat Crescent is transitional between the dry and humid climates. The western part is definitely semiarid or steppe. The eastern margins are subhumid to humid belonging to the Cfa type of the Köppen system. The winters are mild and the summers hot. Bahia Blanca, representative of the southern part of the Wheat Belt, has a temperature of 75° F. in the warmest month, January, and 48° F. in the coolest month, July. The annual rainfall is 21 inches, most of it being in summer (December, January, and February in the Southern Hemisphere), while June, July, and August are comparatively dry. In Montevideo on the eastern extremity of the belt there is 38 inches of rain quite evenly distributed through the year. In Rosario, near the northern part of the Wheat Belt but actually in the Corn Belt, there is an average annual precipitation of 33 inches. In general, the rainfall of the Wheat Belt ranges from less than 20 inches per year on the dry western margin to nearly 40 inches in the most humid localities. The heaviest wheat production is from the district with 20 to 25 inches of annual rainfall. In the northern part of the Wheat Belt the rainfall is fairly dependable, while on the southern and western margins severe droughts are likely to occur. The summer weather is variable. The *norte*, or north wind, brings hot humid weather with thunderstorms, while the *pampero*, which comes from the dry Pampa to the southwest, is cool and invigorating.

In the Argentine Wheat Belt some corn, alfalfa, flax, barley, and oats are produced, in addition to wheat. The total acreage of all of these crops averages over 40 millions, of which wheat represents about one third. Wheat fluctuates more in acreage than the other crops, but production averages above 200 million bushels. Much of the wheat is grown by tenant farmers who tend to increase the acreage when prices are high and to return the land to grazing when prices are low. Yields are also highly variable. The best yields in the Wheat Belt are to the west of Rosario, but as in other countries, the highest wheat yields are from the more humid regions. In the Argentine Corn Belt yields are high, but the total production is small. Yields of wheat decline to the south and west to five or six bushels to the acre on the dry margin. In the more favorable areas on the eastern margin of the belt, farmers grow corn, alfalfa, and flax instead of wheat. Most of the flax of Argentina is grown in the humid Corn Belt instead of in the Wheat Belt.

The methods used in growing and harvesting wheat are similar to those of North America but somewhat less advanced so far as the use of power machinery is concerned. This is a result, in part, of the system of land ownership and the high percentage of tenancy to be described on page 186. The plowing or disking is generally shallow, after which the seed is drilled in or sown broadcast and covered by harrows. In some districts seed is still inferior. The seeding season begins in May in the south and extends through

August in the north. From November through January, the grains are harvested by use of threshers and combines. The combine is best suited to the southern part of the belt where labor is scarce. The yields of wheat are slightly below those of the United States, averaging about 12 bushels to the acre. Poor seed, drought, frost, grasshoppers, and heavy rains at harvest time tend to decrease the yields. Once harvested, the wheat begins its journey to market in large carts or trucks. The costly transportation limits the distance of the wheat farm to about 25 to 50 miles from the nearest railroad. The wheat is transported in bags which are stacked near the railroads awaiting shipment. Elevators for the storage of wheat in the producing areas are few, but there are many large ones in the principal ports. The network of rail lines converging on Buenos Aires, Rosario, and Bahia Blanca handles most of the wheat. About two thirds of the wheat production in Argentina usually is exported, most of it being transported to Liverpool. Because of the nearness to the sea, the total cost of transportation is about ten cents less per bushel than it is from the interior wheat belts of North America.

The pattern of land ownership and farm operation is more like that of the United States Cotton Belt than other wheat belts. Much of the land is still in large estates, the owners of which are reluctant to sell any part. Here sharecroppers lease tracts of a few hundred acres and grow wheat on shares, the crop usually being divided evenly between the owner and tenant. The landlord furnishes machinery, implements, draft animals, and seed. Renters, unlike the sharecroppers, own their equipment, pay cash rentals, and take all the crop. Both the sharecropper and the renter are likely to grow nothing but wheat. The colonists, or independent farmers, own their land and equipment and are most numerous in the north. The wheat farmers are for the most part recent immigrants from Europe—Italians, Germans, French, and Swiss.

The larger estates of the Humid Pampa are especially slow to change over from ranching to grain farming. The owners are satisfied to retain them as large ranches with very little cultivation of crops. Some of the owners live in the United States or western Europe. There is some indication, however, of the increasing subdivision of the large estates by inheritance and sale. It is to be ex-

pected that in the Humid Pampa to the east of the Wheat Belt there will be an increasing crop production with less emphasis on ranching.

In World War II Argentina was found to have a surplus of wheat and a very limited market owing to the naval blockade and the lack of shipping. Heavy stocks accumulated. Accustomed to export more than 100 million bushels, Argentineans were required to utilize much of the crop for feed and fuel. About 60 million bushels of the 1943 crop were sold for fuel; about 18 million bushels for feed. Altogether domestic consumption of wheat ranges from 100 to 175 million bushels, depending on how much is used for fuel and feed. Since the average production is nearly 250 million bushels, a large amount is available for export and the carry-over is often as large as the crop. In Argentina there is a large area of humid pasture land which can be used for wheat with the result that production could be tripled readily if world demand justified.

THE AUSTRALIAN WHEAT BELTS

Wheat is the principal crop of Australia, occupying more than half the cultivated land. In reality there are two wheat belts located primarily between the 10- and 20-inch isohyets in the southern part of the continent. The larger belt extends from Streaky Bay, west of Adelaide, in an arc through Victoria north of Melbourne, to the northern border of New South Wales. See FIGURE 13.2. The other and lesser belt is in the southwestern part of Western Australia (See END PAPER 4). Perth, Albany, Adelaide, Melbourne, Sydney, and Brisbane are the principal export ports, but many smaller ones also are used.

Like the wheat belts of North America, the Australian regions are dependent on an irregular rainfall. Most of the rain comes in the winter, during the crop season. The rains begin in March and continue through the southern winter. Most of the wheat is sown in May or June and harvested in January. Yields vary greatly with the rainfall and, in general, are comparable to those in the United States, Canada, and Argentina.

The methods of cultivation vary slightly from those in the other wheat lands. Machine cultivation is used, but until recently horses furnished most of the power. A large proportion of the wheat is sacked for export, there being as yet comparatively few local elevators. Attempts have

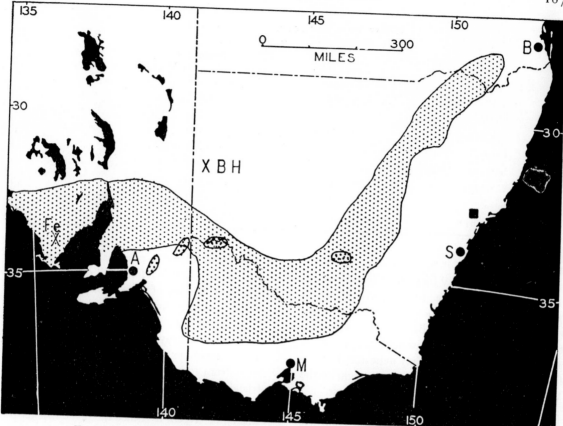

FIGURE 13.2. *Map of the main Australian Wheat Belt. This belt lies between the humid mountains on the east and the grazing lands to the west and north, and includes parts of Queensland, New South Wales, Victoria, and South Australia. The chief export ports are Brisbane (B), Sydney (S), Melbourne (M), and Adelaide (A). A few irrigated areas (indicated by heavy shading) occur in or near the Wheat Belt. Iron (Fe) is mined on the Eyres Peninsula and coal (black square) is produced in the vicinity of Newcastle to the north of Sydney. Silver, lead, and zinc are mined at Broken Hill (BH).*

been made to irrigate wheat on a large scale and thus increase the yield, but this requires much hand labor, which is not available in these thinly populated regions. Possibilities of extending the acreage are good. Using the best methods of dry farming and taking a calculated risk, Australian farmers could probably extend their acreage to four times the prewar area of about ten million acres.

The major wheat area is in the southern part of the great plain which extends across Australia from north to south. Its surface is somewhat like the Great Plains of the United States but at a lower elevation. The Wheat Belt which occupies the southern margin of the plain is principally in the drainage area of the Murray River. This river and its main tributaries, the Darling and the Lachlan, flow slowly across the alluvial plain. During the drier season the tributaries are merely strings of water holes, and even the Murray ceases to flow in the driest years. These rivers furnish some water for irrigation, however, and grapes, vegetables, and citrus fruits are produced. The soils are similar to those in the other wheat belts but have been formed under drier conditions. Black soils are found in some localities, especially in the old river channels. The red soil of other districts suggests the desert rather than the steppe.

The climate of the Australian Wheat Belt is drier than that of any other major wheat producing district. It is a steppe type adjacent to areas of the Mediterranean climate. Since both altitude

WHEAT ACREAGE OF LEADING COUNTRIES (1950)			
Country	Acreage (in millions of acres)	Production (in millions of bushels)	Average yield (in bushels per acre)
United States	61.7	1,026	16.5
Canada	27.0	461	17.0
Argentina	14.0	200	14.2
France	11.5	280	24.2
Italy	12.1	285	23.6
U.S.S.R.	107.0	1,110	10.4
India	24.0	231	9.7
Australia	11.7	183	15.6

and latitude, 27° to 37° S., are low, temperatures are therefore relatively high. In Adelaide on the southern margin of the belt the January average is 74° F. and the July average 51° F. In Broken Hill, to the north of the Wheat Belt, there is an average temperature of 78° F. in January, in spite of the 1000 foot elevation. As already indicated the rainfall is light, especially on the dry margin of the Wheat Belt, which is to the north and west.

In Western Australia the smaller wheat belt receives from 12 to 20 inches of rain annually, nearly all of it occurring in the growing season. Here a part of the area is brushland and must be cleared before cultivation can begin. Seeding begins in April and may extend into June. Harvest begins in December. A typical farm in this district comprises about 1000 acres, approximately one fourth of which is in wheat at any given time. The remainder is fallowed in accordance with usual dry-farming methods. After a field is harvested, probably in January, sheep are turned onto the stubble. During the following winter the land is plowed and harrowed to produce a fine mulch, after which it lies fallow for a year.

Altogether the Australian Wheat Belts exhibit several distinctive qualities as compared with the wheat lands of other continents. The average rainfall is lower. Fertilizers, especially superphosphate, are widely used although not in great quantities per acre. Draft animals and comparatively light machinery are still in use. Much of the transportation from the wheat farm to the railroad is still by wagon and cart. This limits the wheat farms to a distance of 20 to 50 miles from the rails. Increasing use of trucks extends this dis-

tance in some places to 75 miles or more, but large areas in the wheat belts are still used for grazing because of the lack of truck transport.

In recent years Australian production of wheat has increased from 150 to 200 million bushels per year, excepting only unusual years when the production was very high or very low. This crop comes from somewhat less than 12 million acres of land. Average yields are nearly 16 bushels to the acre, slightly less than in the United States, Canada, or Argentina. Since the home market for flour and other wheat products is limited to about eight million people, from 40 to 80 million bushels are exported, either in the form of flour or grain. Most of the export is sent to Great Britain, Egypt (where some wheat is grown), India, China, and the Netherlands East Indies. Domestic use includes flour, breakfast cereals, feed, and industrial alcohol. In some years more than 30 million bushels are used for feed. In this connection it should be remarked that little corn and alfalfa are produced in Australia, and that quantities of wheat are cut green for fodder.

THE RUSSIAN WHEAT BELT

The Wheat Belt of Russia (FIG. 13.3) is the largest of the commercial wheat regions. From the edge of the Carpathian Mountains it extends for 3000 miles eastward to Lake Baikal, and its width averages nearly 400 miles. This vast region in total area is almost as large as all the other wheat belts. In many ways, however, it differs from the wheat belts previously studied: wheat is only one of many crops, although the most impor-

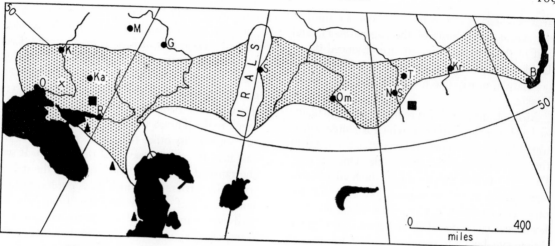

FIGURE 13.3. *The Russian Wheat Belt reaches from Odessa (O) on the north side of the Black Sea eastward to Lake Baikal (B), a distance of nearly 2000 miles. The belt is interrupted in the middle by the Ural Mountains. Odessa (O) and Rostov (R) are the only ports of importance, but other agricultural and industrial centers in or near the Wheat Belt include Kharkov (Ka), Kiev (K), Moscow (M), Gorki (G), Sverdlovsk (S), Omsk (Om), Novo-Sibirsk (NS), Tomsk (T), Krasnoyarsk (Kr). The Russian Wheat Belt, unlike those previously studied, has large and varied mineral resources and has already reached an advanced stage in industrialization.*

tant; the region is old agriculturally and has a fairly dense population; parts of it abound in minerals, some of which form the basis of a rather advanced industrialization.

The zone of surplus wheat production lies on the smooth steppes, the grassy plains (FIG. 13.4), and low plateaus of southern Russia. The climate, surface, and soil are suitable for small grains and, in some places, other crops, but not so favorable for the livestock industries of central Russia. The climate is semiarid in the south and more humid toward the north, so that the Wheat Belt extends into the dry margin of the humid continental climate (Dfb). Annual rainfall ranges from 10 inches on the southeast near the Caspian Sea to more than 25 inches on the northwestern margin, most of the rain coming in summer. Winter temperatures range from the mild Januarys of the Crimea (39° F.), a part of which has a Mediterranean climate, to the severe winter of the east with January averages near 0° F. The winters are severe enough, however, throughout the region so that spring wheat rather than winter wheat is grown in most districts. The summer temperatures are much more uniform, most of the stations having average July temperatures from 68° to 72° F.

The Black Earth or "chernozem" of this region is the type of black soils of the other wheat belts described previously. In the Russian Wheat Belt the soils have been cultivated for centuries without the use of much fertilizer and still they continue to produce but with decreased yields. Not all of the wheat is on the chernozem; in the south the wheat occurs on the chestnut brown soils with higher mineral content and less humus in regions of lighter rainfall.

The Black Earth Belt of Russia, extending from Odessa and Kiev on the west to the southern end of the Ural Mountains, is the oldest and most complex of the regions in which large quantities of surplus wheat are produced. See FIGURE 13.3. Perhaps its very age contributes to its diversity, but there are other factors, such as the abundant mineral resources, access to the sea, and the effect of the various five-year plans which Russia has executed. A preliminary glance at a map of the region shows no outstanding physical qualities as compared with the other wheat belts. It lies on the border of the steppe and the humid lands. The soil is black to dark gray, high in mineral content but not too high.

Although only a small part of the total land

area in Russia is in this region, about one third of
the wheat, two thirds of the sugar (beet), and
half of the coal and iron ore are produced there.
Unlike most wheat regions there is a fairly dense
population, nearly one fourth of the people of all
Russia.

Most of the land in this region is either in plains
or level plateaus, either of which is suited to the
use of heavy machinery. Between the segments of
the plateaus there are rivers—the Dnestr, Bug,
Dnepr, Don, and Volga—all of which are of some
significance in the transportation of grain and
other commodities. For centuries wheat and barley have been produced in this region. Now, in addition, rye, buckwheat, sugar beets, potatoes, and
forage crops are also raised. There are more cattle, sheep, and hogs in this wheat region than in
any other in the world. Even some corn is grown
in the western part, and cotton has been introduced into the southern part of the region. This is
the most mechanized part of the Russian agricultural country and the first where farming has been
developed on a large scale with the use of heavy
machinery.

Largely because of the Black Earth Belt, Russians have nearly 100,000,000 acres in wheat.
Russia is therefore the leading country in wheat
acreage, with a production of 1500 million bushels. In addition, rye, barley, and oats are grown in
the wheat region. Rye and oats are produced
mainly on the poorer soils of the northern fringe
where the yields are better than those of wheat.
Barley is grown near the Black Sea in the drier
districts and on the fringes of the mountains. Although some barley is used for food, most of the
crop is used for industrial purposes. Millet is
grown in the drier regions of the southeast. Corn,
requiring a longer growing season, is produced in
quantity only in the southwestern part of the
Ukraine near Odessa. Rice has been introduced to
the shores of the Black Sea and the northern
fringe of the Caucasus, and cotton is also of some
importance in this region. The sugar beet reaches
its greatest importance in the vicinity of Kursk,
but it is also grown in the marginal regions of the
south. Other crops include flax, potatoes, sunflowers, soybeans, and various grain sorghums.

Interrupted by the Ural Mountains, the Russian Wheat Belt continues into western Siberia
(FIG. 13.3) Here agricultural conditions are more
like those in the wheat belts of other lands. It is a
comparatively new area; the Russians call it the
"pioneer agricultural region." Yet it is older
than the wheat belt of Kansas or Australia. Even
before the advent of the railroad Russian settlers
began to move into this region. Early travel was
mostly by river. It is a fairly easy matter to go up
the Kama, a tributary of the Volga, and "portage" to the Tura, a tributary of the Ob. The Ob
and some of its other tributaries reach far to the
east near the upper reaches of the Yenisei. It was
the railroad, however, which brought the majority of the settlers and which takes out most of the
wheat. A half century ago the Trans-Siberian
Railway, which provides year-round east-west
transportation, was built through the heart of this
region. On the main courses of the rivers, goods
are carried north and south, and by this means
wheat and other commodities are fed to the railway.

The West Siberian Wheat Belt is a very level
region, most of which lies below 1000 feet. From
the Urals to the Yenisei there is scarcely a hill,
but east of the river the land becomes rougher and
the wheat belt narrows. The climate is the most
severe of any of the wheat belts. From October
to April the temperatures are below freezing;
very severe winter weather is experienced. The
summers are rather cool (the July average at
Tomsk is 64° F.) and very short. Some uncomfortably hot days may be experienced, however.
Most of the rain comes in summer and therefore
falls on the crops. Precipitation varies from 12 to
18 inches annually. Since the temperatures are
low, the effectiveness of the rain is high. Snowfall
is light but sometimes drifts enough to block the
roads and the railway.

The chief crop is spring wheat, but lesser
amounts of oats, barley, rye, hay, potatoes, and
sunflowers are grown. At nearly every railway
station, there are large elevators, and at the larger
towns, such as Omsk, Novo-Sibirsk, Tomsk, and
Krasnoyarsk, there are flour mills. Livestock is of
more significance than in most wheat areas, and
meat and butter are exported to western Russia.

Export and Consumption of Russian Wheat

As in the United States, there is in Russia a
large local demand for the wheat crop. The 200
million Russians are large bread eaters and are,
therefore, capable of absorbing a large part of the
wheat and rye from nearly 180 million acres. In-

FIGURE 13.4. *Farm workers harvesting wheat in Russia in the shadow of the Caucasus Mountains. From Keystone.*

formation on Russian grain production in recent years is scanty, but it appears that production is again approaching the prewar volume. Enough wheat can be produced in the Russian Wheat Belt to supply the growing Russian population and also to provide more wheat for export than any other country. It seems likely that all forms of production in Russia will expand, once the worst effects of World War II have been overcome. At the same time it is probable that a larger proportion of the cropland will be devoted to hay and forage crops for the feeding of livestock in connection with meat and milk production, both of which have always been very low in Russia on a per capita basis.

Minerals and Industries

Agriculture is only one part of the production in the Wheat Belt of southern Russia; coal, iron, and oil form the basis of large-scale industry. This explains the density of population, which is far higher than that of the other wheat belts. The most important mineral deposits are the coal of the Donetz Basin within the great bend of the lower Don River, the iron ore of Krivoi Rog in the great bend of the Dnepr, and the oilfields north of the Caucasus.

In the basin of the lower Don (Donbas, the Russians call it) the wheat grows on the smooth plateaus as in other parts of the belt. Beneath the surface are excellent coal, limestone, salt, and glass sands, which form the basis of industries more important locally than the wheat. The coal lies between Kharkov and Rostov on the inside and to the west of the great bend of the Don River, about 60 miles north of the Sea of Azov. There are hundreds of mines, some shallow, some deep, producing more coal than any other coal

FIGURE 13.5. *A view of Kislovodsk in the foothills of the Caucasus. This city is an important commercial center for the grain lands in the vicinity. From "Sovfoto."*

district in Russia, exceeded only by the Pittsburgh and Ruhr regions. Much of the coal is made into coke for the steel mills. The coke, together with the local limestones, dolomites, and the iron ore from Krivoi Rog, makes this Russia's best metallurgical region. On the basis of the steel production a large-scale machine tool industry grew up, and locomotives, railroad cars, and steel rails are made to supply Russia's growing railroad system. Oil is transported to this region by pipeline from the Caucasus Field, the nearest part of which is about 250 miles distant. The Donbas is the industrial center of South Russia, and the Caucasus, Krivoi Rog, and even parts of the lower Volga are tributary to it.

Krivoi Rog, principal iron ore district of southern Russia, lies on the bend of the lower Dnepr, 300 miles west of the Donbas. Quantities of high-grade iron ore, more than all produced in the rest of Russia combined, are mined. Although, as is usual, most of the iron ore is sent to the coal region some of the coal from the Donbas is transported to the Krivoi Rog region to be used in smelting the iron ore. In this same general area, at Nikopol, are large deposits of manganese sufficient to supply the needs of the metallurgical industries of southern Russia and some for export. Including the deposits south of the Caucasus, the largest deposits of high-grade manganese in the world are in Russia.

The Dnepr River, like the lower Don, is used for the transportation of coal, iron ore, and other goods, but it is also of great potential importance as a source of power. In 1932 a huge dam, forming a large reservoir and producing 550,000 kilowatts of power, was constructed in the rapids of the river below Dnepropetrovsk. This dam was destroyed by the Russians on their retreat from the Ukraine in the summer of 1941. Rebuilt after the war, this dam furnishes power to an electric railroad and to factories which produce aluminum, manganese, and many metal products.

A large part of the oil industry of Russia lies in this southern region on the north and south slopes of the Caucasus and in the middle Volga region near Kuibishev. Of all the oil regions the Caucasus is the most important. Although oil is found all along the northern margin of the Caucasus, the most productive district is on the eastern end in the vicinity of Baku, especially on the Apsheron Peninsula where many gushers have been

FIGURE 13.6. *Wheat harvest on a collective farm in the Russian Wheat Belt. The land here is rolling, well drained, and productive. From "Sovfoto."*

brought in. Some of the wells have been drilled in the edge of the Caspian Sea. The production of oil was first begun in the Baku region, and at one time the amount produced there was nearly as great as that produced in the United States. Production declined after 1901, but was rejuvenated by the drilling of deeper wells. The Baku district is now only one of many oilfields in the U.S.S.R. From it, however, oil may be taken cheaply by tanker on the Caspian Sea and the Volga to the heart of eastern European Russia. Pipelines, next cheapest form of transportation, lead to Rostov and the Donbas industrial district. A pipeline, running south of the Caucasus, takes oil to Batum on the Black Sea. From Batum it may be shipped by tanker to western Europe. In consideration of the fact that only in one other European country, Romania, is natural petroleum produced in any quantity, the strategic importance of the Caucasus Field may be realized. Oil is not the only product of this region; salt, borax, and various agricultural products, including wheat and wine, are of significance.

CHAPTER

14

The Mediterranean Lands of Europe, Asia, and North Africa

INTERMEDIATE in character between the dry lands to the south and the humid regions to the north, the maritime mountain-fringed Mediterranean lands of the Old World extend from Portugal and Morocco on the west to Turkey and Palestine on the east. See FIGURE 14.1. To the south are the spacious Sahara of northern Africa and the deserts and steppes of Arabia. To the north lies humid middle Europe with summer rain and winter snow, too cold in winter for agriculture and even too cool in summer for many of the crops which grow in the Mediterranean lands. In the New World other similar lands are found in middle and southern California, middle Chile, the Cape district of South Africa, and parts of southwestern and southeastern Australia. Only in the Old World, however, in southern Europe, northwestern Africa, and southwestern Asia does this type of production include large areas of land. Only here have many diverse peoples modified

and adapted the landscape to their needs through the slow march of the centuries. This is the parent region, the cultural hearthstone of all the Mediterranean lands. From it the other lands have drawn their people, products, and peculiar techniques of making a living. Although the products of the various Mediterranean regions differ in many ways, all have certain fundamental qualities in common and it is appropriate that they be studied together.

The feature which distinguishes the Mediterranean lands, as a whole, is the climate (Cs). In winter the climatic conditions of the northerly humid lands swing southward, bringing variable winds and recurring rains, and then mild temperatures, generally above freezing, prevail. In summer the climatic pattern of the desert is projected northward over the Mediterranean. The winds are usually from the south, and temperatures are high except near the sea. The vegetation, except for the evergreen trees and shrubs, is parched and brown. The length of the rainy and dry seasons varies with latitude and the situation with respect to the mountains and the sea. Near the humid regions the rainy season is long, but adjacent to the dry areas the long rainless summer may last seven or eight months. In Barcelona and Marseille there are long rainy seasons and short dry seasons, while in Alexandria and Tripoli in North Africa there are seven months of drought. Similarly, Casablanca is drier than Lisbon, and Tunis is drier than Rome.

There are also strong local variations in climate: near the coast the summers are usually cool and sometimes foggy; a few miles inland high

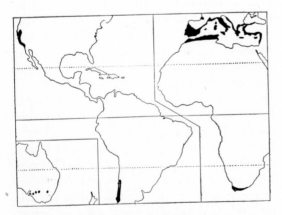

FIGURE 14.1. *The Mediterranean Lands.*

summer temperatures are the rule at low elevations. Precipitation varies locally, particularly with exposure. One side of a mountain in the path of the rain-bearing winds may be quite humid while the other side is very dry. Particularly significant from the standpoint of certain crops, such as the olive and citrus fruits, is the occurrence of frost. Except in localities near the sea, there is a strong possibility that frost may damage the trees. The deciduous fruits, the olive, and the grape can endure some frost and therefore have a wider distribution. In the areas of frost hazard, a site with a gentle slope is favorable because of the good air drainage. During a cold winter night, the colder, heavier air tends to settle in the valleys and other depressions, accompanied by frost. On the slopes, in the meantime, the movement of the air reduces the frost hazard.

The mountainous character of the Mediterranean lands in part compensates for the dry season. The streams from the high mountains, fed by the melting snows of spring and early summer, are the lifeblood of the plains as they provide water for irrigation. In Europe it is the Sierra Nevada, Pyrenees, Alps, Apennines, and the various Balkan ranges which provide water for this purpose. In Africa the Atlas Mountains and in Asia the coast ranges of Syria and Palestine and the upturned margins of the Anatolian Plateau perform the same function, although on the whole less effectively. The mountains collect moisture during the winter partly in the form of snow. The snow melts through the spring and summer, releasing water to the valleys and basins below, which otherwise would be sterile. A lofty, extensive range of mountains with its flanks well exposed to the rain-bearing winds provides more water than a low range with its axis parallel to the wind. Usually only the windward side of a mountain provides much water, while the other flank, in the "rain shadow," is dry and sterile. The lower slopes of the mountains themselves may be terraced and put into cultivation, but the middle and upper slopes are too steep and too cool for most crops.

NATURAL VEGETATION

Depending on the amount of moisture available, there are three general types of natural vegetation in the Mediterranean lands: forest, brush, and grassland. All types are adapted to endure the pronounced dry season which comes at the warmest time of the year. Forests have a limited extent today because of the activities of man in clearing the land to get timber and to make room for agriculture. In the more moist localities, however, large trees, such as evergreen oaks, grow in luxuriant stands. With intermediate moisture conditions, a brush type of vegetation, known as the *maquis* (*chaparral* in California), is likely to be dominant. This type of vegetation gave its name to a famous underground organization in France during World War II. In still drier locations grasses are common, furnishing green pasturage in winter, but dry and brown in summer. Various mixtures of the three types may be found. A parklike landscape with scattered trees and grass is common. One slope of a ridge may be covered with grass, the other with brush, depending on exposure to the rain and sun. Most of the trees and shrubs are evergreen; for example, the live oak, the laurel, and a variety of woody shrubs. The leaves are usually small and leathery so that the loss of plant moisture by evaporation is reduced to a minimum. Aromatic gums and thick bark (e.g., the cork oak) also conserve moisture. The natural vegetation of the Mediterranean lands has been profoundly modified by man. Forests have been cut over repeatedly, brush has been burned, and the natural grasses replaced by cultivated varieties.

AGRICULTURE

Agriculture in the Mediterranean lands is primarily conditioned by climate. The strong seasonal contrast in moisture and the moderate temperature ranges are advantageous and delightful for outdoor activity, but nevertheless impose serious handicaps on the farmer. The long drought comes in the warm season, ordinarily the most favorable time of the year for the growth of crops. Several choices face the farmer, depending on local conditions. He can usually grow wheat, barley, legumes, and some forage crops in winter without irrigation because of the low temperatures and high rainfall. Certain tree crops—olives and, in certain localities, citrus fruits—may be grown without summer irrigation although additional water is an advantage. Grapevines thrive in the hot summer, and most of the world's wine is produced in Mediterranean lands. Where water is available for summer irrigation, a great variety of crops, including all types of vegetables and many kinds of fruit such as figs, peaches, and apricots, may be grown. Crops like sugarcane and cotton, however, are of little significance largely because other crops yield higher returns. Corn is not commonly grown for the same reason. Under exceptional conditions, however, all three of these crops are to be found. Sugarcane grows in southern Spain, a fairly large acreage of corn in Mediterranean Italy, and cotton in Turkey, Syria, and Palestine.

According to acreage, wheat is the most important crop of the Old World Mediterranean lands, for this most valuable bread grain is well adapted for growth in the cool season. It is sown in the autumn in order to take advantage of the largest part of the year's rainfall. Growth is slow but continuous, and ripening occurs before the severe dryness of summer is well advanced. Barley is also grown widely, although in many places it has been replaced by wheat. Barley is used for food, for feed, and in the manufacture of beverages. Both wheat and barley are well adapted to the dry margin of agriculture as indicated earlier in Chapters 12 and 13. In the Mediterranean lands conditions are less favorable for oats and rye, which require more moisture.

Olives are in many respects the most characteristic and distinctive crop of the Mediterranean Agriculture. They are evergreen, require little water, and are not even tolerant of summer rain. They are commonly grown in all the Mediterranean lands and rarely in any other regions. Growth is best on limestone lands near the sea, a similar situation to that found in the olive's original home in Syria and Greece. The growth period is long, the flowers appearing in early spring and the fruit ripening in early winter. The harvest is usually continued throughout the winter. Large quantities of oil, which is at the same time the "butter" and "lard" of the Mediterranean lands, are pressed from olives. This substitute is very significant in view of the scarcity of pasture and the difficulty of stock raising. Olive oil makes a unique contribution to the diet. It is used extensively with green salads and is particularly welcome to a fare which includes little meat or milk.

Grapes, too, have a unique place in the crop system of the Mediterranean lands. In the regions of long summer drought, palatable drinking water is difficult to find and a rather obvious substitute is grape juice. Wild yeasts convert most of the sugar in the grape juice to alcohol. For many centuries the important cultivation of grapevines has been in the summer-dry lands: in Italy, France, Spain, Greece, and later in California, Chile, and Cape Province. In the first four countries grapevines are grown largely without irrigation; in the newer areas irrigation is common.

The citrus fruits—oranges, lemons, limes, and citrons—are widely distributed in the Mediterranean lands although sweet oranges were not introduced from China to Europe until the 15th century, and much later to the other regions. The citrus fruits require large quantities of rain or irrigation water and much care, and have succeeded in the Mediterranean lands only as commercial crops and only in comparatively recent times. The distribution of these fruits in the Mediterranean lands is limited rather sharply by the hazard of frost. The trees cannot endure severe frost for more than a few hours at a time. Oranges are grown in many other climates and in many situations, but the Mediterranean lands are first in importance.

A brief study of the Mediterranean lands shows their striking similarity. A closer study with a comparison of distinct regions reveals the contrasts and differences. All have a similar climate with winter rains and summer drought; most have the mountainous fringe which is so essential. In general, the fundamental qualities of the Mediterranean Agriculture described on pages 194 to 195 apply to all the cultivated lands bordering the Mediterranean Sea. All areas grow winter grains, principally wheat and barley; olives, grapes, citrus fruits, legumes, and vegetables are also widely distributed. The regional differentiation is to be found largely in the varying proportion of these basic crops, in the different methods of production, in the nature of the minor crops such as cotton, tobacco, and the poppy, and in the value of the mineral deposits. Distance to large markets and the nature of the surrounding regions also play an important role. Syria and Algeria, for example, are all but surrounded by arid lands and are inhabited by nomadic peoples with a limited capacity to absorb surplus agricultural products. On the other hand, southern France is part of a compact and productive country with a large domestic market for wine, olives, and citrus fruits. Only the study of the individual districts of the Mediterranean lands can bring out their unique qualities. Some of the outstanding characteristics of the various Mediterranean lands are indicated in the following descriptions.

NORTHWEST AFRICA

In recent years much attention has been focused on Northwest Africa (FIG. 14.2), a region little known to Americans prior to World War II. Although appearing on the map as a rather small part of the huge continent of Africa, it is in reality a large and significant region, very closely related to southern and western Europe. From the western part of Morocco on the Atlantic Ocean to Tunis on the Mediterranean, the airline distance is about 1500 miles, as far as from New York to Dallas, or from Minneapolis to Miami. Northwest Africa includes the northern parts of the Barbary States, French Morocco, Spanish Morocco, Algeria, and Tunisia. Excluding the vast desert portions, Morocco is still as large as Montana, and Algeria is almost as large as Texas. Tunisia and Spanish Morocco are much smaller. This long, narrow region is the only significant part of northern Africa which has adequate rainfall for agriculture.

Of the 21 million people in Northwest Africa 2 million are of European origin—French, Italian, and Spanish. The rest are natives. The largest native group is the Berbers, a name going back to Roman times, meaning "barbarians," "strangers" or, referring to their attempts to speak Latin, "stutterers." Naturally these people never called themselves "barbarians." They used the name "Imaziren." The other native group is the Arabs, who came into North Africa in the sixth century bringing with them the tent, camel, and many new ideas and customs. Of greatest importance were the methods of irrigation and the new crops which were introduced into North Africa and also into Spain and Portugal.

In terms of products and resources North Africa is primarily an agricultural land, having a variety of crops including cereals, grapes, olives, citrus fruits, and various minor crops. Cereals, especially barley and wheat, are the most important according to acreage, and there is usually a surplus available for export. The acreage devoted to cereals includes 7 million in Algeria, 7 million in Morocco, and 2½ million in Tunisia.

Barley is generally more important than wheat because it grows better in the drier districts. It is eaten in large quantities by the natives, both as a green vegetable and as a grain. The native farmers grow most of the barley and hard wheat, while the European farmers grow soft wheat. Other field crops include corn, oats, sorghum, beans, tobacco, flax, silk, sugar beets, and some cotton.

From the commercial export point of view, grapes are the most important crop in North Africa. Vineyards exceed one million acres and large quantities of wine are exported to Europe, mostly to France. The French are very large producers of wine but are also large consumers, and by importing ordinary wines from North Africa they are able to export some of their more expensive wines. Most of the vineyards in North Africa are along the coast, not more than ten miles from the sea. The industry is highly organized and is characterized by the most modern methods and equipment.

Tree crops such as olives and various citrus fruits are well distributed throughout the coastal districts, but in few places are they as important as grapes. Olive trees are best developed along the east coast of Tunisia and northern Algeria. Most of the large olive groves are near the cities and towns and are managed by Europeans. The tree thrives on the low hills of all the coastal belt. The best olives and the best oil come from the vicinity of Sfax, Tunisia, where the European population is dominantly Italian. Much of the oil is sent to Italy and France in the crude form for refining and marketing. Oranges and tangerines are the most important citrus fruits, grown largely in the coastal zone, in the alluvial valleys and basins which can be irrigated.

Most of the crops introduced into North Africa in the last century, such as tobacco, sugar beets, flax, and cotton, are still on trial. The old reliable staples—wheat, barley, olives, and grapes—which are well adapted to the region, remain.

Livestock is important in North Africa in spite of somewhat unfavorable conditions such as the dry summers. Beef and dairy cattle, horses, camels, and mules are the most valuable. The animals are used more for work than for meat. Hogs are scarce, because most of the natives are Mohammedans, who for reasons of religion avoid pork. The drier parts of the country are best adapted to sheep, of which there are 15 million, and goats,

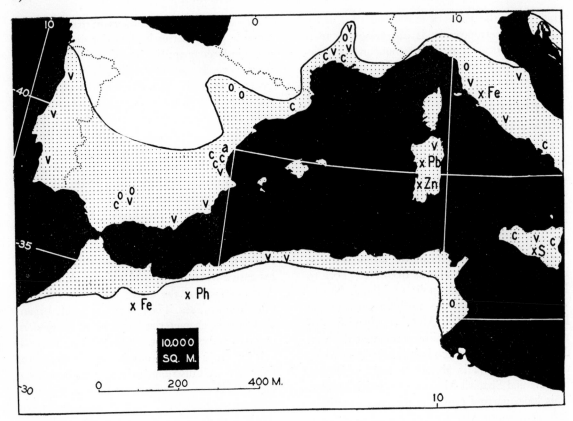

of which there are nearly 10 million. Some of the livestock, especially the sheep, goats, and camels, are found on the desert margins, but most of the animals like most of the people are near the coast.

The forests of North Africa, which cover more than 12 million acres, are not extensive for so large a region. Forest products include pine, useful for building, and cork oaks, which grow near the coast. There are two main zones of the cork, one on the border of Algeria and Tunisia, the other in Morocco. Whatever cork is obtained in North Africa can be readily marketed in the United States.

Minerals

Minerals are important in North Africa, but because of limited transportation facilities they have not been fully exploited. There were some 200 mineral concessions before World War II producing large quantities of phosphate and iron ore and lesser amounts of zinc, lead, copper, antimony, tin, and molybdenum. Most of the minerals are exported as raw ores without smelting or refining. Phosphate, the leading mineral, is mined extensively in Tunisia west of Sfax and Gabés, as well as in western Morocco. The reserves are enormous and the quality is high. More phosphate has been produced in North Africa than in the United States in most years since 1928. Most of the phosphate is used for fertilizer, and since more fertilizer is used in Europe than anywhere else in the world, North African phosphate can easily be sold because of its nearness to the market. High-grade iron ore is mined in Algeria, Spanish Morocco, and French Morocco (especially near Algiers, Oran, and Mellila). Most of it ordinarily is exported to England. North African ore is highly valued because of the high iron content and the relative freedom from troublesome impurities.

In addition to phosphate and iron ore, a variety of other minerals in small quantities are produced in North Africa. Increased production at many places depends on the building of more rail lines and highways. Zinc and lead, which often occur together, are next in importance after iron ore and phosphate. Most of the production is in

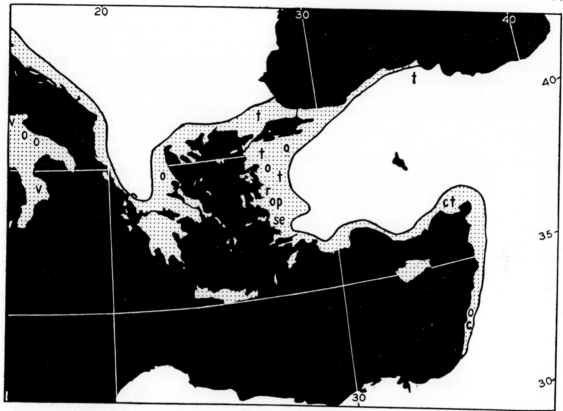

FIGURE 14.2. *The Mediterranean Lands of Europe, Africa, and Asia. The shaded area indicates the area of dominant Mediterranean Agriculture on the fringes of the Mediterranean and Black seas. Districts of crop specialty are indicated by letters: a, almonds; c, citrus fruits; ct, cotton; o, olives; op, opium; r, raisins; se, sesame; t, tobacco; v, vine. This region is not rich in minerals, but deposits of iron (Fe) and phosphate (Ph) occur in North Africa. Lead (Pb) and zinc (Zn) occur in Sardinia and sulfur (S) in Sicily.*

northwestern Tunisia. Other minerals include copper, which awaits larger exploitation, and manganese, which occurs in sufficient quantity to justify the construction of a railroad more than one hundred miles southward from Ouidah in the vicinity of Oran. Small quantities of molybdenum, tin, cobalt, and antimony are mined.

It is unfortunate in view of the variety of resources of North Africa that there is so little coal and petroleum. Although some coal is mined in eastern Morocco and on the Saharan side of the Atlas Mountains in Algeria, it has been little more than enough to supply the railroads. Some promising new fields in Morocco are awaiting railroad construction and the development of the mines. Petroleum is scarce, too, although there are some likely fields in French Morocco along

the border of Spanish Morocco. Some oil has been produced in the vicinity of Bizerte in Tunisia.

MEDITERRANEAN ASIA

The coastal plain of Syria and Israel and the coastal margin of Turkey were part of the cradle of Mediterranean culture. See FIGURE 14.2. In ancient times nomadic pastoral peoples came out of the deserts of the east and fixed their abode in this land which "flowed with milk and honey." Formerly, they had depended almost entirely on grazing animals, with occasional crops of barley if the rains of a particular season happened to be greater than normal, but the pattern of existence gradually changed. The moderate winter rains of the new environment made it possible to grow barley and (later) wheat every season. Additional water for irrigation permitted the cultivation of grapevines, dates, and olives according to methods used in the desert oases. With both summer and winter crops in production, it was inevitable that grazing animals should decline in relative importance and that the people should turn their major efforts toward an intensive form of agriculture later known as the Mediterranean type.

So desirable was this coastal fringe that horde after horde overran it, some coveting the fertile land, others bent on pillage, still others merely resisting the encroachment of the Mediterranean culture on the grazing lands. Phoenicians, Assyrians, Jews, Arabs, Persians, Mongols, Tartars, Romans, and Turks in turn conquered the land. Once established, the essential culture of the region was never disturbed more than temporarily. Small grain cropping in the rainy winters and irrigated tree and bush crops in all seasons have persisted throughout recorded history.

Four hundred miles long and, on the average, 25 miles wide, the Mediterranean portion of Syria and Israel lies on the coastal plain and the lower slopes of the adjoining mountains. The plain is wide in the south, but at its northern end the mountains are close to the sea and thus limit the amount of arable land. In addition to the coastal plain proper, there are numerous broad valleys extending back into the coastal ranges and offering excellent sites for intensive cultivation. The mountains are of moderate elevation, usually 3000 to 6000 feet, but in places extend above 10,000 feet. The significance of the mountains to the plain is difficult to overestimate. If it were not for the rain and snow on the mountain slopes, irrigation would not be possible on the plain.

The climate of the coastal region is a dry and warm variation of the Mediterranean type. The average temperature of the warmest month along the coast is about 82° F., and the coldest month about 52° F. There is little variation from north to south. The rainfall, however, diminishes gradually toward the south. In Beyrouth there is 35 inches annually, in Haifa 27, and in Gaza 16. However, the amount of rainfall is less important than the area of arable land and the quantity of water available for irrigation. The water supply comes from diverted mountain streams, from springs on the margins of the mountains, and from wells on the plain.

In selected parts of the narrow coastal plain and the adjacent valleys, a suitable soil and a supply of water set the stage for a characteristic Mediterranean Agriculture. Wheat and barley are the most important crops from the standpoint of acreage. Corn, introduced from America in recent times, is grown with some success in spite of the summer drought. Of the tree and bush crops, the grapevines and mulberries are most important, but oranges and many kinds of deciduous fruits are also produced. In the vicinity of the towns and villages, tree and bush crops are dominant. Groves of oranges and olives, and vineyards cover the plain and climb the lower slopes of the hills. In the more remote localities the small grains cover nearly all the arable land. In Syria and Israel agriculture is of first importance, while grazing is secondary. Mining and manufacturing are only slightly developed.

Although the basic crop systems of the two countries are similar, the export surplus of Israel differs from that of Syria. Oranges, grapefruit, soap, wines, and olive oil are exported from Israel. Cotton, wool, silk, and fruit are exported from Syria. It is worthy of note that large quantities of grain, flour, and other foodstuffs are imported to both of these countries, in spite of the large acreage devoted to cereals at home.

It is interesting that the ancient land of Israel, one of the oldest of the Mediterranean regions, should be colonized in modern times by Jews. Since 1870 there has been a steadily increasing stream of Jewish immigrants from eastern Europe to the vicinity of Jaffa, in the plains of Jezreal and Sharon. At the close of World War I there were scarcely 50,000 Jews in Palestine and most of these were in the cities. By 1951 there were 560,000, and as a consequence of this influx all of the coastal plain has begun to fill with Jewish agriculturists. Most of the immigrants came from eastern Europe, especially Poland and Russia. In recent years many have also come from Germany and Austria. These newly made farmers are growing crops characteristic of the region—grain, olives, fruits, and grapes. In addition, there is a vigorous development of dairying and the livestock industries, accompanied by the production of forage crops. This immigration of Europeans, aside from its political aspects, has changed the whole production pattern of Israel in a very few years.

The Europeans who are settling in Israel have great plans for the country. They hope to make it a "land of milk and honey" in a very modern way. Further expansion of agriculture depends on the water supply. Israel has a "JVA," Jordan Valley Authority very similar to the TVA of the United States. The plan calls for the utilization of the waters of the Jordan River to irrigate the plains along the river itself and along the coast. This is no ordinary water supply situation. The Jordan flows through a "rift" valley or huge trench which, at the Dead Sea, is 1290 feet below sea level. Thus it is no simple matter to get the water from the lower course of the Jordan up to the plains on the coast. The easiest way would be to divert the water before it enters the Sea of Galilee. However, this would eliminate the use of the Sea of Galilee as a fresh water reservoir. It would also reduce the power which can be produced if the water is allowed to drop all the way to the Dead Sea. According to the plan a great canal will take part of the water from the upper Jordan to the coast plains. Then, to prevent the Dead Sea from drying up, water will be pumped from the Mediterranean over the divide and allowed to drop into the lower Jordan and thence into the Dead Sea, thus furnishing additional hydroelectric energy. The immigration of Europeans with capital and technical skill may, in the course of time, change the whole pattern of production in Israel, which for centuries has been run-down, static, and even decadent.

Turkey is a peninsula of Asia thrust into the European sphere of influence. Asiatic in race and in certain aspects of its culture, Turkey has closer economic and political ties with Europe, and its products resemble those of Spain and Italy more than those of Iran and India. Like Syria and Israel, this coastal fringe of Asia Minor stands at the great crossroads between Central Europe and Asia, between eastern Europe and Africa. World War I had a far-reaching effect on Turkey. Much of her territory was lost, both in Asia and Europe, while the old regime was destroyed and a new country began to appear. Under the leadership of Kemal Pasha, efforts were made to change the customs of the people, to abolish the fez and the veil, and at the same time to reorganize the production of the country. Agricultural machinery was imported, new factories established, mining stimulated, and the transportation systems improved. In the last two decades progress has been rapid, and today, more definitely than ever before, Turkey faces west.

Modern Turkey has an area of about 300,000 square miles (larger than Texas) with a population of 20 million, of which about 12 million live on the Asiatic side of the Bosporus and Dardanelles. Asiatic Turkey is a plateau with a narrow, irregular coastal lowland on the outer fringe. The average elevation is about 2500 feet with higher summits on the rims of lofty mountains in the east. The western part of Asia Minor may be compared to a very irregular saucer, resting on a slightly larger disk. To reach the coast from the interior of the plateau it is necessary to climb the rim or pass down through a gap made by a stream. It is in the coastal belt that most of the people live. In the interior the land is less productive, although some mohair, wool, and grain are produced in a nomadic herding economy.

In Mediterranean Turkey (FIG. 14.2) there is a great variation in surface, rainfall, and opportunity for production. The rainiest portion is near the Black Sea and the Russian border, where more than 35 inches fall annually, some of it during the summer months. There is somewhat less rainfall on the western coast and the southern margin is driest, receiving less than 20 inches per year in some localities. The temperatures also show strong contrasts. Along the Black Sea the January average is 43° F. (Trebizond); in August, the warmest month, the average temperature is 74° F. and the absolute maximum is 97° F. On the mountains back from the sea the winter temperatures are much lower, part of the precipitation occurs in the form of snow, and there are occasional severe cold waves. The temperatures along the south coast are slightly higher in winter and much higher in summer. At Adana there is a 50° F. average for January, an 83° F. average for July, and an absolute maximum of 113° F.

Turkey is an agricultural country with most of the cultivated land located in the coastal plains and in the adjoining valleys. The small grains— wheat, barley, and oats—have the largest acreage and are produced in characteristic Mediterranean fashion. Other important crops include tobacco, opium, olives, figs, raisins, nuts, silk, cotton, rice, and sugar beets. In maritime Turkey, unlike many Mediterranean regions, large quantities of citrus fruits are not produced, nor are olives of more than domestic importance. In Turkey there are large numbers of livestock, sheep, goats, cattle, donkeys, horses, and camels, a large portion of which graze in the semiarid interior of the country.

The climate of the northern coast of Turkey is favorable to the growth of most of the Mediterranean crops on a commercial basis, excepting only the citrus fruits. After the small grains, which are staples, corn and tobacco are the most important crops. It is worth noting that both crops reach their greatest importance where there is some summer rainfall. Tobacco is the chief money crop in this region, and the major areas of cultivation are in the vicinity of Samsun, Bafra, Sinop, and Zonguldak. The domestic consumption of tobacco is very large, but in addition, the annual exports of Turkey often exceed ten million dollars. Production in Turkey and export from it are less than one tenth that of the United States. Evidently the local conditions of soil and climate account for the peculiar quality of Turkish tobacco, since attempts to grow the same varieties elsewhere have generally failed. Greece, however, produces similar varieties. Turkish tobacco is sown in March and transplanted in May or June. It is carefully cultivated and fertilized, and the first harvest is made in late June, at which time the poorer quality lower leaves are picked. The finer quality upper leaves are harvested as late as September.

The most intensively developed agricultural region in Turkey is in the vicinity of Smyrna and in the various valleys and lowlands on the western margin of Asia Minor. Here, as usual, wheat and barley are the most important crops. They are cultivated with oxen, harvested by hand, and threshed by tramping cattle. New methods, however, are coming into use. A little rice is grown in this region (more is imported), and there is the usual crop of beans and chick-peas, which are common in many Mediterranean lands. Tobacco and sugar beets are important. Opium is significant although production has declined in recent years. Smyrna opium is in great demand because of its high morphine content (11 to 14 per cent). In addition, the poppy seed is a source of oil which is used for food in the manner of olive oil. The production of cotton is increasing, aided by government research in crop management. In the Smyrna

region quantities of raisin grapes, figs, olives, filberts, and various other fruits are produced. The Turks lead the world in the export of figs and filberts.

The southern coast of Turkey may be compared with parts of the Great Valley of California. It is the driest part of the coastal belt and has the highest summer temperatures. Cultivation reaches its height in the vicinity of Adana where cotton is the important money crop. The Turkish production is about 500,000 bales. Oranges, lemons, and olives are also produced in this region, the only one in Turkey where much citrus fruit is grown. Sesame is also an important crop.

In summary it may be said that the Mediterranean region of Turkey consists of a series of isolated districts on the coastal border where the characteristic Mediterranean crops are produced. Tobacco, cotton, and opium, however, are somewhat exceptional in that they are not common in most Mediterranean lands. The region as a whole is handicapped by poor transportation. The coastal plain is not continuous and the plateau provides a rather effective barrier between the northern and southern coasts. The greatest handicap, however, is the limited export market. The principal exports are tobacco, vegetables, nuts, fruits (mostly figs and raisins), wool, mohair, cotton, and vegetable oils. It is to be noted that only the vegetables and fruits are characteristic Mediterranean products and that none require much processing before export. The imports include cotton goods, iron and steel, machinery, and clothing.

Minerals

In general, Mediterranean Asia is poor in minerals. Salt is obtained from the Dead Sea in Israel, while in the island of Cyprus there is some sulfur and copper. Petroleum is readily obtained since the main pipeline from Iraq leads to Haifa in Israel and Tripoli in Syria. There are a great variety of minerals in Turkey and production is generally increasing. Most important is chromium which is mined mostly in the northwest and southwest, and the Turks are second in world production. During World War II Allied and Axis agents bid feverishly for Turkey's chromium. Molybdenum is mined near Ankara on the plateau, and coal is found on the Black Sea coast near Ereğli. Small quantities of lead, silver,

FIGURE 14.3. *Piraeus, the harbor of Athens, Greece. The port city completely covers the hill. From TWA.*

zinc, emery, and meerschaum are also produced in Turkey.

MEDITERRANEAN EUROPE

Mediterranean Agriculture in Europe (FIG. 14.2) is much more highly developed than in Africa or Asia, partly because it represents the humid phase of the region, partly because the mountains are more lofty and supply more water for irrigation. Southern Europe is primarily a land of peninsulas —the Balkans, Italy, and the Iberian Peninsula of Spain and Portugal. Each of these is Mediterranean in character, at least on the coastal margins. Each has some special qualities and products of its own.

The Balkans

The Mediterranean margins of the Balkan Peninsula include parts of European Turkey, Greece, Albania, and Yugoslavia. The peninsula consists of a complex group of highlands with some small marginal plains. Along the western side of the peninsula, the mountains come down sharply to the sea with few harbors and few areas of level land. In eastern Greece and European Turkey there is a long narrow plain (Thessaly) with the best agricultural land in the margin of the peninsula.

The standard crops of Mediterranean Agriculture are to be found wherever cultivation is possible. Wheat is of first rank, followed by barley, grapes, olives, and tobacco. Currants and raisins, along with some citrus fruits, are produced for export. Tobacco usually makes up more than half the exports, although the acreage is small. Nearly all the tobacco is marketed as "Turkish tobacco." In spite of the intensive cultivation of the small plains and the use of the mountain slopes for grazing animals, mostly sheep and goats, the people of the coastal portion of the peninsula are not self-sufficient in foodstuffs. The islands bordering the Balkan Peninsula—the Ionic group, the Dodecanese, the Cyclades, and Crete—are of more strategic than agricultural value because of their relation to the Suez Canal and the Bosporus. Small patches of land are cultivated wherever possible and some olives and grapes are produced on the slopes. In good times the tourist industry is more remunerative than the crops.

There is a variety of mineral wealth in the Balkan Peninsula although usually the minerals are in small amounts. Marble for statuary, build-

ing stone, lead, silver, some chrome, and magnesite are produced in Greece. In Albania there is some petroleum, a fact which led to the early invasion of that country by Italy during World War II. Along the coastal district of Yugoslavia lignite and bauxite are produced. Most of the minerals of the peninsula are exported in the crude form, chiefly because of the lack of coal and facilities for smelting.

The Italian Peninsula

Clear summer skies, mild winters with intermittent periods of rain and sunshine, and numerous mountains and basins close to the sea make peninsular Italy a pleasant place to live. Is it a good place to make a living? Some 25 million people attempt to do so, but millions have emigrated in recent years to find a better home or one that is not so crowded. The majority of the people of Italy make their living from agriculture. In spite of many mountains, hills, and swamps, less than 10 per cent of the land is unproductive. Through centuries of labor, even the unfavorable parts of the environment have been brought to a state of more or less permanent production. But why is agriculture so dominant and manufacturing so unimportant? The answer is, in part, that some of the basic raw materials for manufacturing are lacking in Italy. Minerals are found in peninsular Italy, but they are not the sort which support large-scale manufacturing. Coal and iron are scarce and petroleum is practically nonexistent.

Down the rugged backbone of peninsular Italy, no peak lifts itself into the zone of permanent snows and no lofty range presents a major barrier to communication. It is a land of moderately elevated mountains, hills, small basins, and swamps, varying widely in their productive possibilities. Agricultural production is as varied as the natural landscape. Many of the small grains, including wheat, oats, rye, and barley, are grown. All of the Mediterranean tree and bush crops are present—grapevines, olives, and citrus fruits, as well as a variety of vegetables.

Most of the cropland lies at moderate elevations where there is a rough zonation based on altitude and modified by latitude. The first and lowest zone, which includes the lower slopes of Sicily and the lowlands along the coast of the peninsula, is the land of the citrus fruits. The production of oranges and lemons is particularly important in northern Sicily and in the vicinity of Naples. The citrus fruits are not usually grown very far from the sea or at elevations of more than a few hundred feet. Most of the grains are grown in the lowlands, although some are cultivated on the hill slopes in southern Italy. In the second zone olives are dominant, growing on the slopes where drainage is good and prospering in the soils derived from limestone. Olives can endure light frosts better than oranges and consequently have a wider range. The third zone includes the grape, which is still less sensitive to frost and which reaches an elevation of more than 3000 feet in Sicily. The production of wine in Italy, normally more than 900 million gallons per year, testifies to the importance of this hilly and mountainous zone. The fourth, the chestnut zone, lies above the vineyards on the steeper and less fertile slopes. The acreage is large and the chestnut is an important element in the diet of the Italian people. Fifth, above the chestnuts, where both climate and surface make agriculture difficult, is the forest zone.

In peninsular Italy agriculture is more intensive, perhaps, than in any other Mediterranean land. This is indicated by the large amount of "two-storey cropping" and the common practice of intercultivation. On more than half of the cropped land cereals and some tree or bush crop, such as olives, oranges, or grapes, are simultaneously produced. In spite of the general importance of the tree and bush crops, only 6 per cent of the cropped land is devoted to their specific culture. The larger percentage of the trees are grown along with some other crop. The patterns of "second-storey cropping" and intercultivation are various. For example, on the plain north of Florence the olive trees are planted in rows about 40 feet apart with irrigation ditches halfway between. Along the ditch are two rows of grapes with a strip of wheat occupying the space between the grapes and olives. In "two-storey cropping" trellises support the grapes several feet above the ground in such a manner that other crops may be grown beneath them.

As in most Mediterranean lands the cereals are the most important crops, occupying more than 50 per cent of the arable land in all Italy. Two thirds of the cereal land is in wheat, which occupies a larger proportion of the arable land than in any other European country. The greatest production of cereals, to be sure, is in the Po Plain, but on the small farms of the peninsula the peasants try to produce enough wheat for their bread and macaroni. Whereas in France wheat is grown on the best land, much of the grain in Italy is found on the poorer soils and consequently the yields are low. Thus, in spite of the widespread production of wheat, there is not enough for the needs of the people. In some districts, however, the methods of production have improved and the yield is high. Italians need about 320 million bushels of wheat per year, but produce, on the average, only about 80 per cent of this amount. In spite of the "battle of the grain" and the effort to "liberate ourselves from the servitude of foreign bread," Italians continue to import grain. Wheat yields have been sufficiently increased to replace corn production in part, since Italians prefer wheat to corn.

Olives, first ranking tree crop, have a wide distribution in Italy, but the areas of intensive production lie along the toe and heel of the "boot" in Apulia and Calabria. Lesser quantities are produced in the vicinity of Naples and along the Riviera. Since the decline of olive and olive oil production in Spain, Italians have become the first ranking exporters. Even so, most of the oil is consumed at home. For many years the methods of extracting the oil were inadequate and the quality was poor, but in recent years large refineries have been constructed and standards have been improved. In fact, oils from Spain and Algeria are now refined in Italy. In spite of new developments, the olive groves of Italy are being pushed back before the extension of the grapevines and fruit trees, especially in the north.

In Italy, as in other countries, the cultivation of grapes is by no means limited to the Mediterranean portion. Greater acreage is devoted to grapevines in Italy than in any other country in the world, and in the production of wine Italians usually rank second to the French. The average production of wine in recent years represents a decrease over previous years, owing to the ravages of plant diseases. The Italian vintages are distinguished by their variety. In addition to ordinary wine, there is Chianti, Asti, Orvieto, Castelli, Romani, and Marsala. Italy is increasing the production of table grapes and raisins.

The poverty of Italian mineral resources can scarcely be exaggerated although small quantities of many minerals occur. The minerals produced in Italy, however, are not those which could be used in large industries. The sulfur of Sicily is the most valuable mineral, but Italian sulfur cannot compete in the world market with the cheaper, better product of Texas and Louisiana. Coal production was stepped up to nearly 4 million tons during the early years of World War II, but the average output is less than 2 million tons as compared with an import of 10 times that amount. The coal is mostly lignite and even the other varieties are not generally suitable for use in smelting. Limited quantities of lead and zinc are produced in Sardinia, mercury in the central Apennines, and bauxite in various localities. The iron ore reserves of Italy are estimated at 40 million tons, less than one year's production in the United States. The annual production of iron is generally less than one million tons, most of which is taken from the island of Elba and the adjacent portion of the mainland.

Le Midi *of France*

The French call the Mediterranean portion of their country *Le Midi*, a region including the lower Rhone Valley and the delta and the plains leading toward the Pyrenees. The hot summers, abundant sunshine, and the light, "warm" soil make this a favorable locale for the grape. Production of wine exceeds that of any region in Europe, although the wines from this part of France are not considered the best. Almost every bit of available land is cultivated, except only the space necessary for roads, towns, and houses. Marginal slopes are terraced to increase the acreage of the vine. Other Mediterranean crops are grown to a lesser extent. Citrus trees grow well near the sea and olive trees are grown rather widely. Many kinds of early vegetables and fruits are produced for the northern market, with a well-developed seasonal system. In October, cauliflower and the green salad vegetables are shipped; from November to February parsley, spinach, and leeks; in April, early asparagus and onions; in May, peas, potatoes, and cherries; in June, apricots, peaches, and beans; in August and September, grapes and other fruits. On lands not suited for cultivation grazing cattle and sheep are to be found, but in general, livestock other than draft animals are scarce.

Marseille is the great port of southern France and the outlet of the lower Rhone, although located at one side of the delta. Marseille, unlike most great European ports, is not primarily international in character. Its chief function is to collect and distribute commodities from the French colonies. To Marseille are shipped oilseeds of all kinds, palm oil from equatorial Africa, cottonseed, and copra, as well as tallow, hides, cereals, and sugar. Dried fruits, nuts, wine, cork, olive oil, tea, coffee, spices, and leather are transported from various parts of the world to this port. The industries at Marseille are based on the imports. Soap making, sugar refining, leather industries, and chemical works are representative industries. Heavy industries like steel manufacturing are generally lacking.

Mediterranean Spain and Portugal

If one approaches the south shore of Spain at Gibraltar, Málaga, or Almería, the strongest impression is that the mountains come down abruptly to the sea and that there is little level land for cultivation. Here and there, however, white towns and cities stand out against the dark verdure of the lower slopes. These settlements are based on intensive agriculture. First, there is a fringe of sandy beach, above this the town, and beyond that the area of irrigation. Still higher is the Sierra which supplies the community with water. If it were not for the lofty slopes, there would be very few people on the small fragments of coastal lowland. A great variety of products are grown in the coastal belt. Wheat, olives, and grapes are all staples. Oranges and lemons grow along the entire southern and eastern coast of Spain. In addition, because of the nearness of the sea and the early contact with foreign lands, many strange products have been brought to these shores. Some of them have been adopted with considerable success. Figs, brought centuries ago from the Barbary Coast, have been quite successful, and figs were once exported from Málaga to the Indies. Some of the introduced crops, such as sugar beets, sugarcane, cotton, and sweet potatoes, have met with only mediocre success.

Along the east coast the plains are wider, irrigation is more extensively developed, and the population is denser. One large plain, about 175 miles long and 25 miles wide, extends from Almería to Cape Nao, and another of about the same size reaches from Valencia to Barcelona. On the plain in the vicinity of Valencia, large quantities of wheat, rice, grapes, and citrus fruits are produced. Enough almonds, figs, chestnuts, filberts, onions, peppers, and olives are produced to permit export. From the agricultural standpoint this is the most intensively exploited portion of Spain. Terraces have been built, rivers have been diverted to irrigate the fields, and nearly every inch of available land is in use.

Farther to the northeast in the most industrialized region of all Spain is Barcelona with more than a million people. There is a good harbor which has been greatly improved, and there is abundant hydroelectric energy at the eastern end of the Pyrenees. No great supply of the basic raw materials of industry is near Barcelona, but by the importation of coal, iron, and cotton many industries have been developed there. Cotton textiles represent the most important industry, but there are also flour mills, glass and chemical factories, and canneries for preserving foodstuffs, especially the fruits of the immediate hinterland.

The heart of the olive industry in Spain is in the valley of the Guadalquivir on the south slopes of the Sierra Morena and on the north slopes of the Sierra Nevada. Other outstanding areas include the eastern coast, the basin of the Ebro, and various favored spots on the plateau. Spaniards have long been large producers and exporters of olives and olive oil. The industry has its fluctuations, especially in times of war, but some regions have continued to produce for thirty centuries. The olive industry in the basin of the Guadalquivir alone yields more than 100 million gallons per year, the principal centers being at Sevilla and Córdoba.

The climate of southern Spain is especially favorable for the olive. The tree can endure frost and temperatures as low as 10° F. for short periods of time, but excessive humidity is a handicap, increasing susceptivity to disease. Severe drought does not injure the tree although it may reduce the yield temporarily. Most of the olives are grown where the rainfall is less than 20 inches and where the total summer rain is less than two inches.

More than 25 varieties of olives are found in Spain. Some of the larger sizes are used exclusively for pickling, other varieties entirely for oil. The trees begin to bear after 6 or 8 years but do not reach full production until 20 to 40 years. Most of the trees live for 300 years and some have continued to bear for 1000 years. The average planting is about 40 to the acre with the trees arranged in staggered rows so as to utilize the space with greater efficiency. The picking season usually begins in southern Spain at the end of October and continues through December, sometimes as late as February.

The products of Portugal are similar to those of Spain. In the north, summer rain makes it possible to grow corn in addition to large quantities of grapes. In the hinterland of Porto is the port wine district, where more wine is produced than in any other section of the country. Wheat and rye are the chief cereals and the olive grows in the middle and southern part of the irregular lowland. Cork oaks grow best in the southern part of the lowland, and more than half of the world's supply in past years has been produced in Portugal. In recent times cork oaks have been transplanted to other regions, including southwestern France, but the Portuguese continue to be the largest producers and, considering the brisk demand for cork on the world market, suffer little from the competition.

The most important mineral deposits in the Iberian Peninsula are to be found on the margins of the plateau. The best copper district is in southwestern Spain in the hinterland of Huelva. Mercury is mined chiefly in the vicinity of Almadén, halfway between Sevilla and Madrid; tungsten is taken from southern Portugal and the Sierra Nevada of Spain. Both coal and iron ore are mined in northern Spain; coal from near Ovideo and iron ore from near Bilbao. Most of the iron ore is exported. The Peninsula contains many widely scattered mineral deposits, not all of which are in production.

15

The New Mediterranean Lands

THE Mediterranean lands of the Old World have been occupied by man for many centuries. Similar lands in California, Middle Chile, the Cape District of South Africa, and small parts of Australia are scarcely a century old so far as effective settlement is concerned. It is not surprising, therefore, that production should vary somewhat from that of the type area along the shores of the Mediterranean Sea. Most of the physical qualities needed for the development of Mediterranean Agriculture are present in all the areas. The climate (Cs) is substantially the same; the mountains supply water for summer irrigation, although in varying amounts. Furthermore, most of the new lands have received immigrants from Europe who brought with them the crops, methods, and ways of life well adapted to this environment. Other conditions, however, are notably different. The new lands are not so densely populated although California is rapidly achieving a dense population. Subsistence crops for local consumption are less important than commercial crops to be sold outside the region. Californians have the whole United States for a market. Foodstuffs from Middle Chile are sent to the mining districts in northern Chile, while for the Cape District of South Africa and for southeastern Australia there is only a limited market near at hand.

CALIFORNIA MEDITERRANEAN

From San Diego northward almost to the Oregon boundary and inland to the foothills of the Sierra Nevada (FIG. 15.1), the climate of California is similar to that of the European Mediterranean lands. The summers are dry, and the winters mild and rainy, facts which have a profound influence on the occupance of the land. California with an area of 156,000 square miles is the second largest state in the United States; and second in population with more than 10,000,000 people. The amount of land which can be cultivated is relatively small, however. Large areas are too dry, while other areas are too mountainous. The mountains serve the very useful purpose of collecting and storing quantities of water which are used to irrigate the low alluvial slopes and the valley bottoms. In the United States more almonds, apricots, cherries, dates, figs, grapes, lemons, oranges, olives, pears, peaches, plums, prunes, and walnuts are produced in California than in any other state. In addition, large quantities of grapefruit, early vegetables, apples, barley, cotton, rice, and alfalfa are produced in this state. Petroleum is an important product, as are several metallic minerals. All things considered, California is the most commercial of the lands with Mediterranean climate, and a very large part of the goods produced is sold outside the state.

The origin of the Mediterranean Agriculture in California and the stages of its development are well known, since the growth has been recent. Aside from the Indians, who utilized only primitive agricultural methods, the first stage was ushered in by the Jesuit missionaries and the Franciscan and Dominican monks who entered California from Mexico in the 18th century. They brought the products of the Old World, grapes, various fruits, and the small grains. The missionaries and friars were interested in the salvation of the Indians and were less concerned with the development of large-scale agriculture. The settlers who accompanied them, however, brought livestock, and for many years the use of the land aside from the small irrigated areas near the mis-

FIGURE 15.1. *Mediterranean Agriculture in California occupies a strip along the coast, the east side of the San Joaquin Valley, all of the Sacramento Valley, and the San Francisco Bay Region. The combination of Mediterranean climate and the water supply from the adjacent mountains makes it possible to cultivate part of this region very intensively. Top of map is to the northwest.*

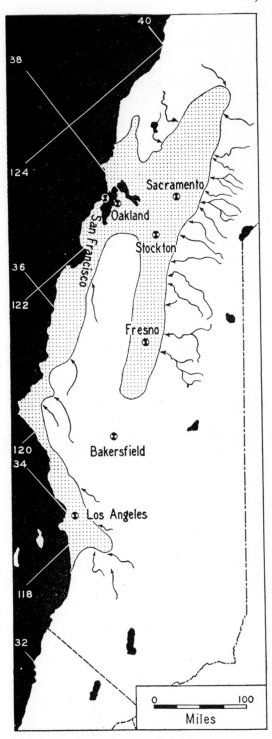

sions was largely for grazing. Thousands of cattle and horses were raised by friar and rancher alike. Wheat and barley were grown without irrigation in the more favored basins. Thus, at the beginning of the 19th century, the stage was well set in California for the development of Mediterranean Agriculture. To put it in another way, the various elements of Mediterranean Agriculture were transported lock, stock, and barrel from Spain to California via Mexico. A few details were lacking, such as citrus fruits and olives, but they were introduced later without difficulty.

During the Spanish and Mexican periods of settlement, California was handicapped by its isolation from areas of dense population which might, on the one hand, supply settlers and, on the other, afford a market. It was a long slow journey by sea or by land to the parent settlements in Mexico. It was even farther to the eastern coast of the United States. Thus California developed slowly in the first half of the 19th century, but the Gold Rush which began in 1849 changed the whole picture. Thousands of immigrants arrived from eastern United States, not only to dig gold but to produce the things which the miners needed—more wheat for flour and beverages, vegetables, implements, and entertainment. The effect was to stimulate agriculture, especially wheat growing in the Great Valley. After a time wheat was exported from California. But wheat declined after 1885 when production in the Kansas, Dakota, and Minnesota regions got under way.

The stages in the evolution of California agriculture are described by Professor John Leighly (Yearbook of Agriculture, 1941, pp. 200–203).

Agriculture was introduced into California along with other elements of Spanish-colonial ways of life late in the eighteenth century. In the early days of Spanish colonization the missions were the centers and examples of agricultural practice. The Spanish mission-

aries were undoubtedly the best equipped among the early European immigrants into California to introduce agriculture there. Much of Mexico, whence the colonists came, is dry; horticulture, production of grain under dry-farming methods, and the herding of livestock, all well-established in Mexico, were easily transplanted to Upper California. The Spaniards had brought from Spain, also a country with dry summers, tree crops and grains that could flourish in this part of North America. Mission agriculture included extensive herding of livestock on the ample tracts assigned to the missions, grain farming, the production of tree crops such as figs, olives, and grapes, and garden cultivation with the aid of irrigation from the streams of the Coast Range. It represented an efficient use of land and of climatic resources when the population had to produce only a little more than was consumed locally and export markets and transportation were limited.

Successive shifts in emphasis on different agricultural products were the reflection of a prevailing speculative interest in the use of land. Production of one crop after another, each promising large returns, was expanded until prices were depressed and the use and sale of land for that crop ceased to be profitable. Then the attention of speculative producers and vendors of land turned to a new product. The speculative sale of land to newcomers from the Middle West and East has been a means of dividing large land holdings into tracts of one-family size.

Intensification of the use of the land, the consequence of continued heavy immigration, has involved particularly an increase in the area devoted to fruits and vegetables grown for eastern and foreign markets and has been associated with steadily increased use of water for irrigation. From north to south irrigation increases in importance as the total annual precipitation de-

creases. But only in dry interior valleys and in southern California does it dominate agriculture to the extent of being absolutely necessary for crop production. Throughout the greater part of this climatic region irrigation is a supplementary source of water for crops and so is a feature of intensification of agriculture rather than a necessary basis for it. The place of irrigation in the summer-dry climates differs in this respect from its place in the true dry climates.

Although the climate of California is favorable to the growth of the small grains in the winter season, the production is not large, owing to the competition of cheaper and better grains from the wheat belts. See FIGURE 15.2. Moderate quantities of wheat and barley are grown in several districts. They are sown in the autumn in order to take advantage of the winter rain, and since most of the season's rain falls on the crop, fair yields are obtained even in some districts where the total rainfall is less than 10 inches annually. The rate of growth is slow, but ripening occurs before the severe dryness of summer is well advanced. Wheat and barley are used for feed and in the manufacture of fermented beverages; of the locally grown grains only a small quantity is used as food.

FIGURE 15.2. *Barley cultivation on the level floor of the west side of San Joaquin Valley, California. The arid east face of the Coast Range furnishes almost no water for irrigation.*

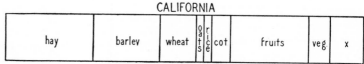

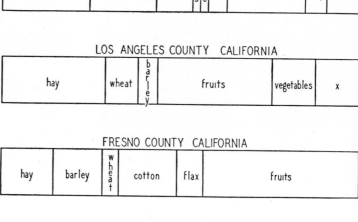

FIGURE 15.3. *Crop graphs for California as a whole and for three selected counties. Fruit and vegetables rank high except in Sutter County in the Sacramento Valley where field crops are dominant. Abbreviations: cot, cotton; veg, vegetables; x, miscellaneous crops.*

The chief commercial crops of the California Mediterranean are fruits—oranges, lemons, peaches, prunes, and grapes—vegetables, and hay. Production varies with the locality, particularly from south to north. See FIGURE 15.3. In the Los Angeles Basin citrus fruit is dominant. In the San Joaquin Valley grapes, citrus and deciduous fruits predominate. In the Sacramento Valley deciduous fruits, hay, and rice are the chief crops. In various other valleys and basins there is usually a specialty crop; rhubarb and lettuce in the Salinas Valley, where experiments have also been made in growing guayule for rubber; prunes and apricots in the Santa Clara Valley. Only a few of these districts will be described. See FIGURE 15.4.

The Los Angeles Basin

The Los Angeles Basin of southern California is one of the most intensively cultivated regions of North America. It is not a large region as farming regions go; it extends about 60 miles to the east of the city of Los Angeles and a similar distance to the southeast. The largest acreage lies at the foot of the San Gabriel Range and in plains to the southeast of the city. The basin is bordered on two sides by mountains, on the north by the San Gabriel Range, on the east by the San Bernardino and several smaller ranges. These moun-

tains furnish most of the water used to irrigate the district. To the west and south is the ocean, which serves to modify the climate for several miles inland. The amount of cultivated land is limited by the mountain slopes which are too steep, by the valley bottoms in which the frost risk is too great for citrus fruits, and by the amount of water available for irrigation.

The water supply for the city of Los Angeles comes from Owens Valley in the southern Sierra Nevada and from the Colorado River, through hundreds of miles of aqueducts, but most of the water for irrigation comes from the adjacent mountains, which receive snow in the winter and a small amount of rain in summer. Some of the orchards are irrigated directly from streams from the mountains, but for many others wells which tap the underground waters are used. These subterranean sources are supplied in turn with water from the mountains. In winter the rainfall is often sufficient to carry the crops for some time without irrigation.

In many parts of the Los Angeles Basin, the crops growing on the gently sloping alluvial fans are marked out in rather definite zones with citrus fruits at the higher elevations. The citrus fruits are followed successively by zones of deciduous fruits, vegetables, and small dairy farms at lower elevations. Professor H. F. Raup ("Piedmont

CALIFORNIA—ORCHARD AND VINEYARD DISTRICTS

A SAN FRANCISCO BAY
  Koppen's Csb climate
B SACRAMENTO VALLEY
  Csa climate
C SAN JOAQUIN VALLEY
  BWh and BSh climates
D SOUTHERN CALIFORNIA
  Csa and BSh climates
E SIERRA FOOTHILL
  Modified Csa climate
F SAN LUIS OBISPO
  Csa and BWh climates
G IMPERIAL-COACHELLA
  VALLEY
  BWh climate

FIGURE 15.4. *A map of the California orchards and vineyards, showing the climate of various districts. Map by P. Meigs in "Economic Geography." See Appendix A for definitions of symbols.*

Plain Agriculture in Southern California." Yearbook of Assoc. of Pacific Coast Geographers. Vol. 6, pp. 27–30, 1940) has described these zones as follows:

The citrus zone, in which the principal orange is the Washington navel, or winter-ripened orange, presents a sharp contrast to the unused upper fan slopes. Here everything is ordered; in place of the thickets of native vegetation, the citrus groves are carefully planned to get the maximum number of trees into minimum space. Their welfare is watched, and they are fed, watered, protected against frost damage, and tended so carefully that there is little about them to suggest either fruit-growing or agriculture to the visitor from the east. These groves appear as artificial and unnatural in a rural region as the most complex industrial areas appear in an urban landscape.

Most of the groves have been so profitable for their owners that the houses of the district are uniformly of high quality, equipped with all the conveniences which are usually associated with urban life, and are usually occupied by their owners. The typical ranch consists of a large one or two-story dwelling house, garage, tool shed, storage shed, well rig, and reservoir. In the orange and lemon groves, standpipes indicate the necessity for irrigation. Piles of smudge pots, the new types euphemistically referred to as "orchard heat-

ers," may be stacked under the trees during summer, or distributed through the grove in winter, one pot to each tree. Some of the best groves are now equipped with pipelines which feed the fuel to the heaters without the necessity for effort on the part of the rancher during frost threats. Most ranchers make use of some form of frost protection service, which forecasts the location of freezing temperatures for some hours in advance, and notifies them by radio, warning signals, or telephone. In parts of this zone, almost nothing can be seen but citrus trees and an occasional ranch house and well rig. Kitchen gardens are rare, although every house has its lawn and flowers. Poultry houses are almost nonexistent. If the ranch is in a location which suffers from high winds, the groves are surrounded by tall eucalyptus windbreaks. If it is near a "wash," the rancher may have collected the largest stones from his grove and assembled them in huge rock piles which put a New England stone wall to shame. Landholdings are relatively small, and certainly agriculture is intensive in this citrus district. . . .

The deciduous fruit zone, lower than the citrus zone, presents some sharp contrasts. The quality of the ranch houses, for one thing, is far below that of the houses in the citrus groves. Some of them are only shacks. They, too, lack poultry sheds or kitchen gardens. The most attractive landscape in this area is that of the walnut groves, with their clean cultivation, showing brown earth under bare limbs in winter, and dark shadows on the ground beneath dense foliage in summer. In general, the boundary between the citrus and deciduous zones has changed little . . . [in recent years] . . . but the most stable boundary defines that part of the deciduous zone which is planted to wine grapes. Landholdings vary in size, from the thousands of acres planted in grapes to the small orchards of peaches or groves of walnuts . . . .

At the southern edge of the region, the walnut plantings give way to small dairy ranches, in which the conspicuous features are the open fields of alfalfa or grain hay. Few trees have been planted, and the houses are of the same order as those of the deciduous zone, that is, of fair to poor quality. Specialization in dairy products has been the primary function of the area near Chino for some years, and this district provides about one-sixth of the fresh milk supply of Los Angeles.

In the Los Angeles Basin live nearly three million people, local consumers who have an increasing influence on the crop system. Most of the oranges, lemons, walnuts, and deciduous fruits are exported from the state, but the local market is significant also. The effect of the local market on the character of the Mediterranean Agriculture is most noticeable. The people of California, unlike those of Italy or Spain, are accustomed to eating quantities of meat and dairy products. California usually imports most of its butter, meat, and some of its milk from other states, a fact which resulted in serious shortages of these items during and after World War II. There is, however, an increasing effort to produce meat and milk in the state in spite of the limited pasture land in summer. Dairy farms in the vicinity of Los Angeles differ greatly from those of the Dairy Belts. The "farms" are small; a few acres are sufficient to give the dairy cows exercise and nearly all the feed is trucked in, most of it from the Imperial Valley and some from Oregon's Willamette Valley. Second-calf cows are also imported in large numbers, are fed and milked heavily for a year or two, and then are resold. Such farms are not typical of California dairy farms in general, but they indicate that milk can be produced under unfavorable circumstances if the demand is great and the price is high.

The growth of manufacturing in the Los Angeles region, to be described on page 462, is having a significant reaction on agriculture, which is tending toward diversification and a partial departure from the strict Mediterranean type.

The San Joaquin Valley

The Great Valley of California owes a large share of its productivity to the Sierra Nevada. This is especially true of the San Joaquin portion of the valley where the rainfall is light, from 5 to 15 inches annually. Water from the various rivers draining the west slope of the Sierra Nevada is used to irrigate the huge, alluvial plains. Only the eastern and central portions of the valley can be effectively irrigated since there is little water to be obtained from the coast ranges nor is there enough to irrigate the entire southern end of the valley.

In the vicinity of Fresno more table grapes, grapes for raisins, and wine grapes are grown than in any other comparable region in the world. Half the raisins of the world are grown and dried there; most of the remainder are produced in Turkey and Greece. The production of raisins is often greater than the demand, and a large surplus may result. Outside the United States the great market for raisins is in Great Britain. Prior to World War I most of the raisins for Britain were bought in Turkey and Greece. During that war British consumers turned to the United States for raisins, thus booming production. During World War II most of the raisins used by the British were obtained in Turkey, partly to pre-

vent them from reaching Germany. This fluctuating demand for California raisins has caused some disturbances in the industry, but raisin grapes can be used in the manufacture of sweet wines, which are in great demand, especially when whiskey production is curtailed to save grain.

Wine grapes are just as important as raisin grapes, since the domestic market for wines has expanded tremendously in recent years. When Prohibition came into force in 1920, many wine grape growers pulled up their vines and planted other crops. But many more continued to grow wine grapes, finding a limited market among the Italian and other European immigrants. Many thousands of home wine makers helped to maintain the industry. One enterprising producer of wine grapes marketed them in a pressed package which bore the injunction, "Do not put these grapes in water with yeast for that will produce wine, which is illegal." With the modification of the Prohibition Amendment in 1933 wine grape production flourished and production in California far surpassed that in New York, Ohio, and other eastern states. The production of wine grapes has been most profitable, in general, since the end product is not perishable, as are table grapes. Also the market is not glutted with wine grapes as it sometimes is with raisins.

The San Joaquin Valley produces a variety of other crops. Deciduous fruits of various kinds are widespread. Orange production is second only to that in the Los Angeles Basin. Small grains are limited in acreage, although the west side of the valley can be described as a small barley and wheat belt. Cotton is grown in increasing quantities, and the acreage of alfalfa is high. Further large-scale expansion of agriculture hinges on a comprehensive irrigation scheme, described in the next section, plus the continuation of a large market at home and abroad.

The Sacramento Valley

The Sacramento Valley is more humid than the San Joaquin, and thus irrigation plays a somewhat less vital role. The Sacramento Valley is also cooler and the danger of frost is greater. Citrus fruits are almost entirely absent although the deciduous fruits are present. The small grains, barley and wheat, have relatively large acreages. Both are used locally for feed, a considerable part of the wheat being fed to poultry and much of the barley used in the manufacture of malt beverages. Rice is the third grain in acreage in California, and almost all of it is grown in the middle portion of the Sacramento Valley. The Sacramento River supplies water for flooding the rice fields. A part of the transient labor is taken from the colonies of Oriental peoples in San Francisco. Large-scale methods of production, including the sowing of rice directly in the fields from airplanes and the use of threshers in harvesting, make it possible for producers in California, like those in Louisiana, Texas, and Arkansas, to compete with rice growers in Japan and China. Prior to World War II rice was exported from California to China and Japan.

Alfalfa is the chief hay crop of the valley. Some wild hay is harvested, however, and a part of the small grain is cut for hay. In the lower part of the Sacramento River Valley, the delta, various vegetables, such as tomatoes, beans, peas, asparagus, artichokes, and celery are grown. A large proportion of the vegetables and fruits grown in the valley are canned on the spot for the eastern markets.

The Great Valley Project

Not all the Great Valley can be irrigated under present conditions, and not all the water supply can be utilized. Floods often carry the surplus water out to sea and damage crops, levees, and property at the same time. Many small reservoirs have been constructed to hold back some of the flood waters, but until recently no over-all plan has been put into effect. The purpose of the Great Central Valley Project (FIG. 15.5) is to store more water from many of the rivers draining the Sierra Nevada in order to irrigate the southern part of the San Joaquin Valley. This section has previously been irrigated from wells only. In addition, dikes will prevent the encroachment of salt water into the delta, part of which is below sea level. A large dam has been constructed on the upper Sacramento River, known as Shasta Dam, which

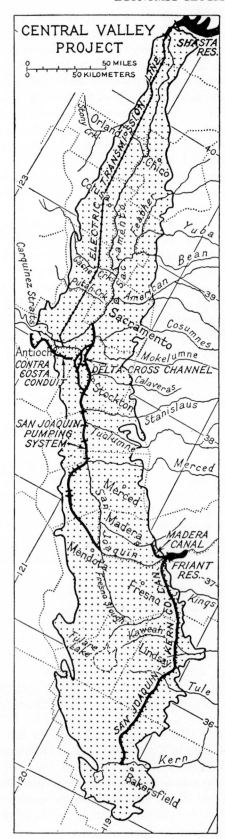

FIGURE 15.5. *The Great Valley Project. Most of the shaded areas will be irrigated when the project is complete. At present a large part of the southern San Joaquin Valley is without irrigation. Modified from a map of P. Meigs in "Geographical Review," April 1939.*

rises 500 feet above the river bed. The reservoir will store over four million acre feet of water, a capacity exceeded only by Boulder Dam and Grand Coulee. Another dam at Friant on the upper San Joaquin River diverts a part of that stream into the southern end of the valley. The first two steps in the Great Central Valley Plan help solve the problems of the lands now irrigated rather than provide water for new areas. Additional dams and canals will be constructed as the population and demand for irrigated land increase.

Marketing the California Crops

Only a small percentage of the California crops can be marketed on the Pacific Coast. Large amounts of citrus, deciduous fruits, and vegetables must be shipped to eastern United States or must be exported. In this respect producers in California run into competition with those from other areas. To be sure, there are a few crops, such as wine grapes, lemons, dried fruits, walnuts, and flower seeds, with which Californians virtually control the domestic market. With other products, for example citrus fruits and vegetables, competition is met from growers in regions which are nearer the market. There are certain advantages in growing products in California; oranges of good quality, for example, can be produced and marketed in every month of the year, which cannot be done in Florida or Texas. The average consumer of oranges, however, is 2500 miles from California, and it costs more than $500 to ship a carload of oranges to New York, whereas Florida growers can truck their oranges to market at a much lower price. The condition in Texas is somewhat similar to that in Florida except that Texas is farther from the market. Californians have been foremost in the development of marketing cooperatives partly because of the distance from the large centers of population in northeastern United States. Not so many years ago the orange growers of southern California were specifically concerned with the problem of inducing the average American citizen to *drink* two oranges instead of eating one.

With a potential surplus of many crops, California growers are interested in the foreign market. Trade agreements and power politics enter the picture. California organizations have been successful in keeping competing Mexican oranges, for example, out of the United States, but have not been so successful in opening and maintaining foreign markets.

Minerals

A variety of minerals, not all of which come from the Mediterranean portion, is produced in California. Gold played a vital role in the development of California agriculture, and it is the mineral most often associated with the state. Gold mining began in the gravel deposits of the Sacramento Valley and spread slowly to the "mother lode" of the Sierra Nevada. Small-scale placer mining is a thing of the past but a small percentage of the gold extracted from the gravel beds is obtained by means of hydraulic mining. During the decade of the 1920's gold production had settled down to about $20 million annually, but the increased price of gold in 1940 stimulated production to a $50 million figure. During World War II production was decreased largely because of the low priority on gold mining equipment. Mercury is produced in the Coast Range south of San Francisco. Since mercury is a "strategic" mineral and in great demand, every encouragement is given to California miners, and they account for half the domestic output.

The most valuable minerals are petroleum and natural gas, particularly since there is no coal in California. Most of the oil is taken from the Los Angeles Basin, in the vicinity of Signal Hill south of Los Angeles, and from various other districts near by. Los Angeles producers export oil in large quantities. In the southern end of the San Joaquin Valley production is increasing, and large quantities of natural gas are sent from this district to Los Angeles and San Francisco. Petroleum is used on all the railroads for fuel and is used for heating homes, as well as for gasoline and lubricants. Silver, lead, copper, and zinc are also produced in California.

NORTHERN MIDDLE CHILE

Northern Middle Chile, the heart of the Chilean nation, is much like Mediterranean California. They are both about the same distance from the equator. Both are bordered on the east by lofty mountains and by low coastal ranges on the western margins. In each there is a Great Valley. There are also some sharp contrasts, however. The seasons have a reverse relation to the calendar, a fact which is of great significance in the

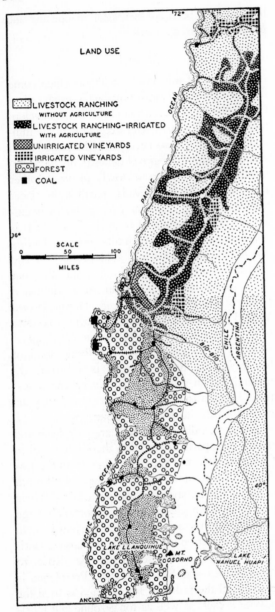

LAND USE

▦ LIVESTOCK RANCHING
   WITHOUT AGRICULTURE
■ LIVESTOCK RANCHING—IRRIGATED
   WITH AGRICULTURE
▨ UNIRRIGATED VINEYARDS
▥ IRRIGATED VINEYARDS
○ FOREST
■ COAL

SCALE
0   50   100
MILES

FIGURE 15.6. *A land use map of Middle Chile. Ranching, with or without irrigation, occupies the largest areas, but the climate and higher values of the grainfields (not shown separately), vineyards, and other cropped land justify placing the region within the Mediterranean Lands. From "Latin America" by Preston E. James. Copyright, 1942, by the Odyssey Press, Inc. Used by permission of the publishers.*

mountain range difficult to cross to the east. There is no great market for citrus fruits, early vegetables, and table grapes in the whole continent of South America at the present time. Even though Chile is no farther from New York than California by water, and can be reached readily by air, the fact remains that the position of the country is a handicap to production and trade, particularly in view of the barrier effect of the Andes. Middle Chile is, therefore, less commercial than California, and less productive.

More than a third of Middle Chile is occupied by the Andes Mountains; another third is taken up by the coast ranges. This makes the Central Valley a sort of corridor along which runs the chief Chilean railway. Only the middle portion, latitude 28° to 42° can be readily cultivated. See FIGURE 15.6. The north is too dry; the south is too wet and rough. The Mediterranean region extends approximately from latitude 32° to 39° S. The climate is like that of California except that it is somewhat cooler in the summer. Santiago, for example, averages 46° F. for the coolest month, July, and 69° F. for the warmest month, January. This is slightly cooler than Los Angeles, California, both in summer and in winter, but the rainfall is about the same, 15 inches, as is the latitude.

The crops and methods of cultivation are in the broad view like those of California or the Old World Mediterranean lands. The small grains, peas, and beans are grown in winter, in general without irrigation. Summer irrigation is common since the melting snows of the high Andes supply abundant water for the crops. In spite of this abundance, however, most of the land is used for pasture. Intensive cultivation, such as is practiced in other irrigated lands, is confined to a few areas.

marketing of Chilean crops. The perishable food crops, melons, grapes, and various deciduous fruits, come into bearing in Chile during the winter season in the Northern Hemisphere. Another difference is in land ownership. In Chile a great many large estates, or haciendas, founded in the days of the Spanish occupation, persist to the present time. Many of the haciendas have more than 12,000 acres, only part of which is under cultivation, the remainder being used mostly for grazing.

Middle Chile is isolated. It faces a vast ocean to the west, a desert to the north, and a lofty

Wheat is the chief crop, but modern machinery for sowing and harvesting is just coming into use. Most of the grain is still sown broadcast and some threshing is still done by primitive methods.

Corn is the second crop in acreage. It does not grow well in the Mediterranean climate but was brought to the Central Valley of Chile by the Incas, and continues to be used as a large part of the food of the workers. Other subsistence crops include potatoes (introduced from the high plateaus of Bolivia and Peru), onions, and peppers. All these crops can be found in the subsistence agriculture of the Central Plateau of Mexico. The more characteristic Mediterranean crops are found only in smaller quantities and only in certain districts, but they are the most significant commercial crops. Olives grow rather poorly because of the cool summers; citrus fruits are limited in acreage by the small home market and by the difficulty of exporting them. Only the vineyards have a large enough acreage to allow wine to be exported from Chile.

The best markets for Chilean crops outside of Middle Chile are the mining districts where relatively high wages are paid, and thus the workers are able to purchase the farm produce. Chief among these are the nitrate pits and the copper mines (FIG. 15.7).

FIGURE 15.7. *Molding "pigs" of crude copper at a Chilean smelter. Copper and nitrate make up a large share of Chilean exports and thereby stimulate agriculture. The production of synthetic nitrates has reduced Chilean exports. From CIAA.*

Minerals

Nitrate occurs in beds of former lakes on the floor of the Great Valley in the desert of northern Chile. It is only necessary to remove a few feet of alluvial material in order to scoop up the crude nitrate. This is done with steam shovels or in some places by hand. From the pits the crude nitrate is taken to an *oficina* where it is refined by soaking the crude ore in vats of warm water and then allowing the water to evaporate, which happens quickly in this dry region. The nitrate is then sacked for export or is shipped in bulk by rail to the coast. The large-scale production of synthetic nitrates in the United States and Europe, however, has reduced the Chilean export drastically. Little food for the workers is produced in northern Chile; most of the wheat, meat, vegetables, and fruits are brought from Middle Chile.

The major copper areas are all in the Andes. There are large reserves in Chile, but the amount exported, as well as the price, is highly variable. In the northern margin of Middle Chile, excellent iron ore is mined, Chilean producers having the largest production in South America prior to the expansion of the Brazilian iron and steel industry. Most of the Chilean ore is transported by freighter through the Panama Canal to the eastern seaboard steel mills of the United States. Some coal also is found along the coast of Chile in the vicinity of Concepción. It is used locally for fuel on the railroads and on coal ships, but does not form the basis of any large industry. Chilean iron and steel production, however, is increasing.

THE CAPE MEDITERRANEAN DISTRICT OF AFRICA

Commercial agriculture in South Africa began in the Cape District in the area of the Mediterranean climate. Here on the eastern slopes of the Cape Peninsula, the Dutch began to grow crops to supply the ships in the East Indian trade, little thinking that South Africa would ever serve as a homeland for two million Europeans. The Dutch had been preceded by the Portuguese, but the latter founded few colonies on the coast of Africa in the early days. Perhaps because the Dutch were more successful traders in the East Indies, they needed a port midway between the Spice Islands and the Netherlands where the slow sailing ships

of that day could replenish their supplies of food and water for the crews. This was particularly necessary because shortage of fresh foods and the resulting scurvy decimated entire crews of the merchant ships. Vegetables, wheat, and the vine were introduced early and cultivation slowly expanded.

Most of the grain—the wheat, oats, and corn—in the Cape District occupies a narrow strip near the coast, extending about 50 miles north of Capetown and over 100 miles to the east of that city. There are numerous small plains within the low coast ranges. These ranges supply a small amount of water for irrigation. The rainfall is light, occurring mostly in winter, and grains, with the exception of corn, are grown in the winter. The grain farms are very large even when compared with those of the Spring Wheat Belt of North America. The average farm is in excess of 1500 acres, and the values and yields per acre are about the same as that of similar land in the United States. Corn was not introduced to South Africa until the arrival of large numbers of British settlers about 1820 and did not become an important crop until the 1880's. Known as "mealies" in South Africa, corn soon became an important article in the diet of Europeans and natives alike. The Cape District is not very favorable for corn, however, and the crop was grown with much greater success after the settlers had made the great "trek" northward into the lands of summer rain, to the district which came to be known as the "Maize Triangle."

It is grapes more than any other crop which distinguishes the Cape District (FIG. 15.8) from the rest of South Africa. Wine production was introduced early and given a good start by the French Huguenots who had experience in the vineyards and wineries of Europe. The growth was normal but slow and is limited at present by the light demand for "foreign" wines in the countries of western Europe. Most of the vineyards, as well as the comparatively few citrus groves, are located near the mountains of the Cape Ranges where water is available for irrigation. Both are marked off in long narrow rectangles by the irrigation ditches on the alluvial slopes of the mountains and in the flood plains of the valleys. In many places the vineyards and orchards are provided with windbreaks to reduce the velocity and drying effect of the winds. Wine production has

FIGURE 15.8. *Mediterranean Agriculture in the Paarl Valley of South Africa. Vineyards, separated by irrigation ditches and interspersed with groves of trees, dominate the production. The mountains furnish water for irrigation. From Bureau of Information, Union of South Africa.*

become fairly stable at about 15 million gallons per year. Table grapes and raisins are produced also.

AUSTRALIA

Mediterranean Agriculture is only slightly developed in Australia at the present time. Two areas of Mediterranean climate occur, one in the extreme southwest, the other toward the southeast but west of the mountains. An examination of the map of Australian climates, Appendix A, will show that both of these locations are on coasts facing west. The lack of lofty mountains, however, limits the area of land which can be irrigated, and the small population of Australia, about seven million, is another limiting factor. As a result, most of the Mediterranean climate is included in the Wheat Belt (FIG. 13.2) and only a few relatively small areas on the Murray River

and near Perth in southwest Australia are irrigated.

Grapes, deciduous fruits, oranges, and berry crops are the most important. There are more than 250,000 acres of fruits and market gardens in Australia. Canning of peaches, pears, and vegetables is increasing in irrigated districts. Jams and marmalades are produced, some for export. More than half the grapes are grown without irrigation. Table grapes, raisins, and wine are the chief products of the Mediterranean districts. The other fruits are somewhat localized. The producers in New South Wales lead in oranges, cherries, and plums, most being grown near the town of Orange. Apples are grown in the wetter parts of Western Australia; peaches and pears are produced principally in Victoria. It should be pointed out that many fruits are grown without irrigation in the Dairy Region of southeastern Australia and in Tasmania.

FIGURE 15.9. *Graph of production and export of oranges and tangerines from various Mediterranean lands, 1951. This graph represents slightly less than two thirds of world production. Note that Spain exports more than half of its production.*

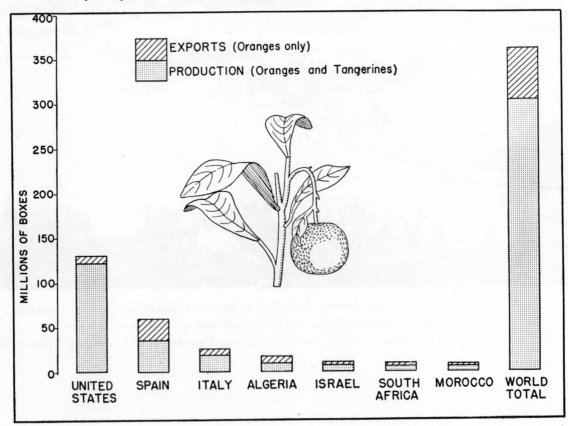

CHAPTER

16

Dairy Regions of North America

From Minnesota to the Atlantic, the principal dairy region of North America (FIG. 16.1) lies south of the Northern Forest and north of the more intensively cultivated Corn Belt. It is the northernmost cultivated region in eastern North America. The summers are cool and wet, too cool for most grain crops to mature in normal years. Much of the country is rough, or rocky, or both, making cultivation difficult. Large tracts are still in woodland, remnants of the former forests; pastures are extensive; crops are relatively unimportant with the exception of hay. The Dairy Belt is an expression of limited opportunities in agriculture, but it is also the result of large urban populations with their great demand for milk and milk products. Many of the largest cities of North America lie in this belt or on its margins. Boston, New York, Montreal, Cleveland, Detroit, Chicago, Milwaukee, and Minneapolis are a few. Stated in another way, the Dairy Belt lies next to and partly overlaps the great Manufacturing Belt of North America and, therefore, there is a very large market close at hand.

Although there is much variation between individual dairy farms in different parts of the Dairy Belt, most people would have little difficulty in recognizing one of the type farms. The large numbers of milk cows in the pasture in the summer season, the large dairy barn well lighted by windows and with a substantial foundation usually of stone or concrete, and one or more silos are perhaps the most striking characteristics to be observed. One can also determine the type of farming by the farm land. So large an amount of pasture land in proportion to cropland is found in no other farming area in North America. Hay is the most important crop, and in addition to cropped

hay, wild hay is cut in many localities. On the northern margin of the Dairy Belt, hay, pasture, and woodland occupy nearly all the farm land and other crops are missing or have very small areas. In the middle and southern parts of the belt, there is substantial acreage of oats, corn for silage

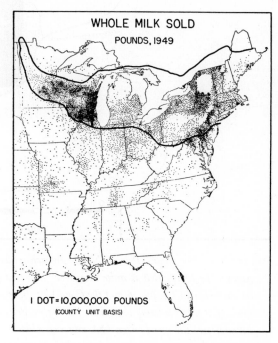

FIGURE 16.1. *A map of the Dairy Belt (indicated by black line) showing the distribution of whole milk sold. The Canadian portion of the Dairy Belt lies in southern Ontario, Quebec, and in the Maritime Provinces. The largest market for whole milk, butter, and cheese is in the large cities located in or near the Dairy Belt. From United States Bureau of Census.*

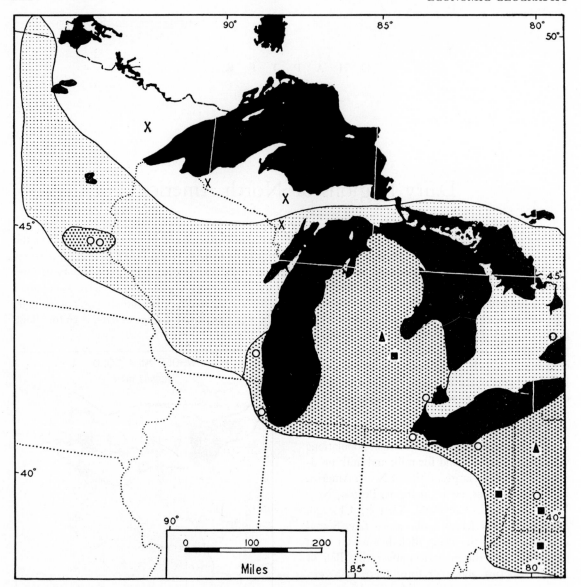

FIGURE 16.2. *The Dairy Belt of North America (west portion above and east portion on next page). The Dairy Belt is quite extensive. Its main part lies between the Great Northern Forest discussed in Chapter 6 and the Corn Belt. In general, it is the northernmost agricultural region. If it were possible to explain the Dairy Belt in terms of a formula it might be said that mineral wealth, mostly iron (X) and coal (black squares), plus transportation (Great Lakes) encourages manufacturing and large cities (open circles), which in turn require large quantities of milk (see Fig. 16.1). But this is merely a part of the equation. It is necessary to add that cool summers and adequate moisture are favorable for hay and pasture, upon which milk production depends. The more heavily shaded areas specialize mostly in fluid milk whereas the remainder of the belt produces butter, cheese, condensed and dried milk. Petroleum (black triangles) and asbestos (A) are among the minerals produced in the region.*

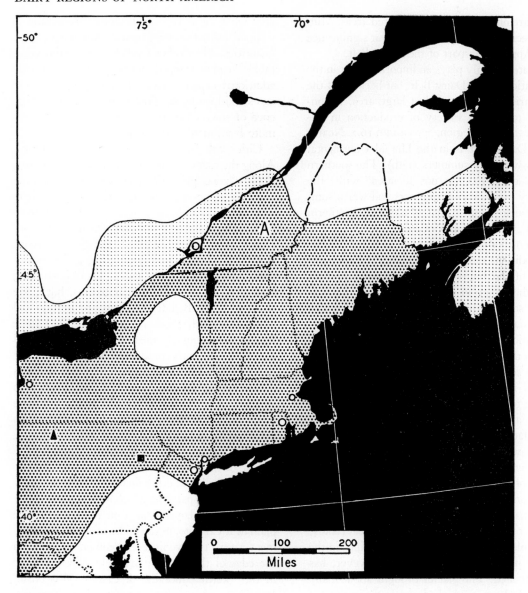

or fodder, rye, potatoes, and various other crops. The regions of Commercial Dairying can be delimited with a fair degree of accuracy by noting where hay and pasture are larger in area than the total tilled land. In the last analysis, the outstanding quality of the Dairy Belt is the large production of milk and milk products, in contrast to the minor place of crops. In other regions, for example the Corn Belt, large quantities of milk are produced. There, however, milk production is secondary to the production of forage, food crops, and meat.

Although milk is the predominant product in the dairy regions, many crops and products of the forests, mines, and lakes yield large returns. The typical dairy farmer produces some meat, such as veal, for the calves not needed or not suitable for replenishing the dairy herd are slaughtered. Hogs and chickens are fed on the skim milk if the farm sells only the cream. Potatoes and other vegetables grow well in the region and are important cash crops. Nearly all the district was originally forested and large areas of cutover land remain unproductive. Pulpwood and even some saw timber are obtained from the forested areas. Mining, especially coal mining, is of great significance in the Appalachian part of the Dairy Belt.

Climate not only plays an important part in the delimitation of the Dairy Belt, but because of the wide variation within such a large area, it contributes to a wide variety of production in different parts of the region. See FIGURE 16.2. Nearly all the Dairy Belt is in the Humid Continental Climate with cool summers (Dfb). The southern limit is close to, but not identical with, the boundary between cool summers and warm summers, which is approximately along the isotherm of 72° F. for the month of July.

The northern limit of the belt is based on surface conditions rather than climate. The southern margin of the Laurentian Shield coincides with the northern margin of commercial dairying, except for small outliers associated with mining districts, islands of clay soil, or other human agglomerations which stimulate the production of milk. In the Shield with its rough, rocky surface and thin soil, conditions are favorable neither for crop nor for pasture. Perhaps it would be more accurate to say that climate and surface combine to limit agriculture at this zonal boundary, but that surface is the critical, immediate factor.

From western Minnesota to the coast of the New England–Canadian Maritime Region, the surface of the Dairy Belt varies greatly; rough, even mountainous land is found in the northern Appalachians and the Adirondacks; level lake plains with their fine textured soils near the Great Lakes; smooth plains or rolling terminal moraines in the western part. The whole region, however, has been glaciated. The glacier brought about many variations: here it plucked the last remnant of soil from the hard rock; there it deposited a thick layer of clay, fertile if difficult to cultivate; or it left broad swamps, which can be cultivated only after expensive drainage operations.

It is no accident that the Dairy Belt is intimately associated with the great urban belt of eastern North America, the great workshop of both the United States and Canada. From Chicago and Milwaukee to Montreal and Boston, it is a land of cities and factories with millions of people depending on it for milk and meat. Because of its bulk and perishability, milk should be secured within a radius of not more than 300 miles of the

city where it is to be consumed. Fresh milk is shipped farther, even overseas, but not in large quantities. Most other foods—meat, grain, vegetables—can be shipped thousands of miles at little additional expense. Likewise butter and cheese can stand long hauls. This accounts for the existence of some dairy regions which are rather remote from urban settlements.

Cities are by no means evenly distributed. Along the east coast from Boston to Washington, D.C., a zone 400 miles long and 50 miles wide contains more than 20 million urban dwellers who daily consume five million gallons of fresh milk. The milkshed for this urban district includes all of New England, the St. Lawrence Lowland, most of New York State and Pennsylvania, and parts of other states. There is no other concentration of cities similar to this, but along the Erie Canal Belt from Albany to Buffalo and along the south shore of Lake Erie and Lake Michigan, groups of cities create a large demand for milk and milk products. Not only do the populations of manufacturing cities and districts demand milk, but in the aggregate the dwellers in small country trading cities and towns consume much milk. On the whole, the attraction of this entire urban area for milk is enough to influence the farm character of the complete Dairy Belt.

Out of the wide variation in surface, climate, urban demand, and other factors is born the great variety of farm patterns which make up the Dairy Belt. At first glance a farm on the smooth lake plain near Chicago, in the midst of urban development, seems to have little in common with one on the edge of the Laurentian Shield of Ontario or in the "kettle" moraine of eastern Wisconsin. Indeed, they have only one outstanding characteristic in common—the emphasis on the production of milk, with other products falling into a secondary place. Although it is difficult to express the variations in the Dairy Belt in a brief chapter, a study of some of the subregions or districts will indicate the range of geographic quality.

THE NEW ENGLAND–CANADIAN MARITIME REGION

When the Pilgrims and their contemporaries landed on the shores of New England, they had little choice of an occupation. Anything to get

FIGURE 16.3. *A Holstein dairy herd in Minnesota. The large well-kept barns, silos, the excellent grass, and the windbreak of trees are characteristic of the better portions of the belt. From Great Northern Railway.*

enough food to keep alive! As time went on, however, the settlements expanded and the choice became wider; the early settlers could farm, fish, and hunt, or build ships and engage in world trade. They did all of these things, but not all the ventures were equally and continuously successful. The early farming had to be of the general type. The consumers of that day needed meat and grain as well as milk. Since in the early days there was no competition from the more favored lands to the west, a general farm could succeed in spite of the rough land, the stony field, and the cool summer climate. As the West was settled, however, and as transportation improved with the building of the Erie Canal and the railroads, New Englanders could no longer compete in the production of grains and meat. As a result thousands of farms were abandoned and many rural areas depopulated.

At the same time there was an expansion of manufacturing and an increase in world trade, which built up the cities at the expense of the towns. Raw materials were brought by clipper ships to New England's ports, and the finished goods were taken to foreign lands. More and more the people crowded into the cities—not only the rural people, for many of these clung to the land, but the millions of immigrants from Europe and from French Canada—until 90 per cent of the people of southeastern New England lived in cities and towns. Meanwhile the production of dairy farms was increasing, and the milksheds of the large cities like Boston were being pushed back farther and farther, touching upstate New York and the Province of Quebec. Some of the abandoned farms were reoccupied on a new basis with the dairy cow in supreme possession of the valleys and hillsides, along with the hay, oats, and other forage crops. New England, however, is not unfavorable for all food crops. Here and there, white potatoes, deciduous fruits, and various vegetables thrive. Fruits and truck crops succeed well on the more favored soils in New England: cranberries in bogs near the coast, onions and tobacco in the Connecticut Valley, apples and other deciduous fruits in various districts, mostly in southern New England.

The southern part of the Canadian Maritime Provinces—New Brunswick, Nova Scotia, and Prince Edward Island—represents the eastern extremity of the Dairy Belt which is rather remote from the large urban markets. As a result dairying is somewhat less intensive, and much of the milk is marketed in the form of butter and cheese. As in New England, many specially favored districts produce distinct crops. The Annapolis-Cornwallis Valley of Nova Scotia, southeast of the Bay of Fundy, is famous for its fine apples. Low ranges of hills protect the orchards from strong winds, and the gentle slopes provide some frost protection. The ice and cold water in the Bay of Fundy retard the budding until the worst danger of spring frosts has passed. The district around the head of the Bay of Fundy is especially favorable for the production of hay and forage crops, as is also most of Prince Edward Island. A considerable portion of the Maritime Provinces, however, is too rough and thin-soiled, as well as too cool in summer for commercial agriculture.

The mineral wealth of the New England–Canadian Maritime Region is limited. There are quarries for granite, marble, and slate in New England. Formerly building stone was exported to various parts of the United States in large quantities, but the competition from other regions is now keen. There is no coal, iron ore, or other mineral in New England which might form a basis for manufacturing. Raw material must be sent to the factories from outside the region. Nova Scotia, however, is well supplied with coal, principally on Cape Breton Island in the vicinity of Sydney and Pictou. Some coal is also produced in New Brunswick. The occurrence of coal in this region is fortunate because of the lack in New England and because of the nearness to the iron ore of Newfoundland. Owners of iron and steel mills in the vicinity of Sydney take advantage of this fact. Other minerals produced in the Canadian Maritime Provinces include gypsum, salt, petroleum, and gold.

THE NORTHERN APPALACHIANS

That part of the Dairy Belt which lies in upstate New York and northern Pennsylvania resembles New England in some respects. It is rather rough although some of the plateau uplands are gently rolling. It has been glaciated, but not with such severe results as New England. It is much more suitable for pasture than for crops, and the nearness to New York City and other urban centers makes it of greatest importance for fluid milk.

FIGURE 16.4. *A dairy farm in southern Ontario. Grain, fruits, and tobacco are also produced on this smooth plain. From Canadian Department of Agriculture.*

Trains loaded with milk exclusively are sent from this district to the large cities. Some crops, however, grow well also. The district is the foremost buckwheat region in the United States. Fruits, grapes, and vegetables are produced in the Finger Lakes district; many vegetables, such as corn, peas, beans, asparagus, are grown for canning. In both eastern and western Pennsylvania, the coal mines are the greatest source of wealth; anthracite in the east, bituminous in the west. Not only do the miners provide a market for some of the dairy and other kinds of produce, but the presence of coal attracts industry which in turn increases the demand.

The anthracite region from Scranton to Allentown is not in itself an important agricultural region. The valleys are narrow and the ridges are steep. The coal has been folded and faulted until in some parts of the region it is difficult and expensive to mine. Anthracite was formerly used largely in the metallurgical industries but has been replaced in large measure by coke made from bituminous coal. Anthracite is clean and smokeless, and so is in some demand for domestic uses, but even here, coke, petroleum, and natural gas give it stiff competition. Some of the anthracite is moved eastward to the Atlantic ports, but most of it is consumed in the steel mills of eastern Pennsylvania and Maryland.

The western part of Pennsylvania along with Ohio and West Virginia includes the best bituminous coalfields in the world and is the district where the most bituminous coal is produced. Here the country is too rough for much farming, but the demand for vegetables and fruits makes possible small farms, often tended by part time coal miner–farmers. This coal, excellent for fuel and for coking, occurs in level beds, most of it near the surface and easily mined. Numerous creeks and rivers afford either barge transportation or routes for railroads facilitating transportation of coal and iron ore. Further discussion of coal mining in this region will be found in Chapter 33.

THE ONTARIO PENINSULA

The Ontario Peninsula is bordered by Lake Huron, Lake Erie, Lake Ontario, and the Laurentian Shield. It extends southward to the vicinity of Detroit and includes the best farming land of Canada and one third of its population. A glance at the map (FIG. 16.2, pages 222–223) shows that this region is in approximately the same latitude as New England, New York State, and Wisconsin. Thus, it belongs to the Dairy Belt although other types of farming exist on the peninsula. On the southern tip of the region next to Detroit, corn is grown for grain, making a small corn belt in Canada. On the shores of the lakes, especially in the vicinity of Hamilton on Lake Ontario, is an important district of fruit production in which grapes play a leading role. Tobacco is grown rather widely, not because the climate and soil are especially adapted to the crop but because of a protective tariff.

On the whole, dairy farms dominate the peninsula. See FIGURE 16.4. The proportion of dairy cows to meat animals is high; milk production per acre of cropped land compares favorably with many parts of the Dairy Belt of the United States. Hay and forage crops occupy a large proportion of the cropped land, and the area in pasture is large. Milk processing plants, creameries, and cheese factories are abundant. It is evident, however, that dairying is much more important in the southeastern part of the peninsula than in the other districts. From London, north of Lake Erie, to Kingston on the eastern end of Lake Ontario, dairy farming is especially well developed. Most of the cities of the peninsula lie in or near this district. In the remainder of the peninsula, the value of crops or meat rivals or exceeds that of milk production. Corn for grain is limited to the very southern part of the region, but hay and forage crops and small grain crops are widespread. To a considerable extent this region is used as a feeder and finisher of livestock from the western ranges of Canada in much the same manner as the United States Corn Belt.

In spite of the tariff and other restrictions to trade, producers in the peninsula of Ontario profit from its nearness to the Manufacturing Belt of the United States. It is easier to get coal from the northern Appalachian region of Pennsylvania than from Nova Scotia or Alberta. Coal supplements the water power from Niagara and other sources. Petroleum, natural gas, salt, and gypsum are the chief minerals produced in the peninsula. Many United States manufacturers have constructed branch factories in Ontario as close as possible to their main establishments. In addition to the branches of United States and British factories, there are many independent factories processing milk and tobacco, packing meat, and making iron and steel with ore from the Upper Lakes and coal from Pennsylvania. Three of the four largest manufacturing cities of Canada—Toronto, Hamilton, and Windsor—are in the peninsula.

SOUTHERN MICHIGAN

The dairy region of Southern Michigan is greatly stimulated by the cities and towns of the Automobile Belt. Aside from this excellent market, the conditions for general farming in Michigan are favorable. Most of the land is fairly level. The glacial deposits are not so rough and rocky as in many other districts in the Dairy Belt, and as a result the crops are highly varied. A large share of the nation's edible beans, sugar beets, potatoes, vegetables, and fruits are produced in Michigan. See FIGURE 16.5. In the western part on the shores of Lake Michigan conditions are favorable for grapes and various fruits. On the level lake plain around Saginaw Bay on the east side of the peninsula sugar beets, as well as hay and forage, are produced. As in other parts of the glaciated districts, the most favorable location for growing vegetables is in the beds of former lakes where the soil is made up mostly of peat and muck. Settlers from the Netherlands found these sites similar to their reclaimed marshland. In the vicinity of Kalamazoo and Holland, they began many years ago to grow celery and later other vegetables and tulips. The old lake beds are favorable for potatoes also.

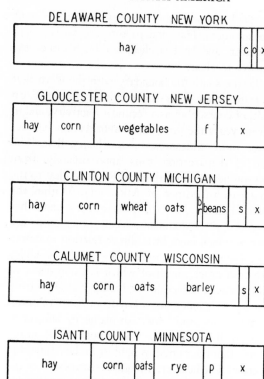

FIGURE 16.5. *Crop graphs of representative dairy counties. The proportions of hay, grain, and other crops are variable; most of the corn is grown for fodder and silage rather than for grain. Abbreviations: c, corn; o, oats; f, fruit; br, barley; s, grass seed; p, potatoes; x, miscellaneous.*

So great is the demand for food of all kinds in the cities of Michigan that many farms give more attention to meat production than is generally customary in a dairy belt. A large proportion of the livestock are meat animals.

Petroleum and limestone for the steel mills are the important minerals of Southern Michigan. Most of the raw materials (some partially processed) must be shipped in for use in the factories. The excellent location of this region with respect to transportation makes coal from the northern Appalachians, iron ore from the Upper Lakes Region, and many other raw materials readily available. The influence of manufacturing on the agriculture of the region is felt throughout the peninsula of Southern Michigan.

WISCONSIN

The western part of the Dairy Belt is not so rough as the New England section. Michigan,

Wisconsin, and Minnesota have no very great elevations although some of the country is too rough or stony to be cultivated. In any event there is great variety in the type of dairying, depending on the surface, the soil, and the nearness to large cities. Wisconsin illustrates the range in conditions fairly well. See FIGURE 16.5.

One of the most specialized and intensive dairying districts in the United States is in the southeast part of the Dairy Belt near the large cities of Milwaukee and Chicago. Most of the surface is gently rolling ground moraine, but the Kettle Hills might be described as heavily rolling with short steep slopes. Large red dairy barns with concrete foundations and the inevitable attached silos dominate the landscape. The residence near the barn is less pretentious though well kept. Nearly all the milk from this district is sent to Chicago, Milwaukee, and the smaller cities near by in the form of fluid milk. Professor Loyal Durand, Jr. ("Dairy Region of Southeastern Wisconsin and Northeastern Illinois," Econ. Geog. 16: 416–428, 1940), describes the function of this region as follows:

The intensive dairy district of southeastern Wisconsin and northeastern Illinois lies in juxtaposition to the nearly continuous urban areas of the Lake Michigan shore, individual cities of which are located from Manitowoc and Sheboygan, Wisconsin, southward through the urbanized Milwaukee conurbation to the string of cities culminating in Chicago and its suburbs, and terminating at the head of the lake in Gary and Michigan City, Indiana. Although it is true that at present the six million urban inhabitants of the Lake Michigan cities furnish the major market area for the adjacent fluid milk-producing regions, it is nevertheless also true that the dairy areas, even in the Illinois portion of the region, were practicing a dairy style of agriculture long before the cities grew to such size that they were forced to draw a milk supply from beyond their immediate environs. Thus the city milk sheds expanded into pre-existing dairy regions; the dairy regions did not grow up entirely in response to an adjacent fluid milk market. Even the Illinois portion of the region was at one time an area specializing in manufactured dairy products; it was dotted with rural creameries and cheese factories, and Elgin gained its position in national butter quotations.

The pattern and shape of the market milk-producing area west of Lake Michigan is most irregular. Only generally is it true that the fluid milk production is carried on near the major city selling points, and only in general is it true that the bulky product of milk is produced in the theoretical locations wherein economic theory presupposes its rooting. Individual milk sheds are highly irregular in shape, and the Chicago milk shed, in particular, is most asymmetrical. The latter region extends in funnel fashion northwestward from Chicago, constantly broadening into southern Wisconsin, then sending scattered tentacles into east-central and northwestern Wisconsin, as far as 325 miles from the Chicago city hall.

In south central Wisconsin lie the sand plains with extensive flats, marshes, and stands of scrub oak. Population is sparse, and the farms are not so prosperous, a fact which can be recognized from the quality of the barns and houses. Rye and potatoes are the chief crops. Dairying is not of great importance owing to the difficulty of producing forage crops and pasture on the sandy soils.

In southwestern Wisconsin is the Driftless Region, a rough, unglaciated area with deep valleys cut into the upland. Both the uplands and the valley floors can be cultivated, but the steep land on the valley walls can be used only for pasture. There are no large cities in the district or the immediate vicinity and most of the milk is dried, condensed, or marketed in the form of butter or cheese.

MINNESOTA

The western part of the Dairy Belt lies in Minnesota (FIG. 16.2) and, to a limited extent, in Manitoba. The chief characteristic of this district is its remoteness from the great urban markets. With the exception of the Twin Cities, Minneapolis and St. Paul, with a total population of less than one million, there are no large cities in or near the district. As a consequence, the marketing of butter, condensed and dried milk, and cheese is more important on the whole than the marketing of fresh milk. The limits of the Dairy Belt in the western portion are somewhat variable with respect to the Corn Belt, the Wheat Belt, and the Northern Forest. The boundary is sharpest with the Wheat Belt of the Red River Valley because of the difference in terrain. Most travelers notice the abrupt change in the type of farming on leaving the rolling terminal moraine country where dairying is dominant and on entering the level floor of the Red River Valley where wheat, sugar beets, potatoes, and flax are the chief crops. Next to the forest the boundary is less sharp. The dairy farmers on the margin of the Laurentian Shield in northern Minnesota and in Manitoba are unable to grow sufficient feed crops for local consumption, partly because of the rocky surface but

chiefly because of the shortness and coolness of the summers. Hay and pasture are fairly good, however, and land is cheap although rather expensive to clear.

To the south the boundary with the Corn Belt is transitional. Dairying continues in the Corn Belt, of course, but as a secondary activity, and in recent years the growing of hybrid corns has become more widespread in the Dairy Belt. The line of demarcation runs approximately from the southern end of the Red River Valley to the southeastern corner of Minnesota. Within the Dairy Belt hay, corn for silage, oats, and other feed crops are dominant. Many other crops are grown which have little direct relation to dairying. Potatoes, flax, rye, barley, and vegetables are cash crops, much of which is shipped out of the state. Production is highly variable from county to county and even from farm to farm. Some of the sandy outwash plains are subject to drought if the rainfall is below normal. Of all the Dairy Belt the rainfall is lightest in the Minnesota section. The heavier, drought resisting soils of the clay moraines are preferred by many farmers even though they may contain boulders and be difficult to cultivate.

THE PACIFIC NORTHWEST

The Dairy Region of the Pacific Northwest is limited largely to the Puget Sound–Willamette Lowland. There, in the trough between the Cascade Mountains and the Coast Range, is a great valley like that of central California. The climate is much more favorable for the dairy farmer. The winters are rainy and mild, the summers cool with light rains. There is no severe weather as in the eastern Dairy Belt and pasture is available for nearly all the year. Thanks to the demand of the large cities near by—Portland, Seattle, Tacoma, and others—and the shortage of milk in the large cities in California, an important region of commercial dairying has developed. In most parts of the valley, milk production accounts for the largest part of the cash income of the farmers, although grains, fruits, and other crops are also sold. In the Puget Sound Trough the annual rainfall ranges up to 50 inches, enough to produce good pasture and forage crops. The greatest difficulty is to find suitable sites for farms and to clear the land of forest or stumps. The best sites are in the valleys of the small rivers which cross

FIGURE 16.6. *Cherry orchards in the Willamette Valley near Salem, Oregon. The hilly portions of this broad valley are more suitable for horticulture than feed crops. From Oregon State Highway Commission.*

the trough. Since such areas are limited, the farms are likely to be small, many less than 50 acres. Other farms are located on the uplands between the streams, where the soil is generally poor. The chief crops include corn for forage, various kinds of hay, oats cut for green feed or for grain, potatoes, and fruit trees, mostly cherries. Most of the milk from this district is marketed in Seattle and Tacoma.

The Willamette Valley is more like a general farming region. Most of the valley floor is level and more suited to cultivation than that of the Puget Sound Region. The climate is a little drier and therefore more favorable to grain crops, of which wheat is the most important. Most of the land, however, is in hay, pasture, and grain crops used for forage. Farms average slightly more than 150 acres, with about 80 acres in cropland and the remainder in woodland or brush pasture. In addition to dairying and grain, prunes, cherries, walnuts, filberts, strawberries, loganberries, and raspberries are produced in the Willamette Valley. See FIGURE 16.6. The surplus is converted into jams and preserves at factories.

On the whole, the Dairy Region of the Pacific Northwest seems to have an assured future. The rapid growth in population on the west coast has increased, and will further increase, its market. The varied resources of agriculture, the forests, water power, and nearness to the sea are all favorable factors. The scarcity of coal and petroleum is a handicap to all-round industrial development, only partially offset by abundant water power. Petroleum is obtained from California, and some coal is available from Vancouver Island and the Coast Ranges of Oregon.

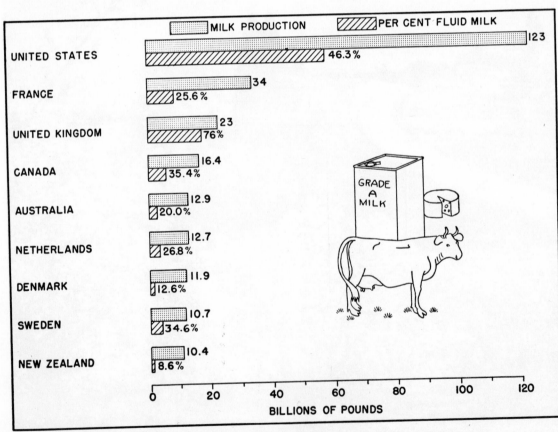

FIGURE 16.7. Graph of milk production by leading countries, showing the percentage sold as fluid milk. The remainder goes into butter, cheese, dried milk, and condensed milk.

17

Dairy Regions of Europe, Australia, and New Zealand

IN WESTERN and northern Europe with 400 million people to feed, there is naturally a great demand for dairy products. In addition, in many areas the summers are too cool and too moist, and the land is too poorly drained for the efficient production of grain. The land, however, is suitable for the growth of hay and other forage crops. It is not surprising, then, that there is a very old dairy industry in Europe. Furthermore, in the last half century the growth in urban population has increased the demand for milk, butter, and cheese. As a result, the land devoted to dairying has been extended usually at the expense of the grain lands. The import of cheap grain from overseas has made it easy for many farms to shift to dairying. These factors are mainly responsible for several well-defined dairy regions and also for the considerable emphasis on dairying in other types of farming in Europe. Emigrants from Europe, mainly from the British Isles, have established dairying in parts of Australia and New Zealand which have somewhat similar environmental conditions.

Although the location of the large urban markets is generally responsible for the great emphasis on dairying in Europe, the major dairy regions are located on the lands too cool and moist for other crops, because of altitude, latitude, or cloudiness. In the Alps dairying is the chief farming type because of the coolness and limited sunshine in the valleys. On the Channel and North Sea coasts of northern Europe, the higher latitude compensates for the lower altitude, and conditions are more favorable for hay than grain. In southern Scandinavia and in parts of Great Britain and Ireland, conditions prevail which are similar to those on the coast of northern Europe.

The dairy regions of Europe vary in surface, soil, details of climate, transportation facilities, and nearness to market. In all regions emphasis is placed on milk production, but most of the milk is sent to market in the form of butter and cheese rather than in the liquid form. In few parts of the dairy regions are there enough fattening feeds produced for the livestock. Corn, cottonseed oil cake, and other feeds are imported from the United States, Argentina, and South Africa. During and immediately following World War II, only small quantities of feed could be imported, and dairy production declined. Even when conditions are most favorable, European producers do not meet home demand for milk, butter, and cheese.

THE ALPS

Flying from Marseille to Vienna, one would cross in 700 airline miles parts of five countries—France, Italy, Switzerland, Germany, and Austria. See FIGURE 17.1. In the alpine portion of all these countries the principal use of the land is for dairying. Other activities include light manufacturing, forestry, and tourism, which in some localities are more important than farming. Dairying, however, is the oldest and most widespread of the occupations. Most of the land is too high, too cool, and the hours of sunshine are too short for the growth of many crops. Hay and pasture occupy most of the level land at the lower elevations.

The average dairy farm in the Alps is a three-storey affair. First, in the lower valley, is the farmstead with the main residence and the barns. The floors of the alpine valleys at the lower elevations are usually flat and often a mile or more in

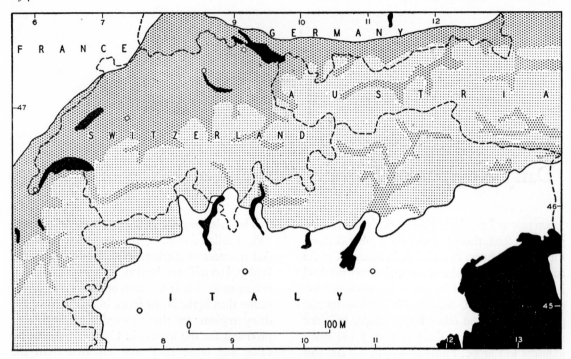

FIGURE 17.1. *A map of the Alpine Dairy Region, including parts of France, Switzerland, Italy, Austria, and Germany. The heavier shading indicates the areas of more intensive development on the smooth plateaus and in the Alpine valleys. The lighter shading represents less intensive development, including mountain pastures. The Alpine Dairy Region, associated with varied patterns of light manufacturing, is represented by cities such as Gênève, Bern, Basel, Luzern, and Zürich in Switzerland and by Torino, Milano, and Verona in Italy. The locations of these cities are shown by small circles on the map.*

width, affording a fair amount of smooth land for cultivation. On the floors of the steep-walled valleys, however, the sun may shine less than seven hours per day even in midsummer. The elevation makes for coolness also, and most of the valleys are not suitable for the growth of grains. On the south-facing slopes of some of the lowest valleys, grapes and mulberries are grown, but this is exceptional. The usual crops are hay, forage, and potatoes. The people spend the winters in the lower valley, but as soon as the snow melts on the nearby slopes, they begin the slow migration up the zigzag trails. The first objectives are the "May" pastures to be found on the benches and terraces at elevations of a few hundred to a few thousand feet above the valley floor. This is the second storey. The dairy animals graze on these pastures until the snow melts in the higher districts. They are moved upward as soon as possible so that the May pastures can produce a crop of

hay in the summer. The third storey is the "alp" proper, the mountain meadow above timberline. Here the animals graze through the summer on the cool humid slopes. The season is short and at the end of August the animals and people begin the descent, carrying with them the accumulation of cheeses and collecting the hay from the May pastures on the way down. It is obvious that, in a situation of this sort, cheese is the logical form in which to market the milk. Exporting milk would be most difficult, especially during the summer.

The regular seasonal migration of the pastoral peoples from the low valleys and plains to the mountain pastures is called *transhumance* and is widely practiced in the Alps, Pyrenees (FIG. 17.2), Massif Central of France, and various ranges in Spain, Italy, and the Balkans. The number of livestock, however, is not nearly so great as formerly. In Spain at one time three million sheep and other animals made the annual trek from north to south. In France the maximum was nearly 500,000; today the number is less than half that figure. Expansion of agriculture with consequent increased production of forage crops, the extension of forest reserves in the mountains, and the opposition of the agriculturists along the roads used by the animals have been contributing factors. Only in the districts with short migrations, such as the Alps, is transhumance practiced with dairy cows. Otherwise, the smaller animals—sheep and goats—predominate.

The French Alps begin at the Mediterranean. Along the Riviera in some of the valleys, characteristic Mediterranean crops such as olives and almonds are produced. But away from the coast dairying and the pasturage of sheep become the chief activities of the region. The most productive part of the French Alps is in the valleys of the Isère and the Drac rivers. There, the lower elevation of the valley floors and the excellent soils make it possible to cultivate a variety of crops, but potatoes and hay are still most important. Irrigation of the meadows is widely practiced to increase the yield of forage crops for the dairy cows. Up to 5000 feet the remnants of the forest are largely mixed species, the hardwood consisting of beech and birch mingling with the spruce and other conifers. From 5000 to 7000 feet conifers dominate. Above 7000 feet the "alps" occur in scattered areas reaching up to the zone of permanent snow at 9000 feet or more. Grenoble is the chief city of this region, with a population of 90,000. Gloves, shoes, and other articles of leather are manufactured there. The skins and hides are derived in part from the Alps and in part from the pastoral areas outside the Alps, including the Pyrenees. Abundant water power aids manufacturing, which includes silk spinning and weaving, cement making, and electrical industries.

The valleys and slopes of the Italian Alps are like those of France except that the Alps in Italy are protected more from the cold winds. Most of the dairy cattle of Italy are in the Alps, especially in the foothills. Several good breeds, such as the Swiss Simmenthal and the Brown Swiss, are found. In spite of the fact that many of the Italians are excellent dairymen, the yield of milk is low, about 500 gallons per cow per year for Italy as a whole. The low yields result from the lack of adequate feed, the cows depending on

FIGURE 17.2. *Two views of the French Pyrenees. The upper picture shows an aspect of the Pyrenees above timberline. These pastures support flocks of sheep which produce milk for cheese making. The lower view shows a cultivated meadow on a valley floor with a village perched on a terrace.*

grass and hay for the most part. The milk cows also double in harness as draft animals, which also decreases the yield. Most of the milk of this region is consumed in the fluid form, but some quantities of cheese, *gorgonzola* for example, are produced for export.

Large numbers of sheep are raised in the Italian Alps, although not for milk as in the Pyrenees, the Massif Central, and the Balkans. The sheep are kept for the wool and meat, and they make the annual migration with the dairy cows. The Alps furnish water power for the factories of the Po Plain, but there is a very limited

FIGURE 17.3. *An Alpine valley in Italy northeast of Bolzano. Some of the slopes, as in the foreground, support vineyards, but the region as a whole is used for dairying. From USAF.*

agricultural and industrial development in the valleys. See FIGURE 17.3.

Switzerland is well known in dairying circles all over the world for fine cattle, skilled dairymen, and a great variety of cheeses. In the Alps the system of cultivation and migration is similar to that of the French and Italian Alps. Most of the valley floors are too high for cultivation of crops other than hay and potatoes. The heart of Switzerland is a plateau lying between the Alps and the Jura mountains. This is a rather rough, rolling country with forested ridges and cultivated valleys. On favorable slopes orchards and vineyards are found, and the well-kept dairy farms with the excellent Brown Swiss dairy cattle are a conspicuous feature. Lakes are numerous, streams furnish water power, and here and there on the plateau are industrial cities. The greatest of these is Zürich. Textiles, machinery, and various other kinds of manufacturing make this the chief industrial city of the country. Zürich and hundreds of smaller industrial cities and towns provide a large market for dairy products, vegetables, and fruits. Most of the grain for bread is imported, but in difficult times wheat, rye, and barley can be grown on the plateau.

In the Austrian Alps the milk yield ranges from 400 to 600 gallons per year per cow, usually with grass and coarse forage and limited amounts of concentrated feeds. Near the sugar beet refineries in eastern Austria, molasses and beet residue are fed to the animals, and in prosperous times grain and imported oil cake are used. Most of the cows follow the usual migrations up and down the mountain slopes with the season. About half the milk is consumed in liquid form, 15 per cent fed to animals, and the remainder manufactured into butter and cheese. Most of the cheese is processed in cooperative factories with the Swiss and Dutch types of cheeses predominating.

After World War I Austria, her frontiers restricted, was sometimes called "a head [Vienna] without a body." The large area of alpine pastures together with the cultivated valleys, however, enabled the Austrians to produce milk and milk products for export. During World War II, the livestock declined in numbers, but the fact remains that the country is suited to dairying and can be again more than self-sufficient in the production of dairy products such as milk, butter, and cheese.

NORTHWESTERN EUROPE

The most intensively cultivated land in Europe lies along the coast of northern France, Belgium, the Netherlands, and the adjacent parts of Germany and Denmark. See FIGURE 17.4. Much of the land now cultivated has been reclaimed from the sea by great labor, and some of it is nearly 30 feet below mean sea level. It is only by constant vigilance that water from rains, rivers, and the sea is kept from covering the fields. To one accustomed to drought and to the irrigation schemes

FIGURE 17.4. *A map of the dairy regions of northwestern Europe. The zone of intensive dairying includes the Channel and North Sea coasts of France, the Low Countries, Germany, and Denmark, also southern Norway and Sweden, and a large portion of the British Isles. The circles indicate the chief cities in and near the Dairy Belt which are the markets for milk, butter, and cheese.*

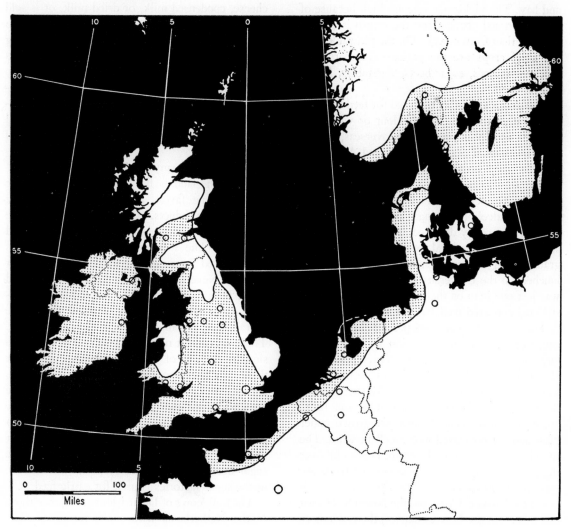

necessary for agriculture in arid lands, it is a strange sight indeed to witness the constant struggle *against* water. When the first settlers came into the region many centuries ago, they found a string of sand dune islands along the coast. Between the dunes and the land was marsh, a shallow part of the sea. The dunes afforded a place to build houses and villages but were not suitable for intensive cultivation. Dikes, therefore, were constructed little by little, and the enclosed land was pumped free of water by windmills. Nowadays, dikes are constructed on a large scale and the pumping is done by Diesel motors or by electricity.

More than 60 per cent of the cultivated land is in grasses. This is partly because the land is so difficult to plow for row crops and partly because of the large return to be obtained from pasture and hay. The yields per acre are high because of the year-round growth, and the return is greater in value than from cereals. On the plowable land the chief crops are the grains—rye, oats, and wheat—potatoes, sugar beets, vegetables, fruits, and flowers.

The grains are ordinarily used for feed for livestock rather than for bread. Flour or wheat for bread is usually imported from overseas, mostly from the United States, Canada, and Argentina, because good bread cannot be made from the local grains. Potatoes are used both for food and feed for livestock and, in addition, for the manufacture of alcohol. During World War II livestock were greatly depleted, and the people consumed all available local supplies of potatoes and grain. In 1945 the author was invited to a student luncheon at the University of Amsterdam. There was just one item on the menu, potatoes; yet the students appeared well fed and mentally alert.

The yields of sugar beets per acre are high because of the careful cultivation and the use of large quantities of fertilizer. However, cane sugar is imported to all the countries of northwestern Europe from the tropical regions. Market gardens flourish, and a variety of vegetables and fruits are produced in them. Grapes are grown under glass and are converted into excellent wine. The tulip bulbs of the Netherlands are famous all over the world. Many of the vegetables and fruits are exported to England.

On the Channel Coast and the North Sea Coast of France and the Low Countries, there are more livestock in relation to the cropped land than in any other part of Europe. Cattle for both milk and meat, pigs, horses, sheep, and poultry are all of importance. Near the west end of this region in France, is Perche, the home of Percheron draft horses. In the English Channel to the west of the Cherbourg Peninsula are the Channel Islands of Jersey and Guernsey which have given their names to famous breeds of dairy cattle. In the Netherlands, Belgium, and adjacent lowlands the dairy cow is dominant. The black and white Frisians from the islands of the same name are the most numerous, since they yield large quantities of milk although with only a moderate butter fat content. The average annual yield of milk per cow is more than 800 gallons, with high fat content. About half of the milk ordinarily is converted to butter; the remainder is made into cheese, condensed milk, or dried milk, or is sold to consumers of whole milk. Skim milk is fed to pigs and poultry, and bacon and eggs have long been important items of export. The forage crops grown in the Low Countries are not sufficient to feed all the livestock, consequently large quantities of corn, oil cake, and other feeds are imported from the United States, Argentina, and eastern Europe, especially from Hungary and Romania.

Denmark has many natural advantages for agriculture. The land is flat and the soil good. The long coastline favors the exportation of bulky agricultural products. The best land is on the islands and on the eastern side of the Jutland Peninsula. The western part of the country is less favored because of sandy soils and poor harbors. Nevertheless, with the aid of imported feeds, both meat and milk are produced for export. Denmark is a nation of small farms, the average farm comprising less than 100 acres. There are almost no large estates. The crops are similar to those of the Netherlands except that there is rather more emphasis on feed grains, barley, oats, and mixed grains. Potatoes are grown for food and feed, and various root forage crops such as the mangel (coarse variety of beet) enable the Danes to feed their livestock without importing too much costly foreign forage. The sugar beet is an important crop, and the residue of the sugar factories is used for cattle feed.

The milk cows of Denmark are similar to those of the Netherlands with slight variations. The two main breeds are the Red Danish and the Black and White Jutland, both of which average about 700 gallons of milk per cow per year. By far the greater proportion of milk, more than four fifths in good years, is made into butter. About one tenth is consumed as whole milk while only small quantities are condensed or made into cheese. In normal times about three fourths of the butter is exported, mostly to Britain. Exports of butter and bacon and imports of feeds, coal, and other raw materials makes Denmark a leading country of Europe in per capita trade.

In south central Sweden and in the Oslo district of Norway dairy farming is dominant. Land available for agriculture is more limited, and the climate is less favorable than in the Low Countries. Nevertheless, hay grows well and occupies a very large part of the cultivated land. The other crops include oats, barley, and potatoes, all of which are used for feed. Owing to the rough nature of the terrain, not more than 15 to 20 per cent of the land is under cultivation. Despite this fact nearly 40 per cent of the people of Sweden live on farms. However, not enough food is produced to satisfy domestic demands. Wheat and various feeds are imported. The farms are small with an average of about 25 acres under cultivation. Many of the farms are part time, and the farmers work in lumber mills and factories or engage in fishing during part of the year. The crop pattern is characteristic of this whole dairy region. Hay, oats, rye, mixed grains, wheat, potatoes, root forage, and sugar beets are, in order, the chief crops.

Fifty million people are supported in the British Isles in an area of about 120,000 square miles, slightly less than the area of the state of New Mexico. With an environment which is not favorable for intensive agriculture, the British long ago turned to industry and trade, and about half of all the employed people are so engaged. Only about 10 per cent are engaged in agriculture. In general, the character of the agriculture is like that of northern Europe. The summers are cool and rainy; the winters are mild with even more rain than the Continent. Thus, the climate is unfavorable for grains, except on the east coast, but suitable for grass, hay, potatoes, and various vegetables. Under the circumstances it is not surprising that a large part of the farm land is used for dairy-

ing, especially if the large urban population is considered. The variety of terrain, of climate, and accessibility to market makes for various types of land use, including commercial grazing in some of the more remote localities.

The eastern part of England and a small portion of eastern Scotland are lowlands on which conditions are most favorable for crops. Parts of the land are level and fertile, and the annual rainfall is lighter than farther west, falling below 25 inches in the eastern part of southern England. The low rainfall is sufficient for grains in these cool northern latitudes. A part of this region is in the Small Grain and Livestock type to be described on page 268. The western part of England and Wales and the greater part of Scotland are more rugged, and while the elevation is not great the country is more suited to pasture than to crop production. Some areas in southern Wales and southern Scotland are used almost exclusively for grazing. The remainder of Britain is used mostly for dairying, although there is emphasis throughout on the production of meat for the home market.

The crops of Britain are like those of most northern countries, such as Denmark and Sweden. By far the largest acreage is in hay. Next are oats, wheat, barley, mangels, and potatoes. A much smaller acreage is in fruit and vegetables, but this production is worth noting. The average farm in Britain is less than 100 acres in size, and most of them are operated by tenants with long-term leases. In southeastern England the farms are much larger; thus the cultivation and harvest of grain can be facilitated by heavy machinery.

Most of the dairy regions of Britain occupy an intermediate position with respect to land quality and climate. The grain lands are found on the best soils and in the most favorable rainfall and temperature belts. Grazing is on the roughest and most humid land while the dairy regions are located near the great urban districts. The largest area includes most of the southern and central part of the English Lowland. Between London and Cornwall on the south, the Dairy Belt is widest and includes even the southern part of Wales. Northward the region narrows, compressed by the grazing region of the highland of Wales on the west and on the east by the grain-producing region of eastern England. Included in this region are most of the cities of England.

Another area of dairying is to be noted in the western part of the Scottish Lowland and parts of the southern Upland. Here, too, the influence of the industrial centers and the other large cities is felt. Glasgow, Edinburgh, and many smaller cities afford a good market for milk and milk products. Early potatoes and various fruits are grown along with the forage crops for the dairy cows, and on the adjacent hills sheep for wool and mutton utilize the land which is not suitable for farming.

Most of Ireland, including both Eire and Northern Ireland, is also primarily a dairy region, although more retarded in its development than Britain. Since there are few large cities in Ireland, the Irish are able to send dairy products and meat to England. The conditions of climate and soil are more favorable to dairying than to grain farming. The rainfall is heavier than in England, and the summers are slightly cooler. The high percentage of cloudiness makes it difficult to ripen grains. Then much of the central plain of Ireland is low and swampy making cultivation difficult. Pasture is good, however, and there is a natural tendency to concentrate on meat production. Some oats and barley are grown, and potatoes are produced everywhere as food for man and beast. The flax crop was formerly of great significance in Northern Ireland, but in recent years, imports of linen fiber from Russia have supplied most of the Irish linen factories.

In spite of the large percentage of the farmland devoted to dairying, it is necessary for the British to import milk, butter, and cheese. Most of the import is shipped from Denmark, the Netherlands, Belgium, and northern France, but large quantities of butter also are imported from Canada, New Zealand, and Australia. Large quantities of meat also are imported by the British, most of it from the Dominions and Argentina. It is to be noted that the increased emphasis on dairying in recent decades has been to a certain extent at the expense of meat production.

AUSTRALIA

The Dairy Belt of Australia extends approximately from Brisbane on the east coast, southward through Sydney, westward through Melbourne, to southwestern Victoria. Tasmania is also a part of this Dairy Belt. The region is east and south of the Australian Mountains which are sometimes called the Great Dividing Range. It is the most humid part of Australia with good pasture for most of the year. Most of the large cities of Australia are in this region.

The general quality of this region differs little from some of the cool humid regions previously described, such as the Willamette Valley of Oregon or parts of the British Isles. Jerseys and Holsteins are the favorite breeds. Most of the pasture is based on sown rather than natural grasses. Ensilage is used for winter feeding in the southern districts especially in Tasmania. Since there is no corn belt in Australia and there is a limited amount of humid pasture, many cattle and sheep from the Commercial Grazing Regions to the west are fattened and finished in this region.

The eight million people of Australia do not represent a very large market for dairy products, and the foreign market is far away in western Europe. Enough milk, butter, and cheese are produced for the home market and, in addition, some butter for export. Butter usually ranks fifth in export value, after wool, wheat, gold, and meat. The fact that the people of western Europe are now using their limited purchasing power to import the cheaper foods, such as wheat, corn, and vegetable oils, has obviously had a restraining influence on the dairy industry of Australia and New Zealand.

NEW ZEALAND

The Dairy Region of New Zealand is located in the northern and western portions of North Island in approximately the same latitude as that of Australia. Humid pasture, parts of which are cleared forest sown to grass, is abundant. Since good grass is available the year round, little attention is given to forage crops. No more wheat and other grains are produced in New Zealand than the local market demands. Butter, wool, and meat are of almost equal export value, and the production of all increased rapidly prior to World War II. The areas of most intensive dairying include the valley of the Waikato River, which flows northward from Lake Taupo in the center of North Island, and the districts around Auckland and Wellington. The chief crops grown in the New Zealand Dairy Belt are turnips, alfalfa, and oats for feed; also wheat, various fruits, and tobacco. Of these only apples are exported. Even in the Dairy Belt of New Zealand, sheep for wool and mutton add to the farm income.

CHAPTER

18

The United States Corn Belt

FROM South Dakota to Maryland and from Kansas to Virginia stretches the Corn Belt (FIGS. 18.1A and 18.1B), the most productive agricultural region in the Americas. Corn is grown in many lands, but here Corn is King. The annual yield, nearly three billion bushels, is enough to provide every person on earth with 80 pounds of grain. Little of the crop is used directly for food, however. Most of it is fed to livestock—cattle, hogs, sheep, and poultry—and the chief cash product of the Corn Belt is meat. Other crops include hay, wheat, oats, soybeans, and tobacco. A longer and more meaningful name for the Corn Belt is "Corn, small grain, hay, pasture, and livestock belt."

The best way to find out how the Corn Belt functions is to study an individual farm, keeping in mind that no single example is absolutely typical of the Corn Belt. Most of the Corn Belt is in relatively flat country and little can be seen from the road; in winter there is little to attract the attention; in summer the tall corn obscures the view and masks other important crops. See FIGURE 18.2. But from an airplane in midsummer an excellent general idea of the crops can be obtained, and later a farm can be visited on the ground for details. From a plane over central Iowa or Illinois, the most striking quality of the landscape is the rectangular road pattern (FIG. 18.3). The roads are usually one mile apart, some paved, some graveled, and others but slightly improved. Within a square marked off by the roads, there are usually four farms, as indicated by the farmsteads, clusters of buildings with windbreaks. The most representative farm size in the western part of the Corn Belt is 160 acres, but there are many larger and smaller farms.

If the pilot can be persuaded to circle momentarily, attention can be fixed on an individual farm. The farmstead, appearing small but very distinct, faces south on a paved road; clearly defined are the various buildings, the two-storey frame residence, the large unpainted barn with silo, the corn crib, granary, implement shed, and several small structures known as "hog houses." Near the residence are a vegetable garden and a small orchard, and to the north and west of the farmstead there is a windbreak of pine trees. Beyond are the fields and in midsummer the crops are not difficult to identify, even from the air. In the northwest "forty" (acres) and in the southwest "seventeen" the dark green, coarse looking crop is corn, 57 acres in all. In the north "twenty" the farmer is beginning to harvest oats with a small tractor and binder. In the west "twenty" the wheat is beginning to ripen, turning from a light green to a golden straw color. Three other fields of about 20 acres each are in hay and pasture, the latter distinguishable by the grazing cattle. In summary, the farm has 57 acres of corn, 20 acres of wheat, 20 of oats, 20 in hay, and 39 in pasture, 2 acres in the farmstead, a total of 158 acres.

Such a view of a corn belt farm from the air in midsummer gives a good idea of the crops but tells little of the farm as a production unit. To understand how the various parts function, it is necessary to study the farm at various seasons, since labor and production on the farm is an almost unbroken cycle of planting, cultivation, harvesting, and the feeding of livestock. The best time to start our study of the Corn Belt cycle is in the fall after the corn crop is harvested. When the corn is in the crib and the livestock have eaten

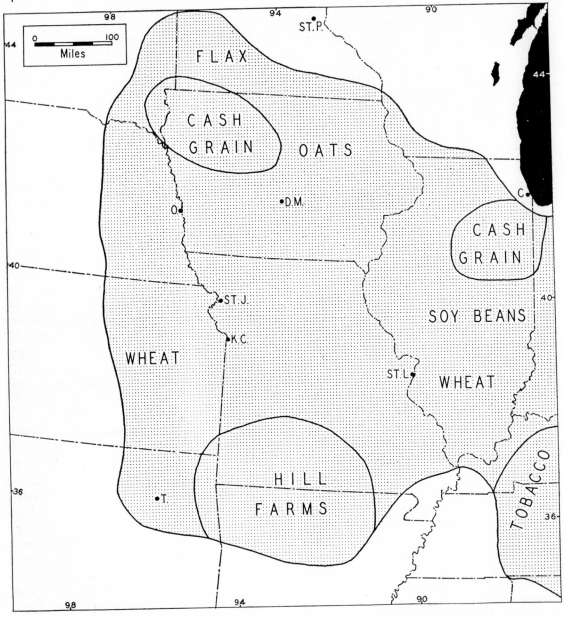

FIGURE 18.1A. *A map of the greater Corn Belt of the United States. The region in which corn is the dominant crop extends from the Winter Wheat Belt to the Atlantic Seaboard and from the Dairy Region to the Cotton Belt. The chief minor crops are indicated for various parts of the belt. Corn, hay, and small grains are found throughout the regions. Three subtypes are shown: cash grain, in which much of the corn is sold from the farm; tobacco; and the hill farms with emphasis on subsistence. Abbreviations: C., Chicago; D.M., Des Moines; K.C., Kansas City; O., Omaha; St. J., St. Joseph; St. L., St. Louis; St. P., St. Paul; T., Tulsa.*

FIGURE 18.1B. *A continuation of Figure 18.1A is shown on the opposite page. Abbreviations: B., Baltimore; C., Cincinnati; I., Indianapolis; P., Philadelphia; W., Washington; L., Louisville.*

the fodder from the field, it is time to plow and prepare the land for winter wheat, which follows corn in the crop rotation. Nearly all the wheat in the Corn Belt is winter wheat (FIG. 18.4) and is, in the aggregate, the most important money crop in the Corn Belt. During the winter the Corn Belt farmer is less busy, having only to feed the livestock and repair the machinery. However, many farmers keep dairy cows and the milking furnishes additional employment. The first crop to be planted in the spring is oats, which can be seeded before the frost is out of the ground and before it is time for corn planting. Shortly after corn planting, May or June, and as soon as the corn is a few inches in height, cultivation is necessary. In July wheat which was planted in the fall and the oats sown in early spring are ready to harvest. The hay harvest also demands the farmer's attention. In late summer the farmer is not quite so busy, but there are weeds to cut, fences to repair, and always the feeding of the livestock. Then comes autumn and the corn

FIGURE 18.2. *A view of a Corn Belt farm in southern Wisconsin. The crops include corn, oats, and hay grown on gentle slopes. The farmstead, consisting of frame dwelling, barns, windmill, silo, and various other structures, occupies a slight eminence. From Soil Conservation Service.*

harvest. There are many ways of harvesting corn —by use of the combine, by shocking and husking later, or by husking by hand directly from the stalk. A small proportion of the corn is harvested by the beef cattle or hogs, saving the farmer the labor.

Since the primary goal of the Corn Belt farmer is the production of meat, the farmer must breed or buy beef cattle, hogs, lambs, and poultry. Most of the animals are bred on the farms, but migra-

tions of cattle and sheep from the regions of Commercial Grazing are heavy. In either case the "stockyard" cities are markets where the farmer can buy and sell livestock. Many farmers purchase thin, young cattle or lambs called "feeders" just as they come from the ranges. Since they are not suitable for slaughter in this condition, the price per pound is low. Fattened on corn, oats, hay, and good pasture the animals are ready after several months to return to the stockyards where

FIGURE 18.3. *Contrasting aerial views in the Corn Belt. In the upper view the smooth surface of the Illinois Corn Belt is divided into rectangular fields. The road pattern is also rectangular except where modified by a shallow stream valley. The lower view shows a hilly aspect of the Corn Belt in central Tennessee. Only a part of the land is cleared for cultivation; the remainder is in woodland. The fields are irregular, many of them occupying fairly steep slopes. From AAA.*

the farmers receive a higher price per pound for many more pounds. The larger stockyards are located on the western side of the Corn Belt near the grazing lands. Chicago, Omaha, Sioux City, South St. Paul, and Kansas City handle the largest numbers of livestock. There are stockyards in most of the large cities farther east, but on a smaller scale. Near the yards are packing houses where the meat is processed for the market.

LIMITS AND DIVISIONS OF THE CORN BELT

Some corn is grown in almost every state in the United States. Along the northern boundary some areas are too cool for corn to ripen and the arid lands are too dry, but the distribution of corn is wide and includes even a part of Canada. Corn grows all the way to the tropics and throughout the temperate parts of the Southern Hemisphere. Corn grows better in some districts than others, however, and the region extending eastward from eastern South Dakota and Kansas to the Atlantic seaboard is, in general, especially well suited for corn.

The Corn Belt has fairly definite limits based on a number of factors. To the north and west the boundaries are principally climatic. Corn requires high temperatures both night and day if the yield is to be heavy. Corn can be grown in regions of cool summers for silage and fodder but not for grain. The development of new strains of hybrid corn has extended the limits somewhat in recent years, but most of the crop is still grown where the average July temperature is above 70° F. On the west corn is limited by low rainfall. Although it is not possible to state a definite number of inches of rain necessary for a good corn crop,

comparatively little corn is grown where the annual rainfall is less than 20 inches. The southern limit of the Corn Belt is determined by the competition with cotton. To be sure, corn is grown throughout the Cotton Belt but usually as a

FIGURE 18.4. *Wheat harvest in the Corn Belt of central Iowa. Corn, wheat, and alfalfa occupy alternating strips of the gently sloping surface. From Soil Conservation Service.*

secondary crop. It may be stated then that the southern boundary of the Corn Belt is determined by the northern limit of cotton.

The Corn Belt is a large region, including all or parts of 20 states; naturally there is a great variety of production with respect to the minor crops and products. The heart of the belt, from Iowa to Ohio, is often called the Inner Corn Belt and is distinguished by the emphasis on corn as a crop and on meat as a money product. On the margins of the region there are, of course, certain resemblances to the adjacent regional types. For example, near the Dairy Region, there is more emphasis on hay and pasture; near the Wheat Belt, larger acreage in wheat. Furthermore, there are other distinct phases which are related to cities, to peculiarities in the climate, and to soil or surface configuration. Many subdivisions could be made, but in addition to the Inner Corn Belt, four will suffice here: the cash grain areas of Iowa and Illinois; the tobacco region of Kentucky and Tennessee; the mountain

hill farms of the Ozarks and the southern Appalachians; and the eastern Corn Belt of southeastern Pennsylvania and parts of Virginia and Maryland.

The Inner Corn Belt

The best part of the Corn Belt corresponds to the prairie which confronted the early settlers. The prairie ran from western Ohio to eastern South Dakota and Kansas. Its smooth rolling grassy surface was interrupted only by the larger stream valleys which provided water and wood for the pioneers. The only slopes too steep to be cultivated were on the banks of the streams. The soils derived in part from glacial deposits were excellent. The long continued growth of tall luxuriant grass produced an excellent humus, and the rainfall was not sufficient to cause excessive leaching. The thick tough sod presented a problem for the first settlers since it was difficult to plow with the light draft animals and equipment available, but once "broken," the soils proved rather easy to cultivate in most places. In some places the settlers found the land so level that artificial drainage was necessary.

At present in the Inner Corn Belt (FIG. 18.5) emphasis is on meat production rather than production of cash crops for sale. After corn, hay and oats are the crops with the greatest acreage and value. In many districts hay has a greater acreage than corn. Some wheat, soybeans, and other crops are grown for sale, but the production of beef, pork, and mutton is the chief concern of the farmer. In general, nearly 90 per cent of the corn crop is fed to livestock while the remainder is sold for food and industrial purposes.

The dominating purpose of the Corn Belt farmer is to produce meat for sale. To do this he must grow quantities of corn, oats, and hay for feed. He must maintain the fertility of the soil, and he must plan his work so that the plowing, seeding, cultivating, and harvesting of one crop will not interfere with that of the others. In this respect corn production works well with hay and small grains. Other row crops such as tobacco, potatoes, and beans require attention at the same time as corn, and therefore the farmer's work schedule is made more difficult. Such crops are grown in some parts of the Corn Belt to be described later.

On most Corn Belt farms some sort of crop rotation is practiced to aid in the maintenance of soil fertility. A three-year, four-year, or longer period of rotation may be followed. A common three-year rotation is corn-oats-hay, and following the hay crop the land may be used for pasture for one or more years. Wheat is grown in place of oats in many parts of the area. The proportion of crops and the number of livestock on the farm depend to a large extent on prices. If grain prices are high and meat low, the farmer is likely to extend the acreage of corn and wheat and sell a larger quantity of grain. If meat prices are high, he may purchase additional grain from neighboring areas so that he may fatten more animals.

The Cash Grain Areas

In several districts within the Corn Belt the farmers produce large quantities of corn and other grains for sale, retaining only a part of the crop for feeding. These cash grain areas include part of eastern Illinois to the south of Chicago and a large area in northwestern Iowa and adjacent parts of Minnesota and South Dakota. The cash grain areas are a response, in part, to the demand for corn for feed and industrial purposes in the large cities. Corn from the cash grain areas is used to feed livestock in the more intensive meat production districts and also in the manufacture of cereal foods, corn oil, and alcohol. Chicago is the market for the Illinois area, while Sioux City, Omaha, and St. Paul are close to the larger area. Both districts are in excellent country for the production of corn on a large commercial scale. The land is exceptionally smooth, the soils good, and the farms are much larger than the average. In the western district it is not uncommon to see a square mile section in one field of corn. The cash grain districts are organized so that corn is grown and marketed on a large scale. Machinery is used for planting, cultivating, and harvesting. If the weather will permit, corn is picked, husked, and shelled in one series of operations by means of combines. There are usually elevators and other storage facilities for handling corn in nearby towns.

The Tobacco District

The Tobacco District of the Corn Belt is in the hilly lands of Kentucky, Tennessee, and includes small parts of Ohio and Indiana. See FIGURE 18.6. The growth of corn is not so intensive in this district as in the Inner Corn Belt, but nearly all the farms qualify as Corn Belt farms. Corn, wheat, oats, and hay are important crops, and much of the corn and oats is fed to livestock. However, the rough land is not well suited for the large-scale production of grain; furthermore, this district is more remote from the large livestock markets than other parts of the Corn Belt. Tobacco grows well because of the excellent soils derived from limestone, the favorable climate, and the skill and experience of the farmers. Included in this district is the well-known Blue Grass section of Kentucky and a similar section of Tennessee known as the Nashville Basin. Other districts are in general less favorable for tobacco because of steep slopes and less fertile soils.

Tobacco is the chief cash crop in all this region although the sale of meat is considerable. Most of the farms are small and the fields of tobacco rarely exceed 10 acres. The transplanting, cultivation, care, and harvesting of tobacco require so much hand labor that a farmer can produce only a few acres together with his other crops. The

FIGURE 18.5. *A hilly phase of the Corn Belt in southern Ohio. Strip cropping is necessary to prevent erosion on these slopes. From Soil Conservation Service.*

expenditure of labor is greater than that of any other crop in the Corn Belt. Furthermore, each farmer has a quota of so many acres in order to avoid overproduction and declining prices. The task begins with the preparation of the seed beds in early spring. The bed is carefully prepared with the best soil, and after sowing is covered with canvas to protect it from late frosts and other hazards. The field is then prepared for transplanting by plowing, harrowing, fertilizing, and laying out in squares. The tobacco plants, now several inches in height, are transplanted to the field usually by hand. Then follows the weeding, hoeing, topping, thinning, harvesting, curing, and stripping, most of which must be done by hand. Only the large cash return per acre makes all this labor worthwhile. On good land the yield is often greater than 1000 pounds per acre and sometimes reaches a ton. If the price is good, the gross return per acre may exceed $500. Many small farms sell more than $5000 worth of tobacco per year, but the cost of production may include $50 per acre or more for commercial fertilizer. In any event tobacco usually accounts for a larger share of the cash income than that derived from the sale of livestock. Three broad types of tobacco are produced in this region, air-cured light burley in the northern part, fire-cured dark tobacco in the west and south, and dark air-cured tobacco in the middle section. Most of the light burley is used in the manufacture of cigarettes, the darker fire-cured types are exported, while the dark air-cured tobacco is used in the manufacture of chewing tobacco and snuff.

The Hill Farms District

In the Ozarks and the southern Appalachians (FIG. 18.6) farming is less well developed than in the smoother parts of the Corn Belt, but corn is still the most important crop. Much of the land is too steep for cultivation, while the land with gentler slopes is often infertile. This district was settled by pioneers who preferred a carefree life of hunting and gathering, with some farming, to the life of hard work and greater reward in the plains. Most of the farms have been classified as subsistence type (FIG. 18.7), on which most of the produce is consumed and there is little to sell, or if a surplus of corn or meat is produced, there is poor access to a market.

The typical farm in this district lies in a valley

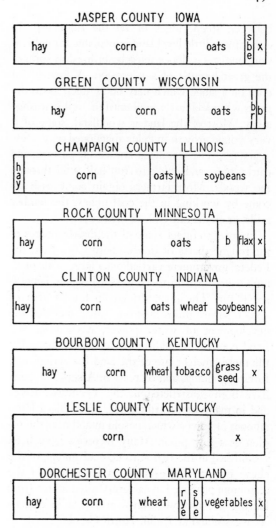

FIGURE 18.6. *Crop graphs of various counties in the Corn Belt. The proportion of hay, corn, and small grain varies widely. Jasper County, Iowa, and Clinton County, Indiana, represent the inner part of the Corn Belt; Green County, Wisconsin, the northern edge with some emphasis upon dairying. Champaign County, Illinois, produces corn and soybeans as cash crops, as does Rock County, Minnesota. In Bourbon County, Kentucky, tobacco is the important cash crop. In Dorchester County, Maryland, large quantities of vegetables are sold from the farm, while in Leslie County, Kentucky, a large proportion of the corn is consumed as food and feed. Abbreviations: b, beans; br, barley; sbe, soybeans; w, wheat; x, miscellaneous crops.*

between steep ridges or on the ridge top. In either place little level land is available for cultivation, and steep slopes must be utilized in spite of the great hazards of soil erosion. A "patch" of corn on a slope which may be as steep as 40 degrees will yield fairly well until the soil is washed away. Most of the land is woodland, some of it very young growth in fields abandoned only a few years ago. The woodland is used for pasture, and cattle, pigs, and chickens run half wild through the woods. Most farmers obtain some cash income by working in the coal mines, the lumber mills, or on the railroads or highways.

In order to offset some of the disadvantages of the rougher parts of the southern Corn Belt, the Federal government carried out a large-scale planning experiment in the watershed of the Tennessee River. The plan, drawn up for an area of 40,000 square miles in seven states, included the development of water power, navigation, and flood control. In addition, plans were made for the more efficient use of the land for agriculture, forestry, mining, and recreation. A series of dams have been constructed in the Tennessee River and in many of its tributaries, providing a large amount of power which is sold in and near the region at a low price. Many factories have been established in the region to take advantage of the cheap power. For example, a large part of the aluminum produced in eastern United States from bauxite ore is now refined at Alcoa in eastern Tennessee and at Badin, North Carolina.

The impact of this plan on the agriculture of the region is most significant. Formerly most of the hill farms were impoverished by soil erosion, and the yields were declining from year to year. Only on the relatively smooth floor of the Great Valley of eastern Tennessee was agriculture on a fairly stable basis. The Tennessee Valley Authority has been able to retire some of the land least suited for agriculture. Soil conservation measures, including terracing, strip cropping, and contour plowing, make it possible to cultivate many of the moderate slopes without serious risk of soil erosion. Yields have been improved by the use of fertilizer processed in the region. The Corn Belt type of farming predominates. Corn, wheat, hay, pasture, and livestock are the important elements. On many of the ridge slopes, apples and other fruit trees have been planted and grow well.

The Eastern Section

The character of the Corn Belt to the east of the Appalachians is influenced by the large urban population as well as by the nature of the terrain and soils. In southeastern Pennsylvania and parts of Virginia and Maryland, a ridge and valley landscape prevails. The rolling valley lowlands are underlain by limestone which weathers to a fertile soil. The ridges, on the other hand, are made up of shale and sandstone and are suitable only for orchards, pasture, and woodland. In the lowlands there is more acreage in corn than in any other tilled crop. Hay, wheat, and tobacco are also important. The nearness of large cities— Washington, Baltimore, Philadelphia, and New York—stimulates the production of specialty crops which are generally unimportant in the more remote parts of the Corn Belt. Fruits and vegetables, the former grown on the ridges and on the ridge slopes, occupy a large acreage. The valleys of southeastern Pennsylvania were settled predominantly by Germans who came to be known as "Pennsylvania Dutch." These farmers prefer the soils of the limestone lowland and are noted for their neat farms and for their thrift. Corn, small grains, hay, and tobacco are the chief crops. The livestock include a large proportion of dairy cows, but in general the farms belong to the Corn Belt type.

CORN BELT CITIES

There are few large cities in the Corn Belt, but there are many small and medium-sized ones. Of greatest significance are the stockyard cities, some of which are outside the proper area of the Corn Belt. The large stockyards are in the western part of the region since these yards have the first chance at the "feeder" cattle sent in from the ranges in the west. The largest stockyards are in Chicago, slightly outside of the Corn Belt, because of superior railroad connections. From almost every state in western United States livestock is shipped to Chicago even though it may pass through some of the other stockyard cities. Chicago and vicinity represents a large market in itself, and its railway connections with the eastern centers of population are excellent. Omaha, near the western edge of the Corn Belt, receives most of its livestock from the overland route directly to the west. Kansas City, on the south-

FIGURE 18.7. *A Corn Belt hill farm in eastern Kentucky. The cornfield entirely surrounds the house while the slope in the background is too steep for cultivation. In this part of the Corn Belt, shifts in cultivation are frequent.*

western corner of the Corn Belt is in a position to receive livestock from western Kansas, Oklahoma, and Texas. Also included in the hinterland of Kansas City is the rich corn land of northern Missouri and a part of the oilfields of the mid-continent region. Another important stockyard city is South St. Paul in Minnesota. Served by several rail lines which reach into the Northwest, this city is marginal to the proper area of the Corn Belt but functions as a distributing center for "feeders" to the northwestern part of the Corn Belt. Other stockyard cities in the western part of the Corn Belt include Sioux City (Iowa), St. Joseph and St. Louis (Missouri). The last named functions not only as a great commercial center for the adjacent part of the Corn Belt but is an important manufacturing city as well.

The cities of the eastern part of the Corn Belt are less noteworthy as stockyard centers; they are more significant for manufacturing. There are stockyards in most of the larger cities from which farmers are supplied with feeders. Meat is packed for the local markets at such yards. The industries of many of these cities are directly related to the Corn Belt. The manufacture of agricultural machinery and the processing of Corn Belt crops, together with other industries, will be described later, in the chapter on manufacturing in North America.

RECENT TRENDS IN THE CORN BELT

The Corn Belt represents a stable system of farming but is not static. Men and methods, crops and products, and land systems are changing under the influence of technological improvements. On the farm the most spectacular change is the great increase in the use of machinery. Formerly a tractor was considered out of place on the average farm; the tractor was too large and too expensive to own and operate; it would do some jobs well, but was ill suited to the cultivation of half-grown corn. The makers of farm machinery have answered both objections; small, inexpensive row-crop tractors and suitable plows, cultivators, and harvesters have been provided for the small farm. Rubber tires on tractors and implements have added greatly to the usefulness of power machinery. In addition to the efficiency of power machinery, the shortage of farm labor has increased the use of power equipment.

Partly as a result of the increase in the use of power the average size of the Corn Belt farm has increased. In 1900 the average farm in Iowa was 151 acres; in 1930, it was 158 acres; in 1950, it was 168 acres. Perhaps the typical farm of 160 acres with horse-drawn machines was an efficient unit. What is the size of an efficient unit with power machinery? One Corn Belt farmer bought five farms close together but not adjacent, all of which could be classed as financially distressed and run down. These farms had acreages of 60, 60, 80, 110, and 110. He reorganized them to make one farm unit of 420 acres which he now operates with two men. Tools are shifted from one farm to another. The trend is definitely toward the larger units and the pace is quickening.

The trend in farm land prices is of greatest significance in the Corn Belt. A few generations ago good land could be obtained for almost nothing; in the early years of this century, especially 1917 to 1921, land prices advanced beyond reason, stimulated by the high prices of farm produce. In 1920 the average price of Iowa farm land was about $200 per acre. By 1951 the price was much higher. In general, when land prices in the Corn Belt go up after a steep decline, more farms are operated by tenants. In 1939 more than half of the farms in the belt were operated by tenants, and contrary to popular opinion some of the tenants are more prosperous than the owners of small farms, since the small farmer is hard pressed, even without the burden of investment or debt. In a long period of farm prosperity and high commodity prices, tenancy usually declines.

Crops in the Corn Belt are slowly but constantly changing. New varieties of old crops, such as hybrid corn, are of great importance; new crops, like soybeans, are just as significant. The effects of such changes are far reaching. Hybrid corn, a new variety, yields much more than the older varieties. In 1933 there was very little planted, but in 1939, 40 per cent of the corn acreage in the Corn Belt was hybrid, by 1951 nearly 95 per cent. It is noteworthy that the acreage restrictions of the Agricultural Adjustment Ad-

ministration stimulated the use of hybrid seeds enormously, since the usual amount of corn could be produced from a much smaller acreage.

Soybeans, the most spectacular crop in the Corn Belt, are not new; this crop has been increasing gradually for years. In 1930 more than three million acres were sown, mostly in the Corn Belt but also in the Cotton Belt. The soybean is an excellent protein producer, easily adaptable for food or feed. Acreage jumped to 13 million in 1951, stimulated by the new demand for soybean oil and by the classification of soybeans as a soil-conserving crop.

MINERALS

Although the Corn Belt, as outlined previously, is primarily an agricultural region, mineral production, especially of coal, petroleum, sand, gravel, and building stone, is substantial. Coal is produced in various fields from Iowa to Pennsylvania, with the best coal being mined in the Appalachian plateaus of southern West Virginia, Kentucky, Tennessee, and Virginia. In Iowa and Illinois some of the coal is strip-mined since it is close to the surface, but shaft mines are also common. In general, the coals of the western part of the belt are not satisfactory for coking but are valuable for fuel.

Petroleum is also found rather widely in the Corn Belt but generally in small quantities. The best fields are in southern Illinois where deep wells have tapped new pools in recent years, and also in Kansas and Oklahoma. Smaller fields are operated in Kentucky, Ohio, and West Virginia.

Since the northern part of the Corn Belt is covered with glacial deposits, supplies of sand and gravel are abundant. Gravel is used widely in road building both in the loose form and in concrete. Various building stones, including limestone and sandstone, are available. In many parts of the region, limestone is quarried and crushed for fertilizer on a large scale. Clay for brick, tile, and other ceramics is available in many districts, a critical resource in a region in which there never have been extensive forests. The lead mines of southern Missouri are the most extensive in North America, but otherwise little metallic minerals are produced in the Corn Belt. The supplies of fuel, minerals, and agricultural raw materials contribute to the variety of manufacturing in the region, to be discussed in Chapter 37.

CHAPTER

19

Corn Belts of Other Lands

THE corn belts outside the United States are by no means so extensive, productive, or so varied as the region described in the previous chapter. See FIGURE 19.1. Each of these smaller corn belts, however, plays an important role in its territory, and from most of them corn and meat are exported to western Europe. In each of the regions listed below, corn is the first or second crop in acreage, and a part of the crop is fed to livestock for meat production. The crop pattern, the proportion of corn used for food, and the general background of production vary greatly. The Corn Belt on the plateaus of southern Brazil is still in a pioneer stage of development. A large quantity of corn is exported from the Argentine Belt, and this region is more significant than its areal extent suggests. From the "Maize Triangle" of South Africa food is supplied to mine workers, and some corn is produced there for export. In southern Europe a line of corn belts extends from

northwestern Spain to the Black Sea with some interruptions. Parts of northern Portugal, northern Spain, and the southwest corner of France represent a corn belt which, for lack of a better name, is called the Iberian Corn Belt. Most of the corn is grown in mountain valleys and is used at home for food and feed. In the Po Plain of Italy, corn is second to wheat in acreage, but the general crop and livestock pattern designates it as a corn belt rather than a wheat belt. The population is denser than in any other corn belt, a large proportion of the crop is used for food, and none is exported. The Danube Corn Belts occupy the basins of Hungary and Romania together with the adjacent hills and valleys. The Balkan Corn Belt includes the hilly and mountainous land of the Balkan Peninsula, excepting the coastal district which is listed under Mediterranean Agriculture.

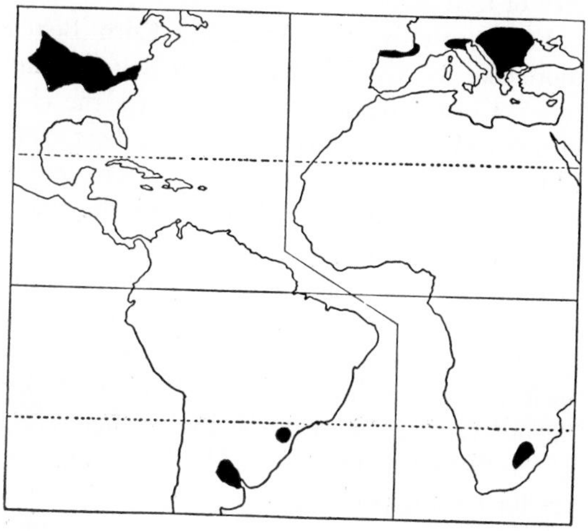

THE BRAZILIAN CORN BELT

The Brazilian Corn Belt lies to the south of the great coffee region of São Paulo, in the states of Paraná, Santa Catharina, and Rio Grande do Sul. The region is a rolling plateau from which only part of the forest has been cleared. The climate is comparable to that of northern Florida, and Porto Alegre on the southern margin of the Brazilian Corn Belt is the climatic counterpart of Jacksonville. Rain is adequate in all seasons and the summers are hot. It is remarkable that a region such as this should not have been effectively settled until the last century. The immigration of thousands of Germans, Italians, and Poles has made this essentially a region of recent European colonization, but numerous Japanese and Brazilians from the north have also moved in. The story

FIGURE 19.1. *The Corn Belts of the World.*

of the pioneer development is similar to that of the eastern part of the United States Corn Belt which was settled more than a century and a half ago. Adventuresome people moved in, cleared the forest, plowed the land, and established homes, only to move on when the settlements around them became too crowded. In the areas remote from the coast this pioneering development still continues.

Once the land has been cleared and put into cultivation, a variety of temperate and subtropical crops can be grown in addition to corn. The winters are too cool for coffee or other crops which cannot endure frost but cassava, sugarcane, and the vine thrive. Corn gives good yields on newly cleared land, furnishing a satisfactory food as well as a feed for swine and cattle. Many of the hogs run wild through the forest as they formerly did in parts of the United States. Because of the remoteness from the coast and the inadequate roads and railroads, almost no corn is exported. Meat in the form of salt pork and salt beef is exported to northern Brazil, while chilled and frozen meat is exported from the more fortunately situated coastal districts. Other crops include potatoes, beans, rice, wheat, fruits, and Paraguayan tea (yerbe maté). The "tea" is widely distributed on the plateau in wild groves and on plantations. The harvest is in winter, from March to September, at which time the Corn Belt farmers move into the forests and plantations as pickers. The leaves are dried in much the same manner as Oriental tea and are then transported to the nearest railroad or to the coast by muleback and cart. The largest market for this tea is in Argentina and eastern Brazil.

The pine forest on the inner margin of the Corn Belt still constitutes the most accessible stand of temperate belt softwoods in this part of the world. Poor transportation limits commercial production to the vicinity of the roads and railroads. Many new roads are in the process of construction, and it is likely that the invasion of the forest will open up more lands to corn belt farmers. The increasing demand for meat in the more densely populated parts of Brazil will undoubtedly stimulate further development. Expansion of corn belt farming southward into the areas of humid Commercial Grazing is also a possibility. This section of Brazil is not noted for a great variety of resources other than its agriculture and forests. It

does contain, however, the country's greatest coal reserves in the vicinity of Porto Alegre. It is this coal which forms the basis, along with the iron ore in the state of Minas Geraes, of the Brazilian iron and steel industry at Volta Redonda.

THE ARGENTINE CORN BELT

The Argentine Corn Belt, located approximately 100 miles to the northwest of Buenos Aires (FIG. 19.1), is a small region with intensive production of corn, wheat, hay, flax, and livestock. The surface of the humid Pampa in this district is like that of prairies of the Inner Corn Belt of the United States. The chief difference in climate is that the Argentine winters are milder, a fact of little significance in the production of corn. The surface consists of alluvial deposits which have weathered into excellent soils, the best in the country. The location of the Corn Belt on the Paraná River makes it easy to export the bulk of the Argentine corn crop through the ports of Rosario and Santa Fé.

Corn was first grown in Argentina on a large commercial scale at the beginning of the present century. In 1901 the production was less than 100 million bushels. For a time the annual production averaged more than 300 million bushels but declined following World War II. Although corn production in Argentina is second to that in the United States, the total is less than that in the state of Iowa. Argentine corn, however, looms larger in the world market than that of any other country. Most Argentine corn is exported to western Europe where there is always a scarcity of feed grains.

Fundamentally, the Argentine Corn Belt is more like the United States Corn Belt than any other. Corn, wheat, flax, and hay are the chief crops, and meat animals, especially beef cattle and hogs, are numerous. The region functions as a fattening ground for animals from the ranges in the west. The contrasts, however, are more striking than the similarities. As much as 80 per cent of the crop is exported. As a result, the "flint" varieties of corn, which will keep and ship well, are grown instead of the heavier yielding "dent" varieties. In addition, the smaller kernels of the flint corn are preferred by European farmers for feeding poultry. Flax grown for linseed is an important secondary crop in the Argentine Corn Belt. Alfalfa is grown on large ranches scattered throughout the belt as a holdover from the day when this was a ranching region. Wheat is an important cash crop.

The system of land ownership and the size of the farms are related to the former dominance of ranching. Some ranches have been converted into huge corn belt farms while others have been subdivided into smaller ones. Today most corn is grown on farms of from 200 to 250 acres, many of which are owner-operated. Others are farmed by tenants who lease land from the ranchers. Many of the tenants are Italians and other recent immigrants from Europe who are thrifty farmers on the whole but have little concern for the maintenance of soil fertility or the permanent occupation of the land.

Since the normal market for Argentine corn is in western and central Europe, any disturbance of the economy of Britain, Germany, the Low Countries, and Denmark reacts quickly on this region. During World War II Argentineans were cut off from this market and suffered severely from overproduction. The local price of corn dropped as low as three cents per bushel at one time, compared to about sixty cents at the same time in the United States. At this low figure corn accumulated in storage until space was no longer available and then was used extensively as fuel.

THE MAIZE TRIANGLE OF SOUTH AFRICA

The Corn Belt of South Africa or the Maize Triangle, as it is called in South Africa, occupies a part of the High Veld region in northern Orange Free State and southern Transvaal. The corners of the triangle are near Mafeking, west of Johannesburg, near the town of Carolina, east of Johannesburg; and at Ladybrand in eastern Orange Free State. The region is essentially a high plain ranging in elevation from 4000 to 6000 feet. The surface is like the smoother parts of the Great Plains in the United States, but farming conditions resemble more nearly those of the western part of our Corn Belt. The summers are warm rather than hot on account of the altitude, and rainfall is generally adequate for the growth of corn, wheat, and hay. In small oases, citrus and other orchard fruits are grown.

Corn has been an important crop in South Africa since 1880, although it was introduced from the Americas about 1820. The crop was not suited to the climate of the Cape District so that wide utilization awaited the settlement of the interior. Mining has played a major role in the growth of agriculture in the Maize Triangle. The gold from the Rand District and from other areas within or near the Triangle represents more than half the total world production. The mining towns and cities provide a market for the corn, wheat, meat, vegetables, and fruits grown in the region. A large part of the corn is used for food, especially for the native laborers in the mines. Some of the Dutch farmers eat small amounts of corn, but the rest of the Europeans prefer wheat, which is usually abundant but more costly. Corn is fed to livestock and some is exported to western Europe. Most of the corn crop is grown on farms operated by Europeans.

On the margins of the Triangle corn is grown by the natives in the various Reserves (areas set aside for exclusive native use). Most of this crop is eaten by the natives and their animals, since export of native crops which compete with those grown by local Europeans is discouraged in South Africa. Prior to the introduction of corn the natives subsisted on kaffir "corn," a grain sorghum which has also been introduced to the Winter Wheat Belt and the drier parts of the Cotton Belt of the United States. Some kaffir "corn" is still grown in South Africa, but the acreage has declined.

THE CORN BELT OF IBERIA

The northern part of the Iberian Peninsula (FIG. 19.3), from northern Portugal to southwestern France, is a humid and rugged region with only small areas of good land on the valley floors. Less favorable for cultivation are the lower slopes of the hills. The summers are rainy and the growing season is long; therefore corn has become the major crop in acreage although grapes surpass it in value in a few small districts. In the very northern part of Portugal and northwestern Spain, corn is an important food and feed crop. The summers are cool, the soils poor, and only a small proportion of the land is cultivated. The remainder includes heath, woodland, and scattered groves of chestnuts. It is a region of small farms which furnish a constant stream of emigrants to the foreign labor markets. The rural people tend to move to the coastal fishing towns, Vigo and La Coruña, for example, where they are recruited by labor agents for foreign service.

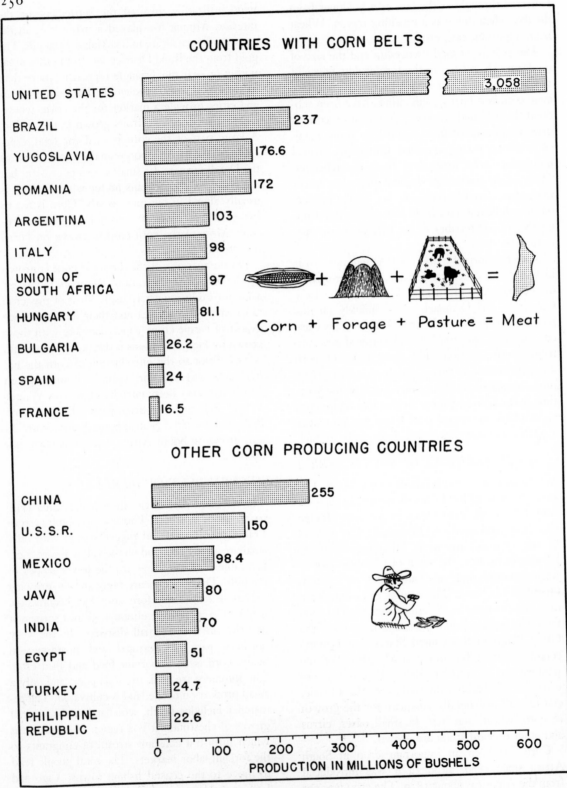

FIGURE 19.2. *Graph of corn production in leading countries.*

In the western part of the Pyrenees Mountains, partly in Spain and partly in France, agricultural conditions are somewhat better. See FIGURE 19.4. Corn is grown on the valley floors and up to 3000 feet. Hay, potatoes, various vegetables, and small quantities of grapes are produced on most of the small farms. Corn, the chief crop in acreage, is grown for food and feed and plays a dominant role in the economy. The livestock include the "blond cattle," which are used for milk, meat, and draft purposes, and sheep, which are used for wool, meat, and milk. The curd from sheep's milk is exported to central France for cheesemaking. Swine and poultry consume some of the corn and other feed crops. Above the cultivated valleys are the mountain pastures, the upper parts of which can be used only in summer. The livestock, mostly sheep, move up the slopes in early summer and down again in the fall. This Iberian region has all the qualities of a corn belt, but it is a far cry from Iowa or Illinois, resembling more the southern Appalachians of eastern Kentucky or West Virginia. Most of the production is on a subsistence basis, although meat, wool, and wine are exported in small quantities.

Mineral deposits in the Iberian region include the best coal and iron ore of Spain. The coal production of the Oviedo District amounts to several million tons per year although it is not usually enough to supply all the needs of the country. The quality of the coal is not such as to attract large industries, even though iron ore is mined a comparatively short distance to the east and both the iron and coal are near the sea. The iron ore, most of which is mined in the vicinity of Bilbao, is of good quality and abundant. Several million tons are exported to England and Germany annually. A small iron and steel industry is located on the outskirts of Bilbao. In spite of the fact that in northern Spain coal and iron are mined, the output of steel is limited. This fact can be explained only by the lack of skill and industrial enterprise in the people and the poor quality of the coal.

THE PO PLAIN

In sharp contrast to the Alps on the north and west and the Apennines on the south, the Po Plain (FIG. 19.3) is an alluvial basin capable of intensive cultivation. It is the agricultural heart of Italy and with only a fourth of the area supports nearly half the people. The plain is essentially a Corn Belt but with variations from the standard pattern. Wheat has a larger acreage than corn, but the whole crop pattern—corn, wheat, hay, pasture, and other food and feed crops—fits into the general Corn Belt type.

The surface of the plain (FIG. 19.5) is mostly level. In the northern part, on the margins of the Alps, there are some areas of rough terminal moraines. South of this is a wide outwash plain sloping gently to the Po River. In many places

FIGURE 19.3. *The Corn Belts of Europe. Most of the corn in Europe is produced between the 40th and 50th parallels in Spain, southern France, the Po Plain of Italy, the middle and lower Danube Basins. Corn for fodder and silage is grown farther north.*

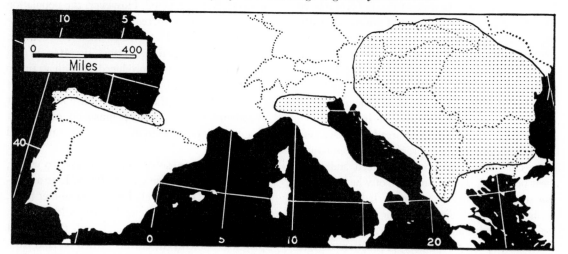

FIGURE 19.4. *Corn cultivation in southwestern France Preparation of the fields for planting involves leveling and rolling. Additional corn is grown on the adjacent slopes. From Edition L. Chatagneau-Bordeaux (France).*

the flood plain of the river is generally too low and level for good natural drainage. The climate is not quite as suitable to corn as that of Iowa, but the summer rain contrasts with the dryness of the peninsula to the south. Most of the rainfall is in spring and fall. Rain in spring is favorable to the growing of corn, but in fall unfavorable. By means of irrigation additional water is supplied for crops which need much moisture in the middle of summer when rainfall is light. Both corn and rice are irrigated.

Wheat has the largest acreage in the plain since this is the most favored part of Italy, and the people need large supplies of bread and macaroni. If it were not for the pressure of population, more corn would be grown for feed and more meat produced. The importance of wheat to Italy can scarcely be overemphasized. It has been described by the Italians as "the most precious fruit of our agricultural endeavor." When Mussolini attempted to increase production to free

Italy from the "tyranny of foreign bread," he initiated the "battle of the grain." Various devices were used to increase production including better seed, draining of swamps, and a high tariff on foreign wheat. Vineyards and olive groves were converted to grain land. However, the population has continued to increase, the per capita consumption of bread is greater than ever before, and at no time before, during, or after World War II have Italians produced enough grain to satisfy their needs. Two kinds of wheat are grown in Italy. In the Po Plain soft winter wheat is grown for bread. In the peninsula durum wheat is grown for the manufacture of macaroni and spaghetti.

The corn crop, second in importance to wheat, is produced mostly in the Po Plain. It is a summer crop and grows well during the summer rains. The harvest extends from August to November, varying with the weather and with the time of planting. Some of the corn is grown on land from which wheat has just been harvested. This usually delays the time of planting and makes for a late harvest. Corn, an important food in the plain, is eaten in the form of meal or a rough pudding, known as *polenta*. Finely ground corn flour is sometimes mixed with wheat flour, a practice which does not add to the quality of the bread. As the population of the Po Plain has increased, the proportion of corn used for food has increased, and less and less has been fed to livestock.

Most of Italy's sugar is manufactured from beets from the fields of the southern and eastern part of the plain. In a good year the production reaches five million tons from which more than 500,000 tons of sugar are extracted, enough to provide about 25 pounds of sugar per capita. Part of the beets, however, were used to make alcohol. Ordinarily, some cane sugar is imported.

More rice is produced in the Po Plain than in any other region in Europe. Indeed, in no other region in the world at this latitude (45°) is the production as great as in the middle part of the Po flood plain. The crop is grown on low, level land near the river with the aid of irrigation. The season is a little short but the yields are fairly good, and the rice makes a substantial contribu-

tion to the food of the plain. Another valuable food crop is potatoes, reaching three million tons in good years. Potatoes are grown in most parts of the plain, and a considerable proportion of the crop is consumed locally. Many other crops such as beans, peas, and various vegetables contribute to the food supply.

The hay crops, although occupying a considerable area, are not sufficient for the needs of the livestock. Alfalfa and clover are prevalent and four mowings per year are possible. But for the priority of food crops, wheat, corn, and rice, the forage crops might be grown more extensively and more livestock raised. Draft animals, especially oxen, are used in agriculture. Because of the industrial cities, the demand for dairy products and meat is good.

It is significant that grapes, a dominant crop of Mediterranean Italy, are mostly an intercultivated crop in the Po Plain where they are found on about 30 per cent of the cropped land. As a separate crop grapes are of slight importance. The same is true of mulberry trees, which form the basis of the silk industry of Italy. Mulberry trees often are used as supports for vines.

The industries and the agriculture of the Po Plain have been mutually stimulating. Agricul-

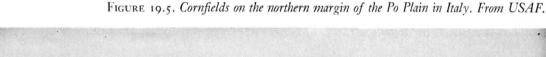

FIGURE 19.5. *Cornfields on the northern margin of the Po Plain in Italy. From USAF.*

ture supplies a variety of raw materials—wheat for the flour and macaroni mills, silk for the textile mills, sugar beets, hemp, and straw from the wheat and rice. Minerals are scarce and industrial production is based on them only to a very slight extent. In the absence of coal in quantities, it is fortunate that the Po Plain has available large quantities of water power from the alpine streams. In northern Italy more than seven billion kilowatts of electrical energy are used per year, and modern industry in Italy dates from the development of this power. Since power is available in all the streams flowing from the Alps, manufacturing is rather widely dispersed. Of greatest importance is the textile industry in which the manufacture of cotton, rayon, and silk are ranked in this order. The cotton must be imported (Italians had hopes of growing cotton in Ethiopia), but the silk is produced locally. Italians are the third largest producers of silk in the world. It should be noted that the dense population of the Po Plain and the peninsula of Italy provides a large labor supply.

THE DANUBE CORN BELTS

The Hungarian or Middle Danube Plain includes most of Hungary and parts of the adjacent countries of Yugoslavia and Romania. Most of this alluvial lowland is similar to the Po Plain, but the northern and western parts are more hilly. The general elevation is less than 1000 feet but is slightly higher than the Po Plain, and since the region is farther north and farther inland, the climate is much the same except that the rainfall is lighter in Hungary. Two contrasting parts of the Hungarian Plain are generally recognized, the Alfold to the east of the Danube, an alluvial lowland, and the western part called Transdanubia where several ranges of low hills and a lake vary the monotony of the plain.

Agriculture is the main occupation in the plain. Forests and minerals are limited, and the products grown in the soil represent most of the food and exports of the Hungarians. The population is less dense than that of the Po Plain, and thus the pressure to produce foods is not quite so great. Since much of the land is operated in large holdings which must show a profit to satisfy the owners, exports of grains and other agricultural products to western Europe have usually been large.

In the Alfold the fertile soil has been cultivated

for centuries without greatly decreased yields. Corn and wheat usually are rotated. Little hay is produced, the animals depending to a large extent on pasture. Corn is fed to pigs and cattle, and small quantities are used for food. Rye, barley, oats, sugar beets, potatoes, and tobacco are the chief crops after wheat and corn. Fruits and various vegetables are cultivated—cabbages, onions, tomatoes, and paprika for goulash, of course. Apricots, peaches, cherries, and walnuts are the chief tree crops although the total acreage is not high. Grapevines cover a half million acres, and enough wine is produced for home consumption and for export.

Since the population of the Hungarian Plain is less dense than that of the smaller Po Plain, more of the crops can be fed to livestock and the subsequent sale of animal products is higher than the average for eastern or southern Europe. Swine are fattened on small farms for the large urban markets to the west. Large quantities of lard usually are exported to fat-deficient western Europe. Beef cattle, poultry, sheep, and horses are also raised. Dairying is only slightly developed, but in good times Hungary exports some butter.

Timber is scarce in Hungary. The hills of the west furnish hardwoods which bring good prices but are of slow growth. Softwoods are very scarce. A variety of minerals, including lead, zinc, gold, silver, antimony, bauxite, and petroleum, are produced in small quantities. Bauxite deposits are extensive, and Hungary has a ready market in neighboring countries for this ore. Most of it is mined in the hilly western portion of the lowland in the vicinity of Lake Balaton. Petroleum is taken from the same general area but somewhat farther south. The scarcity of oil in central and western Europe makes this deposit more valuable than it would otherwise be. Even at the highest peak, however, the production is little more than enough to supply the domestic requirements of the country.

South of the Transylvanian Alps and north of the Danube, the Plain of Romania reaches from the Iron Gate below Belgrade to the Black Sea. The general character of the region is similar to that of the Hungarian Plain, but the agricultural methods are much more primitive. Nearly 50 per cent of the land of all Romania is arable; however, the percentage in the plain is much higher. The chief features of the crop system are the unbroken rotation of corn and wheat on nearly exhausted soils, the extensive use of corn for food, and the feeding of fodder and hay to livestock. By far the largest proportion of the cropland is in corn, wheat, and barley, part of which is usually exported in spite of the low standard of living at home. Grains have ordinarily been the most important items in Romania's export trade, after petroleum. Other crops include apples, plums, various other deciduous fruits, oilseeds, beans, and peas. Potatoes, tobacco, and sugar beets are produced in sufficient quantities to supply most of the domestic demand. Livestock is less dense than in most corn belts. Draft animals, beef cattle, pigs, and poultry are the most numerous, and all except the first of these are exported in large numbers. Milk production is low, since dairy cows are not very numerous and the yield per cow is low.

The most important commercial product in Romania is petroleum. Several small fields are grouped around the town of Ploești, which is the hub of the industry. For many years the production has averaged nearly 50 million barrels, a figure exceeded only by Russia on the European continent. Most of the wells are connected by pipeline with the refineries in Ploești, and pipelines reach the Danube River on the south and the Black Sea on the east. Much of the oil exported ordinarily moves up the Danube by river tanker to central and western Europe. Prior to World War II oil produced in Romania was purchased by representatives of nearly every country in western Europe. Importers in Great Britain, France, and Germany were good customers, and additional oil was moved out via the Black Sea and the Mediterranean to Egypt and Northwest Africa. Within Romania, oil is consumed mostly in the form of fuel oil in factories, locomotives, power stations, and for heating purposes, while a large proportion of the gasoline is exported. There are large reserves of natural gas in Romania, some in the Ploești District and more in the various parts of the Transylvanian Alps.

THE HILL FARMS OF THE BALKANS

In the hilly and mountainous portion of southeastern Europe, including parts of Romania, Bulgaria, Yugoslavia, Albania, and Greece, only a small part of the land is cultivated. Agriculture, nevertheless, is the occupation of more than three fourths of the people. Grain crops, corn, wheat, and rye, occupy most of the cropped land, and most of the grains and livestock are used in the area where they are produced. This region resembles, in many respects, the hill farms of the

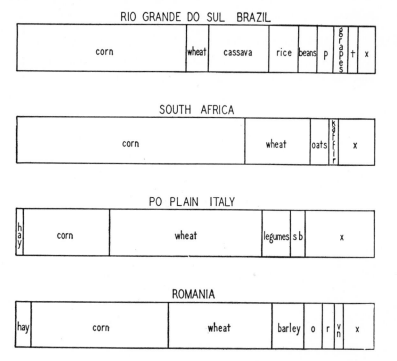

FIGURE 19.6. *Crop graphs of various corn belts. The auxiliary crops include a wide variety, cassava and rice in southern Brazil, kaffir and wheat in South Africa, various grains and legumes in Italy and Romania. Only in the Po Plain does the acreage of wheat exceed that of corn. Abbreviations: o, oats; p, potatoes; r, rye; sb, sugar beets; t, tobacco; vn, vine (grapes); x, miscellaneous.*

southern Appalachians. Land holdings are small, and only a part of each farm is cultivated. In the rougher districts cultivation is limited to patches on the valley floors or on the gentler slopes. In many districts the slopes are too steep and the soil too thin for any cultivation. Much rough brushland is used for grazing, particularly by goats and sheep. Many kinds of tree and bush crops are grown, especially near the border of the Mediterranean Agriculture. Grapes grow well in the Bulgarian Hills and some table grapes and wine are exported. Yields of grapes per acre are not high, partly because of the limited care given to the vineyards. Fruits include plums, which are marketed fresh, dried, or in the form of brandy. Cherries and apples are relatively as important as in the plains described previously. Oilseeds are grown in great variety; the seeds of sunflowers, cotton, sesame, peanuts, and poppies are all pressed for oil. From the poppies a few tons of opium are produced.

Minerals are by no means abundant in the mountainous regions of the Balkans. However, the coal production in the Sofia district of Bulgaria and the oil in Albania should be mentioned. Most of the coal is in the form of lignite, and the oil reserves are not extensive. Small amounts of chromite, copper, and arsenic are produced. Only because of the scarcity of these items in the Balkans are the deposits significant.

CORN BELTS COMPARED

A study of the corn belts described in this and the previous chapter reveals a variety of methods of production and use of corn and associated crops (FIG. 19.6). This is to be expected when the diverse character of the lands and the peoples in the various regions are considered, as well as the stage of their development. In the New World, corn was taken over by invading people and adapted to the feeding of livestock together with a limited use for human food. In Europe, on the other hand, corn production was superimposed upon an already existing agricultural system which included the small grains, hay, and various food and feed crops. Wherever the climate is favorable, a fairly long growing season with warm weather and summer rain, corn has become established in spite of the competition of the small grains. In areas of dense population, of which the Po Plain is a good example, corn is an important food. Where the pressure of population is less, more corn is fed to livestock, and as a result the people eat more meat. In South Africa, however, the presence of a large number of low-wage workers in the mines and on the farms results in the consumption of corn as a staple food, even though no great population pressure exists.

As noted previously, corn has a very wide distribution outside the corn belts. It is grown in southern Canada, in almost every state in the United States, in every country of Middle and South America, in most of the divisions of Africa, and in various parts of southeastern Asia. In regions other than the corn belts, corn is an important crop only in areas of extensive subsistence agriculture, where it is used as a food.

20

Small-Grain and Livestock Regions

THE Small-Grain and Livestock type of agriculture is found in regions intermediate in climatic characteristics between the corn belts and dairy belts. The summers are too cool for corn, but warm enough for wheat, rye, and barley and, at the same time, humid enough for good crops of hay. Except for the absence of grain corn, the resemblance to the corn belts is striking. The bread grains are grown in quantity for food, while hay, oats, barley, root crops, and other types of forage are grown as feed for livestock. Potatoes are of great significance both as a food and a feed, as well as a source of alcohol. Special crops include sugar beets, grapes for wine, flax, and tobacco. Beef and dairy cattle, swine, sheep, horses, oxen (for work animals), and a variety of poultry make up the livestock. The largest region of this type is to be found in Europe and extends from northern Spain to the Ural Mountains. See FIGURE 20.1. Smaller areas are to be found in south Middle Chile and on the South Island of New Zealand.

EUROPE

In Europe the Small-Grain and Livestock Region includes a great variety of surface and soil. On the west is the Spanish Meseta, a subhumid plateau, part of which is suitable for grain growing. The Basin of Aquitaine in southwest France and the Paris Basin are generally described as plains, but many parts are too rough or too sandy to provide good farming land. The North German Plain varies in surface from rolling terminal moraines with lakes to fertile alluvial plains along the present and former courses of the rivers. Southern Germany is a land of low mountains, plateaus, and small lowlands. Much of Poland and central Russia is swampy, suitable for agriculture only after drainage. It is significant that considerable portions of this great region of small-grain and livestock is in forest in spite of the pressure to produce food for the dense population.

The climate is even more varied than the surface. Most of the western part of the region, however, is humid with heavy rain in winter and with less but adequate rain in summer. Winters are mild enough in southern and western France so that vegetables may be grown the year round. In western Europe there is a winter maximum of rainfall, while summer rains account for most of

	Average Temperature (degrees Fahrenheit)		Average Rainfall (inches)		Average Annual Rainfall (inches)
STATION	Jan.	Jul.	Jan.	Jul.	
Bordeaux	40.6	68.2	2.5	1.9	30.7
Hamburg	32.5	63.0	2.0	3.5	27.5
Berlin	31.5	65.8	1.5	3.1	22.2
Warsaw	25.9	64.8	1.2	3.0	22.3
Moscow	13.6	65.7	1.1	2.8	21.0

CLIMATIC DATA FOR SELECTED STATIONS IN EUROPE

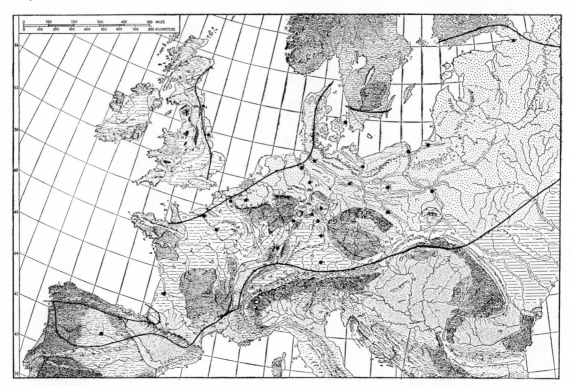

FIGURE 20.1. *The Small-Grain and Livestock Region of Europe. This agricultural type extends from northern Spain through France and Germany to the vicinity of the Ural Mountains. (Consult End Paper 3 for the extension of the region beyond the confines of this map.) It includes also a portion of eastern Scotland and England, and southern Sweden. Notice that much of the region lies on land of low relief. In the middle portion many large cities (indicated by black dots) afford an excellent market for crops and animal products. Base map by A. K. Lobeck.*

the moisture in Poland and central Russia. The winters are colder to the east, but the summers are similar to those in western Europe. Variation in rainfall and temperature is shown in the table on page 263.

Aside from the small area of Steppe (BS) climate in Spain, three types of climate are present in the European region of Small-Grain and Livestock, the Humid Mesothermal with cool summers (Cfb), the Humid Microthermal with cool summers (Dfb), and the Taiga (Dfc) in the elevated areas of the German block mountains and the Carpathians. The most significant general quality of the climate of the whole region is the coolness of the summers.

In northern Europe the growing season is too short and too cool to allow corn and many other crops to mature. In some sections the faster growing varieties of corn are planted, but unless

the season is unusually warm the crop is used as silage, green feed, or fodder; in the northern parts of this region corn is not even grown for silage but is imported, mostly from Argentina. Wheat, oats, barley, and rye, on the other hand, grow well in this region and from them large quantities of bread grains are obtained to feed the dense population. In general, wheat is more important in the west, especially in Spain and France, rye in the east. This distribution depends more on soil and climate than on the preference of the people. The potato grows well in most sections, is an important food in the west, and is both a food and a feed in the east. Sugar beets, mangels, turnips, and other forage crops are produced in certain favorable areas.

Because of the great range in surface and climate, there are many variations in production. In addition, the nearness of the large industrial centers has a definite effect on the agriculture. Except for small areas, it is the surface and soil which clearly mark contrasts in cultivation. On the gently sloping, well-drained plains in the Aquitaine and Paris basins and in western Germany, grain production is dominant, livestock is of less importance. Pastures are small, and hay is of little importance. Most of the land is cultivated on a planned rotation, and long, narrow fields radiate from compact agricultural villages. It is significant that bread grains and, in some areas, potatoes dominate the scene in the immediate vicinity of large cities such as Paris, London, and Berlin, since these cities grew up in part as storehouse centers for rich agricultural districts. Furthermore, the grain farmer is usually protected by a tariff from direct competition with grain from foreign wheat belts. In these areas of intensive grain production there are often less than 20 live-

stock units per 100 acres of cultivated land.

On the other hand, on the poorly drained lowlands, such as the *Landes* of southwestern France, and on the rocky uplands, cattle are more numerous in proportion to the cropland. Hay and pasture are emphasized, especially in the north and east where the winter feeding season is longer. But even there the food crops—wheat, rye, and potatoes—are grown, for it is the intention of the farmer in this region to grow his own food, both vegetable and animal, and in addition, to produce some crop or animal product for sale. Most farmers sell grain, meat, and dairy products. Agricultural practices, although not highly mechanized for the most part, are set up on a permanent basis. Commercial fertilizers and manures are widely used. The fields are carefully and intensively cultivated, and the yields are generally high. See FIGURE 20.7.

FIGURE 20.2. *Graph of sugar beet production in various European countries. Nearly 70 per cent of the world's raw beet sugar is produced in Europe, exclusive of the U.S.S.R. Most of this production is in the Small Grain and Livestock Region.*

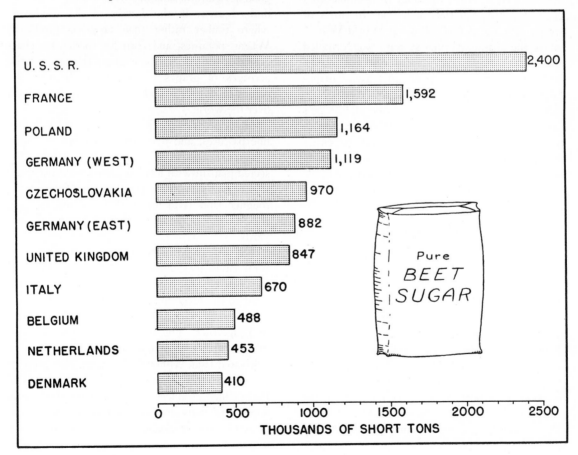

Throughout the Small-Grain and Livestock Region the presence of minerals, especially coal, has an important stimulating effect on agriculture as well as on manufacturing. It is manufacturing, based on coal and, in general, concentrated near the coalfields, which creates an enormous market for the products of the farms. Mention of minerals and manufacturing will be found in Chapters 31–39, but a study of the coal production map of Europe (FIG. 33.6) at this point will throw light on the farming. The effect of the concentration of population in the industrial areas, such as the English Midlands, the Ruhr, Saxony, and Silesia, is felt not only by the farmers in the immediate vicinity but in the entire region. By means of an excellent system of railroads, canals, and coastwise transportation, products of even the remote farms are brought to the urban areas.

In spite of the intensive production of food, it is necessary to import wheat, corn (for feed), fats, and oils as well as meat from regions outside Europe. The whole economy of western Europe has been based on the exchange of manufactured goods for raw materials and food. In times of stress, as in the period following World War II when the manufacturing system was crippled and imports curtailed, serious famines result. From a long-range viewpoint, increase of manufacturing in the "out of Europe" regions has been slowly curtailing the size and scope of Europe's exports. Too many people live in this region to be able to exist on the food produced there; either they must import quantities of food from outside and pay for it with manufactured goods, or some of the people must migrate. This problem will be discussed in greater detail in Chapter 38.

Northern Spain

Old Castile, in northern Spain, represents the dry margin of the Small-Grain and Livestock Agriculture. Its center is the flour milling city of Valladolid, which lies near the center of a basin-like plateau about 100 miles north of Madrid. The basin is almost surrounded by mountains. To the north is the Cantabrian Range, which lies along the north coast of Spain. To the west is the rough edge of the plateau, barring the way to the lowland of northern Portugal. To the south on the road to Madrid is the Sierra de Guadarrama. Wheat, rye, barley, and the chick-pea grow fairly

well, but forage crops are more difficult to produce. Pasture is good in early spring, but not so good at other seasons. Both cattle and sheep subsist on the pasture and on the stubble of the grains. About one fourth of all the wheat of Spain is produced in this region. Population is sparse, since there are no great industrial areas near by to provide a market for large quantities of farm produce even if climatic conditions were favorable for their production. But for the methods of cultivation, this area might well be classified with the wheat belts.

France

The heart of France represents the western phase of Small-Grain and Livestock Agriculture in which wheat is the dominant grain. Only the marginal districts of France, the dairy regions of the north and of the Alps, the Corn Belt, and the Mediterranean Agriculture in the south, fall outside this type. One of the best farming areas is the Basin of Aquitaine which reaches north from the Pyrenees to Brittany. Much of it is good agricultural land but with some low, poorly drained areas in the *Landes* of the southwest where timber rather than crops is produced. Wheat, potatoes, and corn for fodder are characteristic crops. In some areas there are large acreages of grapes for wine and brandy, the names of Bordeaux and Cognac being known all over the world.

The Paris Basin with its wheat, sugar beets, fine pastures, and livestock is perhaps the most productive area of all France. It is a low, dissected plateau with level stretches here and there at different elevations (FIG. 20.3). Much of the rougher land is in forest or woodland pasture, and on many of the slopes there are terraced vineyards.

The French farmers distinguish two types of rural landscapes, *campagne* (or *champagne*) and the *bocage*. For a long time the first has been applied to the level and more open land where the fields extend in long, narrow strips without fences or hedgerows. The farmhouses are grouped in villages and few people live on their plots of cultivated land. Although the name *champagne* is associated most frequently with the area east of Paris which produces sparkling wine, the French apply it to many districts such as the Champagne of Artois and of Beauce. There is great variety

FIGURE 20.3. *A farming area in Normandie, France. In the foreground, vegetable gardens; on the flood plain across the river, pasture. The upland levels are also cultivated, but most of the steep escarpment slopes are in woodland. From "Yvon."*

in farm size. In the more fertile plains, such as Flanders, Picardy, and Brie, the farms are large, and the barns are big enough to store wheat (the grain elevator so common in the newer grain lands is rare in western Europe). The buildings are all arranged around an interior court, which is secluded from the outside world. *Bocage* is another very old term which is applied to a wet, marshy, dismal district or to a granitic or shaly region. The *bocages* are relatively unproductive, and the land is marked out in small irregular fields with areas of grassland and trees. Each field is enclosed by rows of trees or hedges. In Lorraine, Brittany, and in general, in the *bocage* type of landscape the farms are small, often isolated, and the barn and residence are commonly combined in one structure.

Of all the countries of western Europe, France is by far the most nearly self-sufficient. This is

possible because of the careful cultivation of the best land and the fact that only a part of the country is industrialized and densely populated. Then, too, the crops of wheat, rye, corn, oats, potatoes, sugar beets, hay, grapes, fruits, and vegetables furnish a varied diet for man and beast. In addition, the French usually import corn (for feed), wheat, sugar, and vegetable oils in quantity. Most of the imports are from the colonies.

The chief grain crop is wheat, of which the normal production is slightly under 300 million bushels. The principal wheat producing area is in the northern part of France, in the Paris Basin. Wheat is also the first crop in the immediate vicinity of Paris, a rather unusual feature since most large cities of the middle latitudes are surrounded with zones of dairying and market gardening. The second cereal crop is oats, of which about 150 million bushels are produced in a normal year. Oats are fed to livestock, and only a small amount is used for food. A little barley is also grown. Except in the southwestern corner of France, corn is grown for fodder only.

The principal region of sugar beet production is in the northern part of the Paris Basin near the city of Lille. Here heavy, fertile soils and abundant rainfall combine with a dense population and a large labor force to produce most of the sugar needed in France. Many farms are large, 500 acres is not exceptional, and more and more modern machinery is used to cultivate and harvest the crop. The normal production is nearly 1,000,000 tons of refined sugar which, with the addition of small imports, makes it possible to provide nearly 50 pounds of sugar per capita. During and following World War II, production and supplies were greatly curtailed.

About four million acres of good land in France is in potatoes, located in widely scattered areas. French producers are usually able to export a surplus of early potatoes and at the same time supply the cities and industrial districts. Additional crops are flax, tobacco, and

mangels and other root crops for forage. Livestock includes various breeds of cattle and horses for work purposes, beef cattle, dairy cattle, sheep, pigs, and poultry. Beef and dairy cattle are much more numerous in the north where the humid pasture is good nearly all the year. Large quantities of hay in addition to oil cake, root crops, and fodder are fed to the livestock during the winter. The number of sheep has been declining for many years even in the rougher land which is little suited for other purposes. Afforestation of large parts of the southern Basin of Aquitaine reduced the areas of the sheep country. An average of ten million head of sheep furnish about 100,000 tons of mutton in addition to wool and cheese. Hogs and poultry are raised in considerable numbers for local consumption. Horses, including the famous Percherons, are used for draft animals in the north in the rural regions and in the cities. In southern France oxen are widely used.

Great Britain

On the east coast of England and Scotland are small but intensive subregions of Small-Grain and

FIGURE 20.4. *Graph of the acreage of wheat and rye for selected countries.*

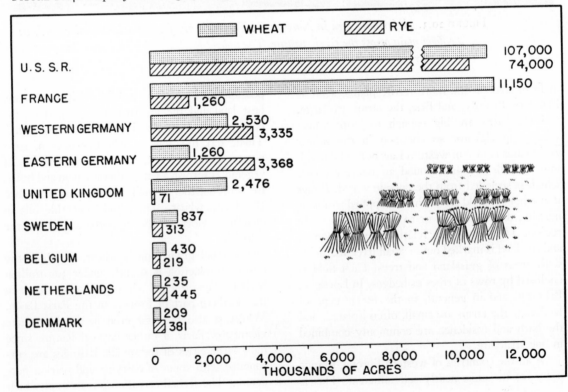

FIGURE 20.5. *A beet sugar factory in England with sugar beets growing in the foreground. Sugar beets occupy some of the best land in the Small-Grain and Livestock Region. From London "Times."*

Livestock Agriculture (FIG. 20.1). The climate of both areas is favorable for crops on account of the comparatively low rainfall and the greater amount of sunshine and slightly higher summer temperatures here than in other regions in these countries. In some localities the annual rainfall is as low as 25 inches, a low figure indeed for northwestern Europe. The crop pattern is typical. Wheat, barley, hay, and root crops, including sugar beets (FIG. 20.5) and potatoes, are of primary importance, along with beef cattle, lambs, and poultry. In these subregions of Small-Grain and Livestock Agriculture most of the domestic bread grains grown in Great Britain are produced. The total amount, however, constitutes about one fourth the domestic requirement. During World War II production of grains was greatly in-creased in these subregions, as well as in the more humid areas to the west. Power machinery was imported from the United States, and tractors, plows, and harvesting machinery were in use day and night. Even at best the British could not pro-duce enough food although they became self-sufficient so far as potatoes and vegetables were concerned. After the war grain production dropped, owing to competition from the wheat belts.

NORTH CENTRAL EUROPE

For the purposes of this discussion North Central Europe may be considered to extend from France and the Low Countries on the west to Russia on the east and from the Alps and Carpathians north to the Baltic. This is a large region with much variety of surface, climate, and other agricultural conditions, but it also has a certain amount of unity. Small-Grain and Livestock Agriculture is dominant, although there is variation in the nature and use of the various crops.

The contrast in surface between the northern and southern parts of this region is clear, from the study of a simple relief map. On the north is the German-Baltic Plain with a fringe of dunes and shallow bays along the North Sea and Baltic Sea. Inland is a belt of terminal moraines describing an arc from Denmark into East Prussia and the Baltic States of Russia. This is rough land with many lakes, not well suited for intensive farming. The southern part of the plain is level and fertile with fine alluvial soils and wind deposited loess. In spite of some unfavorable spots in the plain, cultivation is fairly intensive. Commercial fertilizer is used in large quantities to make the poor land produce. Hay, rye, potatoes, and root forage crops are widely distributed. In the more favored districts sugar beets and wheat are grown. The livestock normally includes large numbers of swine, more than any similar area in the world. The Germans and neighboring peoples consume relatively large quantities of pork and smaller percentages of beef and mutton.

Along the margin of the plains and the uplands to the south, located approximately by the cities of Münster, Hannover, Leipzig, and Breslau, is a zone of variegated manufacturing and high population density. This zone acts as a stimulus for agriculture, and cultivation of food crops is more intensive there than in other parts of the plain.

The uplands of southern Germany together with the northern part of the Carpathians are less favorable for agriculture because of both surface and climate. An elevation of a few thousand feet in this part of Europe rules out most crops on account of the coolness of the summers. Nevertheless, the mountains are interspersed with lowlands, some of which are farmed. The westernmost of these lowlands is the Rhine Graben, part of which lies in France. Here the Rhine flows through a flat-floored valley from Basel to Bingen. The valley is drier and warmer than the adjacent uplands and the growing season longer. Before the winter snows have melted from the plateau, the trees of the Graben are in leaf. Some of the lowland is planted in forest with oak and coniferous varieties predominant. The forests merge with those of the Vosges on the French side and the Black Forest on the German side of the Rhine. Fields of wheat, tobacco, hops, hemp, and a large acreage of vineyards bear witness to the fertility of the region. Small farms predominate, and the dense rural population contrasts sharply with the uplands to the east.

East of the Rhine Graben is a series of uplands and plateaus, of which the Bavarian Plateau is representative. In the north, in the vicinity of Nürnberg the plateau is low, and in the valleys and other sheltered spots a variety of crops is produced. To the south the plateau rises in gentle slopes and abrupt escarpments to the foothills of

FIGURE 20.6. *A combination farmhouse and barn in southern Germany. The left half of the structure is used as a barn while the remainder serves as a residence. Usually the barn portion is placed on the windward side as a protection from cold winds.*

FIGURE 20.7. *Seeding grain in southern Sweden. Most of the fields are small and are surrounded by woodland which is often on rocky ground. From American-Swedish News Exchange.*

the Alps. Parts of this plateau are similar to the Great Plains of the United States except for the much greater humidity and cooler summers. Hay, rye, hops, potatoes, and in the more favored situations, fruits, are the principal crops. Population is concentrated in valleys like the upper Danube and its tributaries. Munich is the largest city, located near the entrance to the Brenner Pass over the Alps. Water power from the Alps is abundant and manufacturing is important, but this area has no coal of any great value.

Poland

After World War II Poland, in effect, moved west. The eastern third of the country was relinquished to Russia because of the large number of Russians who lived there. Parts of Germany, including all but the northern third of East Prussia and the eastern part of Germany proper as far as the Oder River, became a part of Poland. In general, this was an advantageous move for the Poles, especially in view of the fact that now the industrial district of Silesia is entirely within Polish territory. In addition, the Baltic Sea is more accessible. Some of the agricultural land acquired is good, some of low value. The southern section of East Prussia and Pomerania is rough terminal moraine land of low fertility which can be made to yield well only with the use of large quantities of mineral fertilizer. Poland is predominantly an agricultural country with rye, potatoes, hay, barley, oats, and sugar beets the chief crops. The western part of the country has always been more commercial in character than the eastern section, partly because of better soils and transportation. In the past Polish agriculture has been characterized by many small farms and large estates, to the exclusion of the medium-sized farm. The large estates, to be sure, tend to be concentrated on the poorer soils where forest and rough land make intensive cultivation difficult. These large units have, nevertheless, handicapped production. Many of them have now been subdivided.

In Silesia in Poland there are valuable mineral deposits, of which coal, lead, and zinc are the most valuable. The Poles are in a position to produce a large surplus of coal for export to northern and southern Europe. Petroleum in limited quantities is found along the northern fringe of the Carpathians near Kraków. Lumber, pulp, and fuel are supplied from the forests.

Russia

In Russia the region of Small-Grain and Livestock is called the "Central Agricultural Belt." The northern limit is the Taiga, where it is difficult to grow crops because of the shortness and coolness of the summer. On the south is the great Wheat Belt of Russia, in which soils and climatic conditions are more favorable for wheat than in the Central Belt. Almost the whole of the Central Agricultural Region lies in a triangle with Leningrad, Lvov (Lemberg), and Molotov (Perm) near the corners and Moskva (Moscow) at the center. The plain is drained by the Volga and its tributaries, which are navigable except in winter.

For many decades this has been a region of rye production rather than wheat. The podzols and the cool, rainy summers favor a good yield of rye but make it difficult for wheat to mature. Thus black bread, made largely from rye and molasses, has been the staple food. Improvements in seed and methods of cultivation, however, have made it possible to grow spring wheat, and just prior to World War II the acreage of wheat equaled that of rye. The potato, which grows well in this region is also a staple food. Flax grown for seed and fiber has long been one of the main exports to western Europe. There is a substantial acreage of sunflowers also, although not as extensive as in the Wheat Belt to the south. Livestock includes cattle, pigs, sheep, goats, horses, and poultry. Much of this region is still in forest, from which timber and fuel are supplied to the farmers. As agriculture becomes intensified, more and more of the forest areas will be cleared and put under cultivation.

SOUTHERN MIDDLE CHILE

Traveling southward from Santiago, Chile, is like traveling northward from the Mediterranean Lands of Europe. One leaves the land of dry, warm summers and mild, rainy winters and enters that of cool, moist summers similar to those of northern France and the British Isles. One factor is missing in southern Middle Chile, however, the stimulation of many large cities. Concepción, Valdivia, Puerto Montt, and many others act as commercial cities, but the urban population is not large and there is no nearby market for large surpluses of grain and livestock products. As a consequence, the farms are less intensively developed than those in Europe. Indeed, the agriculture of southern Middle Chile has been described as livestock ranching with agriculture playing a secondary role. A considerable number of cattle are fattened exclusively on pasture. The chief crops are soft wheat, potatoes, oats, barley, and hay. Thus the pattern of crops and livestock places this region in the Small-Grain and Livestock type.

The cultural aspect is all the more European because of settlement, about a century ago, of small groups of Germans. The period of immigration was short and almost no Germans have migrated to the region since 1864, but the industry and skill of these pioneers left a permanent imprint on the region. Like the early German immigrants to the United States, these settlers soon gave up any allegiance or interest in Europe. They have intermarried with the Chileans, who have moved into the region by the thousands. Some land is still available for settlement.

NEW ZEALAND

The Canterbury Plain on the east side of South Island, New Zealand, is very similar in general character to the eastern part of southern England described earlier in this chapter. The plain is about 150 miles long and 40 miles wide. It is a natural grassland with a rainfall of 20 to 30 inches. The largest city of the plain, Christchurch, is similar climatically to Cambridge, England. The first use of the land was for grazing, but by 1875 wheat was introduced as a bonanza crop and spread rapidly. For a time the region was essentially a wheat belt, from which grain was sent to the mining districts of New Zealand and to western Europe. Gradually more livestock were introduced and the crops diversified. Today the chief crops of the plain are hay, wheat, oats, and root crops, mostly turnips and mangels. Oats are often cut early and used as green fodder.

Since New Zealand was settled by people from various parts of the British Isles, it is not surprising that production should be similar. The remoteness from market has been one of the factors influencing the decline of the grains and the increase in dairy and meat production. The decline in the production of wheat has been most marked although both wheat and oats still are fed to livestock. Coarse turnips are grown on the Canterbury Plain but are of greater relative significance farther south. On the whole, the Small-Grain and Livestock economy in New Zealand has almost as much diversity as in western Europe. In addition to the staple grain and forage crops, fruits, tobacco, and hops are grown in small quantities. At the same time an effort is being made to maintain the pasture in good condition by the prevention of overgrazing and by reseeding. The chief exports are butter, meat, wool, cheese, and skins. Small quantities of wheat, apples, and gold are also exported. Most of the export goods are only slightly processed, although manufacturing is increasing. The abundant water power, only a small part of which is developed, is used to freeze beef, to mill flour, and for various other purposes.

21

Extensive Subsistence Agriculture and the Plantation

In the tropical and subtropical parts of North America, South America, Africa, and Australia, the production of food crops for local consumption dominates the agricultural scene. In the more favored areas with better soil, climate, and transportation, plantations (FIG. 21.1) for the production of cash crops are well established. In other forms of production, such as forestry, grazing, fishing, mining, and manufacturing, only a small proportion of the people is employed. The regions in which extensive subsistence agriculture, the plantation, and various other comparatively minor types of production are intermingled include the Cotton Belt of the United States, a large part of Middle America, most of the highlands of South America, and sections of central Africa together with smaller districts in Australia and many islands of the South Pacific. In addition, plantation crops are associated with the Oriental agriculture of southeastern Asia and the East Indies, regions to be described in Chapters 26–30. For the sake of convenience and brevity, the extensive type of subsistence agriculture of the Americas and Africa will be designated simply as "subsistence" agriculture, while the more intensive type of southeastern Asia will be called "Oriental" agriculture. Both, of course, are essentially subsistence types.

A variety of food crops (some native, others introduced from overseas) is produced in the regions of subsistence agriculture in the Americas and Africa. A few crops have a very wide distribution. In the Americas corn, beans, and cassava are grown to supply a large proportion of the food and are followed in some districts by bananas, potatoes, and wheat. In Africa corn is replaced by millet and is generally grown in

association with cassava, bananas, palm nuts, and peanuts; while sugarcane, rice, cacao, and various oilseeds are used for local subsistence in some districts.

The small areas of plantations in the tropical and subtropical lands are of more general significance to the outside world than the much larger areas devoted to subsistence crops. Commercial agricultural production began in these lands with the plantation, and although there is a recent tendency toward small-scale commercial farming, the plantation is still dominant. It is an interesting and significant fact that some four centuries ago the institution which came to be known as the plantation, appeared independently and almost simultaneously in America, Africa, and southeastern Asia. As a device for producing tropical crops in quantity for use in the middle latitudes, the plantation has survived, although with many modifications. Since, as a system of production, it differed markedly from the mid-latitude types of agriculture, it will be worthwhile to examine its origin and character.

ORIGIN OF THE PLANTATION

Five hundred years ago most of the products of the tropical lands were unfamiliar to the peoples of western Europe. Sugar, except in the form of honey, was unknown. Few spices were obtainable, and cotton, corn, and coffee were either unknown or very rare. During the course of the 16th century men traveled widely over hitherto unexplored parts of the world in search of spices, sugar, jewels, pearls, cotton, silk, and gold. Indeed, this was "the age of discovery," not only of new lands and peoples but also of new commercial products. In the minds of the hardy sailors,

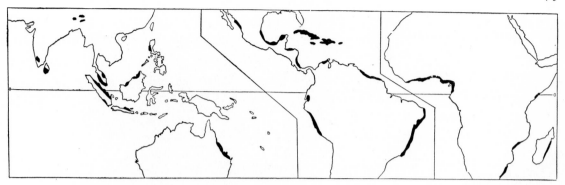

FIGURE 21.1. *The chief plantation areas of the world. This map does not show transitional regions such as the United States Cotton Belt and the Brazilian coffee district.*

the new products and the profits they would bring were more important than increased geographic knowledge.

The search for spices led all the rest, a fact which in this modern era of refrigeration and fresh foods is a little difficult to understand. In the Europe of the 1500's, however, food was limited in variety and quality, and the diet was monotonous and insipid. Something more than salt was needed to add flavor to stale meat and vegetables. Many people were willing to pay a high price for such flavoring. So urgent were the demands for pepper, and so precious was this commodity which is so plentiful today, that it was weighed on jewelers' scales.

The explorers who sailed the seas and endured great hardships to find the valuable spices and other tropical products soon found that discovery was not enough. The next problem was to obtain the goods in sufficient quantities to meet the demands of the potential market. The natives with whom trade was established were not prepared to fill the holds of ships even though in those days ships were not very capacious. The fact was that in the regions of subsistence agriculture there were many items desired by the peoples of the middle latitudes, but there was no organized production. Many products were gathered from wild trees and shrubs, and crops were cultivated only in small patches which provided little surplus beyond the needs of the natives themselves.

The Europeans solved this problem step by step. After their ships had been delayed in the Indies for weeks and months while a cargo of pepper was obtained, the idea developed that it would pay to leave part of the crew there be-

tween voyages to accumulate stocks of spices and other articles. For the return voyage the ship could thus be loaded quickly. The next step was to encourage the natives to cultivate larger plots and to gather the wild fruits over wider territories. Finally, it was deemed necessary for the Europeans to take complete charge of production and with the use of native labor, paid or slave, to develop large agricultural units capable of delivering huge quantities of goods of a uniform quality.

Thus the plantation was born. Of course similar institutions using slaves and outside masters had existed before. The Romans and Carthaginians used slaves to cultivate the land, but this practice was not long lived. The plantations established in Virginia, the East Indies, the West Indies, Brazil, and elsewhere during the 16th and 17th centuries, have either survived to the present time or have left a strong mark on succeeding types of production. In our own Cotton Belt, for example, most of the plantations as such have disappeared, but the effect of the "one cash crop" economy is still deeply impressed on the region.

What is a plantation? How is it defined? There is little agreement among geographers or other students of the subject. Most of us have a picture in our minds of the ante-bellum plantation of the Old South with its numerous slaves, fields of cotton, cornfields to feed the slaves, and the "big house" where the owners lived in varying degrees of luxury. The plantation was not like this everywhere, however. Crops, workers, and the character of the management varied in different regions. Times changed and slavery, at least as a legal institution, disappeared.

FIGURE 21.2A. *Panorama of a coffee plantation in São Paulo, Brazil. In the foreground are the drying floors, and immediately beyond, the houses of the workers. The owner's residence is to the left beyond the limits of the picture.*

FIGURE 21.2B. *A continuation of panorama on opposite page. More of the drying fields are shown, together with the warehouses and hulling mill. Narrow gauge railroad tracks reach various parts of the drying floor. In the middle distance coffee trees are to be seen. From Preising.*

In view of the heterogeneous and changing character of the plantation, no rigid definition is attempted here. The plantation may be considered as a large commercial agricultural unit, usually with both cash and subsistence crops. In addition, it seems desirable for the sake of brevity and simplicity to include the major areas of small commercial farms producing the same crops as the large plantations.

REQUIREMENTS OF THE PLANTATION SYSTEM

The plantation, as an institution, was developed to fill a definite need: the production of large quantities of tropical goods for use in temperate lands. The conditions under which the plantation can exist are rather rigid. At least five general requirements have to be met or the plantation is doomed to failure. The first requirement is cheap, fertile land which is level and well drained. Fortunately, there is an abundance of cheap land in the tropical areas. However, it is not all fertile. Fertility must be measured in relation to a particular crop. Since, in general, plantation cultivation is relatively intensive, a thin, infertile, or poorly drained soil would not justify the necessary expenditure for operation. Large parts of the tropical areas would not be suited to plantation development even if there were a much greater demand for plantation products than at present.

A second major requirement of the plantation system is an adequate supply of cheap, docile labor. Again the requirements vary with the crop and local conditions. For example, the skill needed on a rubber plantation is of a much higher order than that needed on a sugar plantation. In any case, the labor supply must be abundant, and the workers must be capable of learning the methods of cultivation and preparation of the plantation crop. Furthermore, in the interests of competition with small native farms as well as other plantations, labor must be cheap. The quantity and quality of the labor needed by the various plantations vary with the crop and the season. Sugarcane plantations require a large force of slightly skilled laborers at planting and harvest time, while the replanting and harvesting of bananas provides almost continuous employment for semiskilled workers under the direction of experts. Tapping the trees on a rubber plantation,

on the other hand, calls for greater skill in order to obtain maximum yield without permanent injury to the trees. The need for cheap labor with the necessary skills is a primary factor in the location of plantations.

A third requirement is efficient management, which usually comes from outside the region concerned. Europeans and peoples from the other temperate lands have supplied most of the management for the plantations of the tropical zone. Management not only includes the manager or overseer but frequently technicians, soil experts, and entomologists as well.

The fourth requirement is the capital needed to establish the plantation. If the crop is a tree crop, several years may elapse before the first harvest. Naturally more capital is required to finance a coffee or rubber plantation where years must elapse before the first crop comes in than a sugar plantation where the first harvest is obtainable in about one year.

A fifth requirement is a cash crop. The whole aim of the plantation is to produce some kind of product which is in demand in densely populated areas. There must be a sufficient demand and the price must be high enough to make the growing of the crop profitable. Here the question of competition enters, especially in crops, such as sugar and cotton, which can be produced in parts of the intermediate zones as well.

Each plantation requires adequate transportation in order to send its product to market without undue expense. It should be noted, however, that the nature of the transportation varies widely according to the specific crop. Cane sugar and bananas are generally grown near the coast, the first because of the low value per unit weight, the second for the same reason plus perishability. Coffee, on the other hand, may be shipped from plantations far removed from the sea and still be sold at a profit. For example, some of the coffee from the high plateaus of Colombia begins its journey to the market on muleback and is shifted in turn to trucks, railroad, river steamer, and back again to rail before it reaches the coast.

CLIMATE AND THE PLANTATION

Many people have the notion that the plantation is restricted to the humid tropical climates, in spite of the fact that the system has flourished in such diverse regions as Virginia, the highlands of

FIGURE 21.3. *A variety of plantation crops growing on an experimental farm in El Salvador. Various kinds of tree and vegetable crops are being tested for commercial use. From CIAA.*

Mexico, and the valleys of Middle Chile. It is not possible to define or limit the plantation in terms of climate. Attempts have been made to explain the plantation as a tropical phenomenon and thus justify an existing social order in which the workers are essentially a subject people. There is no reason, however, why the plantation as an institution cannot exist in any climate where commercial agriculture can be carried on, provided the requirements mentioned previously can be met. The fact is that in most middle latitude areas neither land nor labor is cheap enough to enable the farmers to compete with plantations in more tropical climates. Thus most plantations are found in the tropical and subtropical climates but are not necessarily restricted by purely climatic factors.

Climate does play a major role in the distribution of specific plantation crops. Rubber and cacao are confined largely to the Rainforest Climate (Af), sugar and rice produce best in the Savanna Climate (Aw), while most coffee is grown in the Winter Dry Temperate (Cw). Other crops such as cotton grow well in various climates. See FIGURE 21.3.

THE PLANTATION CROPS

The products of the tropical belt are so numerous that the list of potential plantation crops is very long. Of these only a few products are well established on a large scale. The most important cash crops are sugar, coffee, and rubber. Cane sugar has competition from the sugar beet grown in the middle latitudes. Plantation rubber has a rival in the synthetic product. All three of these crops are competing with similar products grown on native farms in the tropical belt. Less important as plantation products, since some of them are produced on small native farms or in association with some other type of agriculture, are cacao, bananas, tea, cotton, coconuts, pineapples, sisal, and manila hemp.

In addition to the cash crops listed in the previous paragraph, a variety of subsistence crops are grown on many plantations to feed (and sometimes to house and clothe) the workers on the plantation. The particular crops grown depend on the locality, and to a certain extent, on the eating habits of the natives. In the New World the common food crops are corn, beans, cassava, sweet potatoes, and bananas. In the plantation regions of southeastern Asia rice is important because so many of the workers are normally rice-eating peoples. Wheat and barley are lacking on many plantations because they do not thrive in the tropics and because the natives are unaccustomed to eating these grains. In addition to the subsistence crops on the plantations, certain foods are usually imported. Some, such as canned meats and milk, are obtained from nearby regions of surplus production, and others are imported from the temperate zones. Such foods are usually too costly for the native laborers.

DISTRIBUTION OF SUBSISTENCE AGRICULTURE AND PLANTATION REGIONS

In the low latitude plantations, small farms and various kinds of subsistence agriculture are so mingled that it is difficult to distinguish them. For example, one may see a modern dairy farm on the Plateau of Mexico or a small farm in Nigeria which produces only cotton. In São Paulo, Brazil, is a genuine corn belt farm, and on the plateau of East Africa is a small group of nomadic herders. It is evident that one must turn his eyes from the irregular and unusual and focus his attention on the items of more general distribution. Even so, the definition and delimiting of the types is not satisfyingly clear cut.

It is difficult to define and locate Subsistence Agriculture and the Plantation precisely. The purpose of this discussion is to formulate certain broad concepts and to focus attention on the core of the type. It must be kept in mind that the types are dynamic, in an ebb and flow of constant change. In some regions the large plantations are giving way to small farms. In our own Cotton Belt this transition is largely completed, and parts of the coffee lands of southeastern Brazil are not far behind.

The order of study of the plantation and subsistence regions is as follows (Refer to plantation crops in chapters on Oriental Agriculture.):

1. THE UNITED STATES COTTON BELT (Chapter 22) is a good example of a plantation region in the process of transition. Most of the farms are small single family units, and many of them are operated by tenants. The region, however, does have a major cash crop—cotton—and a number of subsistence crops. Furthermore, it differs markedly from the middle latitude types of agriculture in which livestock or bread grains, or both, are significant.

2. PLANTATIONS AND SUBSISTENCE AGRICULTURE REGIONS OF MIDDLE AMERICA (Chapter 23) show great variety of cash crops, subsistence crops, and geographic background. Sisal thrives on the dry plains of Yucatán; bananas and cacao on the humid coasts of Central America. In addition, there are good markets in the United States and Canada for sugar, coffee, and tobacco grown in this region. Of all the diversified plantation regions in the world, this one is favored with the best market near at hand.

3. PLANTATIONS AND SUBSISTENCE AGRICULTURE REGIONS OF SOUTH AMERICA (Chapter 24) are much like those of Middle America in many respects, but the producers in South America suffer by their remoteness from markets. The large interior area of tropical land remains largely unused either for subsistence or for commercial agriculture. Most of the subsistence agriculture is in the highlands.

4. SUBSISTENCE AGRICULTURE AND PLANTATION AREA OF AFRICA (Chapter 25) has a very different background from that of Latin America. Corn, in general, is a minor food crop. Native crops such as the palm nut are significant, but introduced crops such as cacao, sisal, and coffee also thrive.

HAWAII, An Example. The Hawaiian Islands represent an almost pure development of plantation agriculture. With less than 300,000 acres in cropped land, sugarcane and pineapples together account for nearly 275,000 acres. The change from a subsistence agricultural status with fishing an important form of production to plantation agriculture came rather rapidly after the occupation of the islands by missionaries and traders. At the time of discovery of the islands by Captain Cook, the natives lived usually near the coast, depending upon fish and the cultivation of taro and various vegetables mostly in the valleys

FIGURE 21.4. *A sugar plantation on Hawaii Island. A part of the cane fields, the mill, and the residences of the workers are shown. From Hawaii Visitors Bureau.*

close to the sea. The interior sections of the large islands were scarcely occupied.

After a number of traders and missionaries had settled in Hawaii, some people looked for a cash crop. One of the first crops selected and tried was sugar. It was felt that cane sugar would grow well in the climate and that an export business could be built up. The chance of establishing this business was especially good after Hawaii became a part of the United States and was therefore inside the tariff wall. Exports of sugar from Hawaii to the mainland of the United States began about 1875 and increased rapidly. The quota system (limitation of sugar production in various parts of the United States) allows Hawaii less than one million tons per year. The acreage has declined in recent years, but production has been kept up by the large-scale use of fertilizer and by improved varieties of cane and better cultivation practices. The industry has also been highly mechanized, and very little hand labor is now used. Only 27,000 workers are needed to grow all of the sugarcane, most of which is produced on 28 plantations (FIG. 21.4).

The first preparation for planting is the plowing of the fields, which is done by large tractors that plow very deeply. The planting is done by a machine which digs a furrow, applies fertilizer, and lays cut sections of the cane in rows and covers them with dirt. Irrigation is necessary for many of the sugar fields, and water is brought many miles, sometimes through tunnels and closed aqueducts, so that the cane may have sufficient water at the time when it is needed. After the young cane comes up, weeds are controlled by spraying rather than by hoeing. Fertilizer is again applied when needed. At harvest time the leaves are burned from the cane, making it easier to cut and handle and in no way interfering with the quality of the sugar. Bulldozers often knock over the cane, and hand cutting is limited to hilly sections where large machinery cannot be readily used. In most of the plantations three or more crops are obtained from one planting (after the first harvest the crops are called "ratoons"), but some planters replant every year. After harvest the cane is moved to the sugar mills where it is shredded and crushed to squeeze out all possible juice. The by-products, chiefly molasses and fiber, are used for stock feed, fuel, and in the manufacture of wallboard. The refining of the sugar usually takes place on the mainland of the United States, mostly in the vicinity of San Francisco. The sugar industry of Hawaii is concentrated on four islands—Hawaii, Maui, Oahu, and Kauai.

The other plantation crop (FIG. 21.5) in Hawaii, the pineapple, is worth more than $60 million a year. Commercial production started in Hawaii about 50 years ago. The fields are prepared for planting in somewhat the same way as for sugarcane. The pineapples are planted in the form of slips or crowns from selected plants and seeds are used in only a limited way. After the plants come up, the fields are mulched with paper to conserve moisture and to keep down weeds. This paper is applied by machine which also applies fertilizer as needed. Unlike sugarcane, most pineapples are grown without irrigation in areas where there is sufficient rainfall. It takes about 18 months for a crop to mature. Since the pineapple is perishable, most of the product is canned in Hawaii and shipped to the mainland in that form. Export of fresh pineapples has been restricted by the rigid inspection in the California ports for fruit flies.

Although many other crops, both commercial and subsistence, could be grown on Hawaii, the production is very low. The islands depend upon the mainland of the United States and upon other regions for their food supply. Small quantities of coffee, vegetables, nuts, taro, and rice are grown on the islands, however.

Coffee is grown on small farms in the Kona district of the Island of Hawaii, at elevations of 1000 to 2500 feet on the lower slopes of Mauna Loa. The coffee crop ranks a poor third after sugar and pineapples, averaging about $2 million annually. Bananas are grown as a local food crop on more than 1000 acres. Papayas, mangoes, citrus fruits, figs, coconuts, Macadamia nuts, guavas, and many other fruits and vegetables are grown for local consumption. Production could be increased if a larger market were available.

Hawaii represents a clear-cut development of highly specialized plantations with but little attention to subsistence crops. In part this is a result of remoteness from the mainland; in part it is related to the scarcity of good crop land and the high cost of production. Tourism is the third industry of the islands, bringing in nearly $50 million annually. The military establishments bring a large payroll, most of which is spent in the islands. Manufacturing employs about 20,000 persons, commerce and trade an even greater number. But the plantation crops, sugar and pineapples, form the fundamental base of production in Hawaii.

FIGURE 21.5. *An aerial view of pineapple fields in Hawaii laid out on the contours. Notice the network of roads reaching to all parts of the fields. The valley floor and sides are mostly in woodland. From Hawaiian Pineapple Company.*

22

The United States Cotton Belt

For more than a century most of the world's cotton has been produced in southeastern United States, known usually as "the South." In other countries—India, Russia, China, Egypt, and Brazil—cotton is important. In some of them it is of increasing importance, but in the United States production is largest. The significance of this statement is emphasized when it is recalled that cotton ranks first among all the fibers used by man. Almost everyone wears cotton in some form. Even in cold countries where wool is preferable, cotton often supplements the warmer, more costly fiber. In the warm lands millions of people wear cotton exclusively. The average annual world production of cotton is about 13 million tons as compared with 4 million tons of wool.

The Cotton Belt is no longer a land of plantations and tropical agriculture. It represents, rather, a transition between the plantation of the ante-bellum days and the small tropical farm on the one hand, and a middle latitude commercial farm of the corn belt type, on the other. The crop patterns of the Cotton Belt are like those of the plantation in the great emphasis which is placed both on a cash crop and on the cultivation of a subsistence crop, chiefly corn. Many Cotton Belt farms, however, are more like those of the Corn Belt in the methods of cultivation and operation by individual farmers. Livestock in "the South" is relatively unimportant as compared with the Corn Belt, but the number of dairy and meat animals increases year by year. Hay and forage crops occupy only small acreages because of the long period in which pasture is available.

In addition to crops, significant quantities of petroleum, iron ore, coal, sulfur, phosphate, baux-ite, lumber, paper, turpentine, rosin, and various other commodities are produced in the Cotton Belt. It is the first region of the United States in petroleum production and second only to the Pacific Northwest in the value of its forest products. On the basis of the varied regional raw materials plus water power and water supply, manufacturing is increasing.

LIMITS OF THE COTTON BELT

In a large measure climate sets the limit of the Cotton Belt, and the boundaries are sharp though not static. The northern boundary, extending from southern Virginia to the Texas Panhandle, corresponds closely to the line of 200 days growing season. See FIGURE 22.1. It is here that the boundary is the sharpest, particularly along the margins of the Appalachians and the Ozarks. The western limit, from the Texas Panhandle to the Gulf, is marked by dryness. West Texas is too dry for cotton, and no lofty mountains supply water for irrigation (cotton is not usually irrigated in the Cotton Belt). New varieties which require less moisture have, however, enabled cotton to be grown westward in the drier land and to rival wheat as a cash crop. No satisfactory western limit for cotton can be stated in terms of inches of rainfall; the 20-inch annual rainfall line in north Texas and the 25-inch line near the Gulf represent, however, reasonable approximations. The southern limit is not, as many suppose, at the Gulf but generally many miles inland. The heavy autumn rains near the Gulf, the prevalence of the boll weevil, and the sandy or swampy nature of the surface make it difficult to grow cotton within a 50-mile wide coastal strip along both the Gulf and Atlantic. This coastal region will be described separately at the end of this chapter beginning on page 293.

The Cotton Belt, as described above and shown on the map (FIG. 22.1), includes parts of thirteen states. In two of these, Kentucky and Missouri, there is very small production; in two others, Virginia and Tennessee, there is only slightly more. Of the nine remaining states the average annual production is greatest in Texas with nearly 4 million bales of 500 pounds each. Cotton growers in the other states contribute from one to two million bales each. The total annual production in the Cotton Belt averages nearly 12 million bales.

EVOLUTION OF THE COTTON BELT

The plantation was born independently in many different parts of the world about three centuries ago. In the Cotton Belt this agricultural system has passed through its entire life cycle—a boisterous youth, a rather hectic middle age, and a feeble senility. The plantation is now almost a relic of the past. The shift from the plantation to the tenant farm in the Cotton Belt has been graphically described by Rupert Vance. (Reprinted from *Human Geography of the South* by Rupert B. Vance, by permission of The University of North Carolina Press. Copyright, 1932, by The University of North Carolina Press.)

Historically cotton fastened its hold upon the South through the plantation. The plantation made its appearance in America before either cotton or slavery. The first southern colonies were called plantations and the promoters expected no doubt that the returns of their venture would come from some sort of adaptation of feudal land tenure to America. The first organization of labor in agriculture worthy of the term plantation included indentured servants and was applied to the growing of tobacco. Well known as it is in the tropics, the plantation would in the course of time have given way to a frontier yeomanry had it not been for the fortuitous introduction of the Negro slave and the cotton plant. The plantation according to Phillips has demanded four factors: land, fertile, plentiful and level; a labor supply, docile and of low status; management involving social as well as economic supervision; and a staple crop. In the South it has found five staples: tobacco, rice, indigo, sugar, and cotton, but cotton has outdistanced them all. Cotton early commanded an enviable place in the world's commerce. It also fitted into a regular and easily supervised routine of tasks to be accomplished by plow gangs, hoe gangs, and picking gangs, in all of which, except the plowing, women and children could participate. Technology came to the plantation's aid when the system seemed about to

wane, and the invention of the cotton gin insured on the one hand cheap fabrics, on the other the extension of the cotton kingdom and the perpetuation of slavery.

How the plantation contended with the frontier and how it made an aristocracy, America's first, out of part of that frontier has been recounted. How the plantation, staggered by the shock of the abolition of slavery, after a brief hiatus reorganized its labor into a tenancy and share cropping system is more important for our chronicle. A stricken upper class possessing nothing but lands met a servile population possessed of nought except the labor of their hands. In what must have been an era of primitive barter, a system was arrived at whereby labor was secured without money wages and land without money rent. Up and down the Cotton Belt southern states after 1865 vied with one another in passing crop lien laws. Accepted as the temporary salvation of a wrecked economic structure, the system has increasingly set the mode for southern agriculture. Under the crop lien system the unpropertied farmer mortgages his ungrown crop for the supplies necessary to grow it. He also pledges a portion, third, fourth, or half of his crop, for use of the land. The most outstanding commentary one can make on the South is to point out the fact that from that day to this the percentage of those who must secure their year's livelihood by crop liens has steadily increased.

The breakdown of the plantation was, in some places, more apparent than real. The "Big House" still remained. The former plantation owner became a landlord and leased out his land in small parcels. Slaves were replaced by tenants, most of them white. More than a million white tenant families and 700,000 Negro families now produce most of the American cotton. The remainder comes from a few large modern plantations. Theoretically the tenant is free to tend his small plot as he likes so long as he returns a share to the owner. In practice, however, the landlord has a large measure of control as to the crops planted, as well as to the time and methods of planting. Of the three classes of tenants the "share-cropper" is the most common. He rents strictly on shares, and the landlord usually furnishes a mule and implements, taking in return a large share of the cotton. The "share-tenant" is a step higher economically, furnishing his own livestock and implements. Highest of all is the "cash renter," who pays cash for the use of the land and takes the entire crop. All classes of tenants grow subsistence crops—corn, potatoes, beans, sugarcane, sorghum, and vegetables—for their own use.

The size of the average farm in the Cotton Belt is increasing but is still less than 100 acres. See

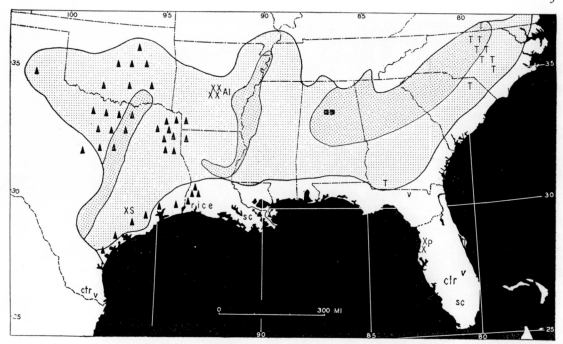

FIGURE 22.1. *The United States Cotton Belt. Three zones of more intensive production, the Black Prairie of Texas, the Mississippi Lowland, and the Piedmont, are indicated by slightly heavier shading. The last named has declined in recent years, partly as a result of soil erosion, while production of cotton has increased in the west where machine methods of cultivation and harvest are more prevalent. In addition to cotton, the region produces a variety of other crops, tobacco (T), corn, forage, fruits, nuts, vegetables, a variety of minerals, including coal (black squares) and iron in Alabama, aluminum ore (Al) in Arkansas, and petroleum (black triangles). The Gulf and Atlantic margin of the Cotton Belt produces rice, sugarcane (sc), vegetables (v), fruits including citrus (ctr), also petroleum, phosphate (P), and sulfur (S).*

FIGURE 22.2. In Alabama the average is 98 acres, in the Texas Black Prairie about 110 acres. Of this only a part is under cultivation and the rest is woodland, pasture, or idle land. Cotton picking by hand is a slow laborious process, requiring many workers. It has, therefore, been the accepted practice, until recently, to perform all of the other work by simple methods. The invention of several workable mechanical cotton pickers is slowly changing the whole character of the Cotton Belt. In a short time the small tenant farm may be entirely replaced by the large mechanized unit, a modern version of the plantation in which machines take the place of slaves.

AREAS OF INTENSIVE PRODUCTION

Cotton is unevenly distributed across the Cotton Belt. In some districts almost none is produced, while in others, because of favorable soils, cotton is grown intensively. Three fairly large areas of intensive production are outlined on the map (FIG. 22.1): (1) the Piedmont, (2) the Mississippi Bottoms, and (3) the Black Prairie of Texas. On the other hand some sandy districts produce little.

In the Piedmont subregion in the western Carolinas, northern Georgia, and Alabama, cotton is grown on hilly land next to the mountains. Here the soils are derived from hard crystalline rocks. These soils were originally more fertile than those in most parts of the Coastal Plain. Drainage is good (in many places too good) and the region has suffered more severe soil erosion than any other part of the United States. The color of the "red hills of Georgia" is derived from the subsoil, the rich chocolate brown topsoil having long ago washed down to the sea. The Piedmont, unlike the Coastal Plain, was settled largely by "small farmers" and plantations were comparatively

FIGURE 22.2. *Piedmont Cotton Belt farms in York County, South Carolina. This gently rolling hill country is surprisingly subject to erosion, hence the strip crops. Most farms are small— more than a dozen farmsteads can be spotted in this photo—and corn, tobacco, vegetables, lespedeza, and other crops are grown in addition to cotton. From Soil Conservation Service.*

rare. These farmers tried various crops, but cotton and tobacco proved most successful as cash crops although both rapidly exhaust the fertility of the soil. Toward the north, in North Carolina and Virginia, tobacco is dominant, while in the southern and western Piedmont cotton is the main cash crop. In all the Piedmont, corn, beans, oats, wheat, and hay are also grown.

Most of the Coastal Plain east of the Mississippi River lies in the Cotton Belt, but the surface conditions do not everywhere favor the growth of cotton. Some areas are too sandy or swampy, while others have suffered severe soil erosion even on gentle slopes. One of the earliest areas of intensive plantation and cotton development was the "Black Belt" of Alabama and Mississippi. The Black Belt took its name from the dark soil derived from a layer of chalky limestone, outcropping in a broad belt. Originally very fertile with tall grass rather than forest vegetation, the Black Belt offered a favorable setting for the plantations which were usually located on the best land. For more than a generation excellent yields of cotton and corn were produced from the dark soils, and the existence of many old plantation houses still testifies to the former prosperity of the area. The good topsoil was, however, gradually depleted, and production has declined. As a relic of the old plantations the population is dominantly Negro.

The Mississippi Bottoms from western Kentucky to middle Louisiana are a unique part of the Cotton Belt. The river has built an alluvial plain 50 to 60 miles wide and 400 miles long. Every flood brings a new layer of silt to renew the soils of the lowest land. The floods are so severe that few cities of any size are located in the "bottoms." On the bluffs adjacent to the river, however, cities like Memphis and Vicksburg have evolved as commercial centers serving this part of the Cotton Belt. Not all of the land can be cultivated because swamps and lakes are numerous. The natural levees of the river, including the abandoned channels, afford excellent sites for farms even though they are constantly subject to the flood hazard. Most of the farms are small, but a few large plantations remain. Second to cotton is corn, followed by potatoes, sugarcane, melons, and various kinds of vegetables. It should be noted that cotton is of minor importance in the delta proper of southern Louisiana.

The Black Prairie of Texas, like the Black Belt

of Alabama, is derived in part from chalky limestone. The climate is drier, however, and the soluble minerals so necessary for fertility are more abundant. The land is more rolling, in places even hilly, so that terracing and contour plowing are sometimes necessary to prevent erosion. This district was settled, for the most part, after the War between the States and consequently there were few plantations and few Negroes. To a certain extent Mexicans—some migratory, some permanent residents—make up the labor supply, especially during the picking season. In a very real sense this is the heart of Texas, and most of the large cities are located in or near the Black Prairie. From San Antonio on the south the Black Prairie stretches northward through Austin, Waco, Fort Worth, and Dallas into southern Oklahoma. See FIGURE 22.3. Cotton is by far the leading crop, but large quantities of corn, grain sorghum, and hay are grown to feed a much larger number of livestock than is found in most parts of the Cotton Belt.

Throughout the Cotton Belt the areas of intensive production account for most of the cotton. Within these subregions cotton occupies nearly half the total crop acreage, as will be noted in the graphs (FIG. 22.4) of Washington County (Mississippi) and Falls County (Texas). The secondary crops show some variety. Grain sorghums flourish in the drier western part of the Cotton Belt, while tobacco is a secondary cash crop in the eastern part. In the areas of less intensive production, very little cotton is produced in some counties which are generally included in the Cotton Belt. This is true of Person County (North Carolina), where tobacco is the chief cash crop. It will be noted that corn has from one fifth to one half the total acreage in all graphs excepting that of Polk County (Florida), which is outside the Cotton Belt.

The method of growing cotton and other crops varies in different districts. On the smaller farms and more especially in the middle and eastern parts of the Cotton Belt, mules, simple plows, and hoes are used to prepare and cultivate the crops. A single mule is a low-cost, fairly efficient instrument for the cultivation of row crops on small farms. On such farms the cotton is picked by hand, and since this tedious task restricts the acreage which can be tended by one family, the fields and the farms are small. In the western part of the

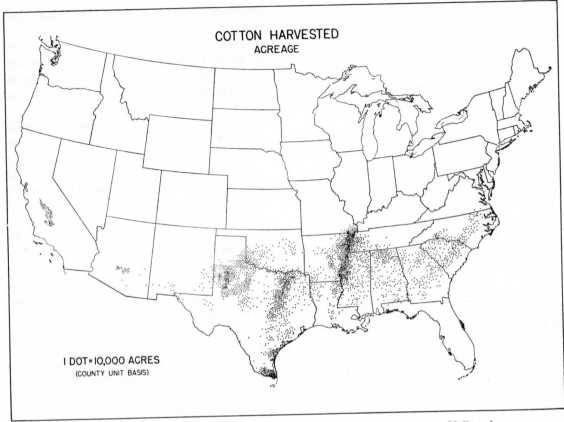

FIGURE 22.3. *Map of cotton acreage harvested. Notice the acreage in the San Joaquin Valley of California and in the Salt River Valley of Arizona. Also notice the uneven distribution of cotton acreage in the Cotton Belt. From Bureau of Census.*

Cotton Belt, great progress has been made in the mechanical picking of cotton as well as in the use of power machinery for plowing, harrowing, and cultivating. Power machinery is well suited to large farms on smooth and gently rolling land. Gradually the improvements in mechanical pickers and their wider distribution are bringing about a revolution in the Cotton Belt. The tenant farm with its small fields of cotton, corn, and vegetables seems doomed. Changes are likely to be accelerated by the competition of cotton producers in other lands and by the increase in synthetic fiber manufacturing.

In view of the disastrous effects of the old-style methods, it is well that changes are coming about. The rougher parts of the Cotton Belt have suffered severely from soil erosion. Even the smoother areas have lost soil by sheet erosion and fertility by continuous cotton cropping. The heavy rainfall which continues throughout the winter when the soil is bare tends to accelerate erosion. In the Piedmont Region gullies large enough to hold a house are all too frequent. Then, too, the fertility of the less eroded soils has been partially exhausted by continued cultivation, especially in the older, eastern part of the region where yields per acre have declined sharply. This, together with the ravages of the boll weevil, has contributed to the definite shift of production from the east to the west. Production has declined from the Carolinas to Mississippi. Farther west production has increased. Fortunately, many of the old practices which tended to accelerate erosion are being abandoned. Newer methods of contour plowing, terracing, and the rotating of soil-conserving crops, such as soybeans with corn and cotton, are tending to check erosion.

FOREST INDUSTRIES

The Cotton Belt at the time of its settlement nearly two centuries ago was almost completely forested except for a few scattered grasslands. To the north was an abundance of hardwoods—oak, maple, gum, hickory, and walnut—while to the south pines and cypress covered large areas, the latter in the swampy land. The first exploitation of the forests on a large scale was for "naval stores" —turpentine and rosin. Even if the district was remote from transportation, in the early days it was possible to haul out turpentine by wagon and make a profit. Later the lumbermen came and found almost ideal conditions for the rapid, ruthless exploitation of the forest. See FIGURE 22.5. The stands of longleaf pine were nearly pure. A minimum of undergrowth facilitated the cutting, and the sandy soils with their cover of pine needles provided good roads everywhere through the forest. In the cypress districts conditions for lumbering were not so favorable, but at least the

stands were pure. Most of the forests of the region have been cut over not once but several times. However, tree growth, especially among the conifers, is rapid, and in 15 or 20 years a new cutting can be made although with much lower yields. Today with the greatly increased demand for lumber, many small portable "peckerwood" sawmills are cutting away at the remnants of the forest and production in the Gulf States is second only to that in the Pacific Northwest, for the United States. The hardwoods in the northern part of the region form the basis of many furniture and woodworking industries, even though most of the hardwood has been cut and the regrowth is slow. Only the rougher lands on the margins of the Appalachians and some of the swamps contain much hardwood.

FIGURE 22.4. *Crop graphs for representative counties in the Cotton Belt and in the adjacent Horticulture Region. Washington County, Mississippi, is in a zone of intensive cotton production near the Mississippi River. Falls County, Texas, represents the Black Prairie district; Person County, North Carolina, the Piedmont; while Acadia Parish, Louisiana, lies in the margin of the rice district and somewhat outside the Cotton Belt proper. St. Mary Parish, Louisiana, in the lower Mississippi Delta, and Polk County, Florida, grow almost no cotton and represent the horticultural district to the south and east of the Cotton Belt. Notice that corn is grown in all these counties. Abbreviations:* veg, *vegetables;* x, *miscellaneous crops.*

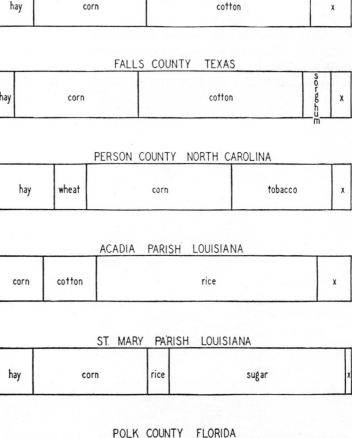

A number of items in addition to lumber and naval stores are produced in the southern forests. The pulp and paper industry has advanced rapidly in the last decade. Paper mills have been established in most of the states, but are most numerous on the southern margin of the Cotton Belt and in the horticulture coastal region to the south. New methods of using the resinous woods for newsprint production have been introduced in recent years, and newsprint has increased in volume. With the rapid growth of the southern softwoods to pulpwood size, it is likely that paper production in this region will increase still further. Many other wood products, including several kinds of fiber boards and insulating materials, are manufactured. Spanish moss, which grows as an epiphyte on many trees, is gathered, processed, and used as an upholstering material.

MINERAL PRODUCTION

In addition to its agricultural wealth the Cotton Belt is also rich in minerals. The outstanding mineral is petroleum, but coal, iron ore, bauxite (for aluminum), sulfur, and phosphate are of considerable significance. In 1950 in the United States 1970 million barrels of petroleum were produced,

and of this amount more than half was taken from Texas, Oklahoma, Louisiana, and Arkansas. Petroleum is widely distributed in the Cotton Belt but most of it comes from three districts: the Gulf Coast of Texas (see Chap. 34) and Louisiana; East Texas, with northwest Louisiana and southwest Arkansas; and the mid-continent field of Oklahoma and north central Texas. The importance of this resource cannot be overestimated. The drilling and maintenance of wells, refineries, and transportation services give employment to many thousands. However, aside from the fact that royalties supplement the income of some farmers and ranchers, there is little relation between petroleum and agricultural production. The petroleum industry will be given more detailed consideration in Chapter 34.

The bauxite deposits of central Arkansas are the richest in the United States. The bulk of the production is in two counties, Saline and Pulaski, but recently the increased demand for aluminum has led to mining in other states, mostly in southeastern Alabama and in Georgia. The first step in the making of aluminum is the mining of the bauxite, which is usually done by stripping off the overburden of soil and rock and scooping

FIGURE 22.5. *A lumber mill at Crossett, Arkansas, in the Cotton Belt. The region is second only to the Pacific Northwest as a producer of lumber. From U. S. Forest Service.*

up the mineral with power shovels. The crude bauxite is then crushed and dried to eliminate as much water as possible. It is later calcined, a process which drives off surplus water and converts the bauxite to alumina, or aluminum oxide. This process requires large amounts of fuel, and thus it is more economical to ship the bauxite to a cheap supply of coal. The nearest meeting place of both coal and the Arkansas bauxite is East St. Louis, Illinois. Much of this bauxite is moved by barge via the Arkansas and Mississippi rivers. For the final processes of refinement, the alumina is shipped to various points where cheap water power is readily available. Large plants are located at Alcoa (Tennessee), Badin (North Carolina), Niagara Falls (New York), and in eastern Canada (see Chapter 6). It should be mentioned here that large quantities of bauxite are received from British Guiana. Metallic aluminum is only one product obtained from bauxite. Bauxite is also used as a source of abrasives, for the manufacture of aluminum salts such as alum and aluminum sulfate, in the refining of oil, and in the manufacture of cement.

Coal, the basic power resource for most heavy industries as well as many lighter ones, is available in quantity in only one locality in the Cotton Belt, in the vicinity of Birmingham, Alabama. Furthermore, the eastern part of the Cotton Belt is close to the Appalachian coalfields and additional coal can be obtained easily. Abundant water power in the eastern part and petroleum in the western part provide excellent additional sources of power. Iron ore production will be discussed later in the section on iron and steel manufacturing.

MANUFACTURING AND CITIES

The abundance and variety of the resources of the Cotton Belt favor manufacturing, but only since 1880 has there been any large-scale development. Particularly in the last decade, industrialism has advanced in the region so that Southerners can boast that they have the largest hosiery mill and cigarette factory in the world, the largest paper pulp mill and aluminum plant in the United States, and that their region also ranks third in blast furnace capacity in the United States.

Most of the manufacturing in the Cotton Belt lies in the Piedmont, which extends from Birmingham, marginal to rather than in the Piedmont, on the south, to southern Virginia on the north and includes parts of Alabama, Tennessee, Georgia, South and North Carolina, and Virginia. The Piedmont is in the forefront of industrial development largely because of water power, water supply, nearness to coal, and the large production of tobacco.

Tobacco Manufacturing

The widespread use of cigarettes has been largely responsible for the rise of tobacco manufacturing in the North Carolina Piedmont. To a certain extent the converse is true: the manufacturers of cigarettes have by advertising and clever management increased the demand for cigarettes while the use of pipes and cigars has relatively declined. Tobacco is the cash crop in parts of the Northern Piedmont to the almost complete exclusion of cotton. Fields are shifted to maintain yields. Tobacco is more difficult to grow than cotton, but the dollar yields per acre are higher also. Tobacco manufacturing is centered in the North Carolina and Virginia Piedmont, especially at Durham, Winston-Salem, Reidsville, Petersburg, and Richmond. Water power, labor supply, and access to various kinds of tobacco are among the advantages of this district for manufacturing. Production began on a large scale more than half a century ago and since that time the Piedmont district from Richmond to Winston-Salem has accounted for about four fifths of the cigarettes produced in the United States. A few factories are located on the western side of the Appalachians, notably at Louisville (Kentucky), while Florida has a vigorous cigar industry based on the import of Cuban tobacco.

Textiles

From 1840 to 1880 the growth of the textile industry located in the Cotton Belt was rather slow but steady. After 1880 development was rapid, and by 1930 the industry in the southern region surpassed that of the North (New England) in production volume. In recent years rayon has become an important addition to cotton textile manufacturing. Some of the advantages of this region for cotton manufacturing, such as the nearness of raw materials, are obvious. Other factors, such as cheap land, somewhat cheaper labor, and better water supplies, are more obscure. It should be pointed out, however, that there is not enough cotton produced in the Piedmont to supply the southern textile mills. A part of the cotton must be brought long distances, for example from Texas, and in such cases the advantage over New England is greatly diminished. Also since freight rates are higher on finished goods than on raw cotton, it is desirable for the textile mills to be located in or near regions of dense population.

The South leads in rayon production as well as cotton textiles and for much the same reasons. Most rayon is made either from wood pulp or from cotton linters (fuzz). In addition to these basic raw materials various chemicals, including sulfuric, acetic, and nitric acids, caustic soda, and carbon disulfide, are used in the manufacturing process. Large quantities of soft water, most of which is derived from the Appalachians, are also used in the processing of rayon. Each of the several methods used in the manufacture of rayon requires more skill than is ordinarily needed in a cotton textile mill. In the plentiful labor supply of the South, increasing numbers of skilled laborers are available. As the quality of the rayons continues to improve and the price declines slightly, these new fibers will be able to compete more successfully with cotton, wool, and silk.

The Iron and Steel Industry

At the southwestern extremity of the southern industrial area is Birmingham, a center of iron and steel industry. No other district in the world possesses equal advantages of raw materials. In Red Mountain, near Birmingham, there is abundant iron ore, not too easily mined, but easily moved to the furnaces by short rail hauls. Coal is near by and as easily obtained. Limestone and dolomite for flux are plentiful. In the Birmingham district there are, therefore, all of the bulky raw materials for the industry, an advantage over other iron and steel districts. Pittsburgh operators, for example, must bring most of their iron ore from the Upper Great Lakes at a cost of several dollars per ton. There are disadvantages, however, which prevent the producers in Birmingham from leading those of Pittsburgh in the production of iron and steel. The greatest disadvantage is the cost of shipping steel to the consumer, since the southern market is limited.

Birmingham producers have the advantage with respect to southern markets, including the Latin American market, but this has not provided a large outlet. Water transportation is available via the Warrior River to Mobile on the Gulf.

The Birmingham district includes several satellite towns. The district extends from Irondale to Bessemer, about 15 miles in a northeast-southwest direction. The width of this zone is about eight miles and within it are Birmingham, East and North Birmingham, Irondale, Bessemer, West Bessemer, and a half dozen other smaller towns, all engaged in some activity relative to the iron and steel industry.

References have already been made to many of the cities of the Cotton Belt. In the following discussion it should be borne in mind that some of the outstanding cities mentioned are actually outside the Cotton Belt and that some of them which belong primarily to the Cotton Belt have significance for other regions also. Urban growth is still in an early stage in this region. In the last decade most of the larger cities have displayed a continued growth while many cities in other parts of the country were showing a declining population.

Cities along the Gulf and Atlantic coasts which are not strictly in the Cotton Belt but do functionally belong to it include Corpus Christi, Houston, Galveston, Port Arthur, New Orleans, Mobile, Tampa, Jacksonville, Savannah, and Charleston. All are ports handling some of the products of the Cotton Belt. A few of them are discussed in the following paragraphs.

Houston, with a 1950 population of 596,000, is the chief city of Texas. It is located in the low coastal plain several miles from the Gulf, but a connecting ship canal makes it a very important ocean port. It ranks first in cotton tonnage and is outstanding also in other commodities. The city is a distribution center for a large hinterland with a rich variety of resources, including petroleum, natural gas, timber, cotton, livestock, and rice. It has had a rapid growth in recent years. In 1920 the population was 138,000; in 1930, 292,000 (an increase of more than 100 per cent); and by 1950 had increased an additional 100 per cent.

New Orleans, the "crescent city," with nearly half a million people, may be regarded as the largest Cotton Belt city even though it is not actually in a zone of important cotton production. For many years it was the leading port for the export of cotton. Later with the shift of production westward, Houston assumed first place. New Orleans is still an important cotton port, and in addition large quantities of oil, bananas, and various other products are imported from Latin America. The city is 100 miles from the Gulf of Mexico by river, but a canal to Lake Ponchartrain provides a shorter passage to the Gulf for small vessels. The Mississippi River has a 35 foot channel as far as New Orleans and above that a 9 foot passage to Minneapolis and, via the Ohio, to Pittsburgh.

Charleston, to take an example of an Atlantic Coast city dependent on the Cotton Belt, was once the outstanding city of southeastern United States. Like its neighboring ports—Savannah, Wilmington, and Jacksonville—there has been little growth in recent years. Several factors have contributed to the slow development of these cities. The hinterlands are small and in the immediate vicinities are not very productive. Also the main line railroads are located farther inland and do not serve these ports directly. Between these cities the coastline is swampy, sparsely settled, and difficult to reach.

Most of the Piedmont cities owe their growth to manufacturing in some form as well as to trade. This is in contrast with the cities previously described which are largely commercial with manufacturing only incidental. However, Atlanta, the largest city of the Piedmont, is dominantly commercial rather than industrial. There is some manufacturing, primarily cotton textiles, paper, and furniture, but Atlanta owes its importance to its position at the southern end of the Appalachian Mountains. It is the greatest rail center in the South having easy access to both flanks of the Appalachians, to the Gulf, and to the Atlantic. There is tobacco manufacturing in Richmond (Virginia), and Winston-Salem and Durham (North Carolina). Macon, Augusta, and Columbus in Georgia, Columbia in South Carolina and Charlotte in North Carolina are in the edge of the Piedmont, near the "fall line," and are important textile manufacturing centers. Dozens of smaller cities with cotton textile industries are to be found in the Piedmont and other parts of the Cotton Belt.

In summary, it may be pointed out that eight cities in, or dependent on, the Cotton Belt had a population in excess of 200,000 in 1940. In the table on this page the growth from 1930 in thousands and in percentage increases is shown. It should be noted that during this period many cities of the United States lost population.

THE COASTAL MARGINS OF THE COTTON BELT

Along the Atlantic and Gulf coasts from Virginia to Texas, the land is low, often swampy or sandy, and generally unsuited to intensive cotton production. Here and there some cotton is grown, but of greater significance are the large quantities of early vegetables, rice, sugarcane, and citrus fruits. In many respects it is like the Cotton Belt proper though it is a little warmer in the winter and somewhat rainier in all seasons. The chief differences are the scarcity of cotton and the greater area of land in forest and woodland.

The main rice district lies in the southwestern part of Louisiana and adjacent southeastern Texas. Another rice district is located in east central Arkansas. With the exception of these

A Comparison of Population Growth in Cities of the United States			
City	Population (in thousands) 1930	Population (in thousands) 1940	Population (in thousands) 1950	Increase (per cent) 1940–1950
New Orleans	459	495	570	15.1
Houston	292	384	596	29.2
Atlanta	270	302	331	9.5
Dallas	260	295	434	13.2
Memphis	253	293	396	35.2
Birmingham	259	267	326	23.8
San Antonio	232	254	408	60.5
Oklahoma City	185	204	243	18.7

two, the only other important rice producing district in the United States is in California. The methods of rice culture in Louisiana and Texas are unique. The techniques of growing wheat have been partially adapted to rice with considerable success.

Most of the level land in this part of the coastal region was a natural grassland. As in other similar districts cotton was tried with indifferent success. Much of the land was once used for grazing and it never passed through the more typical evolution of plantation to tenant farm. In 1885 some settlers from the wheat lands of Kansas began to grow rice, using the methods and implements of the wheat farm. The gang plow, the disk harrow, the drill, and the binder, though not the combine, were introduced. The mule and single plow were borrowed from the Cotton Belt for cultivation of the rice rows during the period of growth. Borrowed too was a system of irrigation, for the 45 to 50 inches of rainfall is not sufficient for rice. Irrigation is easy because of an abundant supply of artesian water near the surface. Another favorable factor is the tight subsoil which holds water.

This combination of circumstances has developed a rather unusual farm pattern, distinctly different from the adjacent Cotton Belt and certainly unlike the Oriental areas of rice production. A comparison of acres per laborer in the various rice regions follows.

A Comparison of Acres per Laborer in Rice Regions of the World	
Country	Acres per Laborer
United States (Louisiana and Texas)	80
Japan	$\frac{1}{2}$ to 1
China	$\frac{1}{2}$ to $2\frac{1}{2}$
Egypt	4
India	3
Italy	5

The total production of rice in the United States is slightly less than four billion pounds annually. Of this total Louisiana and Texas are the largest producers, followed by California and Arkansas. The United States is a surplus producer and a large part of this crop is exported since the people of the United States eat comparatively little rice. See table on rice production, App. C.

The "Sugar Bowl"

In the spreading delta of the Mississippi and its bordering lowlands is the Louisiana "Sugar Bowl." This is the most important area of sugarcane cultivation in continental United States. Here the land between the sluggish Mississippi distributaries and bayous is level and fertile, and the sandy subsoils are well drained. The fields of cane are large, well kept, and patterned by straight roadways or narrow gauge railways. This is by no means an ideal locale in which to grow sugarcane and only with protective tariff can it be made profitable. The soils are more favorable than the climate. Frosts and the dormant winter season cut the sugar content of the cane far below that of Cuba, for example. Furthermore, land and labor are generally more costly than on most tropical plantations.

Here the plantation system has persisted and all of the holdings are large. In Lafourche Parish, which includes both farms and plantations, the average size of the holdings is large as compared with farm sizes for the state of Louisiana as a whole. Most of the plantations are organized around a mill or "central," although several plantations may supply one mill. A mill with one or more plantations may represent an investment of a million dollars or more and, unlike the cotton farm, must be operated with the highest efficiency if it is to show a profit. The "Sugar Bowl" differs from most other cane plantation areas in the greater costs of labor and land, but most of all in the special methods necessitated by the climate. If there is an early winter frost, the cane must be cut at once, piled in windrows, and covered to prevent freezing.

The annual cycle of labor on the "Sugar Bowl" plantation illustrates some of the unique features of this district. The cane may be planted either in the spring or in the fall. Since it cannot reach maturity until over a year after planting and it rarely fully matures in this region, the harvest and planting seasons coincide. An acre requires eleven man-days for harvesting, transporting, and planting. Cultivation requires twelve days. Windrowing, removing from storage, and other tasks require additional time so that in all, an acre requires nearly forty man-days and twenty mule-days of labor. Labor-saving machinery is difficult to use since the cane grows very rank and is hard to cut, top, and strip by machine. Nor is the small farm type of production suitable since each mill must have several thousand acres of cane available for efficient operation, and the whole must be carefully organized.

The only other significant area of sugarcane production is located in the recently drained portion of the Florida Everglades, near Lake Okeechobee. Here the conditions for growing cane are more like those of Cuba. Frosts are light and infrequent, and several crops may be obtained from one planting. Yields per acre are nearly twice those of Louisiana, and in time this district may become the most important domestic producer of cane sugar. At present the quota system which limits sugar acreage in each region is disadvantageous to producers in this comparatively new area.

In spite of the high cost of production, sugar is increasing in these districts. An additional stimulus was provided in World War II since trade was cut off or restricted from a number of competing areas. However, the beet sugar areas of the United States are far more important and generally capable of more significant expansion.

The Truck Farms

In strong contrast to the rice and sugar districts of the coastal belt are the areas of truck farming, the production of early vegetables. The crops are perishable and the season of marketing is very short. The soil requirements are quite different, most vegetables thriving on sandy soils which warm readily in early spring. Another contrast is the small amount of land required. Only a small proportion is cultivated and the remainder is in woodland or forest.

The truck farm region, extending with some interruptions from the Rio Grande to eastern Virginia, is highly specialized. Each little community must produce one or two crops in carload quantities to be able to serve the market. Thus Crystal City (Texas) symbolizes its interest in spinach with a statue of Popeye. In Hammond (Louisiana) and Plant City (Florida) early strawberries are grown. In Sanford (Florida) only celery is grown, while in Hastings (Florida) and Wilmington (North Carolina) there is special-

ization in potatoes. Tomatoes are raised in the Chesapeake Bay region.

Citrus Groves

Orange and grapefruit trees will grow in most of the Gulf Coastal Belt, but only two areas—central Florida and the lower Rio Grande Valley—are of great importance for citrus fruit. All of this region has some advantages and some disadvantages for citrus culture as compared with California. It is nearer the market, needs little irrigation, and land prices are lower. On the other hand, the production of oranges which will ship and keep well the year around is difficult in the Gulf citrus region.

The orange was brought to Florida by the Spaniards, but it was the bitter Seville orange and was scarcely edible. The wild groves along the lakes and rivers of central Florida went almost unnoticed when the wave of settlement moved into Florida a century ago. Some used the juice as a substitute for vinegar, some made wine, and one French Company from New Orleans harvested the blossoms to make perfume. But when someone discovered that the wild orange trees could be grafted with sweet oranges, the orange industry began almost overnight. In 1894–1895 came the "Big Freeze," which killed many of the trees and led to the shifting of the industry from central to southern Florida. Now most of the oranges and grapefruit are grown in the Florida Peninsula, but there is still the danger of frost which sometimes damages the fruit although it does not kill the trees.

Minerals

Most of the sulfur produced in the United States comes from the Gulf coasts of Texas and Louisiana. The known reserves are enormous and supplies sufficient to serve market demands a year in advance are usually maintained above the ground. Since sulfur is used in the explosives industry, in the manufacture of sulfuric acid and fertilizers, as well as in the paper industry, its strategic value is apparent. The mining of sulfur is simple and cheap. A multiple pipe (a pipe within a pipe) is driven into the sulfur-bearing beds, which range from 25 to 300 feet in thickness. Live steam is forced down the outer pipe and through perforations into the surrounding sulfur which, having a low melting point, becomes

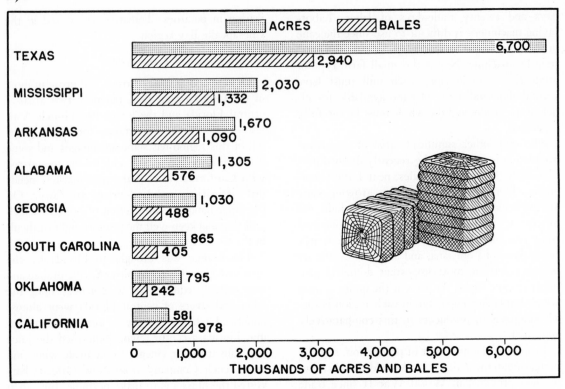

ACRES   BALES

	ACRES	BALES
TEXAS	6,700	2,940
MISSISSIPPI	2,030	1,332
ARKANSAS	1,670	1,090
ALABAMA	1,305	576
GEORGIA	1,030	488
SOUTH CAROLINA	865	405
OKLAHOMA	795	242
CALIFORNIA	581	978

0   1,000   2,000   3,000   4,000   5,000   6,000

THOUSANDS OF ACRES AND BALES

FIGURE 22.6. *Graph of cotton acreage harvested and cotton production by states.*

liquid and is forced to the surface in the inner pipe. Phosphate is mined by open pit methods in Florida, north and east of Tampa. Treatment with sulfuric acid is necessary before the phosphate becomes soluble enough to be effective as a fertilizer.

Tourism

From the Rio Grande along the Gulf and Atlantic coasts of the United States to Virginia, tourism is a major industry. The greatest concentration of resorts, however, is on both coasts of the Florida Peninsula, the most favored loca-

tion for winter vacationists. Millions of people come from almost every state and from foreign countries by rail, ship, automobile, and plane to enjoy the mild winter climate and to get away from the severe winters farther north. Tourism, in addition to being a major business, is a stimulant to local agriculture, including the production of fruits and vegetables. The tourist industry is decidedly seasonal, however. In summer most of the Gulf Coast is warm and humid. Parts of the Atlantic Coast afford relief from the warmer interior and a rather limited summer resort business prevails, usually at cut rates.

23

Plantations and Extensive Subsistence Agriculture
Regions in Middle America

IN MIDDLE AMERICA—the lands between the United States and Colombia—the major types of production are: commercial grazing, forestry, fishing, mining, the plantation, and extensive subsistence agriculture. Of these the first three have been discussed in previous chapters. The latter two are by far the most diverse and extensive in their occurrence. Although Middle America lies almost entirely in the tropics, there is such a variety of relief that some parts take on climatic qualities generally associated with the middle latitudes. High plateaus and rugged mountains rise above the hot, humid coastal plains. Most of the crops of the intermediate zones, such as small grains, potatoes, hay, and forage crops, are found within the region, in addition to the crops ordinarily associated with the tropics.

In Middle America extensive subsistence agriculture is the rule, excepting only the large area of commercial grazing in northern Mexico. Almost everywhere, however, the plantation exists in some form, and on parts of the coastal plains and in the West Indies it is the main production type. It will be convenient to discuss Middle America under five broad headings: the Central Plateau of Mexico, in which subsistence agriculture and mining play leading roles; the Mexican Coastal Lowland; the Highlands of Central America; the Lowlands of Central America; and the West Indies.

THE CENTRAL PLATEAU OF MEXICO

Southward from the United States the two great mountain ranges of Mexico, the eastern and western sierras, join in a series of lofty peaks near Mexico City, D.F. Between these converging ranges lies the Central Plateau, the heart of Mexico. See FIGURE 23.1. Most of the people of the country live here in broad basins, such as Toluca and the Valley of Mexico, where alluvial deposits from the surrounding mountains provide large areas of relatively level land. These basins have few streams and the average elevation exceeds 5000 feet. Rainfall is rather light and the importance of the nearby mountains, some with snow-covered peaks, as a source of moisture can scarcely be exaggerated. Lofty and extensive as they are, however, the mountains cannot furnish enough water to irrigate all of the basin land. The varied surface and mineral resources in different parts of the plateau provide the basis for a variety of products. The raw materials, in turn, have enabled the numerous cities of the Plateau to show a vigorous though belated industrial growth.

The climate of the Central Plateau ranges from Steppe (BS) on the north to the treeless Tundra (ET) on the crests of the higher mountains. In extreme localities one can be uncomfortably warm or freezing cold at any season. However, the climate of most of the basins, where the majority of the people live, is the moderate tropical highland (Cw), with summer rainfall, winter drought, and moderate temperatures the year round. The winters are cool, with occasional snow and freezing temperatures. At such times the Mexicans emerge at dawn from the comfortless interiors of their adobe houses to greet the sun and the warmth that comes with the day.

Temperatures vary with elevation and exposure. The average temperatures of the coldest month, January, range from 50° F. at Toluca

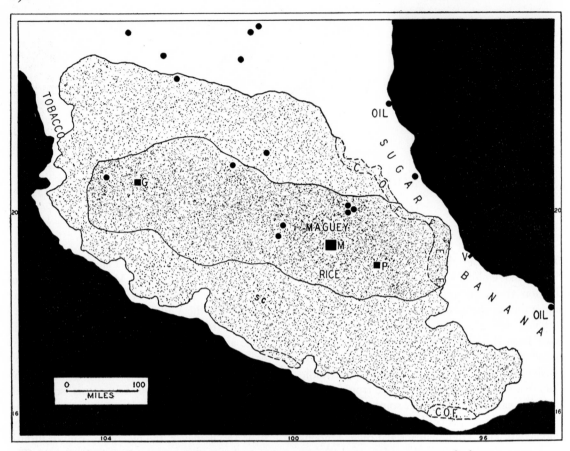

FIGURE 23.1. *The Central Plateau of Mexico, a zone of subsistence agriculture except near the large cities where commercial crops predominate. The middle section (more heavily stippled) has denser population and more intensive agriculture. Throughout the central plateau the chief crops are corn, wheat, beans, and alfalfa. Some maguey (for pulque), rice, and sugarcane are also produced. Oil, sugar, and bananas are produced on the east coastal lowland. The large dots indicate important mining districts. Abbreviations:* G, *Guadalajara;* M, *Mexico, D. F.;* P, *Puebla;* V, *Veracruz;* SC, *sugarcane;* COF., *coffee.*

(8500 feet) to 65° F. at Cuernavaca (5000 feet). The corresponding July averages are 57° and 75° F. respectively. Mountain temperatures, of course, are much lower. The summers are rainy, often cloudy even when there is no rain, and they are by no means hot. In general, the rainfall increases from north to south, averaging from 15 to 30 inches a year on the basin floors.

The Central Plateau of Mexico is dominantly agricultural; 70 per cent of the people are directly dependent on crop production for a livelihood, partly because of inefficient methods of cultivation. The most widely cultivated crops are corn, wheat, alfalfa, beans, and various fruits and vegetables. Corn is of greater importance on the

plateau than in any other region in the world. It occupies two thirds of the cropland and supplies more than one half of the region's food. It is grown on the coastal lowlands, in every basin on the plateau, and on steep mountain slopes up to 10,000 feet, above which grain scarcely matures. If water is available the crop is irrigated, and if not, though the yields are very low, it is still grown. Average yields do not exceed 10 to 12 bushels per acre, but methods of cultivation are being improved and yields are increasing. Low yields are related to cool summer temperatures, low rainfall, poor seed used in parts of the region, and depleted soils. Planting takes place from February through August and harvesting four or five months later. Most of the corn is eaten in the form of thin, unleavened cakes, *tortillas*. Very little is converted into corn meal.

Second only to corn as a food crop is the bean, a large reddish kidney variety which the Mexicans call *frijole*. It is not a very conspicuous crop since it is grown in small gardens or intercultivated with corn, but its distribution corresponds closely to that of the rural population.

Wheat is second in acreage to corn, but is more restricted in its distribution, especially at lower elevations. Conditions for growing this cereal on the Central Plateau are more favorable than for corn, since it thrives well in a cool dry climate. Yields per acre are, therefore, greater than for corn. Most of the wheat is grown in the winter, some of it on land used for corn during the summer. Long continued cultivation has depleted soil fertility, but with improved seed and methods wheat yields are slowly being increased and the area under cultivation extended. It seems likely that wheat production will continue to increase on the Central Plateau and that eventually that of corn may show a slight decline. At present

both wheat and corn are imported mainly from the United States.

Of the numerous other important crops cultivated on the plateau only a few can be mentioned. Alfalfa (FIG. 23.2) is increasing in importance as a livestock feed. Formerly natural grasses provided most of the forage. Deciduous fruits, such as the apple, peach, pear, quince, and fig, grow well. Various native plants including cacti and agave have been adapted to special uses. The *tuna* cactus produces an edible fruit which is eaten locally and is also shipped to the low country. The *maguey de pulque* is grown on large haciendas (plantations) to provide a mild alcoholic drink, called *pulque*. See FIGURE 23.3A at the top of the following page.

When the mineral production of Mexico is mentioned, one commonly hears the comment: "Mexico is a land of vast, undeveloped resources." Unfortunately, this statement is not borne out by the facts. It is true that a variety of minerals, some of them in quantity, are produced in Mexico, and the country does lead the world in the production of silver. However, the total value

FIGURE 23.2. *Alfalfa harvest on the Mexican plateau in Hidalgo. Alfalfa, like many other crops from middle latitudes, is being introduced into many parts of the Central Plateau. This cultivated basin with its row of trees along the main irrigation ditch and mountains in the distance is representative of hundreds of similar basins on the plateau.*

FIGURE 23.3. *Three views of Mexico at varying altitudes.* A. *The upper view shows part of a large pulque hacienda on the Central Plateau. The maguey plants are about eight feet high. Between the rows of maguey, which takes several years to mature, corn has been cultivated.*

B. *The middle view shows the drying floor of a small coffee "mill," located on the lower slopes of the plateau escarpment. The frequent rains make it difficult to dry the coffee properly. Pack animals are used to collect the coffee from the adjoining hills.*

C. *A Mexican farmer is preparing a brush drag to be used in harrowing this field, near Monterrey. His only conventional implements are a simple plow and a hoe.*

of all the silver produced in the world in one year is not enough, in itself, to make even a moderate-sized country prosperous. The sale of silver abroad helps support the value of the *peso*. The value of agricultural products far outranks that of minerals. Nevertheless, it cannot be denied that the mining of some minerals makes an important contribution to the Mexican economy. Furthermore, mining stimulates agriculture in some districts where, otherwise, farming would not exist.

The production of metallic minerals on the Plateau of Mexico is difficult to describe for three reasons: the variety of minerals; the mixture of different minerals in the same ores; and the variety of mines and mining methods. In varying degrees of importance gold, silver, tin, mercury, copper, iron ore, lead, zinc, antimony, and bismuth are produced in Mexico. Although some ores contain a predominance of one metal, such as silver or copper, most deposits are mixtures. Furthermore, in the smelting and refining of the minerals, ores from many different mines are mixed, so that it is difficult to point out districts associated solely with one metal. This mixed character of the ores is an advantage since those that would not be worth the mining for a single mineral pay well when the several minerals have been separated.

For many centuries the most sought after mineral in Mexico has been silver. The Aztecs extracted it extensively from mines that later were driven deeper by the Spaniards. Modern engineers have more recently been able to take large quantities of good ore from mines once abandoned by the Spaniards. Although silver is mined widely on the plateau, a large portion of it has come from a few districts, such as Pachuca (in the State of Hidalgo, north of Mexico City) and San Luis Potosí in the state of the same name. Silver has been mined in these districts since the days of the Aztecs and is still mined there although at a decreasing rate. Hundreds of mines are found throughout the states of the Central Plateau and in the arid areas farther north. There is basis for the belief that the silver of Mexico is near exhaustion. Certainly the best and most accessible ores have been mined. The higher prices for silver, however, have stimulated production in deposits formerly considered too poor to warrant exploitation.

THE MEXICAN COASTAL LOWLAND

On the eastern coast of Mexico from the Tropic of Cancer to the northern part of Yucatán there is a mixture of small primitive farms and large estates concerned mainly with the production of sugar, bananas, and sisal as commercial crops, and corn, beans, and many kinds of fruits and vegetables for subsistence. In addition, all the petroleum of Mexico is produced in this subregion. From Tampico, near the Tropic of Cancer, to the Isthmus of Tehuantepec the area becomes progressively wetter, whereas eastward from the Isthmus toward Yucatán drier conditions prevail. This is largely a low, hilly piedmont marginal to the Mexican Highland rather than a true coastal plain. The soils are generally fertile and, in view of the excellent situation, it is surprising that the land is not used more intensively. The middle portion of the state of Veracruz, however, is almost completely utilized. Elsewhere there are stretches of forest land where little is produced. This is a strange state of affairs indeed, when one considers the fact that the Mexican government is making great efforts to develop the arid lands of the northern interior.

Sugar is one of the important products of the Coastal Lowland. On haciendas and small farms from Tampico to Tehuantepec, the subregion is well suited to cane production, but until recently there has been little surplus for export. This region is in many respects suitable for the production of large quantities of sugar, but the Mexican government has had little interest in the development of the lowland, since most of the people live on the Central Plateau. Furthermore, sugarcane can be grown on the fringes of the highland as well as under irrigation on the west coast. Part of the sugar produced on the east coast is refined in Mexico City, Veracruz, and Monterrey, but much is consumed as crude sugar in various parts of the country.

The most important lowland crop from the standpoint of exports is bananas, grown mostly between Veracruz and Puerto México. Although bananas have been raised widely in Mexico on the Coastal Lowland and on the fringes of the highlands as a subsistence crop and for sale in local markets, it has been only recently that they have become an important export. This retarded development was fostered by the reluctance of foreign capital to enter Mexico and by the lack of interest on the part of the Mexican government.

On the border of the Coastal Lowland and the plateau, mostly in the state of Veracruz, is found the oldest and most extensive area in which coffee is produced in Mexico. The production units vary from the large, well-kept, and efficiently organized plantation to the small coffee "farm" on a steep hillside with a drying floor scarcely as large as a tennis court. A large part of the coffee is grown in the forest with the native hardwoods providing shade to protect the young trees from the sun. For this reason many of the coffee districts are not conspicuous to the observer unless a cross section is exposed, such as a road or railway cut. The quality of the coffee varies greatly, since many of the smaller establishments do not grade their product. Transportation is primitive in some districts; the coffee is moved miles on pack animals before reaching a drying floor and a hulling mill. The best coffee is produced in the southern part of the area, near the rail lines from Veracruz to Mexico City, D.F. Here conditions are more favorable for both growing and drying.

In northwestern Yucatán sisal is the cash crop. This is the driest part of the east coast, a real Steppe (BS) climate, but sisal, the coarse, strong fiber from which rope and binder twine are made, grows well. Here the land is flat and underlain by limestone so that no surface streams are to be found. Water supply is a problem in some districts, but shallow wells are able to tap underground water. The sisal is cut, machined to remove the pulp, dried, and baled for export. Most of it is sent to the United States. As a cheap, strong fiber sisal has few rivals, and in times of emergency, as during World War II, it served as a substitute for Manila fiber and hemp. Corn and beans are the main subsistence crops of Yucatán. The subsistence crops of the sisal plantations are especially important since the only easy traffic with the rest of Mexico is by water or air. No railway or highway connects Yucatán with the remainder of the country.

The most important single industry in the northern part of the Mexican Coastal Plain, in the vicinity of Tampico, is petroleum. The first oil wells were drilled here in 1901, and rapid expansion followed in response to a strong foreign market. The discovery of a rich pool in the vicinity of Tampico on the east coast brought in gusher after gusher, and millions of barrels of petroleum flowed into the sea before the wells could be controlled. Production declined rapidly after 1921, when over 200 million barrels were produced in Mexico, and in recent years, the production has been little more than 50 million barrels. The Mexican oils are heavy, of the asphaltic type, and not suitable to the manufacture of high-grade gasoline. This resource is of the greatest consequence to Mexico because of the shortage of coal. Almost all Mexican locomotives burn oil, and since the railroads are widely spaced, supplementary truck transportation is necessary. Additional petroleum is available for export, most of it going by tanker to the United States. New fields have not been located, although there are promising indications of oil in other parts of this eastern coastal area. Explorations in other parts of Mexico have failed to reveal any considerable deposits of petroleum.

THE HIGHLANDS OF CENTRAL AMERICA

The Highlands of Central America extend from southern Mexico to Panama, the highest areas being in Guatemala and Costa Rica. Like the Central Plateau of Mexico this is primarily a region of subsistence agriculture with some small but significant areas of coffee plantations (FIG. 23.4). The average elevation is somewhat less than that of Mexico, and the area is more completely dissected. Better lines of communication exist between the highland and the coastal lowland, but the areas of level land on the summit of the upland are more restricted than those of central Mexico. Recent volcanic deposits which weather to produce fertile soils cover large stretches of upland.

Coffee is the chief cash crop on the southern margin of the upland in Mexico, Guatemala, Salvador, Honduras, Nicaragua, and Costa Rica. Most of the crop is grown at elevations of 1500 to 5000 feet. Because of the cool and pleasant climate of the uplands and the ease with which coffee and many other crops can be grown, the population density is higher than on the lowlands. Each of the six main coffee areas possesses a distinctiveness of its own. In the Mexican segment, near the Guatemalan border, cultivation of the crop is on the margin of the Chiapas Highland. This area has turned to coffee on a commercial

FIGURE 23.4. *The chief plantation regions of Central America. Many relatively small plantations, producing bananas, sugar, and cacao, are located near the coast. In the interior are large areas of subsistence agriculture and forest, in which some coffee plantations are to be found. Owing to the variety of soil, elevation, and climate, the list of crops is long. Corn, however, is the chief subsistence crop. Abbreviations:* Au, *gold;* bn, *bananas;* cc, *cacao;* cf, *coffee;* ct, *cotton;* sc, *sugarcane. Notice that this map is oriented with the top toward the northwest.*

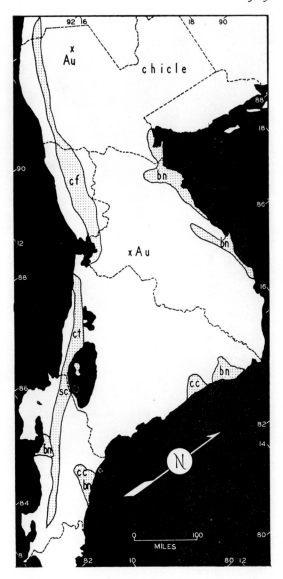

scale in the last few decades. Before World War II many of the plantations were operated by Germans, some of whom even used airplanes to get the coffee to the east coast. The potential coffee producing area is large. However, the competition of other areas is very keen and rapid expansion is unlikely. The coffee district of Guatemala reaches from the Mexican border to Salvador. A railroad and the Pan-American Highway are marginal to the highland and branches of each reach into the coffee country. Coffee, the second ranking export of Guatemala, is moved out by rail to the eastern coast at Puerto Barrios and to the Pacific ports of Ocós and San José. Wheat, tobacco, and cotton are also produced in the highland. Salvador is the smallest of the Central American countries and the most densely populated. Coffee is grown in nearly every part of the country with the exception of the coastal lowland. This product is shipped out via Puerto Barrios in Guatemala or via the Pacific and the Panama Canal. Little coffee is produced in Honduras for export, and the only important area in Nicaragua is near Lake Managua. Costa Rica has a compact but important coffee district near the capital, San José. Most of the people of Costa Rica are of Spanish stock in contrast with the other Central American people in which the Indian element is dominant. Nevertheless, the agricultural pattern in the different political segments of the highlands is much the same, coffee for export, corn, beans, and bananas for subsistence. The details of farming are better managed in Costa Rica, and the farmhouses are plastered and possess tile roofs,

in sharp contrast with the adobe huts with thatched roofs so common in the other portions of the highland.

The mineral resources of the Central American Highland are varied although the production is not great. Some lead, silver, copper, manganese, antimony, and gold are mined in various places on the highland, but no large mining enterprises are in operation because of the difficulty of transportation.

THE LOWLANDS OF CENTRAL AMERICA

On the low coastal plains marginal to both the Caribbean and Pacific sides of Central America, plantations and small areas of subsistence agri-

FIGURE 23.5 *A young banana plantation in La Lima district, Honduras. The plants are being sprayed with Bordeaux mixture to prevent disease. From CIAA.*

culture are the chief forms of production. Taking the region as a whole, the important products are bananas, coffee, sugar, cacao, coconuts, gold, lumber, chicle, and subsistence crops, especially corn. The Caribbean Coast has some very significant advantages over the Pacific Coast of Middle America. The rainfall is heavier as well as more evenly distributed throughout the year. Sea routes to eastern United States are much shorter, in spite of the Panama Canal which has been so great a boon to the west coast. This latter advantage is important in the transportation of

bananas though of little significance in the shipment of coffee.

The coast of British Honduras is only slightly developed. The few people living there produce mahogany or other cabinet woods and tend small subsistence farms. The small section of the Caribbean Coast which belongs to Guatemala, however, is well developed. The United Fruit Company has extensive banana plantations on the lowland bordering the Gulf of Honduras, and Puerto Barrios has been a thriving banana port for many years. Because of the advent of plant diseases in the east there has been a partial shift of production to the Pacific Coast, near San José. This area is connected to Puerto Barrios by rail. Thus, the disadvantage of a Pacific Coast location has been somewhat offset, but the rail haul is relatively long and, therefore, costly.

The northern coast of Honduras was long neglected by the Spaniards because of severe handicaps, principally the prevalence of malaria. However, the United Fruit Company, using Negro labor imported from Jamaica, has developed banana plantations (FIG. 23.5) to the point where there is a larger acreage in bananas in that country than in any of the other Middle American Republics. This area is relatively isolated from the more populous portion of Honduras on the Pacific slope. The east coast of Nicaragua is less developed than that of Honduras. This is called the Mosquito Coast after the Miskito Indians who inhabit it, but, for this inordinately swampy and rainy area, the change in spelling is amply justified. In spite of many difficulties some plantations have been established, the principal crop being bananas although some cacao is also produced.

In Costa Rica the principal development is in the hinterland of Limón from which a railroad leads to the Pacific Coast via San José on the highland. The banana plantations were originally established to provide a pay load for the railroad,

and the district is one of the oldest banana producers in all of Middle America. With the decline of production owing to plant diseases in recent years, many Negro workers were unemployed and thus forced to undertake small-scale subsistence farming.

The Pacific Coast of Middle America differs in several respects from the Caribbean. The climate is more comfortable, with a distinct dry season during the periods of low sun. This means that the marginal highlands are suitable for coffee and that grazing is more feasible. The less favorable location has retarded development, but at present there are signs of expansion of both banana and coffee culture, and also cattle raising. A notable increase in banana production has occurred in western Guatemala.

THE WEST INDIES

The West Indies—Cuba, Hispaniola, Jamaica, Puerto Rico, and hundreds of smaller islands—are lands of plantations (FIG. 23.6) and small subsistence farms in which sugar, bananas, coffee, tobacco, cacao, corn, beans, and various tropical fruits are produced. The total area of all of the islands is nearly 100,000 square miles, about the size of Colorado; the population exceeds 15 millions. Three independent countries are included—Cuba, Haiti, and the Dominican Republic. Most of the other islands are colonial possessions of the

FIGURE 23.6. *The plantations of the West Indies are indicated by shaded areas. In Cuba, Hispaniola (Haiti and Santo Domingo), Jamaica, and Puerto Rico (inset) the chief plantation product is sugar. Other products include bananas* (bn), *cacao* (cc), *coffee* (cf), *henequen* (hn), *and tobacco* (t). *Mineral production* (X) *includes manganese, iron, copper, and chrome.*

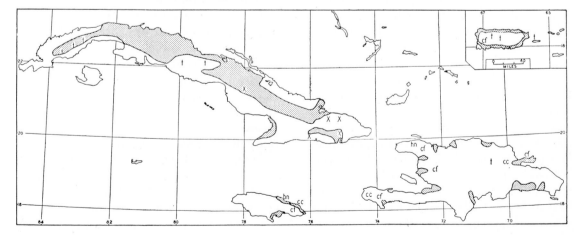

FIGURE 23.7 *Sugarcane harvest in Cuba. Much of the heavy cane is still cut by hand, after which the leaves are removed and the canes hauled to the mill. At harvest time and at planting, additional laborers are needed. From Sugar Research Foundation.*

United States, Great Britain, the Netherlands, France, and Venezuela. The character of all these islands is as diverse as are their political affiliations. Some are low-lying and sandy, while others are mountainous and rocky. Some are dominantly commercial, exporting sugar, rum, molasses, bananas, and coffee, and importing foodstuffs. Others are more self-sufficing and have only limited exports.

Cuba is the largest of the islands of the West Indies (FIG. 23.6), though not the most densely populated. It is as large as Pennsylvania, but instead of being a compact mass, it is nearly 800 miles long and averages little more than 50 miles in width. This shape is significant in that no part of Cuba is very far from the sea, and the export of relatively heavy commodities such as sugar and bananas is thus facilitated. Much of the island is mountainous, yet more than half is level enough to

be cultivated. The most rugged portion is the Sierra Maestra in the east. Other hilly or mountainous areas include the Trinidad Mountains in the center and the Los Organos Mountains in the western end of the island.

The diverse products of Cuba include sugar, molasses, rum, tobacco, corn, bananas, rice, sisal, hides, manganese, nickel, coffee, and copper. By far the most important is sugar. It is cultivated in all parts of the island except in the extreme west and in the mountains. On this island sugarcane is king, and Cuba is one of the world's three largest producers (the other two are India and Java) and easily the most important exporter.

At the time of European settlement the first use of the land was for grazing. The wide, easily accessible savannas encouraged the establishment of large ranches, a number of which are still of some importance. Sugar cultivation began early but did not attain outstanding importance until 1903 when the United States placed Cuba on the preferential list so far as sugar imports were concerned. This gave the island republic an enormous advantage over other countries exporting sugar to the United States and, as a result, the acreage of cane was increased, methods of production were modernized, and inland transportation was improved. Most of Cuba is well suited to the cultivation of cane. The soils, derived in part from limestone, are generally fertile. Most of the island has a Savanna Climate (Aw) with a distinct dry season. The dryness increases the sugar content of the cane and affords more favorable conditions for work in the fields as well as for transportation of the crop. Frost is almost unknown. As a result of the fertile soils and the favorable climate it is possible to harvest several additional crops from one planting. See FIGURE 23.7.

The characteristic production unit of the sugar areas is the large plantation with its *central* or nucleus, consisting of the mill for grinding the cane and evaporating the sap, the machine sheds, the stores, the home of the manager or owner, and the houses of the workers. The *central* is in reality a small town. Surrounding it are the fields, where not only the cane is produced, but also the food crops for the laborers—corn, bananas, beans. In addition, the plantation includes pasture and perhaps some woodland. Cane can be planted in February, April, and September, and the main harvest period follows more than a year later. Planting involves a great deal of labor in the preparation of the ground, after which the joints of the previous year's cane are planted in rows. The dry season in Cuba begins in December, at which time the first harvest takes place, the cutting continuing until April or May. The canes are cut mostly by hand and transported to the *central* by cart pulled by oxen or tractor. Some of the larger plantations have narrow gauge railways for the long hauls. The cane must be ground almost immediately; otherwise it will sour. Heavy machines are used to press the maximum amount of juice from it (FIG. 23.8). The flat, dry canes, which are called *bagasse*, are used for fuel, for making wallboard, and for a variety of other purposes. The juice or sap flows into the evaporating pans, where it is cooked slowly until excess water is evaporated. The residue is crude sugar, ready for export. Little sugar is refined in Cuba

or in any of the other cane producing regions of the world. Most of the refining takes place near the points of consumption, such as New York City, Baltimore, Philadelphia, and Boston.

Cheap labor is an important factor on the sugar plantation, and in Cuba the demand is heavy from December to May, the principal harvest season. Added to the local supply are migratory workers, most of them coming from the more densely populated islands of the West Indies, Hispaniola (Haiti and Dominican Republic), Puerto Rico, and Jamaica. In contrast to the busy harvest season, the rest of the year is a period of general unemployment.

Sugar comprises nearly 80 per cent of Cuba's exports. The concern of the Cubans with the United States tariff, the increased production in the United States possessions, and the large production of beet sugar in the continental United States can well be understood. Other products of some importance are grown in Cuba, tobacco being outstanding. There are several areas of tobacco production, of which the most important is in the western part of the island at the foot of the Los Organos Mountains. Here the sandy soils are not suitable for sugarcane but, with the aid of fertilizers, do lend themselves to the intensive cultivation of tobacco. Excellent cigar tobacco is produced along with some poorer varieties.

The other main islands in the West Indies are somewhat like Cuba. The products are similar but the amounts produced vary. The Island of Hispaniola, with the two independent countries of Haiti and the Dominican Republic, is more than half as large as Cuba and has about the same number of people, but only one sixth as much sugar is produced there. The island is much more rugged than Cuba, and the cultivated land is limited to numerous small plains near the coast. The largest sugar production is on the plains of the southeast, entirely within the limits of the Dominican Republic. In the north central parts of both countries cacao, corn, bananas, and coffee are the chief crops. Coffee is also produced in some quantities on the two western peninsulas and on the smaller peninsula to the east. Other commercial products include tobacco, sisal, cacao, and cotton, as well as large quantities of subsistence crops, mainly corn and bananas. There are also ample pasture lands on the mountain slopes.

Production in the smaller islands of the West

FIGURE 23.8. *The interior of a large sugar mill. The cane enters at upper left, passes through a crusher, then through three sets of rollers. After all the juice is extracted, the pulp, called bagasse, is dry enough to be used as fuel. From Sugar Research Foundation.*

Indies is similar to that already described for the larger islands, with some minor variations. Puerto Rico, as a consequence of its position inside the United States tariff wall, produces a large amount of sugar on the narrow lowland fringe of the island. At higher elevations coffee and subsistence crops have a wide acreage in order to supply the dense population of the island. In Jamaica, a British colony, sugar, bananas, and a special brand of coffee known as "Blue Mountain" are grown. This coffee owes part of its excellence to the local soils and to the fact that it is grown in the shade of the forest trees. Some sugar, corn, bananas, beans, cacao, mangoes, avocadoes, and various other crops are produced in most of the other islands, but very little for export.

Although mineral production in the West Indies is neither large nor diversified, some minerals do have strategic importance. The manganese deposits in eastern Cuba were sufficient to supply nearly one fourth of the needs of the United States during World War II, when some of the usual sources of supply, Russia and India, were not accessible. Nearly all of Cuba's manganese is mined in the immediate hinterland of Santiago and is exported from that port. Iron ore and some nickel are produced in the same district. Chromite also is obtainable from eastern Cuba.

24

Plantations and Subsistence Agriculture Regions in South America

IN SOUTH AMERICA, as in Middle America, extensive subsistence agriculture is dominant in the tropical highlands and less significant in the lowlands. The plantations are for the most part located near the sea, with the notable exception of the coffee plantations of Colombia, which are rather far inland. In many areas the subsistence farms are interspersed with commercial farms and plantations and, like the Cotton Belt of the United States, some of the plantations are being converted into small commercial farms. Two large areas of subsistence agriculture stand out: the Andean Highland, extending from northern Venezuela to Bolivia; and the highland of eastern Brazil, from Ceará to eastern Paraguay. See FIGURE 24.1. Most of the plantations are near the northern coast, in Colombia, Venezuela, and the Guianas, near the eastern coast of Brazil, or in Ecuador.

The chief plantation crops are coffee, sugar, bananas, cacao, and cotton. The areas of all the plantation crops could be increased, but the market demands for most of them are generally insufficient to warrant expansion. The subsistence crops are similar to those of Middle America. Corn is grown in all cropped areas up to about 9000 feet and, together with beans, cassava, bananas, sugarcane, white and sweet potatoes, and in some areas rice, is the common food of the people. The distribution of all crops, commercial and subsistence, is defined by different combinations of climatic, soil, slope, and cultural factors.

PLANTATIONS OF THE NORTHERN COAST

Near the northern coast of Colombia, to the east of the lower Magdalena River, is the Santa Marta banana plantation district. It is located on the alluvial fans at the foot of the small but lofty Santa Marta Mountains, and the cultivated land lies between the mountains and the great swamp, Ciénaga Grande, bordering the Magdalena River. The alluvial soils are well drained and easily cultivated. The abundant water supply from the mountains is necessary for irrigation, since the rainfall is insufficient to grow good crops of bananas. By means of a railroad with several short spurs, bananas are collected for quick shipment to the United States in refrigerator ships via the port of Ciénaga. The labor supply is largely Negro, while capital and management are furnished from the United States. On the mountain slopes are the coffee plantations of the Santa Marta area.

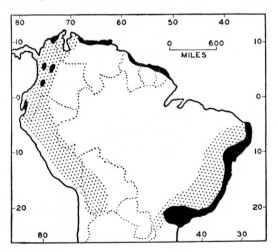

FIGURE 24.1. *A map of the chief Plantation (black) and Subsistence Agriculture (dotted) areas of South America.*

Eastward along the coast of Venezuela the plantations are located for the most part on the lowland, except the coffee plantations which are farther inland and higher. Coffee is the primary export crop, but important quantities of sugar, cacao, bananas, and the usual subsistence crops are also produced. Coffee can be grown in the coastal zone on steep slopes not generally suited to other crops. Most of the plantations are located at elevations between 1500 and 6000 feet. The quality of Venezuelan coffee is high, and the price which it commands is usually above the world market average. Food crops have long been imported to Venezuela, especially to supply the workers in the oilfields. However, there is a growing tendency for the local plantation owners and farmers to supply the needs of the petroleum districts, and it seems clear that oil production will continue to stimulate crop production in this area for some time to come.

Most of the Venezuelan oilfields are located in the vicinity of Lake Maracaibo (FIG. 24.2), but production has been gradually extended eastward to the delta of the Orinoco River. This fresh-water lake is 120 miles long by 60 miles wide and has a narrow riverlike connection with the sea. The shores are low and swampy, and although conditions are not favorable for oil drilling, the utility of the lake for transportation more than compensates for the disadvantages. Shallow-bottomed tankers, which can negotiate the narrow channel to the sea, take the oil from the wells to the refineries on the Dutch islands of Aruba and Curaçao off the coast. The zone of petroleum production extends also westward into Colombia where in the Barco (in the Maracaibo Lowland) and the De Mares fields in the Magdalena Valley substantial quantities are produced. There is a strong possibility that oil will some day be produced in all of the eastern Andean area, as far south as Argentina.

It is evident in the Maracaibo area that petroleum dominates the economy of Venezuela. The landscape has been almost completely transformed. Where fishing villages and small subsistence farms formerly existed, there are now forests of derricks, oil tanks, pumping stations, pipelines, and houses for the workers and technicians. Following World War I and the beginning of oil drilling on a large scale, Venezuela became prosperous. The royalties on 200 million barrels of oil paid to the government of Venezuela by the pro-

ducing companies, provided for large imports of food, clothing, and machinery from abroad. But with the advent of World War II, many of the sources of Venezuelan imports were cut off. The pinch was felt immediately in food and steps were taken to increase food production, especially corn, in various parts of the country. The Orinoco Lowland, previously used only for commercial grazing, is now used for the growing of many subsistence crops. Government assistance in the form of loans, agricultural experiment stations, and improved roads has enabled Venezuelans to produce a much larger share of their basic needs than they had previously.

The coast of the Guianas, British, Dutch, and French, is low and characterized by numerous tidal marshes and lagoons. The Dutch were the first to establish plantations there, finding the situation in some respects like their homeland, where the struggle against the sea and too much water is never ending. The native Indians did not prove to be suitable as plantation laborers, and as a result Negroes, East Indians, Javanese, and some Chinese were imported. Sugar is the chief money crop, but the large proportion of oriental laborers, together with the favorable climate and swampy nature of the coastal lands, encourages the raising of rice as the chief subsistence crop.

The most valuable product of the Guianas is bauxite (see page 291), which is mined near the coast along the Demerara and Berbice rivers. In Surinam (Dutch Guiana) and British Guiana the production of bauxite averages more than 3,000,000 metric tons. The bauxite is close to the surface so that strip mining methods can be used. The ore is brought down the rivers in boats to the sea at Georgetown and New Amsterdam, British Guiana. Then the ore is taken in freighters to the United States and Canada for concentration, calcining, and refining by electrolytic methods. Small amounts of gold and diamonds are also mined in the Guianas.

THE ANDEAN HIGHLANDS

From northern Colombia to southern Bolivia, the Andean Highland supports more people than the adjacent lowlands. See FIGURE 24.3. Most of the people live by subsistence agriculture, growing corn, beans, wheat, barley, *quinoa* (a small grain), and various other crops, depending on altitude. At low elevations in the valleys bordering the rainforest, sugarcane, oranges, bananas, and other

FIGURE 24.2. *Oil wells in Lake Maracaibo, Venezuela. Shallow-draft tankers can reach many of the wells. From CIAA.*

tropical fruits can be grown. Corn and beans are cultivated up to 10,000 feet, wheat and barley as high as 12,000 feet, *quinoa* and the white potato, a native of this part of the continent, at even loftier elevations. The general pattern of land use is similar to that of the Central Plateau of Mexico, although settlements reach greater elevations in the Andes, and the topography is more rugged and diverse. Sheep, cattle, and llamas graze on pastures in the valleys and high plateaus. Small patches of land are irrigated. Throughout the area mining stimulates the local production of food crops, and in some localities coffee is grown for export. Although this general description of Subsistence Agriculture—plantation-mining-grazing economy—applies to all the region, specific descriptions of smaller districts will indicate the variety of production within this major framework.

Colombia

Most of Colombia lies in the low country, but most of that nation's 11 million people live in the Andean Highland. Here the Andes form three great ranges with many smaller branching spurs.

Within each range, valleys and basins as well as benchlike plateaus afford favorable sites for settlement. The great diversity of surface, soil, altitude, and climate explains the many variations in land use. In the low northern plains (llanos) grazing is important along with subsistence agriculture; in the more humid sections of the plain, bananas and cacao are grown. It is the coffee plantations of the highland, however, lying chiefly between 3000 and 7000 feet, which provide the principal export product. Coffee trees dot the slopes on both sides of the three ranges, but the most important districts are found in the vicinity of Medellín, Bogotá, Cali, Girardot, and Puerto Berrío. In none of these districts is there easy access to the sea, and only Cali, in southern Colombia, is connected by railroad to an ocean port.

Most of the coffee is moved out of the highlands via the Cauca and Magdalena rivers. From the plantations pack animals take the coffee to the nearest short railway, from which point, using alternately rail and river transportation, the coffee is moved slowly to Cartagena near the lower Magdalena. The rivers carry heavy traffic but

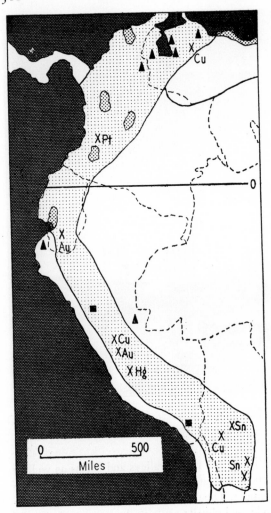

FIGURE 24.3. *Plantations and Subsistence Agriculture of the Andean Region. The chief plantations (heavy shading) are in northern Colombia and Venezuela (bananas, sugar, and cacao), western Colombia (coffee), and western Ecuador (cacao). Minerals include petroleum (black triangles), coal (black squares), gold (Au), copper (Cu), platinum (Pt), mercury (Hg), and tin (Sn).*

this subregion, together with its many feeder roads, is very useful for local transportation and when completed will be of great value.

Colombian coffee growers specialize in *cafe suave*, a mild, aromatic type which is widely used to mix with Brazilian and other coffees. The harvest season varies with latitude. In the south around Cali it occurs from April to July, while in the north most of the picking is in November and December. In most districts there is a smaller "between-harvest." Thus some coffee is being picked in almost every month of the year, and since the raw bean coffee keeps well, there is a constant stream of coffee moving to the coast. In addition to coffee and bananas, which are the chief export crops, Colombia produces corn, wheat, beans, cassava, sugar, tobacco, cotton, mostly for domestic consumption; and enough rubber, cinchona (source of quinine) and balata (a gum used widely as an insulating material) for export. Colombian mines supply gold, platinum, and emeralds for export.

Ecuador

In Ecuador the Andean Highland consists of two main mountain ranges bordering an intermontane valley which is composed of a series of basins. Most of the people live in the basins. To the west of the highland is a coastal lowland, parts of which are fertile alluvial plains. East of the highland is a land of tropical forest, few settlements, and very little commercial production. Quito, at an elevation of more than 9000 feet, is in the best known of the intermontane basins and bears the same name as the basin. The surface varies from rough, hilly land to fairly smooth uplands. Cultivation is restricted by the cool climate which has been described as "universal spring." Since the average temperature of the warmest month is 58° F. and that of the coolest, 56° F., crops will grow equally well at most times of the year. Potatoes, barley, beans, and various vegetables are cultivated. Livestock includes both cattle and sheep. In some of the lower basins south of Quito, corn, coffee, and cotton are also produced but not in large commercial quantities.

The small plantation region of Ecuador is in the Guayas Lowland north and east of Guayaquil, the chief port. This alluvial lowland, about 40 miles wide and 100 miles long, is made up of the flood plains of three small rivers and the alluvial fans

only with difficulty. Numerous sand bars, sudden floods, and periods of low water are among the major handicaps. By boat and train, alternating as many as eleven times between Bogotá and Barranquilla, the journey can be made in 180 hours. By air the trip takes a little over two hours. Little wonder that Colombia was the first nation in South America to develop commercial air transportation! The Pan-American Highway through fronting the nearby mountains. Unlike well-drained alluvial fans, the lowest part of the plain is subject to floods. The chief crops of this area are cacao, sugar, bananas, corn, rice, and cassava, while on the margins of the mountains coffee is the outstanding product. In 1916, at the peak of production, the largest percentage of cacao in the world was exported from Ecuador, but the plantations became disastrously infested with disease, especially "witches'-broom," a parasitic growth on the cacao trees. Ecuadorian yields declined at the same time other cacao producing areas were increasing their acreages. Although now only two per cent of the world's cacao is exported from Ecuador, it is still the most valuable export of the country. Coffee, bananas, tagua nuts (vegetable ivory), rubber, and balsa are also exported. An important industry based on the toquilla palm is the making of "Panama hats." This activity is located chiefly in the vicinity of Cuenca to the east of Guayaquil in the Andean Valley. Ecuadorians also produce most of their domestic requirements of cotton textiles, shoes, beverages, soap, and furniture. Mineral production includes oil from the coastal belt near the Peruvian border and gold from the mountains. In summary, it is important to note that under the present economy the three million people of Ecuador are almost self-sufficient; they produce most of the things they use either in the lowland or in the intermontane basins of the Andean Valley.

Peru

Aside from the desert lowland along the Pacific and the humid rainforest of the upper Amazon on the east, there are a variety of products and production types in Peru. In the highlands, subsistence agriculture and mining are the leading occupations and the plantation is not common, but with the continuing development of the eastern part of the country, large estates devoted to the production of rubber and other tropical products

FIGURE 24.4. *Young rubber trees on a plantation at Belterra, Brazil, formerly owned by the Ford Motor Company, now owned by the Brazilian Government. From Ford Motor Company.*

are being established. The products of the eastern lowland of Peru reach the market only after great difficulty. However, a recently constructed highway connects the Peruvian coast with the headwaters of the Amazon. Currently the most important Peruvian exports are petroleum, cotton, and sugar from the lowland and copper from the highland.

The crops produced are similar to those of Colombia, and again their distribution is largely dependent on altitude and slope. Bananas and oranges grow up to 6000 feet; sugarcane reaches 8000 feet; corn is rarely grown beyond 10,000 feet, wheat beyond 12,000 feet, barley beyond 13,000 feet, and the potato, in some districts, is cultivated at 14,000 feet. The numerous mines in the Andes have carried agriculture with them to the upper cultivation limits of the various crops. It is evident, then, that subsistence agriculture is the dominant activity of a very large proportion of the nation.

Since the early days of Spanish settlement the mines of Peru have been famous. Minerals still are the chief exports although agricultural products mean more to the internal economy. Petroleum is the most valuable mineral in terms of domestic consumption and foreign trade. The largest producing field is in the northern part of the coastal region near the Ecuadorian border. Other fields with increasing production are located in the eastern lowland on the tributaries of the Amazon and in the southern part of the country near Lake Titicaca. Since the domestic demand is not great, most of the petroleum is exported. The extent of coal reserves in Peru is not well known and some known deposits are not readily accessible. One workable coalfield is located inland from the port of Chimbote, another inland from the port of Mollendo.

The metallic products of the Peruvian mines include copper, silver, gold, lead, zinc, tin, tungsten, antimony, bismuth, molybdenum, and vanadium. Most of the ores are complex, containing several different metals. For example, a variety of metals are produced at Cerro de Pasco, one of the oldest mining communities in America. The first mineral produced in this famous district located on a divide at an elevation of more than 14,000 feet was silver. After the silver ores were nearly exhausted and the settlement had declined in population, new installations allowed the working of the copper ores, which yield also small quantities of silver, lead, zinc, bismuth, gold, and vanadium. Many other districts produce the same metals, as well as some mercury. On the islands off the coast of Peru, guano, used widely for fertilizer, is obtained.

Bolivian Puna

Bolivia, an inland country, lies in the widest part of the Andean Highlands. Most of the people live on the broad plateau or *puna* (or a Hiplano) between the distended eastern and western ranges of the Andes. This immense basin, which reaches into southern Peru, is 400 miles long and from 40 to 50 miles wide. Almost all of it lies above 10,000 feet, and important centers such as La Paz are above 12,000 feet. As would be expected, therefore, crop production is extremely limited. Most of the *puna* is too high for corn. In its place as staple foods *quinoa* and large quantities of white potatoes are grown. The climate is dry as well as cool, and irrigation is employed wherever feasible. Yields are, in general, very low, and if it were not for the market stimulus provided by the concentration of people in the vicinity of the mines, agriculture would amount to very little indeed.

Most of the mines are located at high altitudes, some above the zone of potato production. Large quantities of tin (FIG. 24.5), silver, lead, tungsten, zinc, antimony, and copper are produced in Bolivia. Of these tin, tungsten, and antimony were of greatest strategic value to the United States manufacturers during World War II. Although tin mining is very old, production was small before 1900. By 1929 the peak in tin production in Bolivia was reached with 46,000 metric tons. Since then production has slowly declined, and not even the war emergency could bring back former production levels. Ordinarily the country's tin, in the form of concentrated ore, is shipped to Wales for smelting and refining. But during World War II refineries were built in Texas to insure a supply of tin for the United States. Although minerals will continue to dominate Bolivian exports for some time, the eastern slope of the Andes and the plain below hold the greatest promise for future growth. In this so-called Yungas region tropical and subtropical crops, such as sugar, will grow, and the possibilities of large-scale petroleum development are also promising in the Gran Chaco.

FIGURE 24.5. *A Bolivian tin mine near Catavi. Houses of the workers on the upper slope, crushers and concentrators in the valley. Both the altitude and the scarcity of water are handicaps to production. From CIAA.*

THE FORD RUBBER PLANTATIONS

In sharp contrast to the primitive subsistence agriculture and gathering economy of most of Amazonia are the rubber plantations at Fordlandia and Belterra on the Tapajóz River. In 1929 the Ford Company, anxious to have an independent source of rubber, began operations on large land concessions totaling more than 2,400,000 acres, obtained from the Brazilian government. Although this region is the home of millions of wild rubber trees, a number of serious obstacles had to be overcome before plantation production could begin. Diseases attacked the rubber trees. In many places soil erosion damaged the slopes before the young trees could get started. Labor was inadequate and untrained, since it had to be obtained from eastern

Brazil. However, three of the four requirements of the plantation, discussed in Chapter 21, were substantially fulfilled: cheap, fertile land, a cash crop, and skilled management. Not even high wages were sufficient to guarantee the fourth requirement, adequate labor at all times.

The sites of the plantations are favorable, especially at Belterra. A low plateau borders the Tapajóz River, providing level, well-drained land with suitable soils and very little erosion hazard. The climate is satisfactory with a yearly average of from 60 to 100 inches of rainfall, and mean monthly temperatures ranging from 76° F. to 80° F. Most of the rain falls in a period of seven months, from November to May. The remainder of the year is relatively dry, a fact which delays the maturity of the rubber trees. Both Fordlandia and Belterra are easily accessible. Ocean steamers can ascend the stream as far as Belterra at all seasons and to Fordlandia except during the so-called dry season when the river is low. The development of these plantations has thrown a great deal of light on the possible future development of plantations in Amazonia. However, the high cost of operation and the competition from southeast Asia and from synthetic rubber influenced the Ford Company in 1946 to sell the plantations to Brazil.

THE BRAZILIAN EAST COAST

The east coast of Brazil, from Cape São Roque southward, is a narrow tropical lowland, up to fifty miles in width. The outline of the coastal lowland is irregular. It is narrow at Cape São Roque, widens near Baia, and narrows again at Vitória. This belt receives rain the year round thanks to the trade winds and to the convectional equatorial storms. Conditions are favorable for the cultivation of tropical crops (FIG. 24.6) as far south as Rio de Janeiro. The chief cash crops are cotton in the north, cacao in the Baia district, and sugar farther south. Corn, beans, cassava, and bananas are grown everywhere as subsistence crops. This coastal lowland taken as a whole has the densest average population in Brazil.

Sugar was the first plantation crop to be introduced. The Portuguese found that it would grow well on clearings in the forest, especially on the residual soils. Large plantations were established, sugar mills constructed, and Negro slaves imported. In addition to the slaves, some Indians as well as poorer classes of Portuguese workers were used. With the gold rush to the interior in the early part of the 18th century the plantations lost many of their workers. The abolition of slavery in 1880 further reduced the labor supply. In spite of many ups and downs, however, produc-

FIGURE 24.6. *Tapping a rubber tree in the state of Baia, Brazil. The incisions are made at a 30° angle. During his round the tapper has collected several pods of cacao, which grows in the same environment as rubber. From CIAA.*

tion of sugar is sufficient today to meet the demands of Brazil's 52 million people.

Cotton followed sugar as a plantation crop. The first planting was made about 1750, but production did not really begin on an important scale until the period of the War between the States in the United States. Although competition on the world cotton market is very keen, Brazilians with their cheap land and cheap labor have been able to compete with fair success.

Cacao was introduced to eastern Brazil at about the same time as cotton. Climate, soils, transportation, and labor have favored the production of cacao to such an extent that producers in Brazil are now second only to those of the Gold Coast of Africa in total output. Most of the cacao plantations are located near river transportation and on soils derived from crystalline rocks. The cacao tree grows well in the shade of the forest trees, which protect it from strong winds and excessive sunlight. The beans are taken in river boats down to the sea, and coastwise shipping concentrates the product at São Salvador, the chief port of Baia. This part of Brazil, noted for its plantation production, has at times furnished laborers for the rubber stations in Amazonia as well as settlers for the interior plateaus. See FIGURE 24.7.

THE INTERIOR HIGHLANDS—SUBSISTENCE AGRICULTURE

From eastern Amazonia to the border of Paraguay the interior plateau of Brazil is a region of uplands and valleys, of subsistence agriculture and grazing. Extending from the Equator to about 25° S., the region exhibits some striking contrasts in climate and production. Brief descriptions of two phases will suffice: one in the north, between latitude 10° S. and the Equator; the other farther south, where mining is of particular interest.

The rough, northern margin of the plateau is comparatively dry, much of it having a steppe (BS) climate. Pastoral industries have a wide distribution. Farmers have invaded the region, too, attempting to grow cotton along with subsistence crops. For some years agriculture achieved moderate success, but a series of severe droughts has caused many of the farmers to leave. Fortunately, many of them could shift to Amazonia, where workers were needed on the rubber plantations and at the stations gathering wild rubber.

The discovery of gold and diamonds in the southern part of the plateau in the interior of the state of Minas Geraes attracted many people, some of whom remained to become farmers after the mines were partially exhausted. Most of the mines are in Minas Geraes near such cities as Diamantina, Bello Horizonte, and Ouro Preto. The decline of mining set the stage for the rapid development of agriculture during the closing decades of the last century, but mining is still of great significance to this part of Brazil. Today the iron ore and manganese of this region have a greater significance than the gold and diamonds even though the area does lack coal for the processing of the ores. The high-grade iron ore is located about 250 miles north of Rio de Janeiro, in the headwaters of the Rio Doce near the 20th parallel. This is the richest and largest deposit of iron ore in the world. Unfortunately, there is no coal nearer than Porto Alegre in the state of Rio Grande do Sul, approximately 1000 miles south. In the early days iron ore and charcoal were used in iron making. In recent years, small amounts of coal have been brought from southern Brazil and from the United States for the manufacture of iron and steel. The iron ore, however, has scarcely been touched. A recent development is a modern steel mill located immediately to the west of Rio de Janeiro at Volta Redonda (FIG. 24.8). Ore is brought in by rail from the north, coal by sea and rail from the south. The declining iron ore reserves in the Great Lakes Region of the United States may have an important influence on the future development of the Brazilian deposits. The same district in which the iron ore is found also produces manganese, used to make manganese steel and to control the oxygen content of steel. Industrial diamonds, gold, chromium, nickel, quartz crystal, and manganese occur in this subregion. The amount mined, however, fluctuates widely with world market conditions.

THE PLATEAU OF SOUTHEASTERN BRAZIL

Above the narrow coastal lowland of eastern Brazil with its sugar, cacao, cotton, and corn is the Brazilian Plateau. This plateau rises abruptly in a steep escarpment which imposes a substantial barrier to transportation even though it is by no means as serious as many other highlands. The highland is not a simple plateau, but rather a series of plateaus at varying levels with mountains rising above them. Elevations reach more than

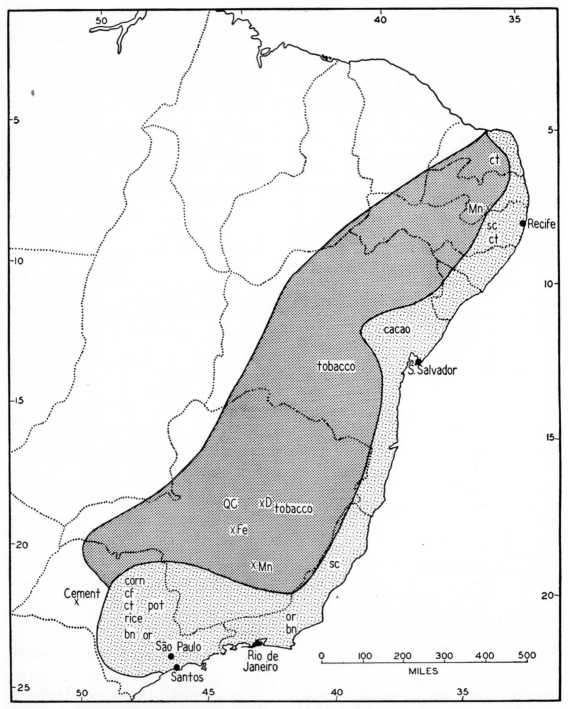

FIGURE 24.7. *Map of Plantations (light) and Subsistence Agriculture (dark) in eastern Brazil. (Dotted lines indicate boundaries of states.) The plantation region is near the sea. Only in the south, in the states of São Paulo and Minas Geraes, where coffee is dominant, are large numbers of plantations found on the plateau. Coffee (cf), cotton (ct), sugar (sc), oranges (or), and cacao are important cash crops. Subsistence crops include corn, white and sweet potatoes (pot), bananas (bn), beans, and cassava (manioc). Subsistence agriculture occupies the plateau and is being extended to the west. Mineral production includes iron (Fe), manganese (Mn), diamonds (D), quartz crystal (QC), and cement.*

7000 feet, but a large part of the plateau lies between 2000 and 3000 feet above sea level. The highland is cut by a number of streams whose valleys greatly aid communication and provide some low land for cultivation.

The plateau is rich in resources—mineral, agricultural, and forest. The production is equally varied, but the dominant note is coffee. In the last half century coffee planting has extended inland, especially in the state of São Paulo, in which there are now more than a billion producing trees. To be sure, coffee was introduced in Brazil long before this period of expansion. In 1774 the first trees were brought to Rio de Janeiro and planted in the adjacent lowlands. The trees did fairly well, but it was not until they were transplanted to the plateau that Brazilian producers began to take the lead in world production which they still hold.

The plateau is well adapted to coffee culture. The many valleys provide slopes with good air drainage and consequent freedom from frost. Nearly all the coffee is grown on the sloping sides of the valleys or on the ridges, while other crops are grown on the valley floors. The soils also proved to be suitable for coffee production. The most common soil, *terra roxa* (reddish earth), is derived from igneous rocks and possesses a mineral content which permits long continued coffee cultivation. The "coffee" climate (Cw) with hot, rainy summers and mild, dry winters is favorable for the growth, ripening, and drying of the crop.

Coffee production requires a large amount of hand labor. The laborers live in villages on the plantation. Seasonal migratory workers supplement the local force at picking time. The harvest usually begins in São Paulo in May, at the beginning of the dry season, and extends into July and August in some districts. The first operation, the picking of the "cherries," is done by hand. A coffee tree will yield only about two pounds of coffee per year. The "cherries" are washed and then dried on the open-air drying floors. They are husked by machine and the coffee beans, two from each "cherry," are again dried. The coffee is sacked, with about 150 pounds to a bag, and is then ready to start the journey to Santos on the coast. In the raw bean form, coffee will keep indefinitely.

A representative plantation in the plateau country of São Paulo includes approximately six square miles of hilltop, hillside, and valley floor. Half of the total area is still uncleared and, except for lumber which is very useful for building purposes, is unproductive forest. The "village" (it would be the *central* on a sugar plantation) is located on the valley floor. It consists of the huge concrete drying floors, sheds for storing the coffee, the residence of the owner, and numerous

FIGURE 24.8. *A general view of Brazil's new steel mill at Volta Redonda 90 miles west of Rio de Janeiro. This mill is near neither coal nor iron ore. From CIAA.*

FIGURE 24.9. *The world's greatest coffee port is Santos, Brazil. The city lies on a lowland within the bend of the river estuary. The warehouses for storing coffee are in the foreground. From PAA.*

smaller houses for the workers. The remainder of the valley floor is devoted to such crops as corn, beans, cassava, and rice to supply food for the workers. There is also pasture for the work animals, mostly mules. The coffee trees occupy the side slopes of the valley and the relatively flat hilltops, where they are arranged in rows up and down the slopes.

The land on which this plantation was founded was originally entirely in forest, but it was easy to clear by cutting and burning. The young coffee trees were planted immediately after clearing, and during the succeeding years, while they were developing to bearing age, other food crops, such as corn, beans, and potatoes, were grown between the rows. The coffee plantation was relatively easy to establish. Land was cheap, labor was available, and even during the early stages the plantation was nearly self-supporting. This situation led to the overexpansion of coffee production in Brazil and to the subsequent "valorization" schemes, which have included restriction of production and sale of coffee, and the systematic destruction of a part of the surplus. Unfortunately Brazilian producers with their enormous production, found themselves saddled with the sole responsibility of destroying the surplus.

The coffee-producing area of São Paulo is undergoing a rapid change. Some plantations are being abandoned while others are being subdivided. Small properties are on the increase. The immigration of many Italian, German, and Japanese families, all of whom were accustomed to small farms in their homelands, has accelerated this movement. In recent years cotton has replaced coffee as the bonanza crop in this area of pioneer settlement. The world market for coffee has been glutted, but the demand for cheap cotton has been better. With cheaper land and labor than in the United States Cotton Belt, Brazilians have been able to compete successfully on the world market. Also the 52 million people of Brazil consume a large amount of cotton at home. Other crops have attracted the attention of the farmers. Oranges will grow well in parts of this region, since the climatic requirements are similar to those of coffee. The corn belt type of farm with emphasis on livestock is also being established in many parts of the Coffee Belt. It must not be assumed, however, that coffee culture is doomed. In recent years the price of coffee has advanced, and if production can be kept within the limits of world consumption, the plantations will continue to be profitable.

Plantations and Subsistence Agriculture Regions in Africa

Equatorial Africa, aside from the tropical rainforest previously described (see page 134), is a land of subsistence agriculture, plantations, small farms with plantation crops, and various other types of production such as grazing and mining. Contained in this region are West Africa, the Sudan, the African Plateau including the Rhodesias and Angola, and the East Coast Lowland (FIG. 25.1). It stretches from Senegal to Ethiopia, thence to northern Mozambique, Rhodesia, and Angola, Madagascar can be studied as an isolated part of Equatorial Africa. Within this vast territory the landscapes are varied. Lowlands, plateaus, and mountains are represented. The climate is either tropical savanna or winter dry temperate (Aw or Cw), according to the altitude, with the exception of a few areas of steppe (BS).

This region offers many contrasts as well as many similarities to the areas of plantations and subsistence agriculture of the Americas discussed in Chapters 23 and 24. In order to establish plantations in the Americas, it was often necessary to import labor from outside, slave labor from Africa for example. In tropical Africa an abundance of agricultural laborers was at hand to cultivate various subsistence crops. Many of these crops could be adapted for commercial production. It is not to be expected, then, that the course of plantation development would be similar to that of the Americas. With specialized subsistence agriculture already established, it was easy for the native farmers to take over a large part of the commercial production, thus developing areas of plantation crops rather than plantations in the strictest sense. The plantation, *per se*, operated by Europeans is still to be found, however, as on the plateau of East Africa, where native farmers are

prevented by law from producing competing cash crops. Furthermore, the large plantation has certain advantages in the preparation of products such as rubber and palm oil for the market.

TROPICAL WEST AFRICA

Extending from the Senegal River to the Niger Delta, Tropical West Africa is the rainforest area closest to western Europe. Long known to the Europeans and well supplied with native labor, it is remarkable that even today its commercial development is limited to a few small areas near the coast and that even in these places the commercial crops are grown mostly on small native plots. The description of a few districts will serve to indicate the variety of production along this coast. In most areas cassava and bananas are the chief subsistence crops although in Senegal millet is also grown. The commercial crops are also used for food.

Peanuts were originally introduced into Senegal about 1840 by a Frenchman named Rousseau but did not become an important food crop until 1870. The simplicity of the cultivation made it very suitable for a native subsistence crop. Subsequently, the tribal chiefs were easily persuaded to put their people to work growing the crop for export. The fact that it is a welcome food to the natives made its introduction all the easier. The centers of production have tended to shift inland toward the upper Niger as better transportation has been provided. It will be recalled that during World War II the French industrialist Bedeaux interested Hitler in the idea of building a pipeline from Senegal across the Sahara to carry vegetable oils to the Mediterranean. The pipeline was never built, but the project, although visionary, indicates the importance of African vegetable oils to Europe. The peanut growers of West Africa have strong competition from those of India and other areas where production has tended to increase.

In Sierra Leone and Liberia the rainforest is still supreme; only in a few clearings is there commercial cultivation. Palm oil is the chief export, and most of it is taken from wild trees scattered through the forest rather than from plantations. On a few plantations in this subregion, however, there are oil mills. In both Sierra Leone and Liberia settlements by former slaves from the United States still dominate the colonies, and a few thousand descendants of these slaves are in

political control. The "native" Negroes live a rather primitive existence in the forest. At the same time that the Ford Motor Company was establishing rubber plantations in Amazonia (see page 315), the Firestone Tire and Rubber Company began the cultivation of rubber in Liberia, and with similar difficulties. The production of rubber has been small. The Firestone Company began operations about 1927, and within two years approximately six million trees had been transplanted from Sumatra to the vicinity of Monrovia. The original plan called for the ultimate production of 300,000 tons of rubber annually, but local difficulties and competition of producers in

FIGURE 25.1. *A map of Subsistence Agriculture and Plantations of Central Africa. Between the Sahara and arid South Africa agriculture is varied. In a few small plantation districts (heavier shading), agriculture is commercial. Along the Guinea Coast, north of the Equator, and in the Congo Basin, cacao, oil palm, and peanuts are plantation crops. Around Lake Victoria coffee, tea, cotton, and sisal are grown for export. The east coast plantations produce cloves, sisal, and sugar. The subsistence agriculture varies widely, including some grazing industries where feasible. Millet, bananas, and corn are common subsistence crops. Minerals include diamonds (D), gold (Au), copper (Cu), tin (Sn), and uranium (U).*

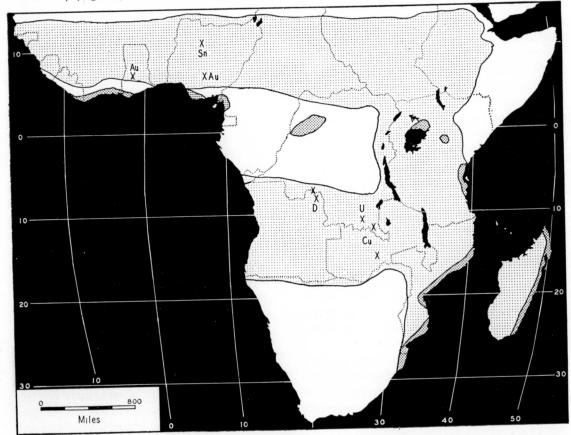

other areas and of manufacturers of synthetic rubber reduced this figure. Export of bananas from French Guinea is on the increase and promises to rival the peanut and palm oil in value. Coffee and pepper are produced in small quantities.

Along the Ivory Coast, the Gold Coast, and the coast of Nigeria cacao is the chief export crop. Climatic conditions—the heavy, even rainfall, the high humidity, and the comparative absence of strong winds—are generally favorable for cacao as on the eastern coast of Brazil. Cultivation did not begin until after 1900 and is largely on small native farms where the cacao trees are often intercultivated with the oil palm. Government instruction in the methods of growing, fermenting, and drying the cacao beans is available to the native farmers.

Although there are plantations of cacao, bananas, coffee, and vanilla along the coast of the Cameroons and French Equatorial Africa, the greatest development has occurred in the basin of the Congo, in the northern part of the Belgian Congo. There the vast stretches of wild oil palms and the abundant native labor formed the basis of the plantations. In 1911 an English soap company, Lever Brothers, obtained a lease on five large "circles" of land. Mills for the pressing and refining of palm oil were set up, one at the center of each circle. It was the plan of the company to exploit the widely scattered wild palm trees while simultaneously establishing plantations. Now this region is practically independent of wild supplies. Some cotton, cacao, and rubber along with cassava, bananas, and corn for subsistence purposes are grown in this area.

In the drier areas of West Africa cotton is produced as a cash crop also. In some districts Egyptian cotton is irrigated, and in the moister regions American cotton is grown without irrigation. Further development depends on expanded irrigation systems.

The mineral production in West Africa and the Congo, mostly gold, diamonds, iron, and manganese, rivals the plantation crops in value. Placer gold is washed out by the natives in many of the river beds and sold to the traders. The Belgian Congo leads the world in production of diamonds with nearly 10 million carats per year, although the proportion of high quality gem stones is low. The chief producers are at the Kasai River placers next to the Angola frontier. There is also large production in Angola, the Gold Coast, and Sierra Leone. Manganese is exported in large quantities from the Gold Coast, while iron ore has been consistently produced in Sierra Leone. No significant deposits of coal or petroleum are known in this region.

THE SUDAN

The Sudan is almost synonymous with the zone of savanna climate (Aw) extending from Senegal on the west to Ethiopia on the east. The western portion is near the sea and at an altitude of nearly 1000 feet while the eastern portion is inland and higher. Primarily, this is a region of subsistence agriculture and grazing although the beginnings of commercial agriculture can be noted. Cotton is grown in the irrigable portions of both the upper Senegal and Niger rivers, but production is small. It is possible to irrigate nearly five million acres in the western Sudan. Peanut production has been extended inland from the coast along the various short railway lines. The chief subsistence crops are millet, sorghum, and peanuts. In northern Nigeria, in the vicinity of the town of Kano, the population is relatively dense for a region of subsistence agriculture, averaging 160 persons per square mile in Kano Province. In addition to the cultivation of millet, peanuts, and cotton, grazing is also important. Hides and skins are exported, along with considerable quantities of tin. As grazing and farming become further intermingled this region approaches a mixed agricultural type with a distinctive quality. However, data are not available to distinguish the areas of subsistence farming from those of commercial grazing and nomadic herding. Communications are poor, except near the Nile River. Population is sparse, since subsistence farming and grazing are the chief activities. The principal district of commercial importance is the oasis of Khartoum at the junction of the Blue and the White Nile. There the acreage of cotton is increasing because of the favored location with respect to irrigation facilities and the rail connection to the Red Sea at Port Sudan.

THE AFRICAN PLATEAU

The great plateau of Africa extends in an arc from Ethiopia and the Red Sea through northern Rhodesia to Angola. This is by no means a simple plateau. Lofty volcanic mountains, such as Kilimanjaro, rise to more than 19,000 feet. Elongated structural depressions, including those occupied by Tanganyika, Nyasa, and Rudolph lakes, represent lower lying portions of the plateau. These great lakes, together with Lake Victoria, are important features of this extensive upland.

The climate is that of a moderately elevated plateau lying on and near the Equator. Except for the mountain peaks, the elevation is not sufficient to modify significantly the high temperatures of the equatorial belt, especially in the vicinity of the warm Indian Ocean. The influence of altitude on mean annual temperature is shown in the table on this page.

It will be seen that the change in temperature with elevation is approximately three degrees for each 1000 feet with some minor exceptions. The temperatures of the lower parts of the plateau are too high for comfort from the European standpoint but at elevations above 5000 feet are quite tolerable, since, in addition to lower temperatures, the air is drier.

The rainfall of the plateau is variable both in amount and in seasonal distribution. Much of the region averages from 40 to 50 inches annually, but some parts of Ethiopia and the vicinity of Lake Victoria and Lake Nyasa receive as much as 60 inches. In most parts there are two rainy seasons of unequal intensity separated by a short and a long dry season. For example, there is a wet season in Nairobi in March, April, and May, another in November and December. These seasons occur at the time of the high sun, the dry seasons at the time of the low sun. In this equatorial region far removed from the ocean, there is little marine influence so far as wind and rain are concerned. Farther east the Lowland of East Africa experiences both trade wind and monsoon influences. The amount of rainfall is highest on the mountain slopes exposed to the east, in some places reaching more than 80 inches.

The waters of the African Plateau flow to three large bodies of water: the Atlantic Ocean via the Congo; the Indian Ocean via various short rivers, such as the Ruvu, Shire, and the Bagamoyo; and the Mediterranean Sea via the Nile. Some large areas, such as that around Lake Rudolph, have no drainage to the sea. Some of the lakes have no outlets and are salty, but most are fresh water. They have a total area of about 60,000 square miles, Lake Victoria alone having over 32,000 square miles. Lake Tanganyika is 400 miles long and has a depth of 4700 feet, the deepest part being 2200 feet below sea level. The outlets of the lakes and the connecting rivers are not favorably situated for interlake communication, but the individual lakes are used for local traffic.

The peoples of the African Plateau have a great diversity of customs. Some are hunters, some primarily migratory agriculturists, and some combinations of the two. The region has been readily accessible to migration. Sudanese Negroes from the north, Zulus from the south, and in more recent years, immigrations of Europeans have added to the variety of people and culture. The native peoples of the African Plateau have been affected profoundly by their European contacts. Although few in numbers, the Europeans have taken a large share of the best agricultural lands and brought about many changes in native customs.

Ethiopia

The Ethiopian Highland, the northern part of the great African Plateau, has a mean elevation of over 5000 feet for a very large portion of the area and is, in this respect, the loftiest part of the plateau. The mountain peaks, however, are not as

			Average Temperature (degrees Fahrenheit)		Average Rainfall (inches)			Average Annual Rainfall (inches)
STATION	Climate	Elevation (feet)	Cool Month	Warm Month	Dry Month		Wet Month	
Mombasa	Aw	0	75	81	Jan.	0.8	May 13.0	47
Mwanza	Aw	3900	68	72	Jul.	0.1	Apr. 8.7	42
Nairobi	Cw	5400	58	65	Jul.	0.8	Apr. 8.3	39
Naivasha	Cf	6300	60	64	Jan.	1.1	Apr. 6.4	32
Elisabethville	Cw	4500	60	72	Jul.	0.0	Dec. 11.4	47

CLIMATIC DATA FOR SELECTED STATIONS IN THE EQUATORIAL BELT OF AFRICA

FIGURE 25.2. *A native market in central Africa. Peanuts, grain, and palm oil are offered for sale, as well as imported manufactured items. In many ways this scene resembles the small town markets of the Central Plateau of Mexico, also an area of subsistence agriculture. Keystone.*

high as those of Kenya and Tanganyika. The Ethiopian segment of the plateau is deeply dissected, but there are extensive areas of nearly level upland. The climate is a little cooler than that of most of the African Plateau because of the greater elevation. In Addis Ababa, for example, the hottest month averages 65° F.

The natural riches of the Ethiopian Highland led to exploitation by Egyptians, Arabs, and later by Europeans. In ancient times caravans of camels, mules, and donkeys carried ivory, ostrich plumes, gums, slaves, incense, and myrrh to Egypt via the Nile and also via the Red Sea and thence to lower Egypt. In modern times the interest in Ethiopia has been in coffee, gold, and petroleum, and in the possibilities of European colonization.

European interest in Ethiopia began in the late 1400's, but little attempt was made at exploitation until the Italians came in 1882. Active colonization was postponed until the conquest of Ethiopia in 1936. Plans for the settlement of many thousands of Italian farmers in the colony were hampered by the lack of roads and the difficulties of agriculture in this land strange to the Italian peasants. The venture was ended in 1940 with the reconquest of Ethiopia by the British aided by the Ethiopians. The limited exports in recent years have been coffee, gold, ivory, leather, gums, and wax. In spite of all the efforts, Ethiopia remains to be developed as a commercial region.

The Lake Victoria District

Plantations have been established on the borderlands of Lake Victoria, in Uganda, Kenya, and Tanganyika. The elevations, especially those above 5000 feet, are favorable for settlement by Europeans. Two railroads, one through Kenya to the northern end of the lake and one through Tanganyika to the southern end, transport the products to the Indian Ocean. In general, cotton is an important cash crop. Short upland American varieties are grown, mostly by the natives on small plots ranging up to five acres. Indian immigrants play an important part in the preparation of cotton for export, and much of the export goes to India. Coffee and sisal are the other plantation crops. Three areas deserve special mention: southeastern Uganda, southern Kenya, and northern Tanganyika.

In Uganda, still "Black Man's Country," both subsistence and cash crops are largely in the hands of natives, a situation more like that of Nigeria than of East Africa. Cotton and coffee are the chief cash crops, while corn and millet are staple foods. Most of the farms are small family plots on which the methods of cultivation are simple if not primitive. The soil is broken by hand or with small plows and cultivated with hoes. Only at picking time is extra labor supplied by migratory workers from neighboring territories. There is some local concern about the dominant status of cotton, and an attempt is being made to develop other cash crops. Coffee, tobacco, and oilseeds are on the increase.

In Kenya the European settlements are between 5000 and 6000 feet and the climate, although equatorial in the sense of little seasonal contrast, is by no means hot. The temperature in Nairobi at 5400 feet averages 66° F. for the warmest month and 60° F. for the coolest. It is interesting to note, however, that apparently the Kenya climate promotes too rapid growth in children followed by debility in early middle age, but evidence of this is not yet clear. Coffee, cotton, sisal, and tea are the chief cash crops. All are grown mainly on European farms (FIGS. 25.3 and 25.4) in contrast with those in Uganda. The farms in the European reserve, mainly near the railroad, average about 600 acres per individual. Native farms, however, are small and mostly subsistence in character, since there are restrictions on the production of cash crops by natives in order that there may be laborers available for the estates. Large areas of relatively poor land are set aside in native reserves and are not, therefore, open to European settlement. In Tanganyika, the chief export crops are sisal and coffee, mostly grown by Indian farmers, who came in when the Germans left at the end of World War I.

Nyasaland

Nyasaland is a comparatively small protectorate on the west side of Lake Nyasa. There is fairly abundant rainfall and the region is favorable for agriculture, but poor communications have limited European settlers to a few thousand. The natives prefer the alluvial soils on the borders of the lake or in the valley of the river Shire, whereas the Europeans prefer the cooler plateaus. In addition to the subsistence crops—corn, beans, and cassava—the principal crop is tobacco, while

FIGURE 25.3. *A plantation clearing on the East African Plateau. There is little indication of native subsistence agriculture in this view. From Mary Light and the American Geographical Society.*

FIGURE 25.4. *A near view of the same plantation as illustrated in Figure 25.3, showing young tea trees growing under shade. From Mary Light and the American Geographical Society.*

the growing of cotton has been unsuccessful. The commercial development of Nyasaland depends on the completion of the railroad from Beira across the Zambezi River to the lower end of Lake Nyasa. The difficulty of bridging the Zambezi has delayed this project for many years.

Northern Rhodesia

The major attraction of Northern Rhodesia to Europeans is the large bodies of copper ores at Broken Hill and Bwanamkubwa. The copper mines, still in an early stage of development, belong to the same mineral zone as Katanga, described in the next paragraph. In recent years Rhodesian copper production has been increasing and has surpassed that of the Belgian Congo. The natives grow corn, coffee, and tobacco in small quantities, and there are a few European farms near the mining towns.

Katanga

In the southern extremity of the Belgian Congo, immediately north of Rhodesia is the Katanga copper district located on the plateau portion of the Belgian Congo. Approximately one fifth of the world's copper is produced in Northern Rhodesia and Belgian Congo together, and the reserves are enormous. Production has been sufficient to upset the world market. For centuries the natives had mined the copper on a small scale, the ore and metal moving by caravan in the days of the slave trade. In 1868 David Livingstone (Scottish missionary and explorer in Africa) met such a caravan with slaves, ivory, and several tons of copper. By 1906 a mining company was organized, and in 1911 work began on a large scale. Since that time production has increased steadily with few interruptions. The smelters and refineries at Elisabethville and Panda (Jadotville) are capable of producing 250,000 tons of copper annually.

The labor problem in these mining districts is a simple one, since many of the natives had been engaged in mining before modern mining began. The Katanga district is not densely populated, but there has been little difficulty in providing sufficient labor for the mines and smelters, since every native must earn enough to pay his poll tax. With the development of the mineral industry, the agriculture of the region has expanded and quantities of corn, cassava, sugar, ground nuts, palm oil, rice, and beans are now produced to feed the workers. A large mining operation always stimulates agriculture if the region is at all favorable for the growing of crops.

Henry Stanley (British journalist and explorer), who is famous for the remark, "Dr. Livingstone, I presume," made a much more cogent statement about this country. "Without railroads," he said, "the Congo is not worth a penny." Reference has already been made, in Chapter 8 on Tropical Hardwood Forests, to the difficulties of navigation on the Congo. The Katanga district has two direct railway connections with the coast and two others are under construction. The first to be built was from Beira on the Indian Ocean to Broken Hill in Northern Rhodesia. This section was completed in 1906 and was extended to Elisabethville in 1910, just as production of copper at Katanga was getting under way. The other route leads from Benguela on the Atlantic to Katanga across Portuguese territory. It was an easy road to construct but serves very little of the Congo. Consequently, a railroad which will eventually reach the lower Congo at Matadi is now being built northwest of Katanga.

Of more significance than the copper perhaps are the uranium deposits in the Katanga area. In 1940, before world production of uranium became a well-kept secret, this, together with the Great Bear Lake district of Canada, was the chief source of the metal. As late as 1941 the *Minerals Yearbook* reported a large surplus of radium and uranium, far above the world demand. The development of atomic fission changed this situation drastically, and the feverish search for new supplies of uranium by all major nations began. Statistics of uranium ore production are not available, but it is known that the Shinkolobwe mine in Katanga is the largest producer of high-grade ore. Other nearby mines produce some uranium.

Angola

Portuguese Angola, the western extremity of the African Plateau, offers fairly good opportunities for European colonization. The central portion of the country is above 3500 feet and certain districts reach 7000 feet. Today native subsistence agriculture is the rule along with pastoral activities. Sisal and coffee could be grown here without great difficulty. The chief effort of the Portuguese, however, has been directed to the narrow coastal lowland, where some sugar and cacao are produced for export. The scarcity of native labor in the coastal belt and the hot humid climate are serious handicaps to further commercial development. The natives realize, apparently, that the best opportunities, or at least the greatest comforts, are on the plateau.

EAST AFRICAN LOWLAND

The low country of East Africa from Kenya on the Equator to latitude 25° S. is a land of small native farms and expanding plantations. It is more of a lowland than the Congo, more maritime than the Belgian Congo, and oriented very definitely to the Indian Ocean. Most of the natives are farmers but some also hunt and fish. In the equatorial portion, bananas are the essential food, and the natives live where bananas can be grown. This crop is easy to cultivate; a small clearing is made, a few shoots are transplanted, and the native Bantu has a grove of banana trees which furnishes shade and food for many years. Grain sorghums, maize, potatoes, and cassava are cultivated in the drier areas where the banana will not mature. Where rainfall is still lighter pastoral life prevails with camels, donkeys, goats, and most important of all, beef cattle. Cattle are used for meat, milk, and hides, but rarely as beasts of burden.

Immigrants from Arabia and India have invaded East Africa for centuries. In the last half century there has been an influx of Europeans in spite of the difficulties of inland transportation and the hazards of disease. To be sure, most of the tide of European immigration passed beyond the low country to the cooler plateau, especially around Lake Victoria. Nevertheless, there are some areas of concentrated development in the lowlands, mostly by Arabs and Indians. The most important commercial crop is sisal, which was introduced from Mexico.

Along the east coast of Tanganyika and on the island of Zanzibar is the first plantation area of importance south of Suez, the African coast of the Red Sea and the coast of Somaliland being too dry to support much cultivation. The Zanzibar district was the first to be developed by outsiders. Arabs and Hindus settled this coast and began to produce tropical crops to send back to their native lands and export to Europe.

Zanzibar, in particular, was an important trading center for the East African Plateau. The Portuguese traders reached this part of the continent about 1490, but it was not until the 19th century that plantations appeared on a fairly large scale. The clove tree was introduced since spices were in great demand, and later sisal, cotton, and sugar were added. Coconuts are grown on plantations near the sea. The Arabs and Hindus have operated these plantations with the help of native labor. With the entrance of the Germans and later the British into this territory, the influence of the Arab declined. Many of the plantations have fallen into neglect, others have come into the possession of Europeans, and some have been subdivided and taken over by native farmers.

Sisal was introduced from Mexico late in the 19th century and has become the most important export of the eastern coast of Tanganyika. It is entirely a plantation crop, since the natives are not allowed to grow this crop for export. Cotton also thrives here and is the second export crop. Both of these crops are also grown in the highlands inland from the coast at elevations up to 5000 feet or more. The subsistence crops in this plantation area include bananas, rice, and corn.

It should be pointed out that although the East African coast from the Equator to Natal is not very productive or well populated by Europeans, it is, nevertheless, of considerable importance as a means of reaching the great African Plateau. The plateau has already seen great development, and further strides will undoubtedly be made in the immediate future. Progress on the plateau will mean progress in the low country, although to a lesser degree.

Along the coast of Mozambique, a Portuguese possession, there are scattered plantations in the more favored localities. The government of Portugal has not actively promoted settlement, however, and production has been static for a long time. The climate favors the production of sugar, sisal, coconuts, and cotton, as well as the small grains. What few Europeans live here are confined largely to the coastal cities. Sugarcane is the most important crop, but the production has been limited to what the Lisbon market could absorb. There is a market for additional sugar in South Africa in spite of Natal's production.

Most of the other crops are exported in minor quantities or consumed in the colony. One very important function of the ports of Mozambique—Beira and Lourenço Marques—is as outlets for the copper, corn, and coal from Rhodesia and the Transvaal.

South of Mozambique is the lowland of Natal, a part of the Union of South Africa. There the acreage of plantation land is limited by the narrowness of the coastal lowland and by the occupation of much of the land by native Zulu farmers. Nevertheless, a large part of the cultivated land is devoted to growing sugar, enough being produced to supply most of the needs of the people of South Africa.

MADAGASCAR

Although the physical qualities of Madagascar are similar to those of East Africa, this large island is isolated commercially and culturally from the continent. Since Madagascar is a colony of France, the trade is with the mother country rather than with Africa. Furthermore, the population is partly Asiatic in origin and rice is an important crop, especially along the eastern coast as well as on the eastern side of the

plateau. Rice is grown in all parts of the island except the southwest, which is too dry. Both paddy and upland rice are cultivated, the former in the lowlands which can be irrigated, the latter on the hill slopes of the highland. Cassava, corn, beans, and bananas are also grown for subsistence purposes and, to a limited extent, for export.

The chief commercial crop is cane sugar, most of which is grown along the eastern coast for export to France. Coffee thrives along the eastern fringe of the highland. Production of cash crops is limited by the inadequate transportation from the interior of the island to the coast. However, a railway connects the capital, Tananarive, on the plateau, with Tamatave on the eastern coast, and a good motor road runs from the capital to the excellent harbor of Diégo-Suarez at the northern end of the island. Other roads lead to the western coast and to the southern part of the plateau. As the transportation system is improved, the production of sugar, coffee, and other cash crops will probably increase. Madagascar is one of the world's important sources of graphite; most of it is obtained from the hinterland of Tamatave.

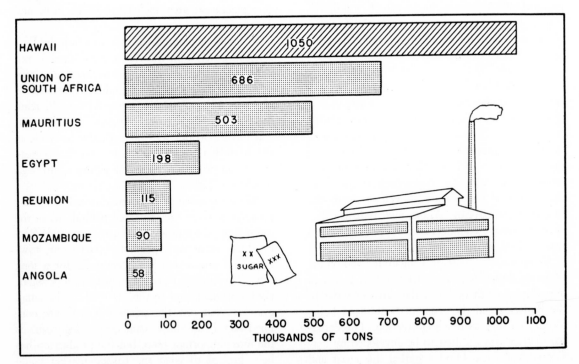

FIGURE 25.5. *Graph of raw sugar production in Africa, compared with Hawaii.*

26

Oriental Agriculture

ORIENTAL AGRICULTURE is characterized by quite small farms, intensive cultivation by hand labor rather than machinery, and emphasis on subsistence crops. The careful cultivation of small plots for two or even three crops a year suggests some of the more intensive phases of Mediterranean Agriculture, but the differences in crops and methods are striking. In the Mediterranean the crop system is adapted to a dry summer and rainy winter; in the Orient the Monsoon climate (Chapter 4) with its rainy, hot summers and dry winters (in some places very mild, in others very cold) is the chief limiting factor. As in the Mediterranean, additional water for irrigation is usually necessary for the full-scale development of the type.

The main belt of Oriental Agriculture extends from western Pakistan to Manchuria and Japan, and includes Indochina, Indonesia, and the Philippines. Smaller patches of this type may be found in other parts of the world, wherever migrating Oriental peoples have found a favorable environment for this kind of cultivation. On the east coast of Africa and on some of the South Sea Islands, migrating Orientals have transplanted their farming pattern, usually with some local modifications. Indian farmers brought rice culture to the coast of British Guiana; the Chinese introduced it to California and Hawaii. But only in Asia has Oriental Agriculture reached its full development through many centuries of adaptation to the varying environments and to pressures of population.

Oriental Agriculture supports approximately one half of the world's people on one eighth of the land surface. This fact, even after allowing for the high fertility of parts of Monsoon Asia, is still the greatest geographic anomaly on the earth's surface today. The people of Monsoon Asia have the lowest resource base per capita of any large group in the world. Why is this region so densely populated? Is it because of the intensive agriculture? Or is the intensive agriculture the result? The answers are by no means clear. It is obvious, however, that in a rather favorable environment, peoples as different as the Indians, the Chinese, and the Japanese have all increased in numbers up to the very limit of the food supply. Indeed, in terms of an adequate diet, they have expanded beyond their food production. It should be noted that, unlike western Europe, which also is densely populated, Monsoon Asia has little industrial development.

In Monsoon Asia, a few places have many people, and many places have a few people. This makes the first statement of the preceding paragraph all the more remarkable. Population density ranges from less than ten persons per square mile in the Thar of India and the interior of China to more than 2500 per square mile in some of the rural districts of Java. Dense populations are almost always supported by agriculture, in which rice is the most important crop, while the sparsely peopled areas are too dry or too cool for rice. Near the equator, where two crops of rice per year can be grown on the same land (double cropping), the highest densities of population are attained. Where good yields of rice are difficult, millet, wheat, barley, oilseeds, and various other foods are substituted. Five rather large regions of dense population can be readily distinguished: the Ganges Plain and Delta in India and Pakistan;

the Island of Java; the Yangtze Basin of China; the North China Plain; and southern Japan.

THE CROPS

Nearly all the important crops grown in Monsoon Asia, rice, millet, cotton, soybeans, etc., have been mentioned in previous chapters in connection with other types of agriculture. Rice is fundamental, and in southeastern Asia 95 per cent of the world's production is grown. However, in the dry areas of western India and China and in the short-summer districts of north China and Manchuria rice cannot be grown efficiently. In its place wheat, barley, and millet, which require less rainfall and will grow during a shorter season, are the staple crops. The grain sorghums also produce well in the drier and cooler areas, and the soybean thrives in north China, Manchuria, and Japan. Oilseeds, such as sesame, rapeseed, cotton, and peanuts, help make up for the lack of animal fat. Commercial crops include sugarcane, rubber, and various plantation crops, but rice, wheat, and millet have the highest acreages and the widest distribution.

Rice is one of the world's oldest cultivated crops. It has been cultivated from the earliest times in southeastern Asia and has been introduced into only a few areas on the other continents. There are many varieties both cultivated and wild which may be classed as either upland or paddy (swamp) rice. Upland rice, sown broadcast like wheat or barley, is grown on hilly lands or uplands without irrigation. It grows on poorer soil and with less work than paddy rice. Yields, however, are correspondingly low and in the rice-growing countries it is distinctly a makeshift crop. Paddy rice must be grown on lands which can be flooded either by heavy rains or from diverted streams or wells. It is, therefore, grown on the river flood plains of southeastern Asia. On the other hand, where level land is not available and there is sufficient labor, terraces may be constructed in order to convert the hill slopes into small patches of level land. Terraces are more common in Ceylon, China, Java, the Philippines, and Japan than in India.

The rice paddy is a small plot of ground with a bordering ridge of earth which will hold water. Before plowing, the paddy is flooded until the ground is thoroughly soaked. Plowing is done in the wet paddy after which the rice plants are set out by hand or the seed is sown broadcast. Where transplanting is practiced (FIG. 26.1), the plants usually go through an initial period of growth in a specially prepared seed bed. After planting, the rice paddy is alternately flooded and drained. The cultivation of paddy rice requires a high degree of agricultural skill. Not only do the operations of transplanting, flooding, and terracing call for unending attention, but the process of securing water for irrigation often requires the cooperation and organization of the whole community.

From the standpoint of the peoples of southeastern Asia, rice has a number of unique advantages as a food crop. In the first place, the yield per acre in terms of food value is very high, higher than any other crop except white potatoes. The maintenance of high yields, to be sure, is coupled with the continuing fertility of the soil, but rice has been produced in China for forty centuries on the same land without great loss of soil fertility. In the second place, rice is a well-rounded food, comparable to wheat as a balanced item in the diet of the people, because it supplies most of the necessary food ingredients. A third quality of rice from the standpoint of the tropical and subtropical lands is the ease with which it may be preserved. Under similar conditions corn and even wheat would spoil. Thus, since rice is largely a warm season crop which must be preserved to feed the people during the dry season, it is especially suitable for growth in the subtropical and tropical lands.

The relative importance of rice in different areas of Oriental Agriculture is a significant indication of the nature as well as the basis of the main agricultural types. The relative acreage of rice depends on climate, water supply, surface, soil, and the competition of other crops. In general, rice occupies the best sites. Rice grows best in the alluvial lowlands where precipitation is heavy or water is available for irrigation. A heavy subsoil is favorable in areas of light rainfall and limited water for irrigation. This soil tends to hold the water in the paddies for several days. See the table on page 294.

There is, of course, great variation in the relative acreage of rice in different parts of the large countries. In the Ganges Delta and parts of the Brahmaputra Lowland, the rice percentage is as high as 75 per cent, and it is less than 5 per

FIGURE 26.1. *Transplanting rice in South China. The plants are removed from the seed bed, tied in bundles, and placed in the water in preparation for transplanting to the paddies. Paddy rice cultivation is practiced throughout Monsoon Asia, excepting only those areas too dry or too cool for rice to grow. From Keystone.*

cent in parts of the Deccan. In western Java rice represents 68 per cent of the cropped land and in the east 28 per cent.

The nonrice crops of Monsoon Asia are so numerous and so widely distributed as almost to defy classification or study in any brief treatment. Tentatively they may be grouped as follows:

Small grains—wheat, barley, and oats
Millets and sorghums
Pulses—beans, soybeans, peas, chick-peas (gram), and
    other legumes
Vegetables—cassava, sweet potatoes, and many others
Corn
Oilseeds—peanuts, sesame, linseed, rapeseed, and
    others
Fibers—cotton, jute, silk and ramie
Sugarcane

The chief areas of production for each of these crops will be discussed in the chapters to follow. It will be noted that most of the crops in the previous list are primarily for food. The people of Monsoon Asia depend on cereals more heavily than those of any other region of the world, and less on meat and dairy products.

TYPES OF ORIENTAL AGRICULTURE

In Chapter 2 Oriental Agriculture was described briefly as the intensive form of subsistence agriculture in which a large amount of labor is applied to relatively small plots of land. Yields per acre are generally high; yields per man remarkably low. In view of the wide variety of climate, surface, and peoples in southeastern Asia, it may be assumed that Oriental Agriculture has as many types as Occidental Agriculture. But data are not available either to define numerous types or to mark them out on a map.

Therefore only the broad, easily recognized types will be studied in the chapters to follow.

THE RICE AND PLANTATION CROPS type occurs in the warmer and moister parts of southeastern Asia, southern and eastern India, southern Burma, Siam, and French Indochina. Here rice reaches its greatest importance, and in many districts two crops are harvested in one year from the same land. The majority of the secondary crops are those already discussed under plantations—rubber, sugar, coffee, tea, quinine, jute, copra, manila hemp, pepper, cassava, and cacao.

THE RICE AND SMALL GRAINS type occurs where the season is too short for two crops of rice in one year; small grains and vegetables are the winter crops. The middle Ganges Plain in India, the lower Yangtze Valley of China, and southern Japan are regions of "rice and winter grain." Many additional crops are produced, such as corn, cotton, mulberry for silkworms, tea, melons, poppy for seed and opium, bamboo for wood and food, and sweet potatoes.

THE MILLET type occurs in western and northwestern India in areas which are too dry for rice and also in northern China and Manchuria where the growing season is too short. Other crops are sorghums, wheat, and soybeans, but millet is the most representative. This type is described in Manchuria as the Soybean–Sorghum type.

The broad types of Oriental Agriculture described correspond to irregular areas on a map. For this reason in the subsequent descriptions the areas will be divided as follows: Indonesia together with the Philippines, Malaya, Burma, Siam, and Indochina; India, Pakistan, and Ceylon; China; and Japan.

27

Indonesia, Malaya, the Philippines, and Indochina

SOUTHEASTERN Asia is the most tropical part of the continent, a result of the combined influences of latitude (10° S. to 20° N.) and sea. There is no cold season, no steppe, no desert, only the ever humid rainforest broken here and there by an occasional savanna. In most places the rainfall and temperatures are uniformly high, and where surface and soil are favorable, all kinds of tropical crops will grow at any time of year. Some of the slight differences in climate, such as the varying length of the rainy season, are significant. The five stations listed in the table on this page are representative of the region, and the data suggest the nature of the variations in temperature and rainfall.

Singapore is an ideal rainforest (Af) station, temperatures and rainfall being uniformly high. Batavia is in the southern hemisphere and thus receives its heaviest rainfall during the winter monsoon in January and February. Manila and Rangoon are much alike with heavy rain in summer and a definite dry season. Port Moresby is drier than the other stations, because it lies in the rain shadow of the Owen Stanley Moun-

tains. Throughout the East Indies, Malaya, and the Philippines the climate is either rainforest (Af) or savanna (Aw), except in the interior highlands of the large islands. In the higher elevations of Luzon, Mindanao, Sumatra, Java, Borneo, and Papua, the climate is cool and temperate (Cfb), affording a cool retreat from the hot, humid lowlands. Baguio and Buitenzorg are summer capitals for Manila and Batavia, respectively.

The climatic data on this page fail to express the abundance of rain. In no other region of such extent in the world is there so much precipitation. In the Dutch East Indies, the average is nearly 100 inches, and in the Philippines more than 85 inches. On the slopes of the mountains in the path of the monsoon, the rain is much heavier, two or three times the general average. Furthermore, the rain often comes in violent downpours, sometimes accompanied by hurricanes. At Baguio, north of Manila, 45 inches have fallen in a 24 hour period. Little wonder that leached and eroded soils are to be found in many cultivated districts unless extreme care is taken

CLIMATIC DATA FOR SELECTED STATIONS IN SOUTHEASTERN ASIA					
STATION	Average Temperature (degrees Fahrenheit)		Average Rainfall (inches)		Average Annual Rainfall (inches)
	Jan.	Jul.	Jan.	Jul.	
Singapore	77.9	80.2	9.7	6.7	95.1
Batavia	77.9	78.7	13.0	2.6	72.1
Manila	76.6	80.6	0.8	17.3	79.6
Port Moresby	82.2	78.1	7.5	1.0	40.8
Rangoon	74.7	78.8	0.2	21.4	99.0

in the methods of cultivation and fertilization.

In spite of the population of nearly one hundred million in this region, much of the land remains in forest. In the districts with even rainfall—Malaya, Sumatra, western Java, Borneo, and the southwestern Philippines—the tropical rainforest is dominant. The variety of evergreen hardwoods, climbing vines, and flowering plants is even greater than in Amazonia or the Congo. In those areas having a definite dry season such as eastern Java and southern New Guinea, the forest is less dense and some savanna grasslands exist, especially in eastern Mindanao and southern Papua.

In the tropical rainforest climate the soils are usually so thoroughly soaked as to have lost nearly all of their soluble minerals and are consequently low in fertility. This is not true in Java, however. Of the hundreds of volcanic cones on this island more than eighty have been active in historic times. Soils derived from these recent deposits have not had time to become thoroughly

FIGURE 27.1. *A map of western Indonesia. Most of the Peninsula of Malaya and the islands of Sumatra and Java may be classed as Subsistence Agriculture (light shading) or as Plantation (heavier shading), whereas the interior of Borneo is covered with tropical forest. Within this small area live more than 60 million people, who subsist largely on rice, cassava, corn, bananas, sugarcane, and millet. The chief plantation crops are rubber (R), sugarcane (sc), sisal (s), together with lesser quantities of quinine, tea, coffee, and kapok. Mineral production includes petroleum indicated by black triangles, coal of poor quality indicated by black square, tin (Sn), and iron (Fe).*

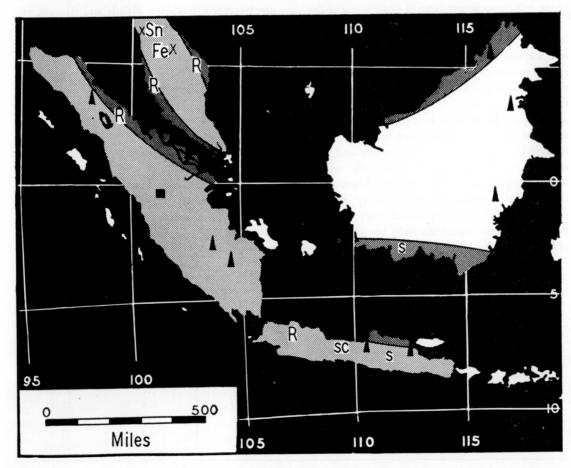

leached. Furthermore, the mountain streams constantly bring down a new supply of soil to enrich the lowlands. Silt deposited by the water used for irrigation is also an important factor in maintaining the productivity of the soils. Because of these factors the soils of Java and other parts of Indonesia are generally superior to those of the Amazon Basin and the Congo Upland.

INDONESIA

Java, the heart of Indonesia, is a long narrow island with a fringe of volcanic mountains on the southern border. These mountains are less continuous and there is much better access to the interior than in Sumatra. Java is more than 600 miles long, generally less than one hundred miles wide, and is smaller than the state of Florida. Only a few centuries ago, before the Dutch had effectively occupied the island, the population was about five million. The increase to 50 millions in the last three centuries, brought many changes in the agriculture of Java. Rice remained the chief crop but there were many new crops introduced: corn, cassava, sugar, coffee, rubber, and sisal. In other words, the plantation system has been superimposed to a limited extent on rice culture.

Rice is the most extensive crop in Java, occupying about 40 per cent of the cultivated land and extending throughout the lowland areas. Most of it is still grown by the natives with their own peculiar methods of farming and, as a result, yields are not high. The production is more than six million tons, but this gives only about 200 pounds per capita, as compared with more than 500 pounds per capita for Japan. The deficiency is made up in part by corn, cassava, and other starchy foods. This does not represent a very high standard of living, but it is above that of Indonesia as a whole.

When Java was first visited by Europeans, production was in a primitive state. Most of the rice was grown by the *ladang* method which consists of the burning or clearing of the forest and the sowing of the grain broadcast without irrigation or tillage. The Dutch, skilled in handling the surplus waters of their homeland, were able to introduce an effective system of irrigation which increased the production of rice and other food crops substantially. Wet paddy cultivation replaced upland rice with a consequent increase

in yield. Permanent dams and drainage channels superseded the temporary structures of the natives; railroads and highways were constructed to afford better movement of goods. In general, however, the Dutch took little part in the actual cultivation of the basic food crops.

At the peak of development, immediately prior to World War II, 1200 plantations with a total area of 1,500,000 acres accounted for only about 6 per cent of the total cropland of Java. The remainder was in subsistence crops, forest, and pasture land. Most of the plantations were established on newly cleared forest land and only a small proportion on land previously cultivated by the natives. Some precautions were taken to protect the land devoted to the food crops of the Javanese from exploitation by plantation owners.

Today, the chief cash crops (FIG. 27.2) on the plantations are sugar, rubber, copra, sisal, jute, tobacco, quinine, coffee, cotton, tea, and the oil palm. A typical plantation produces two or three cash crops in order to employ the labor and land most effectively. Rice, corn, cassava, and bamboo are also grown. The combination of a climate in which two crops of rice can be grown on the same land in one year, a rich soil which is derived from recent volcanic deposits and often renewed by annual flooding of mountain streams, and an energetic native population provide a setting in which plantations can succeed.

After Java, Sumatra is the principal producing area of Indonesia. On the map it appears as an enlarged and tilted Java. Sumatra is a thousand miles long, somewhat larger than California in total area. About eight million people live on it. Like Java it has a mountain fringe along the southwestern margin and a lowland to the northeast. In Sumatra, however, the mountains constitute a relatively serious barrier between the northern and southern coasts. Only a small percentage of the land is under cultivation, but the amount has been increasing in recent years largely because of the expansion of plantation cropping.

As in Java, rice is the chief food crop of the natives. Cassava and corn are also produced. In the northwest, a limited number of beef cattle are raised on the savannas. The plantations produce rubber, coffee, sisal, copra, tea, palm oil, tobacco, and cotton, employing native laborers in addition to Javanese and Chinese who contract for two or three years at a time. Sumatra is the

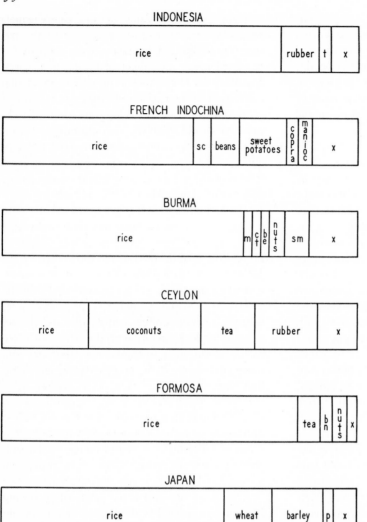

FIGURE 27.2. *Crop graphs of various phases of Oriental Agriculture. Indonesia (the first graph represents the Indonesian islands exclusive of Java. For a graph of Java's crops see page 26) and Ceylon grow quantities of plantation crops as well as rice. Burma, French Indochina, and Formosa (Taiwan) are surplus rice producers, while Japan supplements rice with wheat, barley, potatoes, and other food crops. Abbreviations: t, tea; sc, sugarcane; m, millet; ct, cotton; be, beans; sm, sesame; bn, bananas; p, potatoes; x, miscellaneous crops.*

second largest producer of rubber after Malaya. Part of the crop is taken from the small groves of the natives. The advantage of a location near Singapore, the great rubber market, is obvious.

"The Great East"

The Dutch call the lands east of Borneo and Java and south of the Philippines "The Great East," a part of the Outer Indies. Only recently production in this area has been placed on a commercial scale. Bali, Celebes, Amboina, Halmahera, and New Guinea are only the best known islands; thousands of smaller islands are also included. It was the plan of the Dutch to develop Java to a point where it could serve as an economic center for all of Indonesia before the outer colonies were exploited. In recent years, how-

ever, economic expansion in "The Great East" as well as in Sumatra and Borneo has been in the hands of the new Republic of Indonesia.

Today the native farmers of "The Great East" are living in much the same way as the Javanese did a century or so ago. Temporary forest clearings in which rice and other food crops are produced will in a few years give way to new clearings. In some cases the clearings are devoted to plantation crops, chiefly copra, coffee, and nutmeg. The expansion of plantations, however, has been limited by the small labor supply of the eastern islands. In many places it is necessary to bring in contract labor from Java or China. A further handicap is the poor transportation, since the eastern islands are off the main lines of ocean traffic.

Mineral Production

By far the most significant mineral of Indonesia is petroleum. The total production is not large but so little oil is produced in southeastern Asia that the wells of Sumatra, Borneo, Java, and New Guinea are of great significance. Indonesia, in fact, ranks fifth or sixth in world production of oil. About 65 per cent of its oil is taken from the Palembang district of Sumatra, 20 per cent from Borneo, the remainder from Java and New Guinea. The quality of most of the oil makes it easy to use without the more elaborate refining processes, some being used as ship fuel without refining. The gasoline content is often as high as 50 per cent, and can be separated by simple distillation. The oilfields are widely scattered, however, and it is necessary to bring the oil from remote fields by pipelines and tankers to the chief refining districts in southern Sumatra and northern Java.

The most valuable metal of Indonesia is tin. The island of Bangka off the northeast coast of Sumatra is the largest producer, followed by the islands of Belitong and Singkep. The tin ore occurs in alluvial deposits and is separated by washing in much the same manner as is placer gold. Most of the ore is then smelted on the spot and the crude metal is sent to the Netherlands or to Wales for refining. Some, however, is shipped to western Europe for smelting because of the poor quality of coal in Indonesia. The coal which is used locally in the smelters and also as bunker fuel is mined in Sumatra. The beds are shallow and accessible. Strip mining is used in some localities, and drift tunnels in others. The coal is very soft and, upon handling, crumbles rapidly and forms dust, not all of which is usable.

Gold is mined in various parts of Indonesia, more especially in Borneo, Sumatra, and New Guinea. Deposits of bauxite are worked in the Rhio Islands near Singapore, and the ore is exported in crude form. Phosphate is mined on Java, diamonds in southern Borneo, and mercury in Sumatra. Deposits of copper, iron ore, lead, zinc, and other ores are known, but the production has been small. On the average, the mines of Indonesia employ about 65,000 workers.

MALAYA

The Malay Peninsula is one of the less favored areas of Monsoon Asia for general subsistence agriculture. Much of the peninsula is mountainous, and much of the remainder has poor soil, especially for rice cultivation. The low foothills are satisfactory for rubber plantations, and the proximity of India, China, and Java assures an adequate labor supply. Rice production has never been sufficient to support the people, a possible reason being the rapid growth of rubber planting and the resultant neglect of subsistence crops. Prior to World War II less than one million acres of rice were under cultivation in Malaya, about one third the number necessary to satisfy the needs of the people. The remainder was supplied by the adjacent surplus rice areas described later. (See page 344.) A few large irrigation projects have extended the rice acreage but many Malayans prefer to grow rubber as a cash crop on their small plots. Other crops include coconuts (for copra), the oil palm (cultivated in small groves), pineapples, and various oilseeds.

Malaya has been the chief world source of natural rubber for almost half a century. The common rubber tree, *Hevea brasiliensis*, thrives in the rainforest climate and also on the residual soils of the foothills. The most favored district is near the coast and along the Malacca Strait from Singapore to Penang. Most of the plantations are near the sea, convenient to coastwise shipping and rail connections with Singapore. As noted previously the rubber tree was transplanted to this part of the world largely because Brazil could not produce enough cheap rubber to meet the world demand. In Malaya as well as in Indonesia the conditions of plantation production are adequately met. Cheap land suitable for rubber is still available; cheap labor from Malaya, India, and China can be obtained; and rubber has proved to be an excellent cash crop.

In establishing a plantation the first step is to clear the forest, which means the removal of all trees and stumps. Transplanting of young trees from nurseries, about 200 to the acre, follows. Later the number will be decreased to approximately 75 to the acre, only the best ones being retained. In some places annual food crops are planted between the rows to furnish income while the trees are growing to maturity. In general, however, the rubber plantations have not been self-sufficient producers of food for the workers and have been forced to import rice and other foods from Burma, Siam, and French Indochina.

FIGURE 27.3. *A product map of the Philippines. Most of the land can be classified as subsistence agriculture, plantation, or forest. Since the plantations are intermingled with subsistence farms in many districts, no attempt is made to distinguish this type. More intensively cultivated areas of both cash and subsistence crops are shaded, however. Abbreviations: A, abacá (manila hemp); c, copra; R, rubber; t, tobacco; Au, gold; Cr, chromium; Fe, iron. Corn and rice are grown widely in many places on hilly and mountainous land.*

Tapping begins when the trees are from six to eight years of age, or when they have reached a diameter of from eight to ten inches. Tapping may be done daily, on alternate days, or in alternate periods of several days each. The latex is collected periodically and coagulated on the plantation or on the small native farm. Various methods are used to coagulate the rubber, alum or acetic acid being added to precipitate the rubber. On the modern plantations the latex is sprayed under pressure into a heated chamber so that coagulation takes place without the addition of chemicals. The crude rubber is washed and dried and is then ready for export. Singapore is the exporting port not only for Malaya but for most of Indonesia as well.

For many years the plantation owners feared the competition of the small native groves, many of which, however, produced an inferior quality of rubber. The competition of synthetic rubber is proving to be much more serious. During World War II the rubber plantations of Malaya and Indonesia were occupied by the Japanese. Contrary to expectations, the Japanese resistance collapsed so suddenly that the Japanese had little opportunity to destroy the plantings. To be sure, neglect had allowed many of the groves to revert to forest and production was curtailed. Meanwhile, large factories for the manufacture of synthetic rubber had been set up in the United States and the quality of the new product had greatly improved. It is unlikely that natural rubber will ever reach the production peak of the prewar period.

Aside from rubber, tin is the most important cash product of Malaya, accounting for about one third of the world production. The tin is ordinarily mined by dredges from alluvial deposits in the stream valleys, a form of placer mining. Although lode mining is limited, hard rock deposits are known to exist and will probably be exploited in the future to a greater extent. Other mineral production includes iron, manganese, and bauxite, with iron the most important. These metals were actively mined by the Japanese during their occupation of Malaya.

THE PHILIPPINES

The 7000 islands which comprise the Philippine Republic range in latitude from 5° N. to 20° N. The total area is over 115,000 square miles, ap-proximately the same as Arizona, and the population is about 20 million. On most of the islands, mountains and lowlands alternate, the latter alluvial in character or composed of elevated coral reefs. The general orientation of the mountains and islands is north-south (FIG. 27.3). Although the average relief map suggests that the lowlands are extensive, in reality more than three fourths of the surface is hilly or mountainous, leaving only one fourth capable of intensive cultivation. Furthermore, the coastline is rather rugged and abrupt and, as a result, few good harbors exist.

The climate varies from east to west; the east side of the archipelago is humid all the year (Af climate) while the west side, in the rain shadow of the monsoon, has a dry season. Thus the west is more favorable for sugar, the east more suitable for copra and abacá (Manila hemp). The worst feature of the climate is the hurricanes, which strike usually from the east and are more frequent on the coast of Luzon than on Mindanao.

The people of the Philippines are grouped (FIG. 27.3) in the lowlands and on the coasts of the larger islands. Where feasible, rice cultivation is practiced, but the coral lowlands are not suitable for paddy cultivation because of porosity of the soil. In northern Luzon rice is grown on terraces, a practice which indicates the scarcity of good paddy land. In addition to rice, a variety of crops of which corn is the most widespread are produced in the uplands. Sugar is concentrated on the plains in the west, and is grown extensively on the leeward sides of Negros, Cebu, and Panay islands. The cultivation of sugarcane as the chief export crop is possible only as long as the Philippines are inside the United States tariff wall. The cost of sugar production is higher than in Java, and the amount sold abroad is dependent on the extent of free trade.

The production of abacá or Manila fiber is more favorable. Grown along the east coasts from southeastern Luzon to Davao in Mindanao, this crop enjoys a world-wide reputation as a source of a strong, smooth fiber, superior to sisal and other coarse fibers. The fibers, derived from the long leaf stem, are separated and dried in the same fashion as sisal fibers (see page 302). The most intensive area of abacá production is in southeastern Mindanao in the vicinity of the Bay of Davao. Thousands of small farms are care-

FIGURE 27.4. *A vegetable market in Manila, P. I. From Northwest Airlines.*

fully laid out, cultivated, and protected from erosion. Mineral fertilizers are used to increase the yields, and the strippings from the fibers are returned to the fields. Because of the severe shortage during World War II, abacá was produced in other areas, including Central America (FIG. 27.5), but the greatest production is still in the Philippines. Another crop dependent upon the whim of the Congress of the United States is copra, but since the coconut has no serious competitor within continental United States, the prospect is favorable. The coconut grows in the humid rainforest and on the sandy beaches. Some ramie, which provides a strong fiber, is grown in

this district but the demand is not heavy. Other cash crops include tobacco, which forms the basis of a significant cigar industry, and rubber, which thrives in southwest Mindanao. The Goodyear Rubber Company established a rubber plantation near Zamboanga. Like the producers in the Tapajoz area in Amazonia where the former Ford plantations are located, those in this area will find it difficult to compete in the fierce struggle between natural and synthetic rubber. Only the most efficient plantations with low production costs can succeed.

The mineral wealth of the Philippines is varied but not well balanced. Coal and petroleum are almost completely lacking. On the other hand, iron ore, manganese, chromite, gold, and copper are fairly plentiful. On the west side of Luzon, north of Manila, there is one of the largest deposits of chromite in the world. During the Japanese occupation of the islands, the stoppage of chromite (and abacá) shipments to the United States were most keenly felt. The Japanese made good use of these materials and were interested also in the iron ore and manganese of eastern Luzon and Mindanao.

The development of the Philippines under United States rule presents a curious parallel to the growth of Java under the Dutch. In each case a plantation economy was introduced into an area of subsistence agriculture. In 48 years the population of the Philippines increased from 7 to 18 million, disease was greatly reduced, water supply improved, and roads and railroads constructed. Hospitals and schools are now to be found in various parts of the islands. Subsistence agriculture continues to be the chief occupation

FIGURE 27.5. *An abacá plantation in Costa Rica. During World War II this fiber was transplanted to Middle America. Compare with Figure 23.5 and notice the resemblance to the banana. From CIAA.*

of the people. The average Filipino cultivates his patches of rice, corn, and sweet potatoes, builds his house of bamboo and palmwood, fishes in the rivers and bays, and, in general, takes life rather leisurely.

INDOCHINA

Between India and south China lies the mountainous peninsula of southeastern Asia occupied by Burma, Siam, and French Indochina. The principal mountain range runs southeastward from China along the east coast of Indochina. There are also broad plateaus, interior basins, and four important alluvial lowlands, the Irrawaddy in Burma, the Menam in Siam, the Mekong and Yuan in French Indochina. It is in these river lowlands that most of the 50 million people of the peninsula live. Because of the large areas of fertile alluvial lowland, however, the pressure of population is much less in Indochina than in Java, south China, or the Ganges Lowland of India. Rice, which occupies a larger proportion of the cultivated land there than in any other part of Monsoon Asia, is produced in sufficient quantities for export. In fact, these four alluvial lowlands are the chief rice exporting districts in Asia. The surplus rice usually goes to Japan, to the plantations of Indonesia, and in smaller quantities to India and China.

Burma has a population of about 18 million and an area of 262,000 square miles, slightly smaller than Texas. Most of the country is mountainous forest land with small areas of rather primitive subsistence agriculture. The lowland of the Irrawaddy and Salween rivers is the heart of Burma. Rice occupies more than 70 per cent of the cropland and is the chief export. Oilseeds, including cotton and millet, are also important crops. On the margins of the middle Irrawaddy is the most important petroleum field on the mainland of southeastern Asia. All goods move to Rangoon, the principal port, where there are rice mills and petroleum refineries.

The basin of central Siam, which is the flood plain of the Lower Menam, is an important rice growing region, with more than seven million acres and a production of six million tons. Rice has long been exported from Siam, most of it being moved to Singapore, Hongkong, and Penang. Rice from Siam is supplied to the rubber plantations of Malaya and Sumatra. In addition to rice, small quantities of oilseeds, pepper, and tobacco are exported. From the forests quantities of teak are produced. Siam has a variety of poorly developed mineral resources. Tin and wolframite are mined in the Siam portion of the Malay Peninsula. Gold is taken from alluvium. Deposits of coal, iron, zinc, manganese, antimony, and other minerals are worked slightly.

In French Indochina also rice is the principal crop and the chief item of export, most of it being grown on the flood plain and deltas of the Mekong and Yuan. The production is more than seven million tons, and although the yields are higher than those of China, they are much lower than those of Burma or Java. In addition to rice, there are a number of minor food crops—sweet potatoes, maize, sugarcane, taro, and cassava. Commercial crops include cotton, mulberry, and pepper. Some success has been attained in the production of jute, ramie, peanuts, sesame, and rubber as cash crops. Mining is only slightly developed although there are some deposits of coal and iron ore. The industries of French Indochina include cotton, jute, and ramie textile mills, rice-hulling plants, and varnish and soap factories.

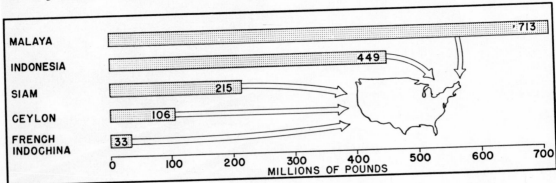

FIGURE 27.6. Graph of the origin of rubber imports to the United States.

28

India, Pakistan, and Ceylon

ALTHOUGH on most maps India seems small, it is in reality some 1400 miles from the Indus to the Ganges Delta, and 2000 miles from the Punjab in the northwest to the southern tip of the peninsula. The area is nearly 1,500,000 square miles, and India supports, after a fashion, 400 million people.

A casual study of the map of India (FIG. 28.1) suggests that this great land mass has a certain unity. In the sense that India is cut off from the rest of Asia by mountains, it is a unit, but it is nevertheless made up of many diverse elements. The contrast between the rice paddies of the Ganges Delta and the parched cotton fields of the Deccan, or between the dry wheat lands of the Punjab and the tea plantations of Assam, are far more striking than any superficial appearance of unity.

Even without the great range of the Himalayas, India has a great variety of landscapes. First in productivity and population are the great alluvial plains of the Indus, Ganges, Brahmaputra, and lesser rivers. These plains are smooth, gently sloping, and almost ideal for irrigation, the more so because the ground water in many districts comes within a few feet of the surface. Wherever rain is sufficient or water is available for irrigation, rice is produced in the plains. In the drier districts sorghum, millet, and the small grains are the staple food crops.

The plateau of peninsular India, the southern part of which is called the Deccan, is a low dissected upland with fringing mountains and hills. On the west the upturned edge forms the Western Ghats, a mountain ridge which reaches an elevation of over 5000 feet. From these mountains the plateau slopes gently eastward, bor-

dered by escarpments on the north and east. Most of the plateau is underlain by lava, which, unlike the Columbia Lava Plateau of the United States, does not always break down into fertile soils. The soils are gray, dark brown, or black, usually quite thick, and sometimes stony. The clay content is high, a circumstance which makes the soil sticky and gives it a good water-holding capacity.

The general qualities of the monsoon climate have been described in Chapter 4. Since crop production is correlated with rainfall, it is essential to describe the variations in different parts of India. The heaviest precipitation is on the windward slopes of the mountains, the west side of the Western Ghats, the south slopes of the Assam Hills, and the Himalayan foothills. In the foothills of the Himalayas, the annual rainfall is sometimes in excess of 200 inches, most of it coming in the summer. The station of Cherrapunji in the Khasi Hills of eastern India averages more than 36 *feet* of rain with a summer maximum. In the rainiest year on record the total was over 75 feet. Conversely, the lightest rainfall is in the rainshadow of the mountains and in the northwest where the effect of the monsoon is negligible. In the lower Indus Plain and in the Thar (desert) the total rainfall is less than ten inches. Karachi on the Delta of the Indus receives an average of about seven inches. Aside from the mountains, the heaviest rain is in the lower Ganges Plain, the Brahmaputra Plain, and the eastern portion of the plateau. In these areas rainfall ranges from 50 to 100 inches. This is sufficient for rice, and most of the paddy rice of India is grown in districts where the rainfall is greater than 60 inches.

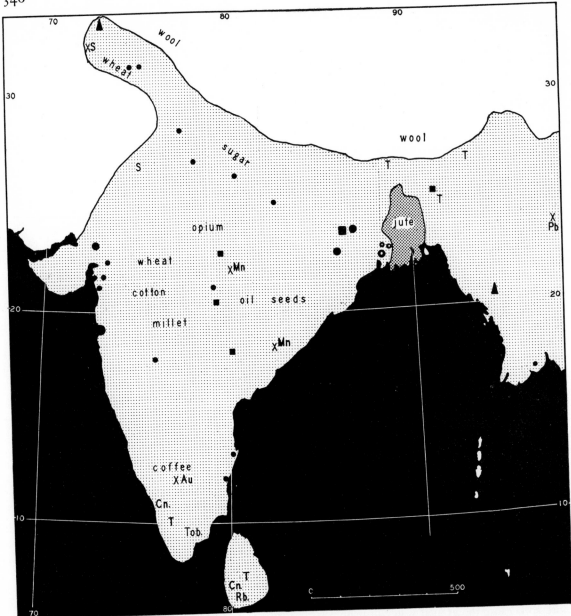

FIGURE 28.1. *A production map of monsoon India, Burma, and Pakistan. Rice is the chief crop in the more humid climates; elsewhere small grains, millet, and oil seeds take its place. Abbreviations: Cn, coconuts; Rb, rubber; T, tea; Tob, tobacco; Au, gold; Mn, manganese; Pb, lead; S, sulfur. Coal production is shown by black squares, petroleum by black triangles, while important cities are indicated by black dots. Most of the jute production is in eastern Pakistan while western Pakistan produces rice, wheat, and cotton with the aid of irrigation.*

Omitting the lofty mountains, there are five types of climate in India. The rainforest (Af), with strong monsoon influence, is found in southwest Ceylon, on the west coast of India as far north as Bombay, and in the Ganges Delta and the Brahmaputra Lowland. The savanna type (Aw) includes most of the peninsula, except the rainforest portions and the steppe (BS) district to the east of the Western Ghats. Most of the middle and upper Ganges Plain is winter dry temperate (Cw), but the winters are so mild that this region might very well be combined with the tropical savanna to the south. The coldest month at Delhi, for example, averages 58° F. The main areas of steppe (BS) and desert (BW) are in the northwest and are, strictly speaking, outside the limits of Oriental Agriculture. It will be noted in the discussions to follow that the distribution of crops in India is very closely related to these variations in climate.

PEOPLE

No matter what criterion is employed—race, religion, language, or customs—the peoples of India are diverse, a fact which makes it difficult for the country to function as a single economic or political unit. The differences are traceable to many invasions of the country in the last twenty centuries and to many contrasting conditions of life in the different regions. By sea and by land many an invading horde has arrived, some to pillage and retreat, some to conquer, remain, and be at least partially absorbed. Alexander the Great reached the Indus in 327 B.C., only to turn back without making any permanent impression on the country. The Mohammedans arrived in the 8th century and remained to become the dominant cultural group in the northwest and east. The Mongols invaded India in the 13th century and left a profound impression on the culture.

The most important invasions in the last few centuries have come by sea. After da Gama first rounded the Cape of Good Hope in 1497, the Portuguese began the conquest of India. The Indians could offer no effective resistance to the weapons of the Europeans and soon the invaders were in possession of all the coastal cities. In addition, by virtue of their sea power they controlled the trade of China and Japan. Portuguese dominance, however, declined as fast as it arose. The Portuguese were displaced quickly by the Dutch, who were in turn driven out by the British. Of all the invaders the British have had the greatest effect on the India of today. They have developed a fairly good system of transportation so that, unlike China, the people in one part of India need not starve while those in another have a surplus. In many districts the system of irrigation has been improved so that production has been greatly increased and stabilized. It should be noted that the population has quadrupled under British rule although the standard of living of most people has not necessarily been raised. British control has led, also, to the development of industrial crops and to the increase of mining and manufacturing.

With the coming of Indian independence the conflict between the Hindus and the Mohammedans, who represent two thirds and one fifth respectively of the total population, was intensified. The Mohammedans, in the majority only in the northwest (the Punjab) and in the east (Bengal), set up a separate state, Pakistan, in spite of the efforts of Mahatma Gandhi to reconcile the differences in religion and customs between the two groups. As additional handicaps, there are 2000 castes in Hindu society with various languages and dialects. Culturally India is at least as diverse as the whole continent of Europe. Pakistan, although politically independent, is not unlike India so far as production is concerned. "India," as used below, includes Pakistan.

AGRICULTURE

Three fourths of the people of India are engaged directly in agriculture and millions more are part-time farmers. The remainder are employed in industry (6 per cent), transport (2 per cent), and mining (0.2 per cent). Most of the farms are small although larger than those of China and Japan. The average farm community is almost self-sufficient, and the individual farmer rarely leaves the community in which he is born. Climate and custom control the pattern of everyday life (FIG. 28.2). Nearly half of all the land surface of India is cultivated and of necessity a large portion is reserved for the basic food crops —rice, millet, grain sorghum, wheat, barley, gram (chick-pea), beans, oilseeds, and sugarcane.

Rice is the staple crop in all the arable lands with more than 60 inches of rainfall and in other districts where sufficient water is available to

FIGURE 28.2. *Dry plowing on the Ganges Delta. In the dry winter season, the land can be plowed dry. In summer, the paddies are flooded before plowing. From Frank Buckley.*

irrigate rice. The total area devoted to this crop exceeds 70 million acres, and the annual production is more than 70 million tons of rough grain (approximately 1500 million bushels). The average yield is about 22 bushels per acre, which is low compared with Japan, but about equal to the yield in the Philippines, Siam, or Indochina. Taking the country as a whole, rice covers nearly 25 per cent of the total cropland. This percentage, however, varies widely in different districts. Where the rainfall is more than 80 inches, rice is the dominant crop in more than 80 per cent of the cultivated land and no irrigation is necessary from wells or streams, since the heavy summer rains will fill the rice paddies at intervals. In such districts two crops of rice can be grown in one season, although this is not a general practice. Paddy rice grows in enclosures to which the young plants are transplanted by hand. An acre of young plants carefully nourished in a seed bed is sufficient to set out ten acres of paddy.

In spite of the large acreage, India is a net importer of rice, and in some years the largest importer in the world. The imports come from Burma, Siam, and French Indochina. The average annual consumption varies from less than 10 pounds per capita in parts of northwest India where little rice is grown to more than 400 pounds in eastern Bengal where rice is the dominant crop. In general, the per capita consumption is between 200 and 300 pounds per year. The daily calorie intake of the average Indian native is slightly more than 2000 as compared with 3200 in the United States. It should be pointed out, however, that the average Oriental is smaller in stature than the average American, and the weather is warmer.

Next to rice the grain sorghums and millet are the chief crops. The various kinds of sorghum—Jowar, Bajra, and Ragi—and several varieties of millet may be considered as one unit since they are similar in character and not always listed separately in statistical records. The total acreage exceeds 60 million. In general, the sorghum-millet crops are confined to the drier areas and to the poorer soils. The conditions for growth are, however, rather varied: some will grow in the humid rice regions; others in the drier districts. The sorghums are much like corn in appearance except that the seed is on the head of the plant rather than on an ear. The harvesting and threshing are done largely by hand with the aid of work animals in tramping out the grain.

Most of the wheat of India is grown in the northern part of the plateau and in the upper part of the Indus Plain. The total acreage is nearly 25 million, a considerable part of which is irrigated. The average yield, about ten bushels per acre, is lower than that in the United States, and the total production is usually less than 250 million bushels. Nevertheless, wheat is often exported from India.

Besides rice, sorghums, millet, and wheat, other food crops are grown extensively. Gram, known in the United States as the chick-pea (although it is in reality a sort of bean), is a winter crop and provides an excellent food. Barley occupies much the same districts as wheat, except that more is produced in the middle Ganges Plain as a winter crop on the ricelands. Most of India's sugar comes from the middle Ganges. The cane area is large, five million acres, second only to Java, but the yield is low and variable. In some years it is necessary for the Indians to import sugar, in others a surplus is available for export. Other food crops include corn, peas, beans, a variety of vegetables, and many oilseeds. Peanuts, sesame, rapeseed, flaxseed, mustard, castor, and cotton are the chief sources of oil. These supply a definite need in the diet, since the animal products are almost entirely lacking.

Cotton and jute are the chief vegetable fibers of India and both are exported. The eastern half of the Ganges Delta and the lower part of the Brahmaputra Valley account for most of the world's jute. The climate is favorable both for the growth of the plant and for the retting (soaking) process which is necessary in order to extract the long, strong fibers. Jute bags and burlap are manufactured in Calcutta, and raw fiber is also exported. Cotton is concentrated on the Plateau of the Deccan to the east of Bombay, where it occupies as much as 40 per cent of the total cropland in certain provinces. Additional cotton comes from the northwest, from the Upper Ganges, and from the southern tip of India. The 13 million acres planted to cotton place India second only to the United States in acreage. But yields are generally very low and the total production is in the neighborhood of two or three million bales. The fiber is short, of poor quality, and suited only for the manufacture of cheap cotton cloth. There is a huge market in India for such goods, but a surplus of cotton is available for export to Japan.

One of the few strictly plantation crops in

FIGURE 28.3. *One of the many ponds or "tanks" on the Ganges Plain. This reservoir provides water for domestic purposes and irrigation during the dry season. From Frank Buckley.*

India is tea. The plantations are on the hilly margins of the Brahmaputra Valley in Assam. Tea is one of the most important of the exports from India. Other crops are mangoes, grapefruit, limes, bananas, papaya, and spices, including curry, pepper, clove, and nutmeg, much of which comes from the southern part of the peninsula.

There are two main crop seasons in India: the wet season (*kharif*) and the dry season (*rabi*). The seasons are defined by rainfall rather than temperature. The wet season crops, sown after the beginning of the summer monsoon, are rice, certain grain-sorghums, cotton, jute, corn, and some oilseeds. The *rabi* crops are wheat, barley, gram, beans, peas, and some millets. The constant cropping summer and winter impoverishes the soil and is slowly reducing the fertility and yields of many districts. Commercial fertilizer is not available and the manure from the numerous cattle is often burned for fuel instead of being applied to the land. Crops are rotated to a certain extent and the legumes tend to improve the fertility of the soil, but on the whole Indian agriculture is in a more precarious position than that of China.

Irrigation in India is one of the brighter spots in the agricultural picture. In all, more than 35 million acres are irrigated by wells, canals, diverted streams, and reservoirs. Much of the water used for irrigation comes from the alluvium of the plains. A shallow well is sufficient to irrigate a small field, but some device is necessary to lift the water a few feet to the level of the field. Oxen are used to hoist the water with the aid of a rope to which is attached a large bucket or leather bag. In many parts of the plateau small reservoirs called "tanks" (FIG. 28.3) have been constructed where water is stored during the rainy season for use during the dry periods. Some of the tanks on the plateau are 1000 years old and serve as laundries, public baths, and for other domestic purposes. Modern forms of irrigation are to be found in the Indus Valley. Huge dams of concrete make it possible to irrigate more than five million acres of rice, wheat, cotton, and other crops.

Livestock plays a minor role in the agricultural economy. About one half the world's cattle are in India, but to the Hindus cows are sacred animals which cannot be killed. They may be used as work animals, however, together with the water buffalo. The numerous cattle probably consume more feed than they are worth. Some goats and sheep are to be found in parts of the plateau and in the northwest. The water buffalo is the all-purpose draft-dairy-meat animal of the humid ricelands, while the camel is used in parts of the Indus Plain.

MINERALS

Although India has long been regarded as a source of precious metals and jewels, there is no large mineral production in this country. In fact, Indians are net importers. Only six minerals are of real significance: coal, iron, petroleum, manganese, gold, and mica. The most productive mineral district is on the edge of the plateau about 200 miles northwest of Calcutta. The best coalfield is there, and within a radius of 100 miles iron ore, limestone, manganese, and other minerals occur. These minerals form the basis of India's principal iron and steel industry. Other coal beds are to be found in various parts of the plateau, but in spite of the fact that the coal is generally close to the surface and easy to mine, production is small largely because of the limited demand. The occurrence of coal together with the low cost of labor enables this fuel to be mined in India at lower cost than in any other country in the world.

The best and most available body of iron ore in India lies in the edge of the plateau to the south of the chief coalfield, mentioned in the last paragraph, and about 200 miles southwest of Calcutta. It occurs in the form of a low "range" about 30 miles long, somewhat similar to the Mesabi Range of Minnesota. This hematite ore averages about 60 per cent iron and is readily mined by open pit methods. The reserves are estimated to be as great as the original deposits of the Lake Superior district, enough to last, at the present rate of exploitation, for 50 centuries or more. Another great iron ore (magnetite) body lies near Salem in the southern end of the peninsula but is not mined at present, largely because of the scarcity of coal in the vicinity. Many other iron ore deposits are exploited in a small way by local iron industries which supply a large share of the rather small demands for iron made by the people of India.

Manganese is the chief mineral export from

FIGURE 28.4. *Threshing rice in India. The threshers beat the rice against a small platform after which the grain is winnowed. From Frank Buckley.*

India, and the amount produced has increased in recent years. The ores are scattered through the plateau but the principal producing areas are in the Central Provinces about half way between Bombay and Calcutta and in Madras Province near the coast. Most of the manganese, in the form of ore, is shipped to western Europe and the United States.

Petroleum production is limited to two small fields, one in the Punjab, near Lahore, the other in Assam, next to the Burma border. The first is an eastern outlier of the Iranian fields while the latter is related to the oilfield of Burma previously noted (page 344). Most of the newly mined gold comes from Mysore Province, west of Madras. The export and import of gold and silver bears little relation to production. Indian princes have long imported the metals in one form or another as a means of hoarding their wealth. When Great Britain in 1931 and the United States in 1933 abandoned the gold standard and the price of this metal soared, the export of gold from India exceeded the total annual world production. India is the best source of mica, a mineral used in the manufacture of electrical devices.

The Province of Bihar, west of Calcutta, and the Madras district are regions where the greatest quantity of mica is produced.

COMMUNICATIONS

As already indicated, India has no significant trade connections with the outside world except by sea. Fortunately, most of the export materials are produced near the coast. Jute is moved out from Calcutta, India's largest city. Most of the cotton is forwarded from the hinterland of India's greatest port, Bombay. Wheat is exported from Karachi on the Delta of the Indus. Good harbors are few, however; coral reefs, shallow estuaries, and violent winds limit the effectiveness of coastwise shipping.

Internally, communications are inadequate but somewhat better than those along the coast. In India there is the best network of railroads in Asia, more than 40,000 miles of track. Unfortunately several different gauges are used, ranging from 2 to $5\frac{1}{2}$ feet. This necessitates a break in bulk along many trade routes. The railway net tends to radiate from Bombay, Calcutta, and to a lesser extent from Madras and Karachi. The best coverage is in the Ganges Plain. Nagpur, in the middle of the peninsula, is an important interior focus of railways. The railroads derive their chief revenue from agricultural products and passengers, since there is a limited amount of industrial goods to be shipped, and there are few automobiles or highways to compete with the rails. The transportation of coal for use on the railways makes up nearly half of the freight, an indication of inefficient operation and the uneven distribution of coal mines.

The rivers of India are not suited for transport because they are alternately flooded and nearly dry. Only the smallest boats can be used on the rivers, and these are restricted to local traffic. A few highways have been constructed in recent years for the use of automobiles. One road leads from Khyber Pass on the border of Afghanistan to Calcutta via Delhi, another connects Delhi with Bombay, and a third reaches from Bombay to Madras. The construction of highways in India is expensive because of the scarcity of materials, such as gravel, cement, and road tar.

INDUSTRY

Since there is a variety of raw materials, cotton, oilseeds, leather, wool, wood, iron, and coal in India, it is natural that there should be many forms of manufacturing. Until recently most of the industry has been of the handicraft type with a large share of the everyday needs of the people being supplied by home industries. In the last few decades, however, the large factory has emerged, accompanied by a decrease in the total number of industrial workers. Modern factories began with the present century and have made great strides especially in textiles.

The cotton textile industry is the most important, owing to the large production of raw cotton in India and the great demand for cotton cloth by the 400 million people of the country. The combined factory, village, and home industries have been unable to meet the demand, and the import of cotton goods from Britain and Japan leads all others. The home and village textile industry is widely scattered in India, but the factory production is concentrated in the Bombay and Calcutta regions, and in the middle Ganges Valley. Altogether there are more than a score of large textile centers in India.

Like cotton textiles, the iron industry was formerly a handicraft and has been replaced in part by larger establishments. This industry, largely in the hands of one company, is concentrated in the coalfields west of Calcutta. A more recent but smaller development is located immediately north of Calcutta on the Hooghly River. Other types of manufacturing in India include the jute industry near Calcutta, silk and woolen weaving, flour mills, rice mills, sugar refineries, oil refineries, sawmills, and tobacco factories.

From this brief account of the production in India it is obvious that there is great opportunity for industrial expansion. Much more coal and iron ore could be mined, production of cotton could be increased, and manufacture of cotton cloth expanded. Perhaps a larger opportunity would lie in the home market if the purchasing power of the masses were increased. Resources in India, however, are not as extensive as those in China, where there is more coal and iron and a greater variety of raw materials. But there is a much better transportation system in India, and the Indians have already embarked on the road to industrialization in the fashion of the western world.

CEYLON

Ceylon, with an area of 25,000 square miles, is about the same size as West Virginia. The population of nearly eight million represents a density greater than the average for all India but much less than the comparable humid rice growing districts. Ceylon is a separate state, having no political connection with India. The general pattern of production, however, is similar to that in southern India, except that plantations are more common and tea, cacao, rubber, copra, and coffee are relatively more significant. The southern part of the island is quite hilly and even mountainous, attaining an elevation of over 8000 feet in the vicinity of Kandy. The northern part is low. In this region there are many coconut plantations on the sandy coasts.

Both monsoons bring heavy rains to Ceylon, the June–August monsoon to the south coast, the December–March monsoon to the north. The south is more humid and is classed as a rainforest climate (Af), while the north is defined as savanna (Aw). A very small part of the mountainous district is high enough to have a humid temperate climate (Cfb).

FIGURE 28.5. *A view of the bay at Bombay, India. A large share of India's exports and imports are moved through the port of Bombay. From TWA.*

354

Rice is the chief food crop, but not enough is produced to satisfy the local demand. Both paddy and upland rice are grown. The land under wet paddy amounts to about 800,000 acres, and the annual production is approximately 200,000 tons. An additional 500,000 tons are imported. Much of the paddy land is on hill slopes where terracing has reached a high level of perfection. Terraces are used also on the valley floors to expedite the flow of water. The construction and maintenance of the terraces require skill and constant labor since small animals bore holes in the terrace walls, and running water carries away some of the soil in suspension. Irrigation of the paddies is accomplished by the diversion of streams and by the use of tanks as in the Plateau of India. Upland rice is grown on hilly land or plateaus which cannot be readily irrigated. The crop is sown broadcast on previously tilled land; it requires less labor but yields poorly.

Tea is well adapted to the environment of the hilly land to the south where the humidity, good drainage, and moderate temperature are favorable factors. In the vicinity of Kandy, tea dominates the hilly land, while rice is grown on the valley floors. The tea trees, which grow normally to a height of about 20 feet, are pruned to a height of six feet, a practice which improves the quality and facilitates picking. Since Ceylon has no cold season, new leaves are constantly appearing and the harvest is continuous. The process of drying, fermenting, and preparing the tea for market is well organized, and machinery is used wherever possible. The tea grown in Ceylon, as well as that in Assam in northwest India, is preferred by the people of Europe and America to the product grown in China and Japan. Rubber has been produced in the foothills to the east of Colombo for almost a half century. Coffee production, formerly quite significant, has declined, largely as a result of plant diseases, and tea, cacao, and quinine have taken its place. Copra and spices, especially cinnamon and cloves, are exported from the marginal lowland, and corn, cassava, yams, and millet are produced by the natives as subsistence crops.

Colombo is the largest city of Ceylon and the chief port of call in the Indian Ocean. It is situated on a small bay with additional artificial protection from the monsoons. Most of the ships on the Suez to Singapore route stop here. Trincomalee, on the east coast, is a superior harbor but is not well situated with respect to the chief crop areas of Ceylon.

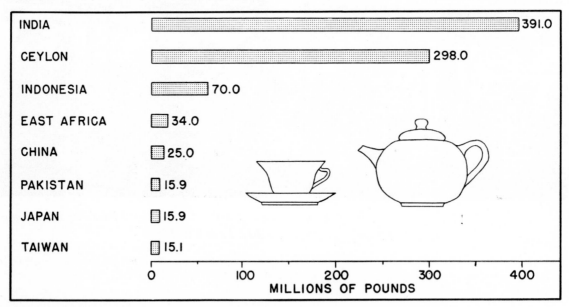

FIGURE 28.6. *Graph showing exports of tea from various countries in 1950. Small additional exports of tea come from Indochina, Malaya, and Brazil.*

29

Humid China

Arid China—the vast reaches of Tibet, the Gobi, and Sinkiang—has been previously described in Chapter 11 on Nomadic Herding. Humid China (FIG. 29.1), the eastern part of Greater China, is 2000 miles long and varies from 250 to 1000 miles in width. It extends from Hainan Island on the 20th parallel to northern Manchuria in latitude 53° N., and from the East China Sea to the eastern edge of Tibet and the Gobi. The land is varied in relief, climate, and culture. On the subtropical southern margin two crops of rice are produced in one year, as well as bananas and other tropical fruits; while in the northern part of Manchuria there are severe winters and short summers, comparable to those in eastern Canada. The plains of the Hwang and Yangtze rivers and of central Manchuria contrast sharply with the rugged plateaus of Yünnan in the southwest. In few countries is there such a large proportion of hilly or mountainous land, and so little arable territory. The culture, although varied, shows more continuity than that of India. The spoken language varies, but the written language is substantially the same throughout.

SURFACE

The basic natural feature in the Chinese landscape is the surface, the contrast between the smooth fertile alluvial plains and the hills and mountains. Where the land is smooth, the population is dense; where it is rough, there are comparatively few people in spite of the terraces on some mountain slopes. The most productive areas, then, are the Yangtze, Hwang, and Manchurian plains and hundreds of lesser flood plains and deltas. The mountains, however, have meaning also as regions of less intensive agriculture, water

supply for the plains, soil supply in some places, and as a source of minerals.

Plains

The Manchurian Plain lies in central and southern Manchuria and includes more than 125,000 square miles of arable land. Hills border the plain on three sides, the north, east, and west, but the Sungari River provides a corridor to the northeast. The most unobstructed outlet is to the south, and Dairen on the tip of the Liaotung Peninsula is the chief port.

The Yellow (Hwang) Plain, somewhat larger than the Manchurian Plain, is in reality many alluvial plains built by the Hwang and other rivers which have merged into one great expanse of alluvium. It reaches from Peiping on the north almost to Shanghai on the south, where it merges with the Yangtze Plain. The surface is quite smooth and too level to provide good natural drainage. The courses of the Hwang and Hwai rivers have wandered back and forth across this lowland, spreading the rich silt derived from the uplands to the west. The fertility is high but poor drainage and floods combine to reduce the productivity.

The Yangtze Plain is divided into two parts, the Delta and the Middle Yangtze Lake Plain. The Delta in the vicinity of Shanghai is low and flat and has many canals for irrigation and drainage. See FIGURES 29.2 and 29.3. Here the Yangtze River flows sluggishly with a very low gradient and a deep channel, providing a splendid avenue for trade. The Middle Yangtze Lake Plain is similar to the Delta but separated from it by a narrow section of the valley. There too, the land is low, subject to flooding, and many shallow

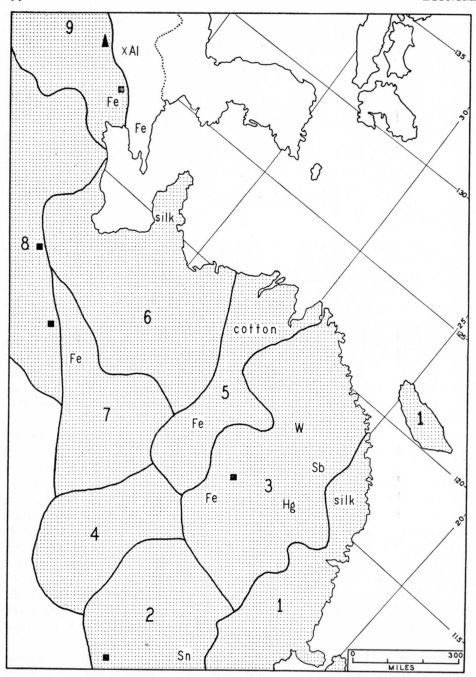

FIGURE 29.1. *A production map of eastern China showing agricultural regions according to J. L. Buck.* 1. *Double-cropping Rice Region,* 2. *Southwestern Rice Region,* 3. *Rice–Tea Region,* 4. *Szechwan Rice Region,* 5. *Yangtze Rice–Wheat Region,* 6. *Winter Wheat–Kaoliang Region,* 7. *Winter Wheat–Millet Region,* 8. *Spring Wheat Region,* 9. *Manchurian Soybean–Sorghum Region. Coal and petroleum production are shown by black squares and triangles, respectively. Abbreviations:* Al, *aluminum ore (bauxite);* Fe, *iron;* Hg, *mercury;* Sb, *antimony;* Sn, *tin;* W, *tungsten. The top of this map, it will be noted, is toward the northeast.*

FIGURE 29.2. *A part of the waterfront at Shanghai. The small craft carry freight as well as furnishing living quarters. Modern buildings indicate western influences and contrast sharply with the native city. From Northwest Airlines.*

lakes are difficult to drain. In this district the river is navigable by ocean freighters which go up to Hankow, more than 600 miles from the sea. The city of Ichang is at the western limit of the Lake Plain. Above this point the river flows in a gorge, and navigation is difficult even for small boats.

The Red Basin of Szechwan to the west of the Lake Plain is often described as a lowland, but it is in no sense an alluvial plain like those described in the previous paragraph. Rather it is a depressed and dissected plateau with hills rising several hundred feet above the valley floors. Parts of the interstream uplands are relatively smooth, however, and afford much land for cultivation.

The Canton Delta is made up of alluvium from three rivers—the Tung (east), Pei (north), and Si (west). Unlike the deltas of the Hwang and Yangtze, the lowland around Canton has many small hills interspersed in the lowland but cultivation is even more intensive than farther north. Victoria, on the island of Hongkong, serves as a trading center for this area, since it has a better harbor than Canton.

Uplands

Most of southern China is a rough dissected upland with little level land. Not more than 15 per cent of the land is level and that is confined to the flood plains of the rivers. In Yünnan and parts of Kwangsi the hillsides leading to narrow ridge crests are almost vertical. In other districts the plateau summits are heavily rolling hills. The highest elevations in the Yünnan Plateau average about 6000 feet, a fact which introduces a serious climatic handicap to agriculture in addition to the unfavorable surface. Locally, as in the vicinity of Kunming (Yünnanfu), small basin plains are to be found, but on the whole the southern uplands are not capable of supporting a dense population.

The Central Upland lies between the Hwang and the Yangtze rivers and consists of several individual ranges such as the Tsinling. The mountains are cut by narrow canyons but between the ranges are broad valleys. The Tsinling Range by limiting the northward course of the monsoon, marks the boundary between south China with its mild winters and the more severe climates of the north. It marks also the northern limit of rice in the western part of Humid China. In the eastern part of the Central Uplands, immediately to the north of Hankow, the hills are low and the valleys wide and open.

To the west of the Great Yellow Plain of northern China are the uplands bordering Mongolia, most of which are a part of the loess hills. Fine, wind-blown silt, called loess, covers the whole region. This material weathers into a fertile soil and has the peculiar property of resistance to erosion on steep slopes. Old cart roads have carved vertical-walled canyons in the loess to depths of 100 feet or more. The productivity of this region is limited by the steepness of some of the slopes and the low rainfall. The Hwang and its tributary rivers owe their yellow color to the loess carried in suspension.

CLIMATE

China lies on the eastern margin of the world's largest continent, a fact of fundamental climatic significance. Extremes are common in all districts, more frequent and more pronounced in the north. A station which has six inches of rain in June of one year may have only one-half inch in the same period of the following year. Floods and droughts are equally probable in many areas, a serious matter in a country where there are so many mouths to feed. In the summer, Humid China is under the influence of the monsoon. Hot humid masses of air move inland to the border of Tibet, Mongolia, and western Manchuria. Wherever elevations are encountered, or wherever the warm air rides up over cold masses from the interior, heavy precipitation occurs. The monsoon is neither as steady nor as apparent as in India. In winter the winds blow toward the sea and very few parts of China receive rain at this time. In late summer the southeast coast of China is subject to typhoons, storms similar to the hurricanes which occur on the southeast coast of the United States.

In many respects the climates of China resemble those of eastern United States and parts of Mexico and Canada. The chief differences are in the very low winter precipitation in China, in the greater variability of rainfall, and in the lower winter temperatures for comparable latitudes. In the table on this page a few climatic stations of China are compared with those of North America in approximately the same latitudes.

Data are not available to mark out the climatic regions of China in an exact manner, but the broad zones can be approximately indicated. As already noted, the sharpest climatic change in China is along the Tsinling Mountains and the Upland of Central China. This district divides the mild winter from the severe winter regions. It is proper, then, to describe the area south of the Tsinling as winter dry temperate (Cw) which covers most of the area, and hot summer humid temperate (Cfa) to be found on the east coast and in the middle Yangtze Plain. This simple classification, however, fails to allow for the local influence of relief and elevation.

North of the Tsinling, the major climate of China is the humid continental (Dwa). In this district the "w" is of little real meaning since the winters are too cold for plant growth. All of the North China (Hwang) Plain and most of the

	A COMPARISON OF CLIMATIC DATA FOR SELECTED STATIONS IN CHINA AND NORTH AMERICA				
STATION	Average Temperature (degrees Fahrenheit)		Average Rainfall (inches)		Average Annual Rainfall (inches)
	Jan.	Jul.	Jan.	Jul.	
Harbin	−1.7	72.0	0.1	5.6	21.0
Montreal	13.0	69.0	3.7	3.7	40.0
Peiping	23.0	75.0	0.1	9.4	25.0
Philadelphia	34.0	77.0	3.3	4.9	41.0
Shanghai	37.0	80.0	2.0	7.3	45.0
Jacksonville	57.0	81.0	2.5	6.7	48.0
Victoria, Hongkong	59.0	81.0	1.3	14.0	84.0
Tampico, Mexico	65.0	82.0	1.5	10.7	44.0

FIGURE 29.3. *River boats and a modern hotel on Suchow Creek in Shanghai. Compare with Figure 29.2. From Thomas O. Milton.*

Manchurian Plain lie in this type. It will be noted from the table that Harbin is on the border between the hot summer and the cool summer areas. In the north it is the coolness of the summers which is most significant. The hilly borders of Manchuria on both sides of the plain are either Dwb or Dwc; the first limits the variety of crops, while the second practically prohibits agriculture.

In general, the rainfall of China decreases from more than 80 inches in the south to about 20 inches in the north. A decrease is noted also westward from the coast. Temperatures decrease in a similar manner, those of winter varying more widely than those of summer.

NATURAL VEGETATION AND SOILS

So persistently and thoroughly have the people of China modified the natural landscape that little of the original vegetation remains. Remnants of the former forests are to be found in the higher uplands of the south where lumbering is still an important industry and in the small patches of trees around the villages and farmsteads. The plains are so intensively cultivated that little or none of the natural vegetation cover remains. In the north, trees are almost completely lacking. Apparently most of the natural forests of the central and southern uplands were mixtures of deciduous and coniferous types. Spruce, hemlock, and fir are mingled with oak, chestnut, and several varieties of gum. Most of the forest has been cleared for cultivation or for pasture. In Szechwan, pine, bamboo, and cypress were the characteristic trees. The banyan tree, an evergreen broadleaf type, is used mostly for shade and was, in former times, an object of worship. In a number of districts conifers and bamboo are grown as crops on hillsides which are too steep for ordinary field cropping.

The soils of China, like the climates, show a sharp contrast between the north and south. North of the Tsinling Mountains the precipitation is light and the temperature average low. The soils, therefore, are high in soluble minerals. These include the chernozem soils on the drier margin, also many varieties of alluvial soils which

FIGURE 29.4. *A Chinese farm on the Yangtze Plain, near Shanghai. Both roof and walls of the farmhouse are of thatch reinforced with bamboo. From Thomas O. Milton.*

have not developed mature profiles. Nevertheless, they have a high mineral content and in poorly drained areas are even alkaline. In South China the soils are more or less leached and deficient in soluble minerals. The brown and gray-brown forest soils are common on the hills and plateaus which originally had a forest cover. Red and yellow soils occur in the extreme south where the rainfall is heaviest and the temperatures never low. The red soils on the hillsides are suitable for tea, tung trees, and miscellaneous forest growth. The yellow soils are more suitable for growing rice either in terraced paddies or as upland rice. The best soils for rice are, of course, on the alluvial plains where long-continued irrigation has produced an impervious layer of fine sediment in the subsoil. This layer prevents excessive loss of water by seepage.

For more than forty centuries the Chinese have cultivated these soils year in and year out without serious loss in fertility. This has been done only by exercising painstaking care, by continual manuring, and the application of large amounts of labor to small patches of land. The methods have been inefficient, perhaps, but this record of continuous crop production is unsurpassed. The farmers save every scrap of organic matter—garbage, sewage, and vegetation. Much of this is carried long distances on the farmer's back from the towns and villages to the fields. The chief fertilizer is sewage, human excrement, which some writers refer to as "night soil."

The silt brought down by the rivers from the adjacent hills is another source of fertilizer. It is scraped from the bottoms of the rivers and carried to the fields. Every farmer grows "green manures," legumes and other plants, which are turned into the soil. Chinese agriculture is not perfect, but it goes further toward maintaining the "good earth" than many others. Improvements now under way include the selection of better seed and the construction of large dams to alleviate the distress of floods and drought.

AGRICULTURE

Agriculture is of even greater relative significance in China than in India, and far greater than in Japan. Even so, not more than 12 per cent of the surface of China is in crops and only a few areas are cultivated intensively. Everywhere the food crops receive the greatest attention. Rice is the chief crop in the southern half but is intensively cultivated only where irrigation is possible. Large amounts of rice are produced in the lowland around Canton, the lower flood plain of the Yangtze River, and the Red Basin of Szechwan. Toward the north, rice is gradually replaced by wheat, the sorghum-millets, and soybeans. These crops supply most of the food of North China. Other less important food crops include corn, barley, and oats. Various oilseeds such as cotton, sesame, groundnuts, and peanuts, and also sugarcane, beans, sweet potatoes and even oranges and bananas are produced in the extreme south. In general, it can be stated that in south China rice is the staple crop; in central China (the

Yangtze Basin including the Basin of Szechwan) rice and wheat are the staple crops; and in the north, millets, sorghum, wheat, and soybeans are the staples. The variety of crops in the south is much greater than in the north.

The methods of growing rice in China are similar to those of India but even more intensive. The farms are smaller, averaging about two acres. This is less than one half an acre of cropland per capita. In south China a farm of 10 acres is considered extremely large. With so little land it is necessary to get more than one crop per year to supply even the minimum needs of the people. In south China two crops of rice are often grown on the same field; in middle China, with less rain and a shorter growing season, a crop of rice and a crop of wheat. In some of the more favorable areas of the south three crops are grown in one year, but this is not a general practice.

Although food crops are of tremendous importance there are also industrial crops in China. Of these cotton is the most important and production in China ranks fourth after that of the United States, India, and Russia. The principal cotton region is in the lower Yangtze, immediately to the west of Shanghai. Another important crop is the mulberry, the basis of the silk industry. The distribution is much like that of cotton; that is, in the central part of China and also in the lowland near Canton.

Agricultural Regions

It is obvious from the variety of crops, methods of cultivation, and agricultural conditions that China can be divided into several agricultural regions. The broad twofold division, already suggested, is based on the cultivation or noncultivation of rice. South of the Central Uplands, rice and dry season grains are the dominant elements in the agriculture. To the north, millet, sorghums, and soybeans are the chief crops. J. Lossing Buck in his "Land Utilization in China" describes eight agricultural regions in Humid China, to which a ninth may be added in order to include Manchuria.

SOUTH CHINA [rice important]

1. Double-cropping Rice Region
2. Southwestern Rice Region
3. Rice–Tea Region
4. Szechwan Rice Region
5. Yangtze Rice–Wheat Region

NORTH CHINA [rice minor or missing]

6. Winter Wheat–Kaoliang Region
7. Winter Wheat–Millet Region
8. Spring Wheat Region
9. Manchurian Soybean–Sorghum Region

1. THE DOUBLE-CROPPING RICE REGION lies mostly in the hilly provinces of Kwangsi and Kwangtung. The flood plains of the rivers such as the Si, Pei, and Tung are intensively cultivated, but so much of the land is in hills that no more than 15 per cent of the total surface is in crops. The growing season lasts throughout the year, and the rainfall is the heaviest in China, thus making two crops of rice in one season feasible. The average population density of Kwangtung Province is *only* 375 persons per square mile of total land, but in terms of the arable land the density is about seven times this figure! The two crops of rice are planted in March and August, respectively, and harvested in June and November.

In spite of the intensive agriculture on the alluvial lowlands, this region is usually an importer of rice from nearby Indochina. Most of the farmers in this region are essentially sharecroppers, returning from one third to two thirds of the rice produced to the landlord. Other crops, grown in small quantities, are sugarcane, sweet potatoes, tea, mulberry, tobacco, oranges, and bananas. The rainfall in this region is somewhat more dependable than in other parts of China and as a result famines are rather rare. The diet, however, is by no means adequate.

2. THE SOUTHWESTERN RICE REGION is the most elevated of the cultivated regions in China. Most of the region lies above 5000 feet. The Province of Yünnan, which includes the greater part of this region, is about the size of California, but has twice as many people, in spite of the fact that only 7 per cent of the land is cultivated. The principal crop is rice, grown during the summer in the valleys, but not enough is produced to feed the people. Corn, wheat, barley, and beans are grown on the hill slopes. Opium and mulberry are ancient crops whereas cotton is just being introduced on a commercial scale. Tung oil, tin, gold, copper, coal, lumber, and other forest products are also produced in this region.

3. THE RICE–TEA REGION is located south of the Yangtze Lowland in the hilly provinces of

Hunan, Kiangsi, and Chekiang. The highest hills and ridges are between 2000 and 5000 feet and the valleys are small but numerous, many of them tributary to the Yangtze. The hills are terraced in part and, in general, more land is under cultivation than in the regions previously described. About 18 per cent of the land is cultivated and most of this is irrigated. Rice is the standard summer crop in the valleys and on the terraced land, while tea, tung nuts, sweet potatoes, mulberry, and oilseeds are produced on the hillslopes and uplands. In winter, wheat, beans, various vegetables, and oilseeds are sown in the rice fields, but the growing season, about 300 days, is not long enough for two crops of rice. This is the chief tea region of China. Both black and green tea are produced. The former is fermented before heat curing. Green tea is obtained by heat curing as soon as the leaves are picked and before fermentation can take place. Formerly this part of China was a large exporter of tea, much of it in the form of bricks for convenience in transport by caravans. The increase in production of plantation tea in India and Ceylon was largely responsible for the loss of China's foreign tea market.

4. THE SZECHWAN RICE REGION is in a basin-like plateau in the middle Yangtze drainage. During the long war with Japan, Chungking, the chief city of this region, became the capital of all China and a focus for the entire productive economy. Formerly this was an agricultural frontier. It became, temporarily at least, the most populous of China's provinces. The general level of this region is about 2000 feet; above this rise numerous hills and higher plateaus. The region is deeply dissected by four tributaries of the Yangtze—the Min, Lu, Kialing, and Wu. The rainfall in Szechwan is moderate, about 40 inches on the average. However, it increases sharply in the higher mountains to the west which give rise to the rivers. The growing season is over 330 days, and the summers are warm considering the altitude. Rice, planted in May and harvested in September, accounts for about 40 per cent of the cropped land. Wheat is a winter crop sown on the rice fields and elsewhere. Corn, millet, sweet potatoes, sugarcane, cotton, and mulberry are chiefly summer crops on the hills and uplands. Tung oil, opium, and tea are produced also, the first two for export. In Szechwan there are some rather valuable mineral resources to be found—coal, copper, iron ore, salt, and gold.

5. THE YANGTZE RICE–WHEAT REGION coincides with the alluvial lowland of that great river from Ichang to Shanghai. The river, because of the humid mountains of its upper reaches, supplies an enormous amount of water to thousands of irrigation canals. The river and canals also serve as arteries of transportation for steamers, junks, and various small craft, the total tonnage of which is greater than that on any other river of the world with the possible exception of the Rhine at the peak of its development. The canals, of course, are navigable only by small boats. The two great risks of this region are drought and flood, too little or too much water. Otherwise the climate is generally favorable for agriculture with a growing season of 300 days and an average annual precipitation of about 42 inches fairly well distributed through the year.

Two crops can be grown on the same land, but not two crops of rice. The winter crops on the riceland are usually either wheat or barley, the combined acreage of these two cereals being nearly equal to that of rice. Cotton is a significant crop in the delta portion of the lowland in the vicinity of Shanghai, and the silk industry thrives in the same districts. The mulberry is, therefore, an important tree crop. Shanghai is the chief port for this region and adjacent regions as well, including in its hinterland most of southern and middle China. This city of nearly four million people has become the most important commercial center of China.

6. THE WINTER WHEAT–KAOLIANG REGION corresponds to the Yellow Plain, or the North China Plain as it often is called. The area of level land here is much greater than that along the Yangtze and the percentage cultivated is just as high. Crop yields are lower, however, and the population in terms of cultivated land is only moderately dense. The middle and upper reaches of the rivers—the Hwang, Hwai, and others—flow through the loesslands to the west and bring in a heavy load of this fertile sediment. As a means of restoring the fertility of the land in the plain this is a blessing, but it is a disadvantage also. The silt, deposited in the bed of a river, builds up the bottom and during floods the banks also, until the river is literally running on a grooved ridge rather than in a valley. The adjacent flood plain is, therefore, lower than the

FIGURE 29.5. *Varied views of China's agriculture. Upper left, plowing paddy with water buffalo; upper right, dry plowing; lower left, harvesting rice; lower right, threshing. All these views are from South China. From Frank Buckley.*

river water. The tendency for such rivers to break through the natural levees and seek lower levels makes this a region of continuous flood risk even without extremely heavy rains in the watershed. Once the banks of a stream give way, it is difficult, if not impossible, to restore the water to its former course.

In spite of the hazards of flood and drought, 80 million people manage to make a living on this rich plain. Conditions are not favorable for rice. The growing season is long enough in the south, but the water supply is not generally adequate. Instead, winter wheat is the chief crop, followed by barley, soybeans, and ordinary beans. Summer crops include millet, kaoliang (a grain sorghum), corn, cotton, hemp, and various vegetables. There is no good port for this important region although Tientsin, a city of 1,200,000 people, is used for shipping in spite of its inadequate harbor. Shanghai serves the southern part of the region.

7. THE WINTER WHEAT–MILLET REGION lies to the west of the Hwang Plain on the loess plateau. There the fine wind-blown silt is in some places more than 100 feet thick. The rainfall is light, averaging from 15 to 20 inches annually, and climatic qualities, in general, are similar to those of the Winter Wheat Belt of central Kansas. Wheat, millet, and cotton are the chief crops, most of the wheat growing in the winter, the millet in summer. Although the population of this region is rather sparse in comparison with the regions previously described, the pressure on the limited food supply is severe. As in other subhumid grain regions the risk of drought is great, and drought often means no crop at all. Very little of this region is irrigated.

8. THE SPRING WHEAT REGION is on the northwestern margin of cultivated China, to the north and west of the Winter Wheat–Millet Region. The land is hilly and high, some of it reaching 8000 feet. The growing season is short (190 days) and the rainfall light. In addition to spring wheat, millet, barley, kaoliang, potatoes, corn, and even a little rice are produced. By means of irrigation in the middle Hwang Valley, this region is extended westward several hundred miles beyond the limits of dry farming. Crop yields are low for the region as a whole and the risk of drought and famine is high.

9. THE MANCHURIAN SOYBEAN–SORGHUM REGION is the northernmost agricultural region of China. Nearly all cultivation is limited to the rolling plain, since a slight increase in elevation at this latitude brings the temperatures below the critical values for plant growth. Winters are long and severe, more so than at similar latitudes in North America or Europe. The agricultural pattern differs markedly from the remainder of China, partly because of the recent large-scale settlement of Manchuria, partly because of the restrictions of the climate. Although Manchuria has been occupied by the Chinese for 2000 years, immigration was restricted until about 1912 when millions of Chinese from the overpopulated provinces to the south poured into the area. A small number of Japanese farmers entered the region after the invasion of Manchuria in 1931, but the population has always been dominantly Chinese.

Crop patterns and agricultural methods are a mixture of Oriental and Western techniques. The fields are larger than in China and yields are large enough for export in spite of the 40 million people who live in the plain. The major crops are soybeans, kaoliang, millets, wheat, and barley throughout the plain, with some corn and rice in the south. For many years Manchuria was the only outstanding source of soybeans in the world, the export going mainly to Japan and the United States. In recent years soybeans have been grown on a large scale in many other regions, including the Corn Belt of the United States. The chief cities of the plain are inland and include Harbin, Hsinking, and Mukden. Dairen and Antung, the only important ports, are not on the plain but are made accessible by river boats, coastwise shipping, and rail. The harbor at Yingkow, on the estuary of the Liao River, is too shallow for the use of large craft.

Livestock

In a land where every mouthful of food is apportioned before it matures, little land can be spared for pasture or forage crops in support of livestock. A limited amount of food for the people is provided by the pigs and chickens which feed on the meager waste of the Chinese kitchen, by the sheep which browse on woodland pastures in the hill country, and by fish from the rivers and the sea. Otherwise the livestock is confined strictly to work animals—oxen, water buffaloes, donkeys, and mules—some of which occasionally provide milk and meat. The various kinds of livestock are unevenly distributed. The sheep, donkeys, and mules are restricted largely to the cooler and drier northern regions. The water buffaloes and hogs are found only in the rice-growing districts of the south, while oxen and chickens are more widely distributed. The minor significance of livestock is attested by the fact that most of the farm work is done by hand, and that on the land much freight is still moved by human carriers or by wheelbarrows.

MINERAL RESOURCES

Agricultural resources in China are developed almost to the limit, but minerals are to a considerable extent unexploited. On this fact much of the future of China depends. To be sure, the Chinese have been picking away at certain mineral deposits for centuries (FIG. 29.1). Gold has been recovered by placer methods from the sediments of many of the rivers. Coal and iron ore have been mined in various localities, but always on a small scale. Enough is known of the mineral resources of China to rank it as the foremost Oriental mining country of the future.

China is well supplied with coal, the first requirement for industry, and with iron ore, which is almost as fundamental. Tin, antimony, tungsten, lead, zinc, mercury, copper, manganese, and other minor minerals occur in varying quantities. On the whole there is less potential mineral wealth in China than in the United States or Russia, but probably greater potential wealth than in France or Germany. Agricultural products such as cotton, silk, and soybeans can, of course, make a great contribution to this industrial economy.

In every province in China there is some coal and in total reserves China ranks fourth among the nations of the world, after the United States, Russia, and Canada. Most of the good coal of China, however, is in the provinces of Shensi and Shansi on the plateaus to the west of the North China Plain and on the margins of the plain in Manchuria. The best mines were in the hands of the Japanese during the occupation of China, a fact which led to the opening of new mines in south China and in the Red Basin of Szechwan. Petroleum is not at all plentiful in China, although explorations have not been as thorough as in the case of coal. Deposits of oil shale are known to exist, but their exploitation is not feasible at present. Water power is only slightly developed

in China, but many of the projects designed primarily for flood control and irrigation will provide a modest amount of power.

Iron ore deposits are found in many parts of China, although only a few deposits are extensive. The total reserves are small in terms of those of some other countries but are sufficient to supply the needs in China for many years to come, as long, perhaps, as the Upper Lakes Region will supply the United States. Good iron ores are found in Manchuria (close to coal), in the plateau west of Peiping, and along the highlands southward to the Yangtze River. In the past most of the iron ore mined in these localities has gone to Japan. From the distribution of iron ore and coal it would appear that the best location for a large iron and steel industry is in Manchuria to the southeast of Mukden. However, the coal in this area does not coke well. The Japanese did have extensive steel mills there which were dismantled at the end of the war. Restoration is a slow and tedious process complicated by the distances between good coking coal and rich ore.

Of the critical alloy minerals so necessary in making good steel, there is an abundance of tungsten and smaller quantities of manganese in China. Lead, zinc, tin, and antimony are fairly abundant and some of these metals in times past have been exported from China. Chromium, vanadium, and nickel are apparently lacking. Salt is mined or extracted from the sea in large quantities in order to supply the great population. The annual production averages three million tons, about one third that in the United States.

INDUSTRIES

Prior to World War II, which began for China in 1937, most of the districts of industrial development were near the coast. The Mukden-Dairen region of Manchuria, with its coal, iron, soybeans as a source of oil, and chemical and cement industries, was, and still is, in a favorable position. There are no minerals of importance in the lower Yangtze region, but transportation is good and light industries, such as cotton and silk textiles, tobacco processing, and rice and flour mills, can readily obtain raw materials from the hinterland. Industrial development around Tientsin, Tsingtao, and Canton is on a similar basis. Obviously these locations on or near the coast have an advantage in obtaining foreign machinery

FIGURE 29.6. *A bamboo store in China. The bamboo plant, which provides food as well as building material, is widely cultivated. From Thomas O. Milton.*

as well as in the transportation of the raw materials and the finished products.

The industrial development of China during and after the war, however, suggests that locations in the interior may become as important as those on the sea. The forced removal of industries from the coast during the war demonstrated the possibilities of expansion in the interior, and many of the emergency developments show signs of becoming permanent. Before the war Szechwan slumbered in a sort of preindustrial lethargy. There were no modern industries in Chungking, no wheeled vehicles, and only a few local handicrafts. As the Chinese Army retreated from the coast, machinery was moved into Szechwan, much of it on the backs of porters. Blast furnaces and steel mills were dismantled and removed bit by bit, and the industry relocated in spite of frequent bombings by the Japanese. The Red Basin is not the best location for an iron and steel industry, perhaps, but the effects of the wartime industries are having a profound influence on the postwar development of this region.

Continued industrial expansion in China depends on improved communications and the coordination of the varied and scattered natural resources. The Shansi coal basin is a focal point because of the abundance and high quality of the fuel. It is on no main line of transportation but is not too far from the sea and from iron ore. Shensi has reserves of petroleum, coal, iron, and salt, and a surplus of wheat and other grains. Flour mills, cotton textile mills, tanneries, chemical and iron works, are already established. The railroad following the Wei River is the first step in connecting this region to the coast. These are but samplings of industrial resources and development in China. If stable political conditions prevail there is a good chance that China will become one of the important industrial countries of the world.

For producers in the United States, the growing industries and the increased use of natural resources in China is a matter of the greatest significance. Chinese are now at least a century behind, and they will continue to be importers of various manufactured goods as well as machinery for their factories. These things the United States can supply in exchange for raw materials not produced in sufficient quantities at home, such as tung oil, tungsten, silk, and tea. To be sure, other peoples such as the Japanese and British will be competing with those of the United States for the Chinese trade, but we are in the best position to supply the producers' goods so necessary to the Chinese in this stage of their development.

COMMUNICATIONS

China has long been considered "a country behind a wall," with little commercial connection with the outside world. This viewpoint was not without justification. During World War II the attitude of the outsiders changed. It became customary to speak of the "lifelines" of China, as if the very existence of the country depended on communication with other lands. First it was the Canton–Hankow Railway, then the route from Haiphong in Indochina to Kunming in Yünnan, then the Burma Road, and finally the Ledo Road. The emphasis on these feeble routes to the outside world obscured the far greater significance of the internal routes of China. Perhaps to many people those run-down railways, the canal boats and small river craft, the improvised roads and the imported trucks, the trails with the millions of human porters, and the hundreds of thousands of wheelbarrows are of no importance. Yet the internal traffic today far exceeds the foreign trade.

Chinese were late in beginning railroad construction and slow to extend it. Most of the lines were built by foreign capital in order to tap the hinterlands of the "treaty ports." The railway from Haiphong in French Indochina to Kunming is a case in point and so are the lines inland from Canton, Tsingtao, and Port Arthur in Manchuria. Later these railways were extended and at the beginning of the war with Japan in 1937, Canton was connected by rail with Hankow. Peiping and several ports were also tied in with this main north-south line. Spurs of these units have been constructed to reach important mineral deposits or other resources. The fact remains, however, that the railroads of China are woefully inadequate for either internal or external trade.

CHAPTER

30

Japan's Production Regions

STANDING room only in Japan! As in China, too many people must wrest a living from small areas of arable land. Eighty five million people live on four islands—Hokkaido, Honshu, Shikoku, and Kyushu—and on hundreds of lesser ones with a total area of only 150,000 squares miles, a smaller area than the state of California. Furthermore, only 16 per cent of Japan is arable and the population density per square mile of cultivated land is more than 3000. Japan is, to a certain extent, industrialized and foreign trade and commercial fisheries have been developed, but the resources are by no means as varied as those in China. Faced with these conditions and possessed of a burning ambition, the Japanese made their bid for an Asiatic empire. The combination of the favorable position in Asia of this clever, vigorous people and a curiously heedless world almost allowed them to bring this to pass. But defeated, stripped of their external empire, and restricted to the home islands, it is obvious that the resources of the Japanese are not sufficient to support the people beyond a bare subsistence level.

If one approaches Japan from the north, perhaps by plane via Alaska, the first large island to be seen is Hokkaido, with an area of 31,000 square miles, about the size of Maine. This island is sparsely populated in comparison with the rest of Japan, having more than three million in 1950. Most of the people live on the coast, while the mountainous and forested interior is very sparsely settled. To the south is the main island, called Honshu or Nippon, with an area of 88,000 square miles, comparable in size to Minnesota. The population is approximately 60 millions. South of western Honshu is Shikoku, the smallest of the "large islands," having slightly more than 7000

square miles (comparable with New Jersey) and four million people. To the southwest is Kyushu with 16,000 square miles (about one half the area of Maine) and 15 million people. Hundreds of smaller islands are found near the large ones, especially in the Inland Sea between Honshu and Shikoku.

In Japan the mountains come down to the sea with the exception of a few small plains which break the monotony of the mountain landscapes (FIG. 30.1). The mountains of Honshu rise to more than 10,000 feet; Fuji, the highest, rises to more than 12,000 feet. This is an active mountain-building zone as the numerous earthquakes and active volcanoes clearly indicate. Although

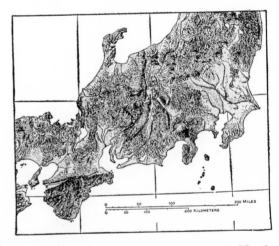

FIGURE 30.1. *This relief map of central Honshu shows the rugged nature of the land and the limited amount of agricultural land. The plains around the bays support most of the people. From Guy-Harold Smith and the "Geographic Review."*

the surface of Japan is for the most part rugged hill and mountain land, the pattern is fine grained. The individual ranges are small, the valleys narrow and short, and the plains tiny.

Most of the people of Japan live on the plains, where easily cultivated land is available. Parts of the lowlands are made up of recent river deposits and the fertility is continuously replenished by the streams flowing out of the mountains. Other parts of the lowlands, however, represent older alluvium which often occurs on terraces well above the rivers. This material is less fertile and has, in fact, lost much of its soluble mineral content by long continued leaching. In still other districts, swamps and rocky river beds cannot be cultivated, and therefore the productivity of even the smoothest land in Japan is further reduced.

The largest lowland in Japan is the Kwanto Plain to the north of Tokyo Bay. The plain is irregular in shape, about 100 miles long in its greatest extension, and less than 75 miles wide. The total area is about 5000 square miles and supports about 15 million people in spite of the fact that certain districts are unproductive because the land is swampy or rough and stony. Several different levels of the plain reveal a variety of surface and material. The lowest level, mainly in the center of the plain, is composed of recent alluvium. Above this the older alluvium rises, often in an abrupt terrace scarp. On the terraces, deposits of volcanic ash have been laid down by recently active volcanoes. Above the terraces alluvial fans border the mountain spurs which are marginal to the plain on all sides. The older alluvium and the fans, because of the high porosity of their soils, are not always supplied with sufficient water for intensive agriculture.

Other similar but smaller plains are found in the vicinity of most of Japan's cities, such as Osaka, Nagoya, Sendai, Hiroshima, Yahata, Kumamoto, Toyama, and hundreds of others. Some of these alluvial plains are barely large enough for a single town and a bit of paddy. The larger plains are nearly all on the coast, but many of the smaller ones lie in narrow basins between the mountain ridges. Wherever the plains and basins are, there is a dense population, except in the northern part of Honshu and Hokkaido where the climate restricts rice culture.

The mountains, sparsely peopled and only slightly productive in themselves, are nevertheless of greatest significance to the plains. Large quantities of water needed in the rice fields and for domestic uses are supplied from the melting snows of the mountains and from the rains, which are heaviest on the intermediate slopes. The rushing streams carry sediment to renew the fertility of the alluvial plains. Hydroelectric power is very significant in Japan because of its applicability to light industry and the scarcity of coal. The timber of the mountain slopes is carefully harvested for lumber, paper, pulp, and fuel, while the lower, gentler slopes are often terraced and used to produce rice and other crops. Only because of the presence of the mountains is production so abundant in the plains.

CLIMATE

The climates of Japan can be compared to those of certain parts of eastern North America. The islands extend from 30° N. latitude to 45° N. and are comparable in this respect to the coast of North America from northern Florida to Maine and Nova Scotia. The summer conditions are similar on these two coasts, but the winters, like those of China, are colder in Japan than in comparable latitudes in eastern United States. Japan is under the influence of the monsoon and in summer the air masses move from the southeast toward the center of the continent. This brings heavy rains and much cloudiness in the summer, which is the season of maximum rainfall. The winter monsoon blows from the northwest and brings sharp temperature contrasts but less precipitation. On the whole, rain is heaviest on the southeast-facing slopes in the path of the onshore summer monsoon, but the northern mountains receive heavy snow in winter also. In terms of temperature, Tokyo is almost the equivalent of Shanghai; Sapporo in Hokkaido compares with Peiping; Nagasaki on Kyushu is only slightly warmer than Tokyo.

In the Köppen system most of Japan is described as the humid temperate type (Cfa). The very northern tip of Honshu and southern Hokkaido are in the cool summer type (Cfb), while the remainder of Hokkaido is microthermal (Dfb). This simple division is not adequate to show the local contrasts in climate brought about by relief and varying exposure. There is a definite contrast, for example, between the coast of the Sea of Japan, called the shady side, and the

FIGURE 30.2. *A farm land-scape in Kyushu show-ing a village, lake, and numerous small fields. From Thomas O. Mil-ton.*

warmer, sunnier coast along the Pacific. The elements of fog and cloud are of considerable significance, both increasing as the Sea of Japan is approached. This is especially true in winter. In summer the least sunshine is at the higher elevations. It should be emphasized, however, that in all the plains of Japan, except in the extreme north, there are adequate heat, sunshine, and rainfall for agriculture.

AGRICULTURE

Japan is first of all an agricultural country. Even the combined value of manufacturing, fishing, and mining is secondary to that of farming. The intensity of the agriculture is a measure of its significance and the good earth of Japan is cultivated with even more care and cunning than that of China or India. The Japanese peasant keeps his small plot of land (FIG. 30.2) neat and clean and makes it produce as much as possible. Only 16 per cent of the total area of Japan can be cultivated, while in Germany 44 per cent is farmed, in Italy 45 per cent, and in France 40 per cent. In the United States, to be sure, only 18 per cent of the land is cultivated, but this is a matter of economic feasibility, not necessity. In North America the cropped land could be doubled.

The pressure of population in Japan and the resulting intensity of agriculture leave indelible marks on the land. The nonproductive use of the land is kept to a minimum. Trees, houses, and roads are not allowed to occupy good tillable land, and on the plains cultivation creeps to the very edge of the salty sea sand. The farms support no unnecessary animals, no dogs, no cows, only the bare minimum of draft animals, and the pigs and chickens which live on the meager waste products. In other countries parts of the farm are left idle for a woodlot, a meadow, or a field corner in which to turn a plow. The Japanese leave no piece of level or gently sloping land the size of a man's shirt untilled. The fertile districts receive the most attention; every field is soaked with manure, the crops are guarded, and after the harvest the crows have no reason to visit the fields. In Japan, man is constantly renewing his impress on the soft alluvium, while on the margin of the plains even the stones show human fingerprints.

As in China, the average size of the Japanese farm increases from south to north. In the extreme south where two crops of rice may be obtained in one year, the average is about 1.5 acres per farm, while in northern Hokkaido at least 12 acres are necessary to support a family. The national average farm size is less than three acres. Small as they are, the farms are subdivided into fields, the average size of which is only one tenth of an acre. As already indicated, special agricultural practices are necessary in order to derive as much food as possible from the small areas of land. These include terraces on the gentler slopes, careful fertilizing and cultivation, multiple cropping, and intercultivation.

Two kinds of terraces are in general use, one for nonirrigated crops and one for rice paddies. The paddy terraces must be nearly level so that the crops can be evenly flooded. The other terraces may have gentle, irregular slopes with enough protection at the scarp or break to minimize soil erosion. In either kind, much labor is necessary to build and maintain the terraces. Prior to World War II, the use of terraces in Japan was declining since more and more rice was imported, but when the Japanese were deprived of their overseas empire and trade, the pressure on all marginal areas increased.

Every scrap of available organic and inorganic fertilizer must be added to the soil in order to maintain fertility. Animal manure and human excrement make up the largest part of the fertilizer. Mineral fertilizers such as nitrates and phosphates, green manures, bone, oil cake, and fish products are also used. The various fertilizers are usually mixed with water in pits or cisterns and allowed to decompose before being applied to the land. Then the liquid is ladled out when needed, but only the soil in the immediate vicinity of the growing plants receives fertilizer. A part of the fertilizer used in Japan, especially the minerals, must be imported, and the total cost of fertilizer is often as much as 25 or 30 per cent of the value of the crop. This in itself is evidence of intensive cultivation.

Except in the north where the climate is not favorable, the good land of Japan produces more than one crop per year. The double cropping of rice is limited to the southern coast of Shikoku; consequently the usual practice is to grow a crop of barley, wheat, rapeseed, beans, green manures or other legumes in winter. The production of the winter crop is not easy, since it is difficult to complete the drainage of the rice paddies in order to prepare for the second crop, and because of the coolness of the winter season. In the middle and southern portions of the country, even the uplands are made to produce a second crop of grain or vegetables. In Kyushu the average field is cropped 1.8 times per year, in the Kwanto Plain, 1.3, while in Hokkaido the figure is 0.8; for Japan as a whole, the average is 1.3. This means that 30 per cent of the cultivated land of the country yields a second crop.

Another practice designed to increase agricultural production is intercultivation. Alternate rows of different crops are sown in the same fields at slightly different times. Vegetables are often sown between the rows of grain in the winter. By careful planning the land can be made to yield additional food, but the crops do interfere with each other to a certain extent.

Crops

In Japan rice dominates the agricultural scene just as it does in south China and eastern India. It accounts for more than 50 per cent of the crops by value, and occupies about the same percentage of the cropped land. Rice production slowly increased from six million metric tons in 1911 to 12 million in 1950. Production has not kept pace with consumption, however, and more and more rice was imported up to the close of World War II. The yield is the highest of any large rice producing country, averaging about 50 bushels to the acre. This is the result of careful cultivation, adequate irrigation, and the heavy use of fertilizer. As might be expected under the circumstances, the cost of production is higher than in Indonesia and Indochina, where the yields are only one third as great. Only in India and China is more rice produced than in Japan.

On the basis of rice production and its relation to associated crops Japan can be divided into four agricultural regions (FIG. 30.3):

1. Double-cropping Rice Region
2. Rice and Dry Crop Region
3. Northern Rice Region
4. Non-Rice Region

The *Double-cropping Rice Region* is limited to small parts of southern Shikoku and the Kii Peninsula of Honshu which lies immediately to the east of Shikoku. In both of these districts the mountains come down almost to the sea and the alluvial plains are very small. The small settlements are usually more concerned with fishing than farming.

The *Rice and Dry Crop Region* occupies all of Kyushu, most of Shikoku, and the southern half of Honshu. This is a region of varied cropping, but the central theme in all the districts is rice (FIG. 30.4), as a summer crop, and wheat, barley, oilseeds, and various vegetables as winter crops. Tea and mulberry are the most common tree crops on the uplands adjacent to the rice paddies. Oranges, grapes, and peaches are also produced on the hilly land.

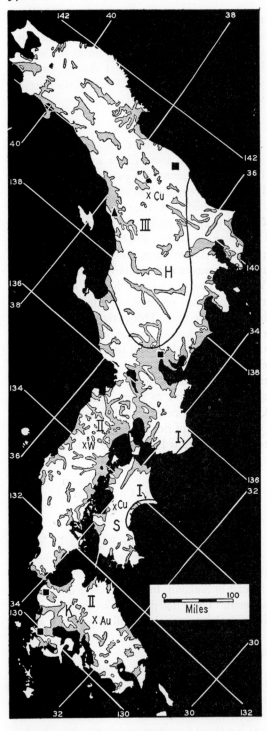

FIGURE 30.3. *A production map of Japan. I. Double-cropping Rice Region [limited to very small areas in Honshu (H) and Shikoku (S)]. II. Rice and Dry Crop Region [in western Honshu and Kyushu (K)]. III. Northern Rice Region (little or no cropping in winter). The chief areas of rice production are shaded. Abbreviations: Au, gold; Cu, copper; W, tungsten. Oil is represented by black triangles and coal by black squares.*

which can be quickly drained or they are grown on the gentler hill slopes following summer vegetables. The acreage of wheat and barley is about equal. Most of the wheat is the soft winter variety which is made into flour. One of the effects of westernization in Japan is the increased consumption of bread. The barley is of two kinds, common barley which has a rather wide distribution, and naked barley which is concentrated in the southwestern part of the region. The chief difference from the point of view of consumption is that the naked barley can be scaled and cleaned more readily. Barley is usually consumed as whole grain, sometimes mixed with rice.

The chief vegetable in this region is the sweet potato. It is widely distributed but is most important in the Kwanto Plain and the plains of western Kyushu. It grows well on the terraces and hill slopes in the summer season. Beans of various kinds, including the red kidney and soybeans, as well as peas, turnips, and taro contribute to the food supply.

Since tea is grown in most of the cultivated districts of southern Honshu and is a rather conspicuous crop, its importance is often exaggerated. Actually, it occupies less than one per cent of the cropped land. Most of the crop is grown in small patches either on the lower hill slopes or in small areas in the villages. Nearly all the black tea and about two thirds of the green tea are ordinarily consumed in Japan.

Mulberry trees occupy a much greater acreage than tea and are somewhat more widely distributed throughout Japan. Most of the silk, however, is produced in central and western Honshu. This may be considered the most important industrial crop in Japan since nearly all other crops are produced primarily for food.

The combined acreage of wheat and barley, the chief winter grains of this region, is equal to that of rice since they are grown in the winter both on the rice paddies and on the uplands. Wheat and barley usually follow rice on the paddies

FIGURE 30.4. *Harvesting rice in Honshu, with tea trees in the middle distance and Mt. Fuji in the background. From Keystone.*

Mulberry trees are grown on the foothills and terraces. The silkworms are fed almost continuously throughout the summer, but the three main crops of cocoons come in spring, midsummer, and autumn. The production of raw silk requires a large amount of skilled hand labor as well as scientific management. The Japanese farmers, who grow mulberry trees and produce the cocoons, obtain the eggs from registered dealers, hatch and feed the worms, and then sell the cocoons to the filatures where the silk is reeled as the first process in manufacturing.

The competition of synthetic fibers and the effects of World War II have restricted the production of raw silk in Japan. Since most of the raw silk is usually marketed abroad, the industry is sensitive to world conditions. At one time more than one fourth of the Japanese farmers received their chief cash income from the sale of cocoons, but it is unlikely that this will occur again because of the competition of synthetic fibers.

The most valuable fruit in Japan is the Mandarin orange grown in southern Honshu and on the margins of Shikoku and Kyushu. Steep hill slopes not suitable for rice production are the usual sites. Navel oranges and bitter oranges occupy small areas, as do persimmons, plums, peaches, pears, cherries, and grapes.

Northern Honshu and southern and central Hokkaido, where rice is the dominant summer crop and winter crops are generally lacking because of snow (FIG. 30.5) and the severity of the winters, are designated the *Northern Rice Region*. Rice is just as important relatively as in the south, in some districts even more so, but the total production is not so great. Winter cropping is not generally feasible, and the fields lie fallow in this season and are sometimes covered with snow. Because of the shortness of the season a number of crops common in the south are missing or are of only minor importance in the Northern Rice Region. Citrus fruits and tea are almost entirely lacking. Mulberry trees and sweet potatoes are found only along the southern margin. On the other hand, white potatoes and oats are grown in Hokkaido and apples are the chief fruit of the region.

Farms are larger in this single cropping region, livestock is more important, and the methods of cultivation are different. Many farmers practice a shifting cultivation, in which the forest is cleared by burning and the field cultivated for some years and then allowed to revert to forest and brushland. Buckwheat and millet are grown on the burned-over land in addition to the more usual crops. Lumbering is important in this region as previously noted in Chapter 7.

The *Non-Rice Region* is limited to the northern and eastern part of Hokkaido. There the growing season is too short for rice, and the chief crops are vegetables—including beans, soybeans, sugar beets, potatoes—oats, millet, and buckwheat. This is a frontier region, sparsely populated. Lumbering and fishing are of greater importance than agriculture in some districts.

MINERALS

In view of the restricted territory of Japan, the pressure on agriculture, and the desirability of industrialization at least sufficient for Japanese needs, the shortage of minerals is critical. None of the common minerals, with the possible exception of copper, is available in sufficient quantity and quality to satisfy domestic needs. Coal, iron, petroleum, and mineral fertilizers are especially wanted. In spite of the poor quality of the mineral deposits, however, the Japanese stepped up their mineral production under the pressure of war. During World War II minerals were a national necessity, and domestic production soared so much that some of the more accessible deposits were almost exhausted. It would appear that in the future the Japanese can produce only a portion of their mineral requirements at home.

Coal is the main source of power in Japan and is, therefore, the most critical mineral of all. Coal is needed for the factories, the steel mills, the chemical industries, the railways, the steamers and fishing boats, for the generation of electricity, and for domestic heating. Most of the Japanese coal is mined in the fields on the northern side of the Island of Kyushu, but small fields of low-grade coal are widely scattered throughout Honshu and Hokkaido. The largest reserves of coal in Hokkaido are the least accessible to the industrial belt which stretches from Tokyo to Nagasaki.

The quality of Japanese coal is so low that statements concerning tonnage are misleading. Production has totaled as high as 40 million tons for Japan, but the ash and volatile content is so high that this figure should be greatly reduced before making comparisons with other countries. Very little of the coal is suitable for making metallurgical coke, and usually high-quality bituminous coal has been imported from China, including Manchuria, and even from as far away as Indochina. Aside from its low heating value, much of the coal is difficult and expensive to mine because of its occurrence in thin seams, many of which are inclined, folded, and faulted.

The best coalfields of Kyushu are on the northern and northwestern coasts, near Yahata, Kokura, Fukuoka, and Nagasaki. The coal is in a good position for shipment to other parts of Japan, especially to the large industrial cities on the Inland Sea such as Osaka, and for the coaling of ships. A part of the Kyushu coal is shipped as far as the Tokyo-Yokohama district and about one third is used in the local iron and steel industries on Kyushu. Some of the coal mines reach into submarine ledges below the level of the sea.

The outstanding coalfield on Honshu is near the east coast, approximately 100 miles north of Tokyo. The quality is very low, but the nearness to the industrial centers in and around Tokyo is a great advantage. The chief coalfield of Hokkaido is on the margin of the Ishikari Plain in the west central part of the island. The isolation of this field from the consuming areas, combined with the fact that the coal is inland and must be transported by rail to the sea, has restricted production somewhat. However, the mines are among the newest in Japan and are the best equipped.

In spite of the scarcity and low quality of their coal, Japanese have been for many years the largest producers in eastern Asia, and only small amounts of high-grade coal have been imported. Fortunately, good-quality coal is available in north China and Manchuria.

Japan is even poorer in petroleum than in coal. Exploration and drilling has been extensive, and it is unlikely that new reserves will be discovered. At the outside no more than 500 million barrels are available, a figure which represents less than half of one year's production in the United States. Prior to World War II it was estimated that the reserves of wells in operation was less than 75 million barrels. The total domestic production for many years has averaged from two to three million barrels, enough to supply about 10 per cent of the domestic demand. The remainder has been imported from various countries, including the United States, Indonesia, Russia, and Manchuria. Three fields account for most of the domestic production: the Akita, on the northwest corner of Honshu; the Niigata, on western Honshu about 200 miles farther south; and the west central Hokkaido field. The largest production is from the Akita field. This field consists of several small pools, in a zone near the coast about 100 miles long and up to 30 miles wide. It is a comparatively new field, which has shown increasing production in recent years. The Niigata field on the other hand is old, with declining production. The Hokkaido fields are the least important and show no signs of greater production. It is noteworthy that most of the petroleum refineries are in the industrial belt along the Inland Sea near the consuming centers. Japanese have long been interested in the production of synthetic petroleum, but the scarcity of coal and other raw materials has been a decided handicap.

To a limited extent the water power of Japan compensates for the scarcity of coal and petroleum, but hydroelectric energy cannot power an airplane or produce cheap iron and steel. The combination of numerous mountains and heavy precipitation is favorable for water power development. The fact that the consuming population is near the mountains is another favorable aspect. Japan ranks third among the nations in developed water power after the United States and Canada. In view of the relative areas of these three countries this is a remarkable situation indeed! At least six million horsepower is potentially available for six months of the year, and of this, half is developed. In contrast, in Canada and the United States less than one third of the potential water power is being used.

The chief producing districts are on the eastern and western margins of middle Honshu where the mountains are highest and the rainfall and snowfall heaviest. The rivers are usually small as compared with the Colorado, Columbia, or the St. Lawrence, but they are swift. The result is many hydroelectric plants, each with a rather small capacity. Many of these small installations are tied together in single power systems which supply the large cities. The industries of Japan,

FIGURE 30.5. *A winter view of the coast of Honshu, near Mito. Rice paddies on the tidal flats, forest, and snow-covered cultivated land on the upland. Several fish traps are to be seen in the bay. From Northwest Airlines.*

especially the lighter ones such as chemicals, light metals, and textiles, use more than half of the hydroelectric energy of the country. The remainder is used mostly for domestic purposes, and it is probable that a larger percentage of homes are wired for electricity in Japan than in any other country in the world.

Japan, the most industrialized nation of East Asia, has been the largest consumer of iron ore, but domestic production has supplied only from 10 to 20 per cent of the demand. Less than a dozen small deposits of iron ore are of commercial importance and the total reserves are estimated at only 40 million tons of magnetite, 30 million tons of hematite, and 10 million tons of limonite. The total reserves are less than one year's peak production in the United States. The largest production is from central and northeastern Honshu and from western Hokkaido; it totals less than one million tons annually. Imports from Korea, Manchuria, and at times, from various other countries make up the deficit in iron ore production. Since the quality of the coal used is low and the ore none too rich, large quantities of scrap iron are usually imported to boost the efficiency of the blast furnaces.

Other mineral production is minor. Copper is produced in sufficient quantities for peacetime requirements, but the ores are of low quality and the cost of production is high. The mines are scattered through northern and eastern Honshu, Shikoku, and Kyushu. The copper ores yield some silver and gold also. Enough sulfur for domestic needs is produced in Japan and building stone is abundant, but critical minerals such as bauxite, nickel, tin, vanadium, mercury, lead, and zinc are either lacking or produced in small quantities.

MANUFACTURING AND CITIES

For many years prior to World War II it seemed to the outside world that Japan was a growing industrial nation. It was impressive that, in spite of limited resources at home and high tariff walls abroad, Japanese could flood the markets of many countries with five-cent cotton cloth, three-dollar bicycles, and one-dollar slide rules, all with the familiar, fine print stamp "Made in Japan." The extent of the Japanese foreign market at its peak of commercial development was the more remarkable when we recall that this people came late to the manufacturing stage and that most of the raw materials used in making the industrial goods had to be imported. Nevertheless, it is evident from the study of the basic Japanese resources in the above paragraphs that Japan cannot easily become a great manufacturing country.

The chief industrial belt of Japan (FIG. 30.6) extends from Nagasaki, on the west side of Kyushu, to the Kwanto Plain, a distance of more than 800 miles. It is not a continuous belt, but rather is composed of several centers separated by intervening sections of hilly land. Most of the manufacturing in Japan is located in four widely spaced districts: the Kwanto Plain, the Nagoya Plain, the Osaka Plain, and the northern end of Kyushu. Of these the Tokyo-Yokohama district in the Kwanto is the most important, although Tokyo is primarily the political and commercial capital of Japan rather than an industrial center. This district has a large population from which to recruit workers, the coalfields of northern Honshu are near at hand, and a supply of electricity from the middle part of Honshu is available. On the other hand, the Tokyo-Yokohama district lies at one end of the

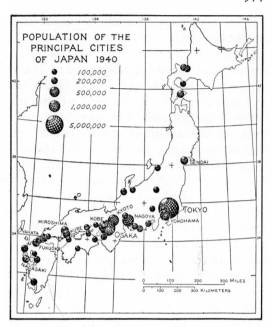

FIGURE 30.6. *The main Urban Belt of Japan extends from Tokyo to Nagasaki. Most Japanese live in cities, towns, and villages, very few on isolated farms. From Guy-Harold Smith and the American Geographical Society.*

industrial belt far from the coal and basic iron and steel of northern Kyushu. The tendency has been, therefore, to specialize in the relatively light industries—textiles, chemicals, light metals, and tools. During World War II, however, a good portion of the iron and steel, airplanes, and machinery were manufactured in this district and also a large share of the imported petroleum was refined here.

The Nagoya industrial district is located near the center of an agricultural region almost as large as the Kwanto Plain. Nagoya, with more than a million people, and a dozen smaller cities in the vicinity provide a large labor force for factories. The harbor is not suitable for large vessels, however, and, unlike Tokyo and Osaka, there is no port city on the bay farther out from Nagoya. This handicap leaves its mark on the industrial pattern. There is very little heavy industry in Nagoya. Instead, the specialties are those which do not require the handling of heavy goods. Textile, chemical, machine tool, and ceramic industries employ the largest number of workers and account for most of the value added by manufacturing. Bicycles, clocks, toys, and various bamboo articles are also manufactured here.

In many ways Osaka is the chief industrial city of Japan, although a poor second to Tokyo in population. Situated at the head of Osaka Bay on a delta formed by several small streams, the harbor is not naturally deep enough for large ships. An artificial harbor construction includes long moles reaching out to sea and channels dredged into the industrial heart of the city. Kobe serves as the deep water harbor for Osaka, and many of the heaviest industries, including iron, steel, and shipbuilding, are in Kobe. Until Japan began to prepare in earnest for World War II Osaka was chiefly a textile center. Large imports of cotton were brought from India, the United States, and Brazil, to be turned into cotton cloth for export to the various markets of eastern Asia. In the early 1930's, however, the producers in Osaka and the satellite cities began to turn toward metal manufacturing. Blast furnaces and steel mills were set up although there is neither coal nor iron in the plain. Metal work and machine manufacturing soon exceeded textiles in value. After the war textiles again became the primary manufacturing activity. Cotton spinning, requiring large factories for efficient operation, is pre-eminent in the city of Osaka, while the weaving of cotton cloth is located in the satellite cities of the plain. Spinning and weaving of wool for the home market are represented in Osaka, but volume is small in comparison with cotton.

The zone of heavy industry hugs the irregular coastline of northern Kyushu for a distance of about twelve miles. The chief cities are, from west to east, Wakamatsu, Yawata, Tobata, Kokura, Moji, and across the strait in Honshu, Shimonoseki. This district has some outstanding advantages as well as disadvantages from the point of view of the heavy industries. It is on the western end of the Inland Sea near the best and most accessible coalfields of Japan and those of the continent of Asia. On the unfavorable side is the fact that the harbors are generally poor and that the hills come down so close to the sea that level land for the location of heavy industries is at a premium. Furthermore, the peripheral position with respect to the manufacturing belt as a whole is unfortunate.

A large share of the raw materials used for the factories are imported to this district. Ores and crude metals are brought from the other islands of Japan and the Asiatic mainland. Oil and sugar pour into these tiny harbors from Indonesia, soybeans from Manchuria, rubber from Malaya, and cotton from India and China.

At the iron and steel mills of Tobata, great docks piled with coal and ore are most conspicuous, dwarfing the smaller sugar refineries, coke ovens, textile mills, and glass factories. Yawata is the largest city in this zone, and the population was more than 250,000 in 1950. Iron and steel in various forms are sent from this port to all parts of Japan. Kokura, to the east of Yawata and Tobata, is located on a somewhat broader plain but has a poor harbor. Iron and steel manufacturing is dominant along the waterfront, but along the canals, accessible only to smaller boats, lighter manufacturing including rice mills and ceramic industries is to be found.

Moji and Shimonoseki are located on opposite sides of the narrow strait which leads into the Inland Sea. The strait is slightly more than a mile in width and above its shores rise steep hills. This is the location of the railway ferry from Honshu to Kyushu. A great variety of goods pass through these ports by either rail or ship; in fact, this is the most important crossroad location in Japan. The industries of Moji and Shimonoseki, therefore, are rather more varied than those of the cities just described. Steel mills, oil and sugar refineries, textile industries, flour mills, rice mills, distilleries, and machine shops are among the important industrial establishments.

COMMUNICATIONS AND TRADE

In little more than a half century the Japanese were able to transform themselves from a feudal, subsistence agricultural people to a modern commercial and industrial nation. No other country has risen so rapidly, expanded so quickly, and fallen so hard. That the Japanese were able to achieve such rapid, if temporary, success is evidence of their ambitions, communications, and trade rather than their resources. Most of the people live in the plains on the margins of the many islands. Coastwise shipping, therefore, connects the chief districts. By the same token, external communications are good. Given ships, it was easy for the Japanese to bring in raw materials from many lands and send out manufactured articles in exchange.

The coastwise movements of goods via the sea are greater than the foreign trade. All the ports, small and large, of which there are over 700, utilize steam, Diesel, and sailing vessels. By means of coastwise shipping coal, ores, steel, cotton, petroleum products, rice and other foods are distributed. The excellence of these shipping facilities takes some of the burden from the railroads and the highways, an important point in view of the mountainous nature of the country. Yet there is a fairly good network of railroads in Japan. The narrow gauge (three feet six inches) is well adapted to the terrain, which requires many tunnels and deep cuts. However, narrow gauge does mean small cars and light loads. Since most of the heavy goods move by coastal steamer, the railroads usually carry passengers and light freight. Furthermore, the limited mileage of good highways and the scarcity of passenger automobiles mean that people must travel more by rail.

The railways reach all the important cities and towns both on the coast and in the inland valleys. A main line double-track railway connects Tokyo to the northern part of Kyushu, passing through all the chief manufacturing centers. Other lines follow the coastal margins of the large islands. Many transverse lines find their way through the mountainous interior to reach the north and south coast of Honshu, and short spurs lead to more isolated valleys which contain mineral deposits. Railroad-car ferries connect the islands, making it unnecessary to break bulk.

Foreign trade means more to the Japanese than to the producers in many countries because of the dense population and limited resources. In the last few decades Japanese have been large importers of raw materials and exporters of finished goods. Japan has been the only important industrial country in eastern Asia. In reaching this unique position the Japanese found it necessary to build up a large merchant marine which sailed all the seas but was most active in the Pacific. Most of this shipping was destroyed in World War II, and the process of rebuilding is slow.

The foreign trade of Japan has been exceedingly variable in the last decades as the Japanese prepared for war, waged war, and went down to defeat. The variability is in the relative amounts rather than in the nature of the imports and exports. The chief imports have been and will continue to be for some years raw cotton, wool, petroleum, oilseeds, sugar, rubber, ores, metals, and machinery. The exports are raw silk, cotton textiles, clothing, light metal goods, chemicals, fish products, and certain kinds of machinery. Most of the trade is with China, the United States, India, and the East Indies.

In the postwar world the Japanese face a very different situation with respect to world trade. Some of their best customers have become or are becoming industrialized and are not likely to furnish the huge markets for cheap cotton textiles in the future. Metal industries in Japan, although flourishing under the stimulus of inflation and war, were never in a position to compete in a free world market. It should be noted, however, that there still is in Japan a large labor force, skilled and cheap, located in a compact country which seems to move and work with considerable unanimity toward its immediate goals.

31

The Metallic Minerals

BRIEF references have been made to mineral production in the preceding chapters in the belief that the geographic significance of world production can scarcely be grasped by the study of isolated commodities. In order to understand the "Maize Triangle" of South Africa, for example, it is necessary to know something about the Rand gold mining district. A study of the United States Cotton Belt would be incomplete without mention of the production of oil, coal, bauxite, phosphate, and sulfur. On the other hand, an appreciation of the value of fertilizer minerals is dependent on some knowledge of agriculture.

Mineral production is important enough, however, to deserve additional discussion. The useful minerals form the very core of our modern industrial economy, and some of them are much more significant than their monetary value suggests. For many minerals there is no satisfactory substitute. Who can suggest a replacement for iron, mercury, tin, or uranium? Furthermore, the production of minerals is of critical interest because the supply is not renewable. The products of the seas, forests, grasslands, and farms with proper management flow on indefinitely, but mining is a "robber economy." This term is used not in disparagement of miners but merely to emphasize the fact that every ounce of mineral removed from the earth's crust leaves that much less to be mined. In some instances this is not critical; common salt is so abundant that we cannot conceive that the supply will ever be exhausted. On the other hand, the United States is producing and consuming about eight per cent of its known reserves of petroleum every year. Even allowing for new discoveries, it would be foolhardy to state

that our petroleum resources are inexhaustible. In varying degrees the same statement holds for iron, sulfur, chrome, manganese, mercury, aluminum, and many others.

As a nation expands its industrial economy, the demand for minerals increases far more rapidly than the population. In the first half of the 20th century the population of the United States doubled, agricultural production increased two and one fourth times, coal two and one half times (coal production has declined in recent years because of increased petroleum and hydroelectric production), copper three times, iron ore three and one half times, zinc four times, crude oil thirty times, and natural gas twenty-six times. The *per capita* consumption of minerals increased three-fold in the period 1900–1950. In the words of A Report to the President, "*Resources For Freedom,*" by the President's Materials Policy Commission, William S. Paley, Chairman, Vol. 1, 1952, p. 5, "This mounting strain upon resources that cannot be replaced has become the most challenging aspect of our present-day economy." See FIGURE 31.1.

It is not possible to discuss the production of all the useful minerals in a few brief chapters. The *Minerals Yearbook*, revised annually and published by the U. S. Bureau of Mines, gives more than 1600 pages of detailed information, a part of which is devoted to production outside the United States. This volume is indispensable to the student of mineral production. *Mineral Resources of the World*, an atlas prepared by the Department of Geography, University of Maryland (1952), limits its treatment largely to 29 minerals. In this and following chapters discussion will be limited to the minerals indicated in the outline below.

1. THE METALLIC MINERALS

    Iron and the Ferroalloys

Iron	Cobalt
Manganese	Tungsten
Chromium	Molybdenum
Nickel	Vanadium

  Nonferrous Metals

Aluminum	(Minor Metals)
Magnesium	Mercury
Copper	Gold
Lead	Silver
Zinc	Platinum
Tin	Uranium

2. THE NONMETALLIC MINERALS (excluding fuels)

3. THE MINERAL FUELS

IRON AND THE FERROALLOYS

IRON is the basic material of the industrial economy of the world. It enters into manufacturing of all kinds, into mining, transportation, building construction, the equipment for commerce. It is important in the tools and machinery for agriculture; in household appliances, automobiles, and food containers of all kinds. Iron is the second most abundant of the metals, constituting nearly five per cent of the material in the earth's crust, but it is present in high concentrations in only a few places. Nevertheless there is no prospect of an immediate shortage of iron ore in the world. Iron is not only a very useful element but one of the cheapest and, therefore, the per capita con-

sumption in the world is high. In the United States more than 1200 pounds of iron are consumed per capita per year. This includes iron and steel, since most iron these days is processed to some form of steel. Even nails and wire are made from a mild form of steel.

Although iron ore production has been mentioned frequently in previous chapters, it will be worthwhile to review the distribution of production and also the distribution of reserves. The graph shown in FIGURE 31.2 indicates that the greatest production of iron ore is in the United States, France, the Soviet Union, the United Kingdom, and Sweden. Other countries produce smaller amounts to make up a world total of around 200 million tons of ore per year. Production varies according to the demand for iron and steel. In wartime, because of the great use of iron and steel in munitions, production expands. In times of depression when the demand is light, ore production goes down. In some cases production has declined because of the exhaustion or near exhaustion of the reserves of iron ore.

Deposits of iron ore are found on every continent and within the borders of almost every country but not always in high-quality deposits. Since as time goes on poorer and poorer deposits are being worked, it can be assumed that at the present rate of production there is enough medium-grade iron ore to last for many centuries to come.

The mining of iron ore depends not only on the richness of the deposits but on their accessibility

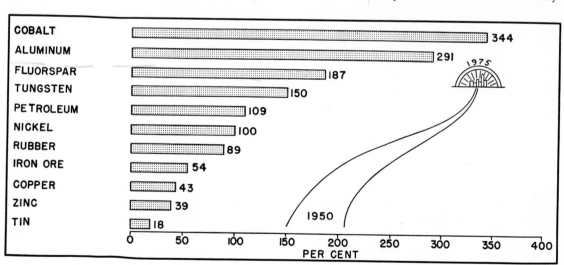

FIGURE 31.1. *Graph of the estimated increasing need for minerals by 1975. From Resources for Freedom.*

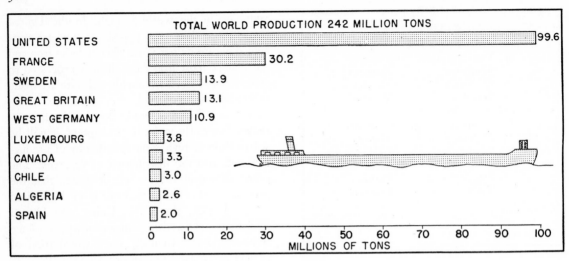

FIGURE 31.2. *Graph of iron ore production in leading countries.*

and nearness to coal and other materials which enter into the iron and steel making process, as well as on the accessibility to markets. In order to make a ton of iron it is necessary to provide the following raw materials: one and three quarters tons of iron ore, about one ton of coke which is usually made from high-quality bituminous coal, and about one half ton of limestone, which acts as a flux in the ironmaking process and removes some of the foreign material. In the whole process of making steel from iron ore a greater tonnage and bulk of coal is needed than of high-grade iron ore. As a general rule, therefore, the iron ore moves to the coal, and only under some exceptional circumstances does the coal move to the iron ore. Some of these exceptions will be noted in the paragraphs to follow.

The most valuable iron ore deposits are those which are near water transportation and also comparatively near coking coal. However, if water transportation is readily available close to the iron mines, as it is in Chile, the iron ore can be sent long distances by ocean freighter at low cost.

Most of the iron deposits of the world that are currently in production are near the surface and can be readily mined either by open pit methods or by shallow shafts or tunnels. In the Lake Superior region of the United States both the open pit method (Fig. 31.3) and the shaft method are used. On the northern fringe the Mesabi ores were shallow and could be scooped up with shovels after removing an overburden of glacial drift. As the miners worked farther south, the ore was deeper, and it soon became more profitable to sink a shaft from the surface to the ore bed than to remove the overburden. If the iron ore is of especially high grade, it is worthwhile to sink deep shafts to the ore body, as is done in the mines of Michigan and in various other parts of the world. Generally speaking, the mining operation starts with open pit or surface mining and gradually develops into shaft or tunnel mining.

One of the problems which arises with the partial exhaustion of high-grade ores is the beneficiation (concentration) of low-grade deposits, a process employed more and more in the various iron mining regions of the world. The ore to be concentrated is usually crushed and then the richer ore is extracted by magnetic, flotation, or other methods.

Very large deposits of high-grade iron ores exist in parts of the world which are not now accessible to modern transportation. These deposits offer a reserve for the future when it may be necessary to build railroads and other equipment to carry out the ore. An example of what may happen to some of these remote areas of iron ore occurrence is shown by the situation in eastern Quebec and Labrador. This large deposit of high-grade ore is roughly 300 miles from tidewater and although its occurrence has been known for some time, production is just getting under way. The development of the Labrador ores encouraged renewed efforts on the part of the Canadian government and others to improve the St. Lawrence Seaway.

MANGANESE, the "starch of steel," is in many respects the most important of the strategic minerals because it is so essential in the manufacture of high-quality steels and is needed in such large quantities. Having by no means as many uses as nickel, manganese is even more vital to a modern industrial economy since there is no satisfactory substitute. Manganese is used in the blast furnaces along with iron ore, coke, and limestone. There a low grade of manganese ore will serve satisfactorily. The chief use of manganese, however, is in the converters where iron is changed to steel. In this process a higher-grade ore is needed to deoxidize and desulfurize the steel. Only a slight amount of the manganese enters into this reaction, but about 14 pounds of manganese is consumed for every ton of steel produced. Small quantities of manganese are required for the manufacture of storage batteries, paints, glass, and china.

In 1950 the United States steel industry consumed nearly two million tons of manganese ore of metallurgical grade. Unfortunately very small quantities of high-grade manganese ore occur in the United States. It is necessary therefore either to import manganese or to work very low-grade deposits in this country. The largest deposits, all low grade, in the United States occur in Maine, Montana, Nevada, South Dakota, and Arkansas. Some of the deposits, especially those of Minnesota, are in iron ore. Except in emergencies, however, the deposits in the United States are not generally worked. In the world production of 1950 the outstanding countries were the U.S.S.R. with about 32 per cent of world production, followed by the Union of South Africa, the Gold Coast, Morocco, and Brazil. This applies only to fairly high-grade ores of manganese. A few decades ago the United States obtained most of its manganese from India. Before World War II the shift was to Russia, but after the war Russia exported very little. It was necessary for the United States to find other sources.

CHROMIUM, the common ore of which is chromite, is one of the important alloys of steel. It is used in armor plate, also in stainless steels, and in high-speed tool steels of various kinds. In the stainless steels rather large quantities of chromium are needed to make the best quality. Since domestic supplies of chromite are rather meager, it is nec-

FIGURE 31.3. *Open pit iron mine at Hibbing, Minnesota, on the Mesabi Range. From Great Northern Railway.*

essary to offer a government subsidy for its production and, in addition, to import chromium from foreign countries in order to satisfy the demand. The principal local deposits are in Montana, Oregon, and northern California. Most of these deposits are being worked at the present time, but the total production in the country can satisfy only about ten per cent of the needs.

The largest producers of chromium are the U.S.S.R., Turkey, the Union of South Africa, southern Rhodesia, the Philippines, Cuba, and New Caledonia. In Turkey there are large reserves in many mines and deposits which are at present inactive. Production could be increased if necessary, but rail transportation in the vicinity of the mines is inadequate. In the Union of South Africa reserves are substantial, but again transportation facilities are not satisfactory. In southern Rhodesia the deposit of metallurgical-grade chromite is large. Difficulties in power and transportation somewhat limit production, but these deposits are being developed very rapidly. New Caledonia in the South Pacific usually ranks high as a producer of chromite, but the high-grade ores were largely exhausted during World War II so that concentration of low-grade ores is now necessary. Deposits of chromite occur also in Cuba, Sierra Leone in western Africa, South Korea, India, Yugoslavia, and Brazil.

NICKEL comes mostly from Canada, a few miles to the west and north of the town of Sudbury in southern Ontario. In this district about 40 mines account for about five sixths of the world production. Other deposits are widely scattered throughout Burma, New Caledonia, Greece, Norway, and Russia. Nickel has long been known as an alloy metal of considerable utility since it was first discovered in meteorites. Nickel was mined first in Germany as an unwelcome ingredient of copper and silver ores. Its name was derived from *kupfernickel* (copper demon). Today the uses of this strategic metal are too varied even to catalog in a brief statement. Most of it is put into steel in percentages from 2 to 35 per cent. The low-nickel steels (up to 7 per cent), tough and ductile, have a variety of uses in automobiles, railway equipment, and in machinery in general. The high-nickel steels are heat resistant and corrosion resistant (stainless). Nickel-silver, nickel-bronze, and nickel-copper alloys also have a variety of uses.

In wartime large quantities of nickel are essential for armor plate as well as for armor-piercing shells. It is widely used for plating, in electroplating, in storage batteries, and in the white alloys such as white gold. It gives the characteristic color to the five-cent piece, although this coin is largely copper. Since nickel and copper often occur in the same ore, "natural" alloys of these metals can be easily produced.

COBALT is a strategic alloy metal because of its toughness at high temperatures. Cobalt is used in magnets of loudspeakers, high-speed tools, and as a pigment. It is mined in the Belgian Congo, northern Rhodesia, French Morocco, and Canada. Total world production is about 6000 tons, of which the United States consumes about three fourths.

TUNGSTEN occurs in several mineral forms, such as scheelite, which is a calcium tungstate, and wolframite, which is an iron manganese tungstate. Tungsten gives a steel alloy which is used in making cutting tools that stand high speeds and high temperatures and still keep their edges. Tungsten is also used widely in the elements of incandescent lights and in radio tubes. A compound, tungsten carbide, is the second hardest cutting agent. The largest producer of tungsten is China, which accounts for about one fourth of the world's production. China is followed by the United States with about 13 per cent and by other countries, such as Bolivia, Brazil, Portugal, Burma, Japan, Argentina, and Korea, which produce substantial amounts. The United States does not produce sufficient tungsten for local demand; so some must be imported, usually to the amount of one third to one half of the needs. Since most of the good deposits of tungsten are overseas, the problem of a good supply in wartime is a serious one.

MOLYBDENUM was first isolated as a metal in 1782, but did not reach commercial importance until 1927. It is used almost entirely as an alloy of iron and steel, where it acts like tungsten. Molybdenum increases the strength and ductility of both steel and cast iron, and only small quantities are needed. Molybdenum steels are used in automobiles, aircraft, high-speed tools, and armor plate. Molybdenum compounds are used also in dyes, inks, and in commercial fertilizers, where small amounts bring about great increases in crop yields. World production of molybdenum has averaged about 12,000 tons in recent years, about

85 per cent of which comes from Colorado, Utah, and New Mexico. The chief ore, molybdenite (MoS_2), is found also in Chile, Mexico, Canada, Norway, and Peru, often as a mixture in the copper ores.

VANADIUM is a hard, brittle metal, which is used widely in steel alloys. It is used in a variety of special steels, particularly in automobile parts, locomotive axles, gears, pistons, gun barrels, and other items, especially those which need a high resistance to torque. Vanadium oxide is also used as a catalyst, in inks and paints, and in glass and ceramic glazes. Vanadium is rather scarce and is produced in quantities in the United States, Peru, northern Rhodesia, and Southwest Africa. Total world production in recent years has ranged from 1400 to 4400 metric tons. Colorado, Utah, Nevada, and New Mexico account for most of the United States production.

THE NONFERROUS METALS

ALUMINUM is the most abundant common metal in the earth's crust. But, unfortunately, the concentrations of high-grade deposits are rare, even more rare than in the case of iron. Aluminum does not occur as the native metal, but is tied up in complex compounds in forms very difficult to extract. This accounts for the rather recent development of aluminum on a commercial basis. Several ores contain aluminum in greater or lesser concentrations. One of these is corundum, which is a native alumina. Because of its hardness and its value as an abrasive, corundum is not used as a source of aluminum metal. Cryolite is another possible source of aluminum which has been mined on a large scale on the west coast of Greenland. Kaolin, or China clay, is a possible ore of aluminum, but kaolin is ruled out in terms of present production because of its low aluminum content and high silica content. The most important commercial ore for aluminum is bauxite, named after the town of Le Baux in southern France where it was first processed. Bauxite occurs in various degrees of purity and is used not only as a source of aluminum metal but as an abrasive and for other purposes. Bauxite is found in tropical climates or in regions that had tropical or subtropical climates at the time of its formation. The best and purest deposit in the United States is in central Arkansas. But numerous other deposits of somewhat lower aluminum content

are found in the southern states, particularly in Georgia and Alabama. The largest reserves in the western hemisphere are in British Guiana, Surinam, and Jamaica. Brazil and Haiti have somewhat lesser quantities. In Europe the greatest reserves are in Hungary and France, while Africa has large reserves in French West Africa, the Gold Coast, and Nyasaland. The reserves of the Soviet Union are not considered to be large, but it is presumed that the U.S.S.R. controls the large deposits in Hungary. China, the Netherlands Indies, and Australia also have reserves of bauxite, and it is probable that exploration will reveal other large deposits in the tropical and subtropical countries.

Once the extraction of aluminum was developed to the point where the costs were not prohibitive, the uses of aluminum expanded. The first large-scale use was for cooking utensils where the conductivity of heat, the light weight, and the nontoxic character of the metal appealed to the consumers. Later aluminum came to be used in automobile and airplane parts and for various structural uses. The uses of aluminum multiplied when alloys were added making it stronger and tougher. Since the specific gravity is only 2.7 as compared with 7.8 for mild steel, the advantages on the side of lightness can readily be appreciated. But the heavier metals, also improved with new alloys, have given aluminum strong competition in nearly all fields.

The processing of bauxite into aluminum metal consists of several distinct steps. In the first place the ore as it comes from the mines is likely to include several impurities, including a considerable amount of clay and silica. If possible, these materials are removed at the mine and also the excessive water is driven off by heating. This saves on freight if the bauxite must be shipped for considerable distance. The next step is to convert the bauxite into alumina. One of these processes involves the digesting of the bauxite in solutions of caustic soda. The alumina comes out in the form of a fine powder which is essentially aluminum oxide. In order to produce aluminum metal electricity is needed in large quantities. The alumina is dissolved in a fused cryolite bath and is reduced electrolytically by the use of carbon electrodes. In order to produce a ton of aluminum, from four to six tons of bauxite are needed. This bauxite yields about two tons of alumina and finally about one ton of aluminum. Quantities of fuels, chemicals, and electricity are needed also in processing the aluminum. One process requires about ten kilowatt hours of electricity for each pound of aluminum, or about 20,000 kilowatt hours per short ton.

The production of aluminum is not clearly associated with the production of bauxite (FIG. 31.4). Usually the smelting and refining operations take place where there is abundant fuel and also abundant, cheap electrical energy. Aluminum production reached its peak during the closing years of World War II when the world produced nearly two million tons. A decline followed, but the production has increased in recent years. The largest production of aluminum, about one half million tons, is in the United States. Canada is second, followed by France, Germany, the United Kingdom, and the U.S.S.R.

In North America two great regions of aluminum production are to be noted. One is in northeastern United States and adjacent parts of Canada, which include the Niagara Falls area as well as the St. Lawrence River and its tributaries. Here hydroelectric energy is cheap. The other large area is in the Pacific Northwest in the states of Washington, Oregon, and the province of British Columbia. Here also hydroelectric energy is abundant and cheap, but in recent years the industries have expanded up to the available supply of hydroelectric energy. It is to be noted that alumina must be shipped long distances to reach either one of these large areas, and in the Pacific Northwest the finished material must be shipped again across the country to the big market in northeastern United States. Much of the Canadian pro-

duction finds its way into the United States, which does not produce enough for domestic needs. Outside of North America the chief producing countries of aluminum may be divided into three groups. The first group, to which the United States could be added, is the deficiency group which does not produce enough aluminum for its own purposes. This includes Germany, the United Kingdom, the Soviet Union, France, Italy, and Japan. The second group includes countries which produce a large surplus, such as Switzerland, Canada, and Norway. And the third group have approximately enough production to take care of their own needs but not a very large amount for export. This group includes Sweden, Hungary, Austria, Spain, Yugoslavia, Brazil, and India.

MAGNESIUM is even lighter than aluminum, having only two thirds the specific gravity. It has come to the fore as a light metal in recent years, particularly during World War II. It was first produced in 1830 but was not used commercially until 1886, when the process of production was greatly cheapened. Magnesium when properly alloyed has great structural strength and can be used for some of the same things as aluminum and of course has the value of lower specific gravity. Magnesium is also used in metallurgical processes as a deoxidizer, and in the form of milk of magnesia it has been known in the medicine cabinets of many homes for a long time.

Magnesium, which reached a production of 183,000 tons in the United States in 1943, declined sharply after the war. After slumping to about 5000 metric tons in 1946, production climbed to more than 100,000 tons. An automo-

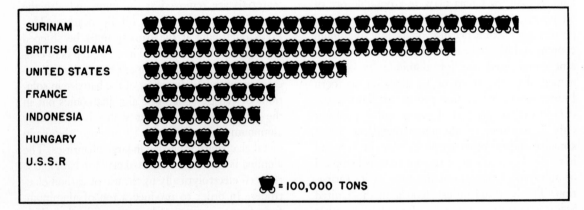

FIGURE 31.4. *Graph of bauxite production in leading countries.*

bile body made of magnesium weighs only 132 pounds while a steel body of the same size weighs about 650 pounds. The cost of magnesium compares favorably with aluminum, volume for volume.

COPPER is one of the oldest metals used by man. This is due perhaps to its occurrence in the form of free metal in nature and also to the ease with which it can be worked with primitive tools. In the pure form it is soft and malleable. It can be combined with tin to form bronze or with zinc to form brass. Furthermore, with pounding it becomes harder and will maintain a fair edge. But copper did not become an important metal in world production until the age of electricity, when it became the cheapest metal which would conduct electricity readily and easily. Another advantage of copper is its resistance to rust or corrosion. For this reason much of the copper used is recoverable so that the reserves are perhaps less important than in the case of other metals, such as iron, that tend to be lost by rusting.

Copper occurs in the native state and also in a variety of ores. These ores for the most part are the various oxides and sulfides of copper. It occurs also in the form of the carbonate and sulfate and in other compounds with iron and sulfur. In the United States ores containing considerable quantities of pure copper are found in the upper peninsula of Michigan. These were the first to be developed on a large scale, but for 75 years or more the principal source has been the various ores, especially the sulfides of copper, which occur in wide distribution. Since it is a rather easy matter to extract copper from the sulfides merely by roasting or applying heat, it is not necessary to have high-grade ores in order to have profitable extraction. It is worth noting that many of the ores of copper contain other metals, including silver and gold and sometimes lead and zinc.

The greatest reserves of copper ores are located in western United States, in Chile, and in central Africa. The greatest producing countries are the United States, Canada, northern Rhodesia, the Soviet Union, and Chile. In western Canada copper production is largely a by-product associated with more valuable minerals. Canada does not require very much copper; so the surplus is exported to the United States. Although the United States is the largest producer, the amount is not sufficient even for peacetime requirements; so Canada, Chile, and Africa supply most of the deficit. As time goes on, poorer and poorer deposits of copper are worked in the United States and higher prices and government subsidies offset the decreasing yield per ton. In Chile the production of copper is a great help in supporting the economy of that country since a tax of three or four cents a pound on all copper exported goes into the federal treasury. In the Belgian Congo and Rhodesia there is a large production of copper, a part of which comes to the United States. Belgium uses a portion of the Katanga copper production, processes it, and sells some of it to other European countries. It is significant that in recent years the relative scarcity of copper and the low-grade ores which are being worked have brought about an increase in price so that copper now sells for more than aluminum. This means that aluminum is being substituted for copper, especially in electrical devices where great conductivity or small wires are not necessary.

LEAD is one of the oldest metals known to man, perhaps because of the ease with which it can be separated from its ores. Lead was used many centuries ago for various common purposes, such as coins, lead pipe, and as a coating on pottery. In modern times the uses of lead are much more varied. The largest quantities go into storage batteries, into coverings of cables or electrical conductors, into leaded gasoline, and into the manufacture of pigments. Lead is also used very widely today as a shield to protect the workers in various processes associated with atomic research and production. Comparatively small amounts are used in ammunition.

Although the ores of lead are widely distributed, most of the production comes from four countries, the United States, Mexico, Australia, and Canada. In the United States production is greatest in southeastern Missouri, which for many years has produced more lead than any other state. Production is also fairly large in several other states, including Arizona, Colorado, Utah, and Idaho. Most of the lead comes from a comparatively few large mines. About two thirds of all the lead produced in the United States comes from 25 properties in the states mentioned above.

In Mexico lead comes from many mines scattered over the northern and central section of the country. In many places the lead ores are mixed in with ores of silver, zinc, copper, and other metals. Smelters are located at strategic points to convert the ores into pig lead. The pig lead is then shipped to a few refining points, such as San Luis Potosi and Monterrey. The cost of long shipments by rail of the crude lead is a serious handicap to production in Mexico, and only the content of silver, gold, and other metals makes the production of lead profitable in many mines.

In Australia the Broken Hill mining district in New South Wales is by far the largest producer of lead. The ores there are rich in lead and zinc, and they contain a fair amount of silver also. This district has good connections with ocean transportation in the vicinity of Adelaide, and large amounts of Australian lead are exported. Lead and zinc are also produced in northwest Queensland and in Tasmania. The last mentioned accounts for about four per cent of the Australian lead production. The ores there contain a large amount of zinc, some copper, silver, and also a little gold. Much of the lead produced in Australia is exported in the crude form to the United States for refining. In Canada the largest lead production is at Kimberley in British Columbia. Ore concentrates from this area are shipped to Trail, British Columbia, for smelting and refining. A number of other mines in British Columbia produce a quantity of lead, including those at Salmo, Hazelton, and Beaverdell.

ZINC has not been used by man as long as lead, perhaps because of the slightly greater difficulty of smelting. Although zinc is found in some of the metals and materials processed by man as early as 500 B. C., it is by no means certain that the metalworkers of those days recognized zinc as a separate metal. In smelting the ores of copper and working with them, undoubtedly some zinc was encountered and some of the zinc metal combined with the copper to form brass. Zinc was known, though, as a separate metal and refined as such as early as 1500 A. D. For many years the uses of zinc were rather restricted, but in modern times the metal is used extensively in industry. The greatest use by far is for galvanizing, that is, coating zinc on various shapes of steel and other metals. The coating of sheets or strips of mild steel with zinc produces a rustproof material. No rust will occur until all of the zinc is removed. Wire, tubes, pipe, and various fittings are also coated with zinc. A substantial although lesser amount of zinc is used in various products, including brass strips, rods, and castings. Zinc is also used as an alloy metal in certain dye castings, in wet batteries, and in some of the light metal alloys.

The pattern of the zinc production in the world follows closely that of lead. The United States is the largest producer. Other large producers include Canada, Mexico, the U.S.S.R., and Australia. The reason for the coincidence of production is that lead and zinc ores often occur together since the sulfides of lead and zinc are formed under similar conditions. In the United States the production by states is not quite like that of lead. Most zinc is produced, more or less in the order of production, in five areas, including the tri-state area of Kansas-Missouri-Oklahoma, the Tennessee-Virginia area, the Sussex County area of New Jersey, the St. Lawrence County area of New York, and in various western states, including Idaho, Arizona, Montana, Colorado, Utah, New Mexico, Nevada, and Washington. As in the case of lead the ores of zinc are smelted near the mines, and refining is done in a comparatively few localities.

TIN was also used early by primitive man because of the occurrence of the ore in a form which could be readily if not accidentally smelted in an ordinary campfire. The principal mineral from which tin is derived is cassiterite, SnO_2. If this ore is heated in the presence of charcoal, metallic tin will be liberated. Tin was used widely in the early days as an alloy for copper. Since the addition of tin hardened the copper and produced a superior metal known as bronze, the Romans were very eager to obtain it. The best known deposits in Europe were in Brittany and Cornwall. The campaign of Caesar in Gaul and the invasion of Britain by the Romans probably were due more to the desire to obtain tin than to any other single reason. In modern times only a small amount of tin is used in the making of bronze. The largest uses are in the manufacture of tinplate, terneplate, solder, and in the various alloys used in bearings, also in type metal. Most tinplate is used in the production of container cans for vegetables, fruits, meat, and so forth. A thin coating of tin added to the sheet of mild steel produces a container which is free from rust. There is no satisfactory substitute for tin in this respect. Containers made from aluminum are satisfactory but much more expensive.

Today most of the tin production of the world comes from southeastern Asia, especially from Malaya, Indonesia, and to a lesser extent from Thailand, Burma, and Indochina. Another area occurs in Bolivia with a very small production in the adjacent part of Argentina. The United States produces very little tin. Small quantities are produced in Canada and in Mexico. In Africa the largest producer is the Belgian Congo, followed by Nigeria. Australia produces a moderate amount of tin also. The scarcity of tin in North America poses a serious problem for the United States. Tin has long been considered a strategic material because so little is produced at home and because it is so necessary in our peacetime and wartime economy.

Much of the tin ore is smelted near the mines in Malaya, Indonesia, and Bolivia. The crude metal is then moved to refining centers. The most important refining center in the world is in southern Wales. People in this area started refining tin when the deposits of Cornwall across the bay were still in production. But the presence of coal and the know-how developed by the Welsh workers has enabled this region to continue as the leading refiner of tins. Refineries of tin have also been established in the United States in coastal areas of New Jersey and Texas. From some of the tin ore production areas concentrates are exported rather than metallic tin. This is especially true in Indonesia. The total world production of tin metal is generally not more than 150,000 tons. This is of course very small as compared with lead, zinc, and some of the other metals. The smelters are located mostly in the United States, the United Kingdom, Malaya, and Belgium.

MERCURY, sometimes called quicksilver, is the only metal which is in the liquid state at ordinary temperatures. Its first use by man was probably in the form of the principal ore, cinnabar, and the use was as a pigment in paint and in coloring. The mineral cinnabar has a bright red color. In modern times mercury is used very widely for medicinal purposes, in insecticides and fungicides for the spraying of agricultural products, in electrical control apparatus of various kinds, and as a catalyst. The most critical use of mercury perhaps is in the form of a fulminate, which is used as a detonator for all kinds of explosive ammunition and bombs. For this purpose there is no satisfactory substitute, and mercury becomes in

wartime a strategic material of great critical importance. The price of mercury, therefore, usually jumps in wartime and declines somewhat in peacetime. As a result, some of the marginal mines are operated intermittently. The common ore of mercury is cinnabar, the sulfide, and the mercury is rather readily recovered by heating the ore in furnaces and retorts. The mercury metal is separated from the sulfur; the sulfur comes off as sulfur dioxide and the mercury as a vapor which is easily condensed in the form of an impure metallic liquid. The liquid is purified by special treatment and is usually marketed in flasks of 76 pounds, each with a purity of 99 per cent or more of mercury. The largest producers of mercury include Spain, Italy, and the United States, with somewhat smaller amounts coming from Mexico, the U.S.S.R., China, and Japan. The largest output of ore has come from a single district in Spain, known as Almaden, in the province of Ciudad Real. This mine has been worked for more than 20 centuries and continues to produce considerable quantities of ore. The content of mercury is from six to eight per cent, but ores of lower percentage can be worked profitably. The largest mercury mines in Italy are in the Monte Amiata district, which is 75 miles north of Rome. Both Spain and Italy produce considerable quantities of mercury for export.

In the United States most of the mercury comes from California, Nevada, Oregon, and Alaska. California is by far the largest producer and in most years produces more than half of the United States output. The principal mines are in Sonoma, Fresno, Napa, San Benito, San Luis Obispo, and Santa Clara counties. In both California and Oregon there are many marginal mines which can operate at a profit only when the price of mercury is fairly high. In other words, the United States has fairly large reserves of low-grade mercury ores.

GOLD is not an abundant metal, but it occurs often in the metallic form and because of its bright color received early attention. It was also usable by primitive man because of its malleability. It could be hammered and shaped readily without the use of heat or any special methods. In modern times the largest use of gold is for monetary purposes. Very few gold coins are produced, but gold bullion is used as a guarantee of paper currency in various countries. The largest stocks by

FIGURE 31.5. *A gold mine in the Rand district of South Africa. Notice the shaft house, the small mine cars, and the heaps of waste material in the background. From Information Office, Union of South Africa.*

far are held by the United States. Gold is also used in some quantities for jewelry, for dental purposes, in photography, and to a very slight extent in medicine. The largest producers of gold are the Union of South Africa (FIG. 31.5), the U.S.S.R., Canada, and the United States. But many other countries produce small quantities of gold that serve to stabilize their currency and bring them considerable income. By far the most important producer of gold is the Rand District of South Africa in and near Johannesburg. This district has produced more gold than any other region and also accounts for the greatest annual production. The Union as a whole usually produces about 12 million fine ounces of gold a year, and the nearest competitor, the U.S.S.R., probably produces not much more than four million fine ounces. Gold is produced both from placer deposits, that is, sands and gravels, and also from lode deposits in which the metal occurs in bed-

rock. Placer mining, which involves washing in various ways, is the simplest method. The most primitive method is to pan the gold by shaking a pan which contains sand or gravel with a small amount of water so that the heavy gold particles will settle to the bottom. Refinements of this method use several devices, and some of them, such as dredge mining, are able to handle large quantities of sand and gravel which contain only small proportions of gold. Gravels which contain only 25 cents' worth of gold per ton can sometimes be successfully worked. In lode mining the gold occurs in bedrock, sometimes rather hard rock, such as quartzite. The rock must be crushed and the ore concentrated before the separation method advances very far. Some ores contain so little gold that it is scarcely worthwhile to mine them at ordinary prices. Thus the mining fluctuates a good deal with the price of gold. If the price goes up, marginal mines can come into production.

Since there has been no great scarcity in gold in the United States in recent years, encouragement for mining has not been great, and gold mining companies sometimes have difficulty in obtaining priorities for mining machinery.

SILVER was also used as a monetary standard and unit in some countries and has been in the past widely used in the production of coins. Silver occurs as a free metal in some mines, but its widest occurrence is in the form of a sulfide. In this form the largest production of ore is from Mexico, the United States, Canada, Peru, Australia, and Japan. Various other countries, such as the U.S.S.R., Germany, and Bolivia, produce moderate quantities of silver. In addition to the uses for money, silver is used in the manufacture of silverware, jewelry, watchcases, pens, pencils, and a great many other similar articles in the luxury class. Photography also accounts for a considerable amount of silver, since silver salts are used in the emulsion of many kinds of films. In the United States the greatest production is in Idaho, Montana, Utah, and Arizona, but small amounts of silver are produced in many other states. Silver often occurs in the ores which are mined principally for other metals, especially lead and zinc.

PLATINUM and five similar minor metals, palladium, iridium, osmium, rhodium, and ruthenium are found together in the Sudbury district of Canada, in the Ural Mountains of Russia, in the Transvaal of South Africa, in Colombia, and in Alaska. These metals are heavy, chemically resistant, scarce, and expensive. The world production is approximately 600,000 troy ounces, ranging in price from $50 to $125 per ounce. The platinum metals are used in jewelry, electrical devices, laboratory apparatus, and as catalysts. Platinum catalysts are used in many processes, including the production of high-octane gasolines.

URANIUM, RADIUM, AND THORIUM are perhaps the most important metals in the world today because of their relation to atomic fission, the production of the atomic bomb, as well as many other uses. These metals have been known for a long time and used in small quantities for medicinal and experimental purposes. Since the principal use for uranium and associated metals in recent years has been in the production of atomic weapons, details of production and refinement have not generally been made public. It is known, however,

that industrial uses are possible and some progress has been made in this connection.

Uranium became a strategic mineral only with the discovery of atomic fission and the development of the atomic bomb. As late as 1940 uranium ores, the most common of which are pitchblende and carnotite, were of interest chiefly as a source of radium, which is used in very small quantities in medicine, as luminous materials, and in research. At that time only two production areas were of much significance, the Katanga district of the Belgian Congo and the eastern shore of Great Bear Lake in Canada. The demand for radium was so limited that operations in the Canadian district were stopped in June, 1940. Then came the development of atomic energy. The mining of uranium and the search for new deposits entered a phase of feverish activity the world over. At Great Bear Lake, mine openings, including both shafts and drift tunnels, were begun, and the uranium ore was moved southward by lake and river as well as by plane. There is also a deposit of uranium about ten miles north of Elizabethville in the Belgian Congo. Reports are also made of uranium in the Union of South Africa, particularly in the Orange Free State. Uranium production in Australia occurs about 300 miles north of Adelaide, about 70 miles west of the lead and zinc mines at Broken Hill. In Europe deposits of uranium are worked in the Erzgebirge region, in the eastern zone of Germany. This belt continues over into Czechoslovakia, which has long been a small producer. All of the production from eastern Germany and Czechoslovakia is controlled by the U.S.S.R. The largest production of uranium in North America occurs in the vicinity of Great Bear Lake, Canada. (See FIG. 31.6.) This production probably accounted in large part for the first atomic bombs produced in the United States. A number of other deposits in Canada show considerable promise. In the United States uranium does occur in very low-grade deposits in various parts of the country. Some of these are being worked at the present time. Every encouragement is given for the discovery of new deposits. Although the production and discovery of uranium ores are top-drawer secrets, it is a matter of general knowledge that a few domestic deposits exist, notably in western Colorado and eastern Utah, but presumably these ores are rather low grade. It is reported that there are some rather

FIGURE 31.6. *Eldorado Mine, Port Radium, on Great Bear Lake, the mine that shook the world. The pitchblende from which the uranium was extracted to make the first atomic bomb came from this mine. Part of the ore was flown out, and a part was moved out by water via Great Bear Lake, the Mackenzie River, Slave, and Athabaska rivers to the railroad. From National Film Board of Canada.*

good deposits in the Urals in Russia, and new discoveries are reported from Sinkiang north of Tibet in China. Other deposits of uranium or thorium, a somewhat similar radioactive element, are reported from India, Ceylon, Indonesia, Australia, New Zealand, Tanganyika, Madagascar, Argentina, Chile, Brazil, and Cornwall, England. In short, uranium is widely distributed, but it is doubtful if many of these deposits can furnish much uranium on account of the very low quality of the ores. Radium is a radioactive metal usually found in small quantities in uranium ores. It is used in the treatment of cancer and in luminous paint.

OTHER MINOR METALS are of strategic importance to us in the United States. Antimony is used as an alloy of lead in type metal and bearings, in pewter, as compounds in paint pigments, and in medicines such as tartar emetic. Antimony is produced in south China, Mexico, Bolivia, and various other countries. Western United States accounts for a small portion of our domestic requirements. A small proportion of beryllium increases the tensile strength of copper. Most of the imports of beryllium come from Argentina, Brazil, Canada, and South Africa.

Titanium compounds have a high degree of opacity and hiding power and are, therefore, valuable in the paint industries, also in the manufacture of paper, cosmetics, and textiles. The largest production is in India, Malaya, and Norway, while small amounts are obtained from Virginia, the Carolinas, Arkansas, and California.

32

The Nonmetallic Minerals
Excepting Fuels

THE nonmetallic minerals occur more widely and in greater variety than the metals and their ores. Many of them, such as sand and gravel, have very low values per unit weight and can be exploited only in the vicinity of a good market. On the other hand, the nonmetallics usually require little processing before they can be used, and the gross value is greater than that of the metallic minerals (FIG. 32.1).

Because of the great variety, the nonmetallic minerals are not easy to classify. A simple "use" classification is given below, but it will be noted that several minerals belong in more than one category. Sand, for example, is used as an abrasive, as a building material, and as an industrial material.

NONMETALLIC MINERALS

1. Abrasives
2. Building Materials
3. Ceramic Materials
4. Chemical Materials
5. Fertilizer Materials
6. Industrial Materials
7. Gemstones

ABRASIVES

Abrasives include many kinds of minerals and rocks which are hard enough to be employed in cutting and grinding and also some softer materials which are used in scouring and polishing. Some abrasives can be used in the natural state while others must be crushed and bonded. Most abrasives can be described in three classes: high grade,

including the diamond, corundum, emery, and garnet; siliceous, including sand, quartz, pumice, and many others; and miscellaneous, such as bauxite, chalk, clay, talc, and lampblack. The automobile industry is one of the largest consumers of abrasives.

DIAMONDS, in the form of carbonado or bort, are widely used in cutting and drilling in spite of the high cost. Most of the carbonados (black diamonds) come from Bahia, Brazil, and are used in drill bits exploring for oil or ores, also for various types of industrial drilling. Bort, which consists of fragments of small stones, is cheaper than carbonado and is more widely used. Most bort comes from the Kasai River district of the Belgian Congo and Angola. Bort is often ground to a fine powder and bonded with molten metal in the manufacture of grinding wheels. It is used also in cutting gemstones. The United States consumes about 12 million carats of industrial diamonds per year, about three fourths of the world production. The average value is about $3 per carat, very low as compared to gemstones but high as compared with other abrasive materials. Since the bulk of industrial diamonds comes from Africa, it is easy for a cartel to control the price and output from year to year. Reserves are large but unfortunately for the United States, rather remote, and industrial diamonds have a high priority on the list of strategic materials.

CORUNDUM includes two gemstones, ruby and sapphire, and emery, which is a mixture of corundum and magnetite. Corundum has a hardness of nine compared with ten for the diamond. The abrasive

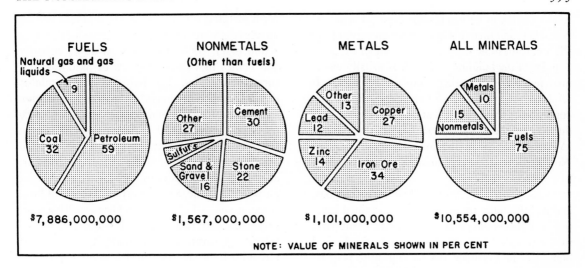

FIGURE 32.1. *Value of mineral production in the United States, by mineral groups in millions of dollars, and by minerals in per cent.*

grades of corundum and emery are used widely in optical grinding, as paper and cloth abrasives, and in abrasive wheels. Most of the commercial deposits of corundum are found in Canada, South Africa, the United States, India, and Madagascar. Ontario in Canada and North Carolina and Georgia are the nearest sources. Emery comes largely from Greece and Turkey, also from New York, Massachusetts, and Virginia.

GARNET occurs in a number of varieties in addition to the gemstone, in New York, New Hampshire, North Carolina, Idaho, Spain, and India. It is used widely as garnet cloth or paper, which is far superior to sandpaper. Garnet powder is used in surfacing plate glass and in sawing building stone.

NATURAL SILICA ABRASIVES include sand, quartz, diatomite, tripoli, pumice, and a variety of sharpening stones. Abrasive sand must be sharp, angular, and clean, and uniform in grain. Three tons of sand are used in grinding one ton of plate glass, and large quantities of ground sand are used in household cleaning powders. Good quality sand is produced in New Jersey, Illinois, and Ohio. Diatomite, used in silver and automobile polishes, in dental powders, and in match heads, comes largely from California, Washington, and Oregon. Tripoli is used for buffing metals and in cleaning and scouring powders. The largest deposits are in Missouri, Oklahoma, Tennessee, and Illinois. Pumice is used in rubbing down furniture finishes, in polishing tools, and in rubber erasers. Large amounts are produced in Califor-

nia, Kansas, New Mexico, Oklahoma, and Oregon.

SOFT ABRASIVES, used largely in polishing, include chalk, clay, lime, lampblack, red, green, and black rouge, and talc, among many others. Most of these materials are abundant. They are selected for their special qualities to give high polish to a variety of materials from ore sections to stainless steel and from rice grains to leather.

BUILDING MATERIALS

A great variety of mineral materials are produced for building and construction purposes. These materials range from building stone, which is quarried into blocks and used directly in construction, through crushed stone, sand, gravel, cement, gypsum, lime, and magnesite. Asphalt, clay, heat and sound insulating materials, such as mineral wool, and various other mineral products, are also used in construction. The chief building stones that are used directly in construction are limestone, sandstone, granite, and marble. A few other kinds of stones are used in special localities and for specific purposes. For example, gneiss is often used for cornerstones and for the groundfloor facing of buildings. The utility of a building stone depends upon several qualities. First of all, perhaps, is the ease of working. Some stones which are hard and resistant are so difficult and expensive to work that their use for ordinary construction is not feasible. Some stone which appears hard in its original state tends to check or split on exposure to air. On the other hand, some types of stone are soft when first quarried but harden on exposure to the air. Limestone is by and large one of the most popular of the building stones. It is usually easily quarried and easy to shape into various forms. It tends to stand up well under ordinary atmospheric conditions. The principal area of limestone production in the United States is in the Middle West, especially in Indiana, where the famous New Bedford stone accounts for a very large part of the production.

BUILDING STONE includes sedimentary, igneous, and metamorphic rocks. Granite, a grained igneous rock, occurs in great variety in different parts of the world. The largest quarries in the United States are in Vermont, but some granite is quarried in a number of other states including Georgia (FIG. 32.2), Wisconsin, and Minnesota. Granite has a varied texture and color and is greatly desired as a building stone and also for monumental purposes. But it is very difficult to work and consequently the amount used is rather limited. Basalt, a heavy, dense, igneous rock, is often crushed to

form material for road surfaces, and also used as an aggregate in concrete structures. Sandstone, a sedimentary rock, has very wide distribution and comes in various degrees of hardness, textures, and colors. The hardness and durability depend upon the cementing material, and some sandstones do not stand up very well when exposed to the weather. The most important centers for sandstone quarrying are in Ohio and the adjacent states. Some of the stones quarried are also used for grindstones and for other abrasive purposes. Marble, a metamorphosed form of limestone, is somewhat harder and has usually a more variegated pattern and color. It is quarried in considerable quantities in Vermont, Tennessee, and Georgia. It occurs also in a few other states in good qualities. Marble is often used for interiors, such as floors and stairways, and also to some extent for monuments in cemeteries. It does tend to weather slowly on exposure to air.

Large quantities of stone, not particularly suitable for building blocks, are crushed to form aggregate for cement, for the covering of roofs,

FIGURE 32.2. *A granite quarry in Georgia. The numerous drill markings reflect the high cost of working this hard rock. From Bureau of Mines.*

FIGURE 32.3. *A caterpillar-mounted mobile electrical loading machine loading broken limestone into a Diesel-powered haulage truck in the deep limestone mine in Barberton, Ohio. From Bureau of Mines.*

and for other purposes. The kind of rock crushed depends upon the local supply. The value per ton is usually so low that it is not profitable to ship crushed stone long distances. Usually the harder stones are crushed for aggregate when natural sands and gravel of good quality are not available in the vicinity.

One of the most important kinds of building materials, in terms of tonnage production at least, is the sand and gravel deposits. Sand and gravel are rather widespread but not always good quality. In order to make good concrete it is desirable to have hard grains of sand which are angular rather than rounded. In the glaciated regions there are abundant deposits of such sands and comparable gravels. But in the nonglaciated regions it is sometimes difficult and expensive to get high quality natural gravels and sand. Usually the sand and gravel are either obtained from glacial deposits, especially outwash plains, or they are dredged up from the bottoms of rivers. The total value of the sand and gravel produced in the United States is very great.

CEMENT, of some sort, has been made for many centuries by using sand or volcanic ash, mixed with lime or other material. Today the most important cement is Portland cement, which is prepared by heating or calcining a finely ground mixture of limestone and shale (FIG. 32.3). The raw materials vary from place to place. In some places limestone contains enough shale or clay so that it can be used directly without other mixtures. In other places the lime is ground with a mixture of clay or marl. In still other places blast furnace clay is used together with limestone to make the cement. In any case, the material is ground finely and heated to drive off all excess water. Then if water is added together with an aggregate or filler, such as sand and gravel, the whole mass hardens into a monolith. Because of its cheapness and its flexibility, cement has become one of the most important building materials of all. Since cement is heavy in proportion to its value, the plants for its manufacture are widely distributed wherever suitable materials are available. Usually, however, the greatest production is in areas of greatest industrialization, as in northeastern United States and in various parts of western Europe. The processes of manufacture vary somewhat according to the raw materials and according to the desired quality, but in general the raw materials include lime and silica, in the form of shale. Some alumina and a small amount of gypsum or anhydrite are added to slow up the setting process. If a waterproof cement is desired, additional ingredients enter into the operation. The raw materials are then ground together fine enough so that the powder will pass through a 40,000th-inch screen. This powder is dumped into a rotary kiln where it is heated to 3000 degrees Fahrenheit. This fuses the powder, after which a second grinding produces pellets the size of marbles, and finally a powder about the consistency of fine flour. There are about 150 Portland cement plants operating in the United States. The United States is the largest producer. By far the greatest production comes from eastern and western Pennsylvania, California, Maryland, New York, Ohio, Michigan, and the Indiana-Kentucky-Wisconsin area. But substantial quantities are produced in other states, especially Texas. California is usually second in production after Pennsylvania. The total production of cement in the United States is about 36 million tons. Other countries that produce substantial quantities include France, Germany, the U.S.S.R., the United Kingdom, and Japan. In Africa the only large producer is the Union of South Africa.

ASPHALT is used very widely as a building material and is especially important in the paving of roads and in waterproofing of concrete in building construction. There are two principal sources of asphalt, one from natural lakes, especially in Trinidad and Venezuela. The other very important source is as a residue from petroleum refining. Petroleum asphalt is used very widely in the United States since we have very little natural asphalt.

CERAMIC MATERIALS

The ceramic materials include various clays, feldspar, bauxite, borax, magnesite, sillimanite, and others. Clay is the chief ingredient of various products from common brick and tile to the most delicate china and vitreous ware. Clay is also used as a building material, as an ingredient of Portland cement, as a filler for paper, in insecticides, and for various other purposes.

China clay (kaolin) comes mostly from Georgia and South Carolina and is used in the manufacture of whiteware and paper. Ball clay is produced in Kentucky and Tennessee and is an ingredient of whiteware, high-grade tile, and enamel. Fire clay is produced in various central states, especially Ohio, Pennsylvania, Missouri, and Kentucky. The chief use is for firebrick (heat resisting) and blocks. Ground feldspar, produced in North Carolina, Colorado, and a few other states, is employed in the manufacture of glass, pottery, and enamel, also in soaps and abrasives. Bauxite, a source of aluminum, is discussed under metals but is also used as an abrasive and as a refractory material. Bauxite increases the strength of ceramics and improves the resistance to heat and abrasion. Arkansas, Alabama, Georgia, and Virginia are the chief sources in the United States. Borax is often utilized in ceramics if pigment is to be added. It also improves the quality of glazes and glass. Magnesite, employed chiefly as a refractory material in the steel mills, is mined in California, Nevada, Illinois, and Michigan, also in Austria, Canada, Greece, and India. Magnesite is also a source of magnesium metal.

CHEMICAL MATERIALS

The chemical industry uses a wide variety of materials, many of which have already been mentioned in previous chapters and some of which will be discussed further in the chapters to come. The chemical industry starts with six basic raw materials, coal, salt, limestone, sulfur, water, and air. In addition, cellulose derived from wood and such intermediary products as chlorine, caustic soda, ammonia, nitrogen, oxygen, and many others are used. Of special concern here are the minerals which contribute directly to the chemical industry. One of the most important and one of the most common of these is salt, sodium chloride.

SALT is widely distributed in solid masses and in salt domes or other deposits from which it can be mined in much the same manner as coal. It also occurs in the form of brines, deep under the surface of the earth, which can be pumped out and evaporated to recover the solid salt. Salt is also contained in seawater, and in many places it is extracted from the sea by normal evaporation. The total amount of salt in the earth's surface is so great that we can scarcely imagine it becoming scarce and yet in some parts of the earth, especially in remote humid regions, salt is very scarce and quite expensive.

Salt has a great variety of uses. The most familiar is as a flavoring for food. It is known that the human body requires a certain amount of salt, and the per capita consumption in the United States is usually about 12 pounds per year. If this rate of consumption were applied to the whole population of the earth of two billion 400 million, the annual direct consumption by human beings would reach nearly 30 billion pounds, or about 14 million tons of common salt. The world production is estimated at about 30 million tons so that 16 million tons are used for purposes other than human consumption, such as the manufacture of chemicals and various other purposes. Considerable quantities of salt are used in the manufacture of chlorine, in bleaches, and in chlorates.

Soda ash, sodium carbonate in other words, is also manufactured from salt, limestone, and other chemicals. Large quantities of salt are also used for livestock and in the meat-packing and fish-curing industry. Other food processing, such as canning and preserving, also accounts for a large part of salt consumption.

Most of the plants for the processing of salt and the manufacture of various chemicals are located near a salt supply and also near cheap fuels. Two areas stand out in the United States, one in the northeastern part, using salt from mines particularly in New York and Ohio, and using cheap coal from the northern Appalachian coalfield. The other zone of chemical plants using large quantities of salt is located near the Gulf in Louisiana and Texas. These plants take advantage of the large supplies of salt in the salt domes and also the large supplies of cheap natural gas from the adjacent fields. Closely related to salt production in the manufacture of various alkalies and derivative products are the saline minerals, which include the chlorides of magnesium and calcium. Also salt production is related to the

FIGURE 32.4. *Loading sulfur into railroad cars in southeast Texas after the walls of a vat have been removed.*

manufacture of compounds of bromine, iodine, and the borates. Salt is produced in most of the countries of the world either from seawater, mines, or from wells, but reliable statistics are not available for all areas. France, Germany, China, and India are all large producers.

SULFUR finds wide uses in the chemical, fertilizer, paper, rubber, and paint industries, in food processing, and in the manufacture of explosives. About three fourths of the United States production is converted to sulfuric acid (which is also obtained from pyrites), in which form sulfur finds its widest industrial uses. Petroleum refining, the iron and steel industry, and textile manufacturing consume large quantities of sulfuric acid. The world production of native sulfur is more than five million tons, most of which is produced in the United States. Deposits of sulfur are found in many countries, but the low cost of production in Texas and Louisiana is a distinct advantage. In the Frasch process of mining, pipes are driven into the sulfur deposits and hot water is pumped in, forcing the liquid sulfur to the surface and into large vats (FIG. 32.4). Sulfur mined by this process is pure enough to be used for most purposes without further refining. World reserves of sulfur and pyrites are large, but the high-grade deposits, such as those of Texas and Louisiana, are by no means inexhaustible.

FERTILIZER MATERIALS

The three basic elements for the fertilizer industry are potassium, phosphorus, and nitrogen. Calcium in the form of lime is also used extensively as a fertilizer, but it is usually applied separately and does not enter into the manufacture of commercial fertilizers. The potassium minerals are often called "potash," a term originally applied to potassium carbonate, later to caustic potash. Nowadays "potash" often indicates the potassium content of fertilizers. Phosphorus usually occurs in the form of phosphate rock or apatite. Nitrogen is usually referred to as "nitrate," a term applied to natural sodium nitrate from Chile, and also to various by-products and synthetic forms of nitrogen.

POTASH is used primarily for the manufacture of fertilizers. But a considerable proportion also goes into other chemical industries, including soap, paper, explosives, matches, and medicines. The largest producers of potash in the world are Ger-

many, France, and the United States. Smaller production comes from Spain, Poland, the U.S.S.R., Chile, and Australia. In the United States the largest production is on the Texas–New Mexico boundary, where large quantities of potash have been produced in recent years. Another source of potash is the Searles Lake district of California, where in a shallow lake basin there is a large deposit of crystalline salts which contains some potash. The outcrop has an area of nearly 12 square miles and the thickness ranges up to 100 feet. By far the most famous deposit of potash occurs in Germany in the deposits known under the general name of Staszfurt. This region lies to the west of Leipzig and more or less between the cities of Magdeburg and Hanover. These are old deposits laid down in Permian times and covered in many places with large thicknesses of sediments. Some of the mines are shaft mines. There are two main salt-bearing formations, and salt beds occur in both of them. But in the Hanover district sylvite occurs in beds up to 25 feet in thickness. The potash deposits there, along with salt and other chemicals, form one of the main bases of the far-reaching chemical industry of Germany. In eastern France, especially in Alsace north of Mulhouse, there are also good deposits of potash. The beds occur in a sort of basin about 14 miles long and half as wide. The total area is about 75 square miles. There are two beds of potash separated by about a 60-foot interval. The depth is from 1500 to 3000 feet. Nearly all of the potash deposits of Alsace are chlorides of potassium, and in addition common salt and other minerals are found. Another area of production in Europe lies in the U.S.S.R. immediately to the north of the Caspian Sea. This deposit is very large in outcrop, at any rate, but production figures for recent years are not available. The Dead Sea, which lies along the border of Israel and Transjordan, has some beds of phosphate and potash.

PHOSPHATE ROCK includes a number of the compounds of phosphorus often referred to as phosphates. These minerals are of very great importance in the fertilizer industry and also in the chemical industry. Many soils are deficient in phosphate, and large quantities of "superphosphates" are used to increase agricultural yields. Most of the phosphate deposits are impure and consist of a number of elements, such as calcium, phosphorus, fluorine, iron, aluminum, and silicon. The total world production of phosphate averages about 20 million tons, somewhat less than half coming from the United States. The most important production outside the United States is in the Soviet Union, in north Africa, and in some of the islands of the Pacific and Indian oceans.

In the United States phosphates occur in the form of phosphate rock, marls, apatite, in limestones, and also in cave guano. The reserves are large and have contributed a good deal to the fertilizer and chemical industries. Florida has long been an important producer of phosphate for domestic consumption and also for export. The principal producing formation lies along the Gulf Coast of Florida in the vicinity of Tampa and consists of hard rock phosphate fairly close to the surface so that it can be mined readily by open-pit methods. The deposits are in places 100 feet thick or more and have about 50 feet of overburden which must be removed. The tricalcium phosphate content is about 80 per cent. One of the reasons Florida phosphate is exported is its nearness to the sea. It can be loaded on freighters very close to the mines, and some is usually exported to western European countries.

Another important deposit of phosphate occurs in Tennessee in the vicinity of Nashville. The Nashville dome exposes the phosphate limestones, which also occur in the Blue Grass region of Kentucky. It is considered that the fertility of these two regions is related directly to the high phosphorus content of the soils. The Tennessee deposits range up to ten feet in thickness and contain 60 per cent of tricalcium phosphate. As the mining continues, there is a tendency for the content to fall off somewhat. In the Rocky Mountain region of western United States the phosphate deposits are worked in Idaho, Montana, Utah, and Wyoming. The deposits here are very extensive, but the mining is somewhat restricted by the remoteness from large centers of processing and consumption. It should be borne in mind that the largest use of commercial fertilizers, of which phosphate is an important part, is in the eastern part of the United States.

In Algeria, Tunisia, and Morocco, the French possessions of northwest Africa, there are large reserves of phosphate, and the production there has increased in recent years. Since this deposit is close to western Europe, which uses more phosphate than any other part of the world, the production largely goes to Europe. Tunisia is usually the largest producer, followed by Morocco and Algeria. Egypt is a large producer also, and its export usually goes to Japan, which also requires large quantities of phosphate in addition to what is mined at home. The Egyptian deposits are near the Red Sea and are consequently easy to export. The best deposits of phosphate in the Soviet Union are in the far north in the Kola Peninsula. Although this is rather remote from agricultural production, it is fairly close to tidewater and also has rail connections with the Agricultural Belt of Russia to the south. There are also large phosphate deposits in the Ukraine and in the Soviet Republic of Kazakhstan. In view of the general low fertility of Russian soils, because of long continued cultivation, these deposits of phosphate are of great significance.

Many of the Pacific and Indian ocean islands contain phosphates associated with the coral deposits. The alteration of the coral in some places has been accomplished by solutions from overlying bird guano. The most important islands are Ocean Island and Nauru, Christmas, and Makatéa. Ocean Island and Nauru are in the Gilbert group and lie very close to the equator. It is easy to export phosphate from these islands since the deposits are near the sea and ocean transportation is cheap. Most of the export goes to Europe, Australia, New Zealand, and Japan.

The largest use for phosphate rock is in the manufacture of commercial fertilizer, most of which goes under the name of superphosphate. Some is also used for the production of elemental phosphorus and various phosphate chemicals, which have their place in industry and in medicine.

NITROGEN COMPOUNDS include natural sodium nitrate and various synthetic forms, such as ammonia, ammonium sulfate, ammonium nitrate, and the synthetic form of sodium nitrate. The leading producers are the United States, Germany, Japan, Chile, France, the United Kingdom, and Canada. However, only Chile produces natural nitrates in quantities. The chief use of the nitrogen compounds is in fertilizers and munition industries, but some are used in the manufacture of synthetic fibers, plastics, and in various chemical processes. The use of liquid ammonia as a source of nitrogen has increased recently.

INDUSTRIAL MATERIALS

A number of minerals have specific uses in industry. Space is available here for the discussion of a few, asbestos, mica, graphite, quartz, and glass sand.

ASBESTOS, a trade name for various fibrous minerals, has the unique qualities of great resistance to heat and also a fibrous character so that it can be spun into threads and woven into cloth or felted into sheets. Deposits of high-grade asbestos are not very common, and the value of the deposits often depends upon the length of the fibers or the thickness of the veins in which the fibers occur. The fibers usually run at right angles to the veins. The most common variety of asbestos is chrysotile. This is mined in eastern Canada in the province of Quebec, in Rhodesia in southern Africa, and also in the U.S.S.R. In Africa some quantities of blue asbestos, which are of considerable importance, are produced. The largest deposit of asbestos is in Quebec Province of Canada to the east of Montreal. At Thetford mines in Quebec asbestos has been produced for many years, and most of the needs of the United States beyond the domestic production are supplied from these mines. This deposit continues into northern Vermont, which is one of the important producing states of the United States. Another deposit of asbestos recently discovered lies about nine miles east of Matheson, Ontario. Exploration for asbestos has been very active in recent years because of the scarcity of this material.

Large deposits of asbestos occur in the Ural Mountains of the U.S.S.R., and these contribute more than any other to making Russia the second largest producer of this mineral. Russia formerly exported some quantities of asbestos but in recent years has been using most of it for domestic industries. In Southern Rhodesia there is a rather large production of the chrysotile form of asbestos. Production has been increasing rapidly in recent years and has reached the neighborhood of 75,000 short tons. Production of asbestos has been fairly large in the Union of South Africa, especially in the Transvaal, where 27 mines have been producing this mineral. Smaller quantities of asbestos are produced in Australia, Austria, Bolivia, Colombia, Italy, and Venezuela. The total world production is generally less than one million tons.

MICA includes several minerals, the most common of which are muscovite, biotite, and phlogopite. These minerals are abundant in many igneous and metamorphic rocks throughout the world, but in only a few places are the crystals large enough for commercial use. Fairly large sheets of mica are very necessary in the electrical industry, where the mineral is used to insulate electrical connections in the presence of very high heat. The phlogopite mica is considered the best in machines which must stand a high degree of heat, such as toasters, flatirons, fuse plugs, and many others. Mica is used as an ingredient in wallpaper coatings, in lubricants, and in the manufacture of tires and tubes. It is sometimes used in the powdered form as a coating for roofs and shingles and as a finish in concrete and stucco. Although flake mica is fairly abundant, the high-quality sheet mica is very scarce, and very little is produced in the United States. It is therefore considered a strategic mineral of rather high critical priority.

India is by far the greatest producer of mica, the most important district being in the province of Bihar, where a belt about 60 miles long and ten miles wide has been worked for many years. The mica is in the form of dikes and veins, and the mining is rather laborious. Large-scale mining operations are not generally practical in the mica mines. Another mining district in India is in the state of Madras, where an overburden must be removed before the mica is exposed. In the United States the largest producer has been North Carolina and after that the Black Hills region of South Dakota. The Minas Gerais region of Brazil has large deposits of muscovite, and the production there has been increasing. Madagascar and Canada have phlogopite deposits and a number of other small deposits are known, but the occurrences are so scattered and irregular that mining is not on a commercial basis. Because of the scarcity of high-quality mica, efforts have been made to produce it synthetically.

GRAPHITE, a form of carbon, is very soft and has a slick, greasy feel, which makes it a good lubricant for many purposes. It also has a very high melting point, which makes it useful in various crucibles where high heat is necessary. Graphite is also used in the manufacture of dry batteries, pencils, and paint. Another use is in the brushes of dynamos and motors, since graphite is a good conductor of electricity and does not wear out rapidly on contact with revolving surfaces.

Large amounts of graphite are produced in Korea, Ceylon, Madagascar, Czechoslovakia, Austria, Germany, and Mexico. Production in the United States is not large, and only a small quantity is produced in Canada. Since for certain lubrication purposes, graphite is a must for which there is no satisfactory substitute, graphite is considered a strategic mineral. The most critical form of graphite is the crucible quality, of which Madagascar apparently has the largest reserves. Synthetic graphite is now being produced in some quantities and is suitable for nearly all of the ordinary uses except the manufacture of crucibles.

QUARTZ crystals are in great demand for the control of frequency in electrical apparatus, such as radios. The best quality of natural quartz comes from Brazil with only small amounts produced in the United States. Since high-quality quartz is sometimes difficult to obtain, great efforts have been made to synthesize it.

GLASS SAND production in the United States averages about three or four million tons. Most of it comes from West Virginia, Pennsylvania, Illinois, and Missouri. For optical glass the sand must be nearly pure silica (99.8 per cent), but for ordinary glass up to four per cent of impurities can be tolerated. Most ordinary glass contains lime, magnesia, and soda. Colors are usually obtained by the addition of small quantities of various compounds of iron, cobalt, copper, manganese, chromium, and calcium.

A number of other nonmetallic minerals are used in some quantities by industry. These include the natural mineral pigments, such as Venetian red, the red oxides, the ochers, the siennas, the umbers, and a number of similar materials. Perlite and pumice are used extensively in plaster and concrete block production.

GEMSTONES

Gemstones may be described as rare, durable minerals which are desirable for adornment or decoration. Such minerals have been known and used for many centuries. After cutting, gemstones become "gems." Hardness, color, and brilliancy are desirable qualities. The "precious" stones include the diamond, emerald, ruby, sapphire, opal, and pearl. Gemstones are used in jewelry, vases, statuettes, in watch jewels, in optical instruments, and as a means of hoarding concentrated wealth. A million dollars in diamonds could be carried easily in a man's pocket, a hundred million in a lady's handbag.

Of the total annual world production of diamonds, about 16 million carats, one half is bort, one fourth off-color and full of flaws, and only a very small amount suitable for high-quality gems of one carat or more. In an average year about 100,000 fine diamonds are produced.

Rubies and sapphires are red and blue varieties of corundum, found largely in Burma, Ceylon, and India. Emerald is a green variety of beryl, obtained from Colombia, the Transvaal, and the Ural Mountains. Aquamarine is also a variety of beryl. Opals, valued for the play of colors, are produced in Australia, Czechoslovakia, and Mexico. The semiprecious stones occur widely and in great variety, including many varieties of quartz, such as amethyst, rose quartz, agate, carnelian, jasper, and onyx; also garnet, turquoise, spinel, topaz, zircon, jade, and lapis lazuli. Several tons of such gems are collected annually by amateurs.

CHAPTER

33

Coal: A Primary Fuel and Chemical

COAL, petroleum, and falling water—the chief power sources—are widely but unevenly distributed over the surface of the earth. See FIGURE 33.1. All these sources of energy can be transported in one form or another but only at considerable cost. Thus, the producing regions, especially those of coal, play a major role in the location and character of the world's manufacturing belts.

The production of coal is one of the world's greatest industries. Coal is found in every continent and in many latitudes, but not all coal beds are worth mining. Some layers are too thin or too deep beneath the surface, or the quality of the coal is too poor for economical exploitation. The best and most accessible deposits are in the Appalachian Mountains of North America, in northwestern Europe, especially Germany and Britain,

in southern Russia, and in northern China. These are merely the chief producing regions of high-grade coal. In all, approximately two billion tons of bituminous, anthracite, and lignite coals per year is mined in about 50 countries. Four countries, the United States, Russia, Great Britain, and Germany, produce about 60 per cent of the world's coal. Other important producers include Poland, France, Czechoslovakia, Japan, and India. Brief descriptions of the major coal regions are given in this chapter while additional data on coal production will be found in the regional descriptions preceding this chapter and in Appendix C.

The character of the solid mineral fuels ranges from peat through lignite (sometimes called brown coal), bituminous coal, to anthracite. Peat is easily mined since it usually occurs at or near the surface, but it is low in heating value, bulky,

FIGURE 33.1. *Graph of the major sources of energy in the United States in 1950, expressed in trillions of thermal units. Small amounts of energy are also obtained from firewood, wood waste, wind, and animal power. In recent years petroleum and natural gas have been increasing in use both relatively and absolutely. Coal has been declining slightly, and water power has shown a steady increase. In the future it is expected that coal will grow in importance as reserves of petroleum and natural gas decline.*

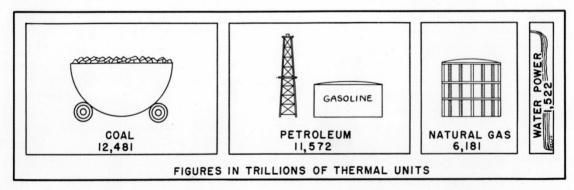

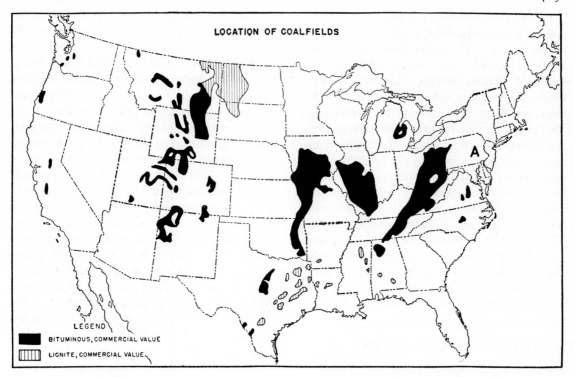

FIGURE 33.2. *Map of the coalfields of the United States, including the bituminous fields* (black), *the lignite* (vertical shading), *and the anthracite* (A). *Because of higher quality and nearness to market, the eastern fields are much more productive than the western ones. From U. S. Bureau of Mines.*

and contains a large amount of vegetable fiber and moisture. Areas with little coal, such as Ireland and parts of Russia, use large quantities of peat. Peat must be dried before use and then burned in specially designed furnaces. Lignite makes up about 15 per cent of the coal mined in the world. Produced mainly in areas of Germany and Russia which do not have better coal, lignite has a high moisture and volatile content, and tends to break up badly on exposure to the air. In the United States lignite is produced in Texas and North Dakota, since both states are rather distant from sources of high-grade coal. More than three fourths of the coal mined in the world is bituminous, often called "soft" coal. Although the quality of this coal varies widely, it is generally black, sooty to the touch, and breaks up rather readily when handled. It does not break up, however, on exposure to the air as does lignite. The heating value is usually high, but the volatile content and the ash are variable. Of greatest significance to manufacturing are the coals from

which good coke, suitable for metallurgical purposes can be made. There are harmful impurities, such as sulfur and phosphorus, in some bituminous coals, which make them unsuitable for certain uses. Anthracite coal is hard and black, with a high luster. Its heating value is high, averaging more than other varieties but not exceeding the highest grades of bituminous coal. The moisture and volatile content are low, and the best grades of this coal can be used without coking in blast furnaces for the smelting of iron. The cleanness of this coal, its hardness which resists degradation, and its slow-burning quality make it a premium coal for domestic household use. Only about 5 per cent of the coal mined in the world is true anthracite, and most of this comes from eastern Pennsylvania (FIG. 33.3), southern Russia, and northern China. Other coals, called "semi-anthracite," with somewhat similar qualities are mined in small quantities in various parts of the world. In the United States "semi-anthracite" is mined in Virginia and Arkansas.

Coal is a prime necessity in this industrial age, and it is being mined almost everywhere that good coal is found near the surface. In the Appalachian Region, especially Pennsylvania and West Virginia, in Illinois, Britain, Germany, Russia, China, and in many a lesser region coal is the most significant raw material. Such names as Pittsburgh, Birmingham, the Ruhr, Newcastle, and Donetz conjure up images of smoking chimneys which bear witness to the production and consumption of coal. In far off Spitsbergen coal comes down the steep slopes in cable cars to the coast for shipment to coal-starved Scandinavia; in China coolies carry coal in baskets; in a part of Tennessee, where there is no coal, a man dug for two years in a worthless bed of dark shale, hoping to find coal. In regions where there is no coal a high price must be paid for this fuel, a fact which limits or prevents industrial development in many parts of the world.

THE APPALACHIAN COALFIELDS

The greatest known resources of high-grade coal in the world are in the Appalachian Bituminous Coal Region (FIG. 33.2). Stretching from north-western Pennsylvania to northern Alabama, this region embraces parts of seven states. It is difficult to overestimate the significance of this region to the industrial life of the United States. Without coal it is doubtful if the Manufacturing Belt of eastern North America would exist. The intensity of coal production varies according to the amount and quality of the coal available and with respect to the accessibility to the main lines of transportation. The most intensive production is in the northern portion—southwestern Pennsylvania, northern West Virginia, western Maryland, and the adjacent portion of Ohio. This region is well served by railroads and by the Ohio River and its tributaries, which provide water routes. Furthermore, it is nearest the Great Lakes and is a definite part of the Manufacturing Belt. In southern West Virginia, eastern Kentucky, and western Virginia is the "middle" Appalachian field, where large quantities of coal are produced, but which is slightly more remote than other fields from the great centers of coal consumption. Of all the fields the least coal is produced in the southernmost field in the vicinity of Birmingham, Alabama, partly because of the

FIGURE 33.3. *A diagrammatic cross section of a coal mine in the Anthracite Field. The layers of coal are tilted and broken, a fact which greatly complicates the mining process. Vertical shafts reach the coal beds and horizontal tunnels extend in every direction following the layer of coal. From Philadelphia and Reading Coal and Iron Company.*

FIGURE 33.4. *A coal tipple and mine in West Virginia. The coal bed is near the top of the ridge on the left. The coal is mined by means of horizontal tunnels and brought down the mountain slope in the covered incline. At the tipple the coal is screened and sorted before dropping into the railroad cars. From N. and W. Railway.*

smaller resources but mainly because of the location of the coalfields.

In a narrow valley in the West Virginia hills lies the coal mining town of "Three States." To one who has never seen a coal mine, the single purpose and function of this elongated town is, nevertheless, perfectly obvious. In the first place, the coal tipple is the most conspicuous feature in the valley; here the coal is weighed, graded, cleaned, washed, and finally dumped into the waiting railroad cars. Extending up and down the narrow valley on a single street are the long rows of small "company" houses in which the miners live. There is also a company store, a school, and a cramped baseball diamond.

From the tipple (FIG. 33.4) an incline railway leads halfway up the steep slope to the mine opening. This is a "drift" mine with the tunnel leading horizontally back into the mountain following the seams of coal. Branches of the main tunnel, like a system of streets and avenues, literally honeycomb the mountain at this level. At the end of each "street" and "avenue" is the "face

of the coal," and here the coal miners are working. The miner's task is simple but arduous, monotonous, and risky; his job is to "shoot down" the coal with small charges of explosive and to load the mine car. He uses a compressed air drill to make the opening for the explosive, and the coal seam is "undercut" along the floor with a machine, so that the coal will come down in lumps rather than dust. The loaded mine cars, carrying 3 to 15 tons each, are moved to the mine mouth and then down the incline railway to the tipple. In descending, the loaded mine cars pull up the "empties" from the previous trip. Some of the coal is loaded directly as "run of mine," but most of it is graded as "egg," "lump," and "screenings" before it is dumped into the railroad car.

Supporting the coal miner are many technicians who keep the mine in working order. The water must be pumped out, the air constantly changed, gas pockets discovered and eliminated, track laid for the mine cars, props placed to hold up the ceiling, and air must be compressed and piped to each working point to operate the machines (many mines use electricity). For every man who actually mines coal at least one other man toils at various other tasks. In shaft mines some of the operations are more complicated and expensive.

Two systems of digging the coal are in general use. The most common is the room and pillar method in which pillars or columns of coal are left standing between the passages to support the ceiling. When the mine is worked out and is being abandoned this coal may be recovered. The other method is the "longwall," in which all the coal is removed along a straight coal face and the roof is allowed to fall in behind the operation. Most mines use large quantities of timber in the form of props to support the ceiling of the mine, the number of timbers required depending on the depth of the mine and the nature of the rock material above the coal.

The latest machinery is used in modern mines to transport the coal and to mine it. In addition to the electric or compressed air drills and the undercutting machines, machine loaders, conveyor belts, and other labor-saving devices are used. In some mines continuous mining machines produce up to four tons of coal per minute.

Coal from the Appalachian Fields supplies most of eastern United States and parts of Canada. From the northern field the principal movement is by rail toward the Lake Erie ports, such as Toledo, Cleveland, Erie, and Buffalo. Transshipped on lake steamers, the coal is easily and cheaply carried to all parts of the Great Lakes. Since iron ore is moved down the lakes from the Mesabi and other ranges, coal makes a good return cargo. From various upper lake ports coal is shipped by rail to inland markets. A fairly large tonnage of coal is moved down the Ohio River and into the Mississippi by barge. This is a cheap form of transportation also and enables manufacturing districts in southern Ohio and Indiana to have high-quality coal at a low price. Much coal is also moved to its destination entirely by rail. For shorter hauls, up to 200 miles or more, coal is often transported in trucks.

Appalachian coal is also moved eastward to the Atlantic Seaboard by rail. In the large cities coal is used for the generation of electricity, also for fuel, coaling ships, and for factories. Some coal enters the coastwise trade. Coal is exported from Norfolk, Virginia, where there are coal docks equipped to pick up railroad cars and dump their contents into the holds of ships. Much of the coal moving out of Norfolk is shipped to some other United States port, such as New York, Boston, or Portland (Maine), but increasing amounts are being sent to Latin America.

The Anthracite Coalfield lies in the Ridge and Valley Region of eastern Pennsylvania. The quality of the coal is excellent, and it can be used in blast furnaces without coking. In addition, this region is very near the large cities of the Atlantic Seaboard. Anthracite is more difficult to mine, however, than bituminous, and the amount produced represents only about one tenth of the United States coal production. Many of the coal beds are tilted, folded, and broken (FIG. 33.3), so that various mining techniques are necessary. Some of the coal is near the surface and can be mined by strip or open pit methods. In others, drift or shaft mines are necessary, and much useless rock must be removed along with the coal. Anthracite is also dredged from the bottoms of rivers which flow through the coalfields. Such an operation is itself a testimonial to the hardness of this coal, since most bituminous coal breaks up if transported by streams. Anthracite is also produced from the "culm banks," which are piles of small-sized coal formerly considered worthless and deposited in the form of dumps near the mines. After washing, this coal is readily marketed. Approximately four million tons of anthracite per year is obtained from culm banks, about one million tons from river dredges, 12 million tons from strip mines, while the remainder, about 30 million tons, is taken from underground workings, both drift and shaft mines. Since anthracite is hard, it is often necessary to break up large fragments in order to remove particles of shale. The tipples which handle the coal, therefore, are often called "breakers." Most of the anthracite is marketed in the vicinity of the mines or to the east of the fields, in New York, New Jersey, and New England.

OTHER NORTH AMERICAN COALFIELDS

West of the Appalachians the quality of the coal declines, and the fields are generally more remote from the market. This means less production, but it should be noted that the reserves are large. In the Eastern Interior Field, in Illinois, Indiana,

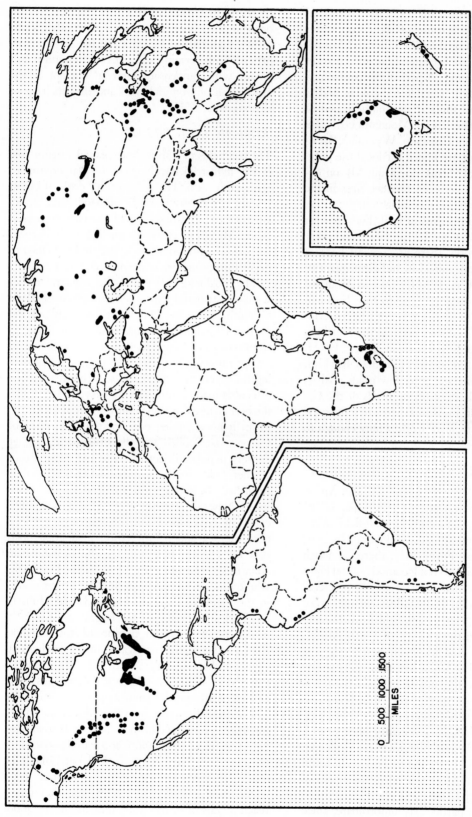

FIGURE 33.5. Map of the principal coalfields of the world. Large quantities of coal are produced in only a few of these fields, and in some fields no coal is mined at present. (Smaller fields are shown by dots.)

and Kentucky, a large amount of bituminous coal is produced, partly because of the cheap water transportation furnished by the Ohio and Mississippi rivers and partly because of the good market in Chicago and vicinity. A part of the coal mined in southern Illinois is suitable for coking and is shipped to the steel mills at the southern end of Lake Michigan. The Rocky Mountain coalfields are scattered through Colorado, Wyoming, Montana, and Utah, but are mined for local use only. Some of these coals break down quickly on exposure to air and may even produce fires in the stockpiles by spontaneous combustion.

There are large reserves of coal, both in west and east Canada. In Cape Breton Island and other parts of Nova Scotia, there are several beds of good coal which are mined in sufficient quantity to supply eastern Canada as far west as Montreal and from which some coal is sent to New England. Coal is imported to that portion of eastern Canada which is west of Montreal from the Northern Appalachian Field of the United States. In Alberta, on the margin of the Canadian Rockies, production of lignite and other low-grade coals is sufficient to supply most of the needs of the Canadian Wheat Belt. In Alaska there are some good deposits of coal which are worked only enough to supply local needs.

LATIN AMERICAN COALFIELDS

One of the greatest handicaps of all Latin America, from the Rio Grande to Patagonia, is the scarcity of good quality coal. A small field on the Rio Grande in the vicinity of Piedras Negras, Mexico, is worked. Fortunately, there is enough petroleum in Mexico to run locomotives and highway transport, so that most of the meager coal supply can be used in the metallurgical industries. In South America one small field is worked in southern Brazil in the vicinity of Porto Alegre. Producers at this field send their best product to the new steel mill at Volta Redonda, a few miles to the west of Rio de Janeiro. In Chile there is a small but productive field on the coast near Concepción, which is used for fuel and in the smelting of metals. Peruvians have recently opened up a new field in the Andean hinterland of Mollendo, and other small fields are in production. In Latin America, however, there is no adequate supply of good coal on which to base a large-scale industrial economy. This is particularly unfortunate, since

there are in Latin America vast reserves of iron ore and other minerals together with other kinds of raw materials to supply large industrial enterprises. To a certain extent petroleum and water power will compensate for coal but not in the production of iron and steel and the smelting of various ores.

EUROPEAN COALFIELDS

The coalfields of Europe have played a major role in the industrial development of that continent. See FIGURE 33.6. The good quality coals of Great Britain, Germany, France, Poland, and, more lately, those of Russia are of the utmost significance. Many raw materials are lacking in Europe, but until the present the coal supply has helped to make Europeans pre-eminent in industry.

The coalfields of Great Britain are rather widely distributed from the Lowland of Scotland to southern Wales. Only northern Scotland and southern England are more than 50 or 60 miles from coal sources, and by use of an excellent system of railways and coastwise barge lines, utilizing the rivers as well as the sea, the distribution of coal is made comparatively easy. In the north, the best coalfield is in Ayrshire south of Glasgow. From it good coking coal for the steel mills of Glasgow is supplied as well as fuel for the rather densely populated Scottish Lowland. From other smaller fields in the vicinity, additional coal is furnished. In northeastern England, in the vicinity of Newcastle on the Tyne River, is another excellent coalfield. Much of the coal is mined near the sea and is, therefore, in a good position for export, especially to the Scandinavian countries, Norway, Sweden, and Denmark, where little or no coal is produced. Farther south, in the vicinity of Leeds, Sheffield, and Hull, is the Yorkshire Coalfield, the largest in Britain. It begins on the eastern margin of the Pennine Range and continues eastward until it reaches out several miles under the North Sea. These underwater veins are reached by way of passages from vertical shafts on the land. Mining conditions in Yorkshire call attention to the difficulties which for many years have been facing the British coal industry. Most of the more accessible portions of the coal beds have been worked out, and it. is now necessary to dig deeper and to mine coal under greater difficulties. Many of the mines reach depths of nearly 5000 feet and mines 4000

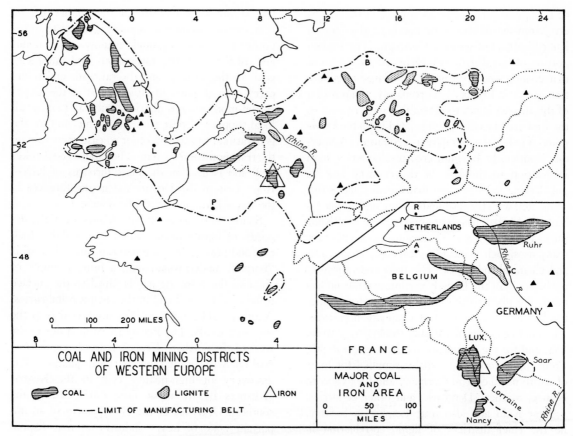

FIGURE 33.6. *The coal and iron producing districts of western Europe. With few exceptions the coalfields correspond, in distribution, to manufacturing. Modified from "Syllabus for Economic Geography," Hartshorne and Dicken.*

feet deep are common. Working conditions at these depths are by no means impossible but the heat, the difficulty of keeping the mine free of water and gas, and the task of lifting the coal several thousand feet add to the hazards and expense. As a result, the cost of mining coal in Great Britain is higher than in the United States, and in times of stress, such as a severe winter, the British find it difficult to supply enough coal for their own needs. Nevertheless, Britain usually exports coal to nearby European countries.

The Lancashire Coalfield, similar to that of Yorkshire but smaller, is found on the west side of the Pennine Range in the vicinity of the port of Manchester. Coal is used to furnish power for the cotton textile mills of this district as well as for metallurgical industries. The Birmingham Coalfield is in a sense a continuation of the Yorkshire and Lancashire fields but located on the southern margin of the Pennine Range. Most of the unmined coal here is fairly deep, but production is heavy and large amounts of iron and steel, as well as many finished products are produced in the Birmingham district. The coal of South Wales, like that of Newcastle, is close to the sea and a part of the production is ordinarily exported to Spain and France, where coal is lacking, and even to South American countries. Much of the coal is consumed in tin and copper smelters, and for many years the chief tin refining and plating district of the world has been in Wales. It should be noted in passing that only small amounts of coal are found in Ireland, mostly in the southern part of the island, and that peat makes up a considerable portion of the fuel used for domestic purposes.

The chief coal district of the continent of Europe stretches from northern France, near the city of Lille, eastward across Belgium and the southern extension of the Netherlands to the famous Ruhr Coalfield of western Germany. The French portion of this district represents the best coal in that country and accounts for the largest production of any in France. Unfortunately, the position of this district is not too favorable with respect to the iron ore of eastern France, and from the viewpoint of political geography it is too near a dangerous frontier. In Belgium coal production is high in relation to the size of the country and its population, and there are many heavy industries associated with the coalfields. Most of Germany's high-grade coal has been taken from the Ruhr mines for many years. The quality is excellent for many uses, such as metallurgical coke, steam, gas, and chemical industries. The field ends abruptly to the south of the Ruhr River but extends underneath the plain to the north, where shaft mines rarely more than 1500 feet deep are necessary. The coal beds are of variable thickness, 5 to 30 feet, and for the most part are at no great depth. From the Ruhr coal is usually supplied for most of western and central Germany and for export to France, Sweden, Denmark, and other countries.

Near Köln and also near Leipzig in Saxony, lie the chief districts of lignite production in western Europe. Although lignite has a low heating value and much volatile material, the Germans have devised methods to use it in the generation of power, in the chemical industries, and for various other purposes. Some high-quality coal is moved into Saxony from the Ruhr for special purposes. The Poles were important producers of coal from their portion of the Silesian Field prior to World War II. The acquisition of most of the German portion of the field gives the Polish people one of the best coal districts of the continent, other than the Ruhr and Russia's Donbas. Silesian coal is used in the heavy industries in the district and is exported to the Baltic States and to White Russia.

RUSSIAN COALFIELDS

Of all the resources in Russia, coal is easily the most significant. Second in quantity in reserve to that in the United States, the coal is scattered through more than 80 fields, the largest of which are in Asiatic Russia far from present lines of transportation. The Donbas Field (FIG. 39.1), north of the Black Sea and west of Rostov, is the largest producer because of the quality of the coal, the ease of mining, and the nearness to transportation. Two thousand shallow shaft mines are used to get the bituminous and anthracite coals to the surface, and the railroads and rivers carry it to all parts of Russia west of the Urals. In the more remote districts, such as Leningrad, local supplies of peat are used for fuel and for the generation of power in order to ease the strain on the transportation system. The Donbas coal cokes well and is used in the blast furnaces of Krivoi Rog, west of the Dnepr, and in the furnaces in the immediate vicinity of the mines.

South of Moscow, in the vicinity of Tula, deposits of lignite occur which are used for fuel, gas, and power. In some parts of this field coal is "burned" underground with a limited supply of air, and the resulting gas is piped to the surface to be used for fuel and in the chemical industries. Another field producing noncoking coal is in the southern Urals. The Pechora Coalfield lies to the west of the northern Urals and supplies good fuel coal but with limited metallurgical qualities. The discovery of high-quality coal in the Kuzbas (Kuznets Basin) about 1400 miles east of the southern Urals led to the development of an important zone of heavy industry in that region. The coal is the best in Russia but is rather far removed from the areas of dense population. Still another coalfield, the Karaganda, lies between the southern Urals and the Kuzbas and is in a better position to supply the southern Urals with coke. Other coalfields lie in the valleys of the Amur, Lena, and Yenisei rivers, but only those in the Amur Valley are in significant production.

OTHER COALFIELDS

In addition to the major coalfields described above, which account for most of the world production, numerous other small fields are found throughout the world (FIG. 33.7). Some of these fields have been described in the preceding chapters (see INDEX), but the smaller fields are too numerous for individual description. In all, from 90–100 commercial coalfields are in production in various parts of the world, about 20 in North America, 7 in South America, 5 in Africa, 15 in Europe, 35 in Asia, and 10 in Oceania. The number of active fields varies from year to year, and from season to season. In wartime a number of additional marginal fields came into production.

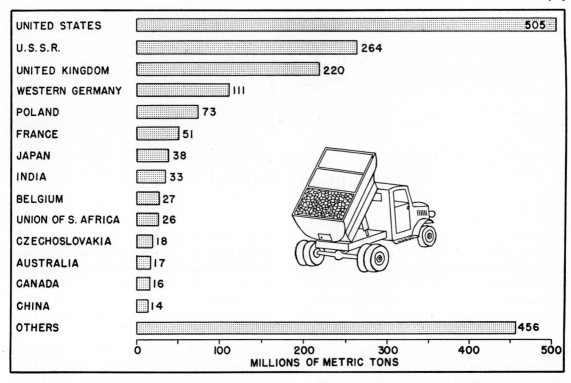

UNITED STATES	505
U.S.S.R.	264
UNITED KINGDOM	220
WESTERN GERMANY	111
POLAND	73
FRANCE	51
JAPAN	38
INDIA	33
BELGIUM	27
UNION OF S. AFRICA	26
CZECHOSLOVAKIA	18
AUSTRALIA	17
CANADA	16
CHINA	14
OTHERS	456

MILLIONS OF METRIC TONS

FIGURE 33.7. *Graph of coal production in leading countries, 1952, in millions of metric tons. Production for the U.S.S.R., Poland, Czechoslovakia, and China is estimated. From* Commodity Yearbook.

COKE AND THE COAL CHEMICALS

In addition to its use as a fuel, coal and its derivatives enter into many industrial processes as chemicals. Coke is by far the most important product of coal. The by-products of the coke ovens, coal tar, ammonia, ammonium sulfates, coal gas, crude light oil, and naphthalene, are the most important coal chemicals. Coke is produced from coal by heating in the absence of air (oxygen). In the beehive type of coke oven, the volatile materials are driven off and lost, but in the by-product coke oven these materials are saved.

Coke is used directly as a fuel and in various metallurgical processes, including smelting and refining of metals. The coal tars and other coal chemicals are widely used in industry in the manufacture of drugs, dyes, and other materials. Coal can also be used in the manufacture of artificial gas, gasoline, diesel oil, and lubricants, but the relative abundance of petroleum limits these processes at present. As reserves of petroleum decline, however, the use of coal will increase, both as a fuel and as a chemical raw material. Even today, in countries without petroleum, coal is more important than it is in the United States.

34

Petroleum and Natural Gas

PETROLEUM affects the daily lives of more people than any other mineral. More homes are lighted by petroleum than by electricity. As a source of gasoline, fuel oil, lubricants, and hundreds of other products, petroleum is an absolute necessity for a modern industrial nation.

Several brief references have already been made to petroleum production in the preceding chapters, since an oilfield affects many other activities in a region. The demands for labor, agricultural products, transportation, and other services increase. In recent years oil discoveries have revolutionized the economies of such places as western North Dakota, western Canada, and Arabia. Interest in petroleum rises as the reserves diminish. During World War II most of us knew what it meant to have only limited supplies of petroleum products, but only the Germans had the unfortunate experience of using up their last reserves of petroleum and seeing their air force and land transport useless for lack of fuel. The world demand for petroleum is increasing today while the reserves are declining, particularly in areas of heavy production such as the United States.

USES OF PETROLEUM

Put very briefly, petroleum is a source of light, heat, lubricants, and power. These are merely the major uses. In the course of a single day, an ordinary person may use petroleum in many different forms: as a household fuel; as gasoline and lubricants for his automobile; or as a cleaner to remove a spot from his coat. Petroleum has been known and used in a small way for centuries. Many people, including the ancient Chinese and primitive American Indians, used it as medicine.

Marco Polo during his journey across Asia observed its use to cure mange on camels. Extensive use of petroleum, however, developed in the present century. The first large-scale use of petroleum was in the form of kerosene for lighting purposes. The increasing scarcity of whale oil and other lamp oils led to the simple distillation of black "rock oil." As much kerosene as possible was obtained from the oil and other products, such as gasoline, were discarded. Today kerosene is less important although it still lights millions of homes and is used widely for cooking and heating purposes. Gasoline, fuel oil, naphtha, paraffin, road asphalt, petroleum coke, and lubricants are the chief petroleum products in the commercial world. See FIGURE 34.4. Fortunately, petroleum products can be transported to all parts of the earth without great difficulty, and it is a remote community indeed which does not have five gallon cans which once contained gasoline or kerosene. Primitive people prize these containers for household purposes often in preference to their native pottery.

OCCURRENCE

Petroleum is widely distributed in certain sedimentary rocks of the earth's crust, but unfortunately it is present in paying quantities in only a few localities. The cost of drilling an oil well is often in excess of $100,000. Obviously a large amount of oil must be obtained to make drilling profitable, more especially in view of the fact that many wells are dry. In the long run the productive wells must pay for the "dry holes" unless the stockholders are to lose money.

Petroleum occurs in paying quantities only in porous sediments, called "oil sands," which have

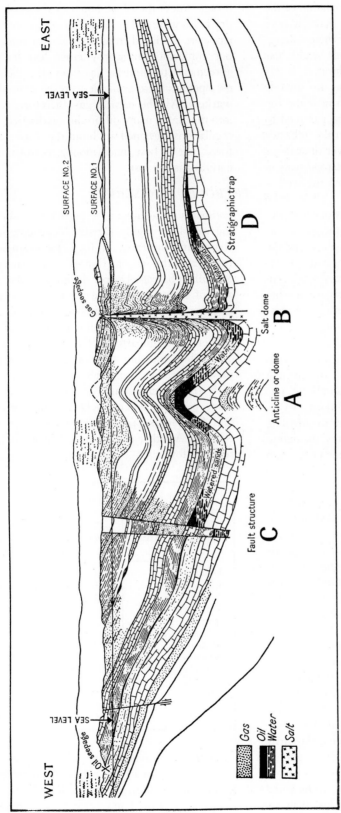

FIGURE 34.1. *An idealized cross section of the central portion of an oil basin. Various kinds of oil traps (structures in which oil accumulates) are illustrated. At A is a simple anticline, the presence of which is clearly evident at the surface. B represents a salt dome with uplift and deformation of the beds, creating numerous pockets in which oil can accumulate. At C a fault trap is formed by a down-dropped block of the earth's crust, sealing the oil-bearing sand. D represents a stratigraphic trap, produced by the pinch-out of the sand. It will be noted that all of the oil occurs in the same formation, a sandstone, which is exposed at the surface, upper left. From* World Geography of Petroleum, *American Geographical Society.*

a favorable structure for the accumulation of the oil in "pools." Many sandstones have a pore space equal to one fifth or more of their volume. This space may be filled with salt water, gas under pressure, or petroleum. If the rock layers are folded or arched, the conditions are suitable for the concentration of petroleum near the top of the arch or anticline, for oil and gas tend to move upward in the structures under the influence of the rock pressure. A capping layer of shale or other dense rock on top of the sandstone seals in the oil and prevents its escape until the well is drilled. Thus it is not unusual for a well to strike the crest of an arched layer of sandstone and produce only natural gas at first. As the gas is exhausted the oil moves up to take its place, and the well then produces oil until the pressure is relieved or the pool is exhausted. Under some conditions newly drilled wells flow freely, sometimes violently, and are known as "gushers," but most wells must be pumped in order to bring the oil to the surface. See FIGURE 34.1.

In spite of the great improvement in the techniques of locating oil wells and in the drilling methods, it is still an uncertain undertaking, one which is often accompanied by much waste. Some of the waste is unavoidable, but overdrilling (too many wells to a given pool), fires, the dumping of oil into streams, and the escape of gas into the air could, in many places, be prevented. To illustrate the wastage one need only witness the exploitation of a new oil pool. Some years ago in central Oklahoma a well was drilled in a district which previously had produced no petroleum. The geologic evidence indicated the possible presence of petroleum, so someone was willing to risk $100,000 to test it. Naturally everyone in the vicinity watched eagerly for the results. Some people quietly bought leases to the mineral rights on nearby farms. When the well came is as a "gusher," there was no concealing the fact. Oil rained from the air in a very unpleasant and exciting downpour. Immediately other wells were started in the vicinity, and soon the race was on to see who could get the most oil from the pool before it was exhausted. The drillers of the original or "discovery" well had to drill additional wells, of course, in order to get as many "pipes" as possible into the pool. As a result, in a few months' time over 600 wells were pumping away at the pool, whereas less than 50 would have been sufficient. Since in the beginning

no one knew the exact limits of the pool, many dry holes were drilled. Large quantities of natural gas were produced from the wells for some time, but companies in nearby cities had long-term agreements to purchase gas from other fields and no pipelines were available to reach more distant markets. All the natural gas, therefore, escaped into the air. In many oil-producing districts today regulations designed to limit the waste are in force, but at best much money, petroleum, and natural gas are lost.

PETROLEUM RESERVES

Estimates of the amount of petroleum reserves in the world are highly variable, depending on the source and the time. In 1937, for example, the reserves in the state of Illinois were estimated at 28 million barrels. Deeper drilling and the extension of a previously known field resulted in the discovery of new pools and two years later the estimate jumped to 432 million barrels! Many a farmer in southeastern Illinois bought a new automobile with his oil royalties. The estimates of world reserves, in general, are not subject to such great fluctuations. As new discoveries are made, however, and old fields extended or as certain fields cease production, the estimates are changed. A rather conservative estimate of world reserves follows.

ESTIMATE OF WORLD RESERVES OF PETROLEUM		
Country or Area	Reserves (in millions of barrels)	Reserves (per cent of total)
United States	27,000	31.0
Iraq and Iran	12,500	14.3
Arabia	20,000	23.0
Venezuela	9,000	10.3
Russia	4,200	4.8
Indonesia	1,250	1.4
Mexico	850	1.0
Romania	350	0.4
Colombia	300	0.3
Trinidad	300	0.3
Others	11,500	13.2
Total	87,250	100.0

Although estimates vary widely, it is fairly certain that most of the petroleum reserves are located in a few areas: the Gulf and Mid-Continent fields of the United States; Venezuela and Colombia; the Caucasus district of Russia; and the Persian Gulf district of Iran, Iraq, and Arabia. Other large fields may yet be discovered, but all the above are known to have large reserves.

If the reserves and present production of petroleum are unevenly distributed, so is the consumption. Only the people of highly mechanized countries are large consumers at the present time, and even in some countries which are industrially advanced, consumption is limited by the high prices of imported petroleum products. The consumption of petroleum in the United States has more than tripled in the last 25 years, and is more than two billion barrels, or about 15 barrels per capita. Nearly half of the petroleum products are used in transportation on the highways, railroads, waterways, and in the air. Industry and agriculture use about one fourth, while residential and miscellaneous uses account for the remainder.

Petroleum and petroleum products are normally exported from the United States, Russia, Latin America, and Asia, mainly to Australia, New Zealand, Europe, and Africa. It will be observed that the consumption of petroleum products is not always related to production within the specific country but rather to purchasing power, to the nature of the transport, and to other factors.

UNITED STATES PRODUCTION

Ever since Colonel Drake "brought in" the first oil well in Pennsylvania in 1859, the United States has led the world in petroleum production. Possessed of a great reserve and a large home market, United States producers have for many years averaged more than one billion barrels annually or nearly ten barrels per capita, per year. The total accumulated production from the United States fields is close to 30 billion barrels, most of which has been obtained since the advent of mass production of automobiles.

Production is distributed through nine major fields from the Appalachians to California and from Michigan to the Gulf (FIG. 34.2):

The Appalachian Field
The Michigan Field
The Ohio-Indiana Field
The Illinois Field
The Mid-Continent Field
The East Texas Field (often considered a part of the Mid-Continent Field)
The Gulf Field
The Rocky Mountain Field
The California Field

The Appalachian Field of Pennsylvania, Ohio, West Virginia, Kentucky, and small portions of adjacent states is the oldest producing area of the United States. Production has declined slowly but steadily for many years and few new pools have been discovered. In general, the oils from this field are of high quality and are especially prized for the manufacture of lubricants. The nearness to the eastern market is also an advantage. The highest production is in Pennsylvania with about 17 million barrels, most of which comes from the vicinity of Bradford. All the wells have to be pumped, and the daily yield per well is less than a barrel. Five and three million barrels are produced in Kentucky and West Virginia respectively. A large quantity of natural gas is produced in the Appalachian Region, and drilling for gas is still active.

The Michigan Field lies to the west of Saginaw Bay in the central part of the Southern Peninsula. In this region, opened only a quarter century ago, production rose rapidly, reaching a peak of 23 million barrels in 1939 and declining since that time. The Ohio-Indiana Field is older and has declined further. Oil quality is good except for the presence of sulfur and water in the oil. About three million barrels are produced in Ohio, and somewhat less in Indiana. (A part of the Indiana production comes from the southwestern part of the state and is considered as part of the Illinois Field.)

Southeastern Illinois is an example of an oilfield which was considered almost exhausted but which staged a comeback. In 1936 producers in Illinois were down to a four million barrel annual production. Deeper drilling in old fields was largely responsible for the increase in 1940 to more than 146 million barrels, making this one of the most important fields of its size in the country. The wells have large initial production but little staying power, however, and since 1940 production has declined.

In the Mid-Continent Field, which includes northern and western Texas, part of New Mexico, and all of Oklahoma and Kansas, more petroleum has been produced than in any other similar field in the world. In certain years more than half the total production of the United States has been taken from this field. Production began in 1889 in eastern Kansas, and gradually spread to Oklahoma, Texas, and New Mexico. The East Texas Field, which includes parts of Louisi-

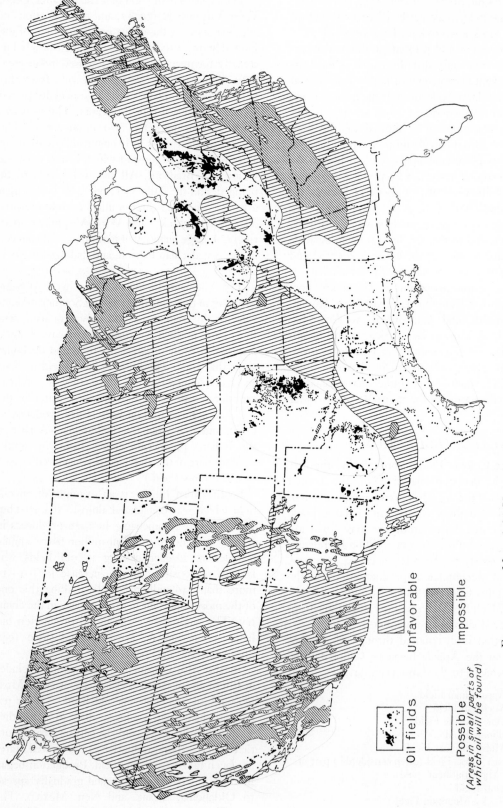

FIGURE 34·2. *Map of the United States showing the distribution of oil fields and unproductive areas classified as to their likelihood of yielding oil. From U. S. Geological Survey.*

ana and Arkansas, sometimes considered part of the Mid-Continent Field, developed somewhat later. The quality of the oil varies widely in this vast region. Some of the shallow wells of Kansas produce heavy oils with little value for gasoline or lubricants, but most of the oil in the Mid-Continent area is of high quality. Largest production in Kansas is in the southeastern part of the state where drilling still continues with good results, but the general picture shows the likelihood of a decline in the near future. Production in Oklahoma is declining slowly, although new discoveries and new drilling are adding to the reserves. Production in Oklahoma declined from 200 million barrels in 1936 (second only to that of Texas) to 164 million barrels in 1950. By far the leading pool in this field is on the outskirts of Oklahoma City where some of the wells are in the backyards and even the front lawns of city residences. From this one pool, not much larger than a good-sized wheat farm, about 35 million barrels were produced annually for several years. The deepest well ever drilled in the Mid-Continent Field is in Washita County (Oklahoma) at 14,482 feet, a dry hole.

Production in the Mid-Continent Field of Texas is in many scattered pools, difficult to describe briefly. For many years Texas has been the leading petroleum state. Outside of the Gulf Coast, which is described separately, the field may be divided into East Texas, Central Texas, North Texas, the Panhandle, South Texas, and West Texas (see map, FIG. 34.2). Of these by far the largest production is in East Texas with an average of 120 million barrels. The total production in Texas is nearly 500 million barrels. In spite of the feverish drilling and high production for many years, the reserves in the Mid-Continent Field are still large.

The Gulf Coast Field of Texas and Louisiana is one of the newest fields in the United States to be extensively developed. The first well was drilled in 1901, but production did not begin on a large scale until 1935. Conditions are quite different from those in the fields previously described. The sediments are softer so that drilling with rotary drills is quite rapid. The oils often contain small quantities of sulfur, water, and even fine sand and are, in general, more suited to the production of fuel oils than of gasoline. Nevertheless, production has increased rapidly in recent years

and will probably continue to increase since the oil pools extend out under the Gulf of Mexico, how far, no one knows. Some drilling is already in progress in the shallow margins of the Gulf, a fact which has raised a rather difficult legal question. Who owns the oil under the waters of the Gulf? The State? The Federal Government? Some recent decisions have favored the states, but the debate continues.

The Rocky Mountain Field includes many small areas of petroleum production mainly in Colorado, Wyoming, and Montana. Canadian production in Alberta, noted previously in Chapter 6, is in this same general region. Production in Colorado is mainly from the new Rangely district in the northwestern part of the state which produces about 20 million barrels per year. Production in Wyoming, on the other hand, has decreased slightly but in some years reaches more than 50 million barrels. Most of the Montana production of ten million barrels comes from the Cut Bank Field in the north central part of the state, near the Canadian border. Of all petroleum fields in the United States the Rocky Mountain Field is the most isolated from the market. Many small scattered pools add to the difficulty of transportation. A pipeline from eastern Wyoming connects with the main pipeline system from the Mid-Continent Field which serves eastern United States.

California petroleum production comes from three main fields—the Los Angeles Basin (FIG. 34.3), the coastal district near Ventura, and the southern part of the San Joaquin Valley. There are several pools in each of these districts. Total production averages more than 350 million barrels, making California second only to Texas in petroleum. Deeper drilling in some pools has increased production. Most of the California oils are heavy, but some are of high quality and production is sufficient to supply the Pacific Coast with gasoline, fuel oil for locomotives and domestic heating, and various other needs. There is a surplus for shipment to eastern United States via the Panama Canal and also for export to the Pacific. This field is all the more significant because of the scarcity of coal on the Pacific Coast.

FUTURE SUPPLIES OF PETROLEUM FOR THE UNITED STATES

Estimates of oil reserves are subject to revision, but it appears at present that within the limits of

FIGURE 34.3. *Historic Signal Hill Oilfield, Long Beach, California, discovered in 1921 by Shell Oil Company, Incorporated, was formerly a residential subdivision. This kind of town-lot drilling with each lot owner demanding a share in the bonanza, resulted in confusion and waste. Today, scientific spacing of wells and other conservation techniques are employed in many oilfields. From Shell Oil Co., Inc.*

continental United States not much more than 27 billion barrels of crude petroleum are available. Since the production annually is only slightly below two billions, and allowing for a probable increased consumption, our domestic supply will not last much more than a decade. New reserves are being discovered in the United States at the present time, and the amount of new discoveries is generally more than the annual production. Furthermore, optimistic observers hold that much greater reserves remain to be discovered in and near the United States, especially in the Gulf of Mexico, that foreign sources of petroleum will be available, and that petroleum products such as gasoline can be obtained from natural gas, oil shales, tar sands, and coal.

Gasoline suitable for use in motors can be manufactured from natural gas with no great difficulty and at low cost. Unfortunately, natural gas is limited in quantity and is already in demand for other purposes. By the time our supply of crude oil is

near exhaustion, natural gas will be scarce also. Enormous quantities of oil shales are available in the Rocky Mountain Region, in which some 90 billion barrels of oil are stored. The cost of extracting the oil on a large scale is not known, but it is many times the cost of crude oil produced from wells. The remoteness of the deposits is a handicap also, but if the price of gasoline should only be doubled by the time oil shales are in use, the relative cost of transportation to market will be low.

During World War II Germans manufactured gasoline and other petroleum products from coal. Only the extreme scarcity of fuel and disregard of the cost of synthetic production made this possible, since the cost of this process is greater than that of extracting oil from shale. Coal is abundant in the United States and if this synthetic process can be cheapened, it may help extend our supplies of natural petroleum. At the close of World War II, Secretary of Interior Ickes strongly recommended the construction of synthetic petroleum factories.

It has been suggested that alcohol derived from grain and other sources be mixed with the gasoline used in the United States in order to increase the supply. If such a plan is to be effective it would be necessary to pass a Federal law indicating the proportion of alcohol to be used. At least 20 per cent alcohol should be added, which would necessitate an additional production of nearly five billion gallons of alcohol and would double the cost of gasoline. While on the whole the best solution of the future oil problem is to secure and develop foreign supplies, the question is one which merits careful thought and long-range planning.

NATURAL GAS

Natural gas and petroleum often occur together and over half the production of gas in the United States is from petroleum wells. In some localities, however, natural gas occurs alone. The largest reserves are located in the Mid-Continent, Gulf Coast, and California oilfields, and Texas, California, and Louisiana are the leading producers.

Natural gas is better adapted to certain uses than petroleum. In a domestic gas heating plant, for example, all that is needed for proper combustion is a simple burner without moving parts, whereas an efficient oil burner must have a high pressure nozzle, a motor, a pump, filters, and other parts which are subject to rather rapid depreciation. Natural gas is very useful as a source of heat in the converters of steel mills. It is also an excellent fuel for oil refineries and glass plants, and is a source of carbon black. As indicated in the previous discussion of petroleum resources, natural gas is an excellent source of gasoline and a large portion of the raw gas product is treated to obtain natural gasoline before being used for other purposes. Natural gas is used also in the manufacture of plastics, synthetic fibers, and various chemicals.

The estimated gross production of natural gas in the United States is in excess of seven trillion cubic feet. Of this amount about one half is produced in Texas. Most of the remainder comes from Louisiana, Arkansas in the Mid-Continent Field, and from the older Appalachian Field, including Ohio, Pennsylvania, West Virginia, and Kentucky. Wyoming and California are also large producers.

PETROLEUM PRODUCTION IN OTHER LANDS

Of the total world production of petroleum (Fig. 34.4), four billion barrels in round numbers, the United States produces 50 per cent, Canada and Mexico together 3 per cent, and Asia accounts for about 20 per cent, mostly in Arabia, Iraq, and Iran. South America produces 16 per cent, and Venezuela alone 14 per cent. The U.S.S.R. averages about 6 per cent, and Europe less than 2 per cent. About half of the European production comes from Romania. Like Europe, Africa and Oceania are also petroleum paupers. World production has been increasing in recent years, especially in the Middle East.

CANADA, a net importer of petroleum a few years ago, has increased production very rapidly in recent years. The largest producing fields, in the Province of Alberta, include the Redwater Field northeast of Edmonton, which has produced more than 23 million barrels in one year, and the Leduc Field, also a large producer. Farther north, the Peace River country apparently has large reserves of oil and natural gas. Although Canada's reserves of petroleum are large, the interior location presents some difficulties in transportation. To supplement rail and truck transportation pipelines for both oil and natural gas connect the fields with the Port of Vancouver, B. C. and with Lake Superior, where cheap tanker transport is available. As the reserves of oil in California decline, the petroleum and natural gas from western Canada should find a greater market.

MEXICO reached its peak of petroleum in 1921 and since that time production has generally declined, although a slow increase has been noted in recent years. The chief fields are near the Gulf, especially in the vicinity of Tampico, Túxpan, and Puerto México, thus facilitating export. Since Mexico has little coal, however, most of its oil production is consumed at home. Although oil exploration for new fields continues in Mexico, little new production has been developed in recent years.

VENEZUELA, usually second in petroleum production, has three main fields, western, middle, and eastern, all along the northern fringe of the country. The field around Lake Maracaibo is the old-

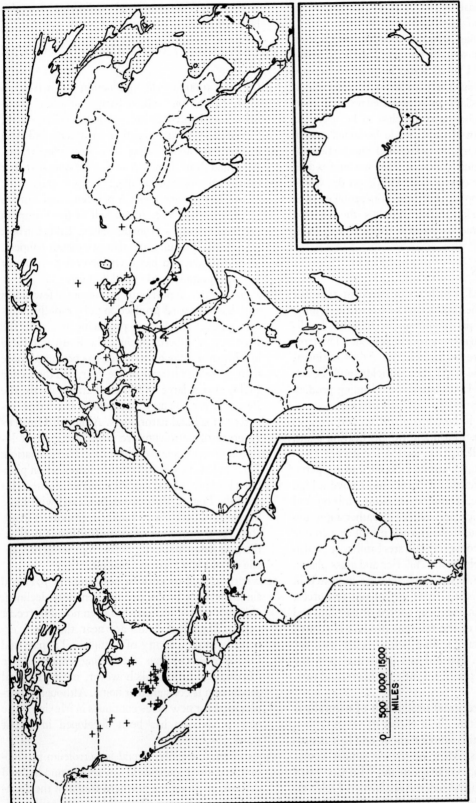

FIGURE 34.4. *Map of the petroleum fields of the world. In most of the fields indicated some oil is produced, but production is variable. (Smaller fields are shown by plus signs.)*

est in point of production. A part of this field lies in Colombia also. The middle Venezuela Field is largely in the State of Guarico, while the Eastern Field is in the Orinoco Delta. (The island of Trinidad nearby is also a producer.) Most of the Venezuelan wells are comparatively shallow, and transportation to the coast is easy. Much of the export oil formerly went to western Europe, but in recent years the United States has been a good customer. It is probable that Venezuela will be able to supply the United States deficiencies for the next decade with some help from Canada, Mexico, and the Middle East. Venezuela also furnishes some oil to other South American countries, since only Colombia, Ecuador, Peru, and Argentina are self-sufficient.

EUROPE has many small scattered oilfields, but only in Romania is there substantial production and the total production is less than that in California. In view of the rather large demands, Europe must therefore import large quantities of oil from the Middle East and elsewhere. At the same time the high cost of petroleum products limits consumption. The largest field is near Ploesti in Romania in the foothills of the Carpathians and north of Bucharest. Oil is moved by pipeline to the Danube River, thence by river tanker to the Black Sea and up river to Hungary. In recent years little Romanian oil has reached western Europe.

THE U.S.S.R. has furnished almost no specific data on petroleum production since 1939, and only estimates are available for subsequent years. The location of the principal fields and their relative production, however, are fairly well known. The first well was drilled in the Maikop region north of the Caucasus Mountains in the year 1866. Its depth was only 70 feet. The chief zone of production stretches from the south slope of the Cauca-

FIGURE 34.5. *The Ras Tanura marine petroleum terminal on the Persian Gulf in Saudi Arabia. Large tankers dock here and transport a large share of Arabian export oil. From Standard Oil Company of New Jersey.*

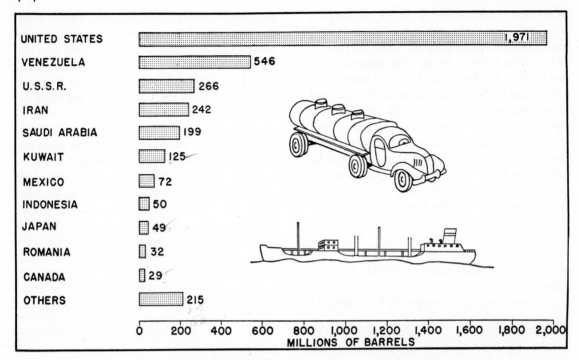

	MILLIONS OF BARRELS
UNITED STATES	1,971
VENEZUELA	546
U.S.S.R.	266
IRAN	242
SAUDI ARABIA	199
KUWAIT	125
MEXICO	72
INDONESIA	50
JAPAN	49
ROMANIA	32
CANADA	29
OTHERS	215

FIGURE 34.6. *Graph of petroleum production by leading countries.*

sus Mountains to the southern Urals and includes the middle Volga district. The largest production is in the Baku district on the Apsheron Peninsula. In 1901 in this rather small district half the world's oil was produced. Oil is shipped from this field via the Caspian Sea, which is connected with the Black Sea by two pipelines, one to Rostov, the other to Batumi. Tankers supply much of west Russia via the Volga River and its connecting waterways. Two other important fields lie to the north of the Caucasus, one near Grozny and the other near Maikop. An additional large field extends from the Kama River, a tributary of the Volga, to the Caspian Sea. The oils from the Volga field are of the heavy type, ill-suited to the manufacture of high-quality gasoline but useful for fuel oil and in chemical industries. Enough oil is brought from Sakhalin Island, off the Pacific Coast of Russia, to permit some export, and the Arctic fields, recently discovered and developed, probably produce three million barrels per year. The Taymyr and Lena districts are especially important.

THE MIDDLE EAST (Iran, Iraq, Saudi Arabia, and Kuwait) has known oil for at least six thousand years and has used it as a bonding material and a medicine, for calking boats and setting jewels.

But until recently production has been very small, although the reserves may be greater than those of any other parts of the world. Remoteness, unstable political conditions, and the quality of the oils have retarded development. Although initial cost of development has been great, the high production per well makes the average cost per barrel comparatively low. The chief producing fields are located on the margins of the Arabian Plateau and the Iranian Plateau, which contain zones of folded and disturbed oil-bearing sediments. Many other parts of the Middle East probably also have petroleum in commercial quantities.

In Iran very small amounts of petroleum have been produced from seepages for many centuries, but modern exploration began in 1855. After many failures, production began on a commercial scale in 1908 and increased steadily. The field is quite compact, and all the wells are within 170 miles, by pipeline, from the large refinery at Abadan. The oil is obtained mainly from anticlines in fissured limestones. The wells are widely spaced, about two miles on the average, and only 70 wells recover most of the oil.

In Iraq also petroleum has been known for centuries, but large-scale commercial production did not begin until 1927 with the discovery of the

Kirkuk Field. This field is located on the crest of an anticline about sixty miles long, and the oil occurs mainly in a porous limestone of great permeability. As a result a few wells account for most of the production. A pipeline, constructed in 1934 to carry the oil to the sea, branches near the crossing of the Euphrates River, one line going to Tripoli and the other to Haifa on the Mediterranean. Pipelines carry 400,000 barrels of oil per day from this field. The reserves in this field may be as large as 7000 million barrels. Oil is produced also in the vicinity of Basra, but some is of inferior quality.

Oil development came late to Saudi Arabia and for many years permission for exploration was not obtainable. An agreement was reached in 1933 and exploration began, under the joint management of four American oil companies, known as the Arabian American Oil Company (Aramco). Production began on and in the vicinity of Bahrein Island in the Persian Gulf and comes mainly from six fields. The Dammam Field is located on a circular dome about 20 miles in diameter and the oil comes from limestone, capped with anhydrite. The Abu Hadriya Field is about 100 miles west of the Dammam and is also on a circular dome. The oil is deep, and further development will be delayed pending greater need for the oil.

FIGURE 34.7. *An oil refinery at Cut Bank, Montana. Refineries are usually located either near the oilfields or large urban markets, or on the seaboard. From Great Northern Railway.*

The Abqaiq Field, one of the largest and most productive fields in Arabia, is located on a large anticline, 50 miles long and 25 miles wide. Production is generally limited only by pipeline capacity and this field is the eastern terminus of the Trans-Arabian pipeline which reaches the Mediterranean at Sidon, Lebanon. Other fields include Qatif, discovered in 1945, Ain Dar, 1948, Fadhili and Haradh, 1949. Part of the oil produced in Saudi Arabia is refined at the Ras Tanura Refinery (FIG. 34.5) and on Bahrein Island. The output is about 25 per cent gasoline, 6 per cent kerosene, 25 per cent diesel oil, and the remainder fuel oil. The United States Navy in adjacent waters has been supplied from this refinery.

Exploration for oil began in Kuwait in 1934, and the first successful well was drilled in 1937. The structure is a low dome with gentle dips, and the oil is found mostly in sandstones at moderate depths. The reserves are very large, making this one of the most important fields in the world.

SOUTHEASTERN ASIA has scattered oilfields from Burma to New Guinea and from northern Borneo to Java, although the largest producing centers are in Indonesia, especially Sumatra, Java, Borneo, and the small island of Tarakan. Oil production began in 1885 with a well in north Sumatra with a depth of only 400 feet. Expansion was slow until 1912 when a number of new companies entered the field. Although many of the wells and much of the equipment was destroyed immediately prior to the Japanese invasion during World War II, the Indonesian fields supplied most of Japan's petroleum for about three years. After Japanese surrender, rehabilitation began and much progress has been made, but production has not reached prewar levels. Perhaps the unstable political conditions in Indonesia are partly responsible.

Australia and New Zealand have produced little petroleum, and there is no indication of large reserves, but a newly discovered field in Western Australia seems promising. The first well, located about 650 miles east of Freemantle, brought in 50 barrels per day. The field is rather remote from rail or other lines of transportation.

SUMMARY

As indicated previously, most of the petroleum comes from a few countries—the United States, Venezuela, Kuwait, Saudi Arabia, Iraq, Iran, and the U.S.S.R. (FIG. 34.6). Many smaller fields are in production, and some of them show promise of substantial increase. It should be noted that Africa (excepting Egypt), Oceania, and western Europe have almost no known resources. The best chances for substantial increases in production in the future lie in the United States, the eastern front of the Andes from Venezuela to Argentina, and in the Middle East. A most important fact is that the United States, with only 30 per cent of the reserves, is producing about 50 per cent of the oil. If this trend continues, it is obvious that in ten to twenty years the United States will be a "have not" nation, and the Middle East, the U.S.S.R., and perhaps a few others will be the "haves." It is in our interest, therefore, to develop the resources of the Western Hemisphere and to keep oil flowing from the Middle East. Consumption in the United States will certainly increase faster than domestic production and imports will have to increase. It would seem desirable, therefore, to encourage foreign oil development and to abolish the tariff on crude petroleum. At the same time every effort should be made to conserve domestic resources, especially in the offshore areas, often called, erroneously, "the tidelands."

35

Water Power and Water Supply

Man has long marveled at the force of falling water and has endeavored through the centuries to harness this energy to useful purposes. Development has ranged from a simple paddle wheel in a mountain stream, turning a grindstone or a millstone, to modern installations with lofty dams, turbines, and generators coupled with a complicated system of transmission lines. Hydroelectric energy still does not equal the energy derived from fuels (often called "thermal energy"), but it has the advantage of being renewable. The water which turns the turbines flows down to the sea, and evaporation brings it back to the atmosphere and to the land in an endless cycle. But hydroelectric energy is not free. The developmental costs are substantial, involving the purchase of water rights and land, the construction of dams, the installation of turbines, generators, and transmission systems, plus constant maintenance. Only on favorable sites or in districts remote from coal is water power likely to be substantially cheaper than thermal generation.

Hydroelectric energy competes with electricity produced from fuels, mainly coal, petroleum, and natural gas. Water power saves fuels. Once the hydroelectric installations are made, the operation is usually cheaper than that of thermal plants, and precious fuels are saved which cannot be replaced. It is estimated that nearly 200 million additional tons of coal would have to be mined in the United States to produce the energy now obtained from water power. In many places hydroelectric and thermal plants are used in conjunction, the water power used to its full capacity and the thermal production stepped up in times of low water or higher demands. The table below shows the relative importance of thermal and hydroelectric power production in the United States in 1950.

Sources of Electric Power in the United States		
Source	Quantity	Per cent of total
Natural Gas	777 billion cubic feet	14
Fuel Oil	93 million barrels	11
Coal	114 million short tons	49
Water Power	—	26

If hydroelectric development is to be worth-while, a number of conditions must be met. A site must be chosen with a natural fall of water or one on which a dam may be constructed to produce an artificial fall. The flow of water must be adequate and fairly even, and this depends in turn on the amount and seasonal distribution of precipitation in the watershed of the stream. In addition, a need for the power must be near enough and large enough to warrant the necessary construction, including transmission lines. Hydroelectric energy can be sent several hundred miles, but only with some loss and at additional cost. Therefore, the investigation of a potential power site begins with a demand or an anticipated demand for power in the vicinity.

One of the first qualities studied is the precipitation over the watershed of the stream. Usually weather records are available for several stations for a period of several years. If the rainfall is light, a large watershed is needed. If a long dry season occurs, a large reservoir is required. Next, the amount of water flowing at the proposed site is measured, preferably over a period of years. If the precipitation and flow are adequate, the next step is to study the site to determine if conditions are favorable for the construction of a permanent dam. Is the bedrock structurally strong and near the surface or is it weak and covered with thick deposits of sand and gravel underneath the stream bed? Is the valley narrow or wide? A wide valley requires a long, relatively expensive dam. Is the reservoir area adequate? Will it hold water or is the underlying rock porous? The nature of the dam site and cost of construction are often the deciding factors in determining whether the site will be developed. In brief, the development depends on the *flow*, the *site* (dam or falls), and the *demand*.

A SMALL POWER SITE

Although less spectacular than the Grand Coulee, Hoover, or TVA developments, small water sites are much more numerous. Many sites lend them-

selves to small-scale power plants, and some of them operate very cheaply and efficiently. The Leaburg plant on the McKenzie River (FIG. 35.1) in Oregon is a good example of a small installation and incidentally energized the fluorescent light by which this chapter was written.

The McKenzie River rises on the west slope of the Cascade Range and is fed by rains and abundant snows. Rain is light in the summer, but the river maintains a fairly even flow, partly because of the porosity of the igneous rocks in the watershed. In the vicinity of Leaburg the river has a gradient of about 10 feet to the mile, including a few rapids but no falls. Here is a favorable site for a small inexpensive dam. A power canal takes water out of the river with the aid of a diversion dam and parallels the river for several miles. At the power plant the canal is 90 feet above the river, producing a satisfactory "head" of

FIGURE 35.1. *The Leaburg Power Plant on the McKenzie River in Oregon. The power canal, diverted from the river five miles upstream from this point, reaches a head of 90 feet. From Eugene Water and Electric Board.*

water. The water falls through penstock tubes to the turbines which turn the generators, and the water flows down the tailrace and rejoins the river. The Leaburg plant produces 14,000 kilowatts at low cost.

LARGE PROJECTS

A good example of a large project in water power development is Hoover Dam (FIG. 35.2) on the Colorado River near Las Vegas, Nevada. This dam, also called Boulder Dam at times, was begun in 1931 and completed in five years at a cost of $120,000,000. The dam produces a head of water of 726 feet, making it one of the highest in the world. It impounds a reservoir more than 200 square miles in area, backing up water well into the Grand Canyon of the Colorado River. This site has all the requirements for good water power development. The watershed of the Colorado River above the dam includes parts of Wyoming, Utah, Colorado, New Mexico, and a small part of Nevada, as well as some sections of northern Arizona. The Colorado River drains snow-covered areas of the Rocky Mountains, and the melting snows provide a heavy flow of water in the spring and early summer. A large dam on such a river has the advantages of storing up much of the flood waters during the period of heavy runoff and of using the water for power development when the runoff is much smaller. Such a large dam with its reservoir provides some measure of flood control as well as furnishing power. However, because of the nature of the country, the dam does not divert water for irrigation, although it does store up water that is used for irrigation in the Imperial Valley farther down the river. During the planning stages of this dam some critics pointed out that there would be no market for power in the vicinity, which is even today sparsely populated. However, the ability to send power long distances overrode that objection, and the power from the dam is used in various places, including Los Angeles. A part of the power produced at Boulder Dam is used in the magnesium and titanium refineries nearby.

Another large site, quite different in character, is located at Niagara Falls on the border between New York and Ontario. Here no dam is needed since the water naturally falls 160 feet over a limestone ledge. The total drop from Lake Erie to Ontario is from 573 to 247 feet; so the potential power is much greater than that developed. Another restriction on development is the scenic value of the falls, since the quality of the falls would be greatly altered if large quantities of water were taken out for power purposes. The power installations are fundamentally very simple. Water is taken out above the falls in penstock tubes, led to a point below the falls, and dropped through the turbines to the river channel below. See FIGURE 6.7. The site of Niagara Falls then is almost ideal. The lakes above furnish perfect natural reservoirs to store the water and provide an even flow. The fluctuations in lake levels from season to season or even from year to year are only a few feet. The only cost is the installation of the penstock tubes, the power houses, and the transmission lines. Furthermore, Niagara Falls is located in an area of fairly dense population, and cities like Buffalo and Toronto can absorb a large amount of electrical energy.

WATER POWER RESOURCES

As noted above, the water power available in any region depends on the amount and evenness of the precipitation, the flow of the stream, and the gradient which can be translated into a "head" of water. The presence of a natural waterfall such as Niagara, or a suitable dam site, or a diversion system to create an artificial fall are also favorable factors. A market for the power is essential, and a demand usually exists in the vicinity before development of the site begins. The potential water power resources of the continents are conditioned, therefore, by precipitation, elevation, and favorable site. Estimates of resources (FIG. 35.3) are measured in horsepower or kilowatts, and may be stated in terms of power available all the time, or part of the time. Power production is often measured in terms of installed capacity, that is, the number and capacity of the generators, even though there may not be enough water to run all the generators all of the time.

In the UNITED STATES the use of electricity has had a phenomenal growth since its beginning in 1882. Each decade has seen a doubling of the amount used. By 1950 electricity was being used in 92 per cent of all houses in the United States including 83 per cent of the rural homes. By far the largest use is in industry, which consumes more than six kilowatt-hours per man-hour. Of the approximate 330 billion kilowatt-hours used

FIGURE 35.2. *A photograph and explanatory diagram of Hoover (Boulder) Dam on the Colorado River. The photograph shows the excellent site, a deep and narrow canyon with rock walls. A portion of the reservoir, Lake Mead, and the power plants below the dam are visible. The diagram illustrates the functional parts of the dam which are not visible in the photograph. The penstocks, intakes, and spillway tunnels are concealed in the rock wall on the Arizona side (right). A similar set of diversion works is located in the wall on the Nevada side (left), but is not shown in the diagram. The principal purpose of the dam is power production, but it also serves for water storage and flood control. From Bureau of Reclamation.*

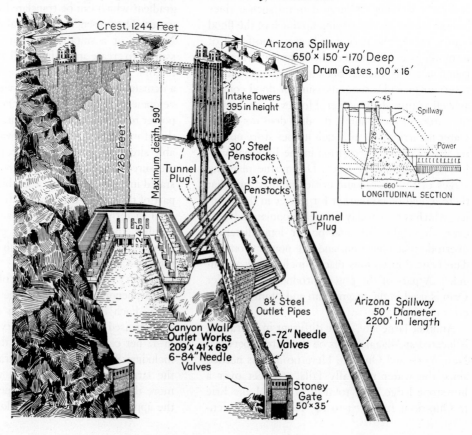

in 1950, about 200 billion were used in industry; residences, including farms, used 75 billion, and various commercial purposes accounted for 50 billion. The total amount generated was 389 billion kilowatt-hours. The difference between the amount generated and the amount used represents losses in transmission and distribution. Slightly more than one fourth of the power generated in the United States in 1950 was from water power. In all probability hydroelectric production will double again in the next ten to twenty years, depending on the growth of industry, but it is expected that it will continue to furnish about one fourth of the power requirements of the nation.

In the United States the greatest potential water power is in the Pacific Northwest because of heavy rainfall and high relief, followed by the Rocky Mountain region, the Great Lakes, and the Appalachians. The Columbia River and its tributaries represent the greatest potential power resource in the United States, even though part of the river is in Canada. Nearly 40 per cent of the potential power of the United States is found in the watershed of this river, only a small part of which is being utilized. The principal developments so far have been in four sites, all providing a large quantity of power: Bonneville Dam, near Portland, Oregon; Grand Coulee Dam, in eastern Washington; McNary Dam, between Washington and Oregon; and Hungry Horse Dam, in Montana.

Bonneville was the first of these power plants to be constructed because a good market is provided for the power nearby in Portland, Oregon, Vancouver, Washington, and vicinity. This is a long, rather low dam. The total length is 1450 feet, the height 197 feet. Because of the tremendous volume, though, of the Columbia River at this point, the capacity of this plant is fairly high, furnishing about 564,000 kilowatts of electrical energy. Energy from this site is transmitted into western Oregon, western Washington, and into networks that reach to California. Bonneville Dam does not furnish water for irrigation and has only limited value for flood control. Its chief use is for power. Grand Coulee Dam (FIG. 35.4) is located on the Columbia River to the northwest of Spokane, Washington. It is a multipurpose dam, built for power, flood control, and irrigation. The length is 4300 feet, the height 550 feet above the foundation. It has a large storage reservoir of about five million acre feet, known as Roosevelt Reservoir, which reaches to the Canadian border. The ultimate power capacity of

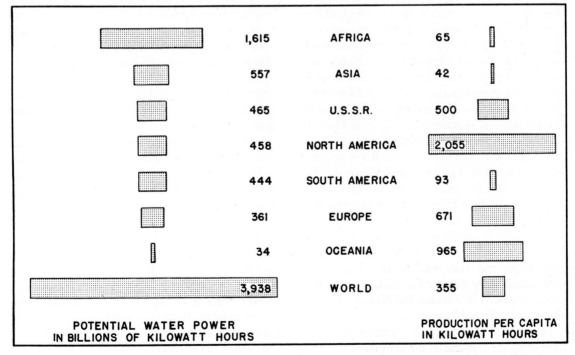

POTENTIAL WATER POWER IN BILLIONS OF KILOWATT HOURS		PRODUCTION PER CAPITA IN KILOWATT HOURS
1,615	AFRICA	65
557	ASIA	42
465	U.S.S.R.	500
458	NORTH AMERICA	2,055
444	SOUTH AMERICA	93
361	EUROPE	671
34	OCEANIA	965
3,938	WORLD	355

FIGURE 35.3. *Graph of power resources and power production by continents.*

this dam is more than two million kilowatt-hours, or about four times that of Bonneville. In addition, the reservoir is large enough and has a surplus capacity sufficient to be used in flood control to some extent. The water is also diverted through the Grand Coulee, by pumping, to irrigate 1,200,-000 acres in the state of Washington. McNary Dam to the northwest of Pendleton, Oregon, is located on the Columbia below the confluence of the Snake River, the Columbia's largest tributary. This dam is 8300 feet long and 158 feet high. The capacity is nearly one million kilowatts. In addition McNary Dam makes it possible to irrigate large areas of fairly level land in the states of Washington and Oregon. Some of the power is used to pump the water to higher levels and thus increase the area under irrigation. Hungry Horse Dam is located on the Flathead River in western Montana. The Flathead is a tributary of the Columbia River, and the dam is typical of headwater installations, used for storage and flood control more than for power. Hungry Horse Dam is 2000 feet long at the crest and has a height above the foundation of 564 feet. The storage capacity is three million acre feet, and the maximum power is only 300,000 kilowatts.

Other parts of western United States have large water power resources. In California many large sites are developed on the west slope of the Sierra Nevada Mountains, usually in conjunction with irrigation, city water supply, and flood control. The slow melting of snow at higher elevations during the summer compensates in part for the dry summers. In the Rocky Mountains and the Colorado Plateau region the greatest development, as previously noted, is at Hoover Dam on the Colorado. Additional power is available, much of it from the Colorado River system, in Arizona, Utah, Colorado, and Wyoming. In order of water power resources, Washington is first, followed by Oregon, California, Arizona, Idaho, Montana, Utah, Colorado, and Wyoming. In installed capacity, California ranks first, followed by Washington, Oregon, Nevada, Arizona, Idaho, and Montana. The completion of a large dam usually changes the rank. Most of the power produced in Arizona and Nevada, for example, comes from Hoover Dam.

In eastern United States the heaviest development of power is in and on the margins of the Appalachian Mountain system. These mountains get heavy precipitation most of the year in rather even amounts. Snow falls on the higher areas in the winter time and melts slowly during the spring, but summer rains are heavy also and the flow of the streams is fairly even. A great many small and moderate-sized power plants are developed all the way from Alabama to New England, and from the Appalachian Plateau country of West Virginia and eastern Kentucky to the Piedmont on the eastern part of the region. One of the greatest developments in the Appalachian region is the Tennessee Valley Project. The Tennessee River and its tributaries drain a large part of the southern Appalachians, including parts of Virginia, West Virginia, Kentucky, Tennessee, North Carolina, Georgia, and Alabama. The river has a rather even flow and furnishes a great deal of power at various sites. One of the first sites developed was at Muscle Shoals, where Wilson Dam was constructed during World War I for the purpose of fixing nitrogen from the air. The nitrate was intended for the production of munitions. Additional dams have been constructed on the upper reaches of the river and on the tributaries to assure a more even flow and to provide power at various points. Power from these various dams reaches such cities as Knoxville, Nashville, and Chattanooga, as well as many smaller communities.

It should be noted that many states have very little water power, either potential or developed. These states include Florida, Louisiana, Texas, New Mexico, Oklahoma, Kansas, and several others. It is fortunate that in some of these states abundant supplies of oil are available for power generation.

CANADA has very large amounts of potential power, and in some places the development has also been very great. The largest amounts of power lie in the Laurentian Shield of eastern Canada, particularly in the provinces of Quebec and Ontario (FIG. 35.5), and in western Canada, more especially in British Columbia. The largest dam in Canada is located at Shipshaw on the Saguenay River in Quebec. Much of the power from this dam is used in the aluminum industry at Arvida. A large power plant at the rapids on the St. Lawrence River west of Montreal supplies power used for that city, which is the largest in Canada. Numerous other rivers coming down from the Laurentian Shield to the St. Lawrence Lowland are used for power. These include the St. Maurice and the Gatineau. In Canada numerous lakes in the watershed of the streams, particularly in the Laurentian Shield, serve as natural reservoirs to provide an even flow of water. British Columbia ranks third in Canada in the development of water power. This is partly because of the rather limited market for power at the present time. As western Canada grows in population, it may be expected that a very much larger proportion of the water power will be developed. In Quebec about two thirds of the potential water power is developed at present, in Ontario one half, and in British Columbia about one seventh. Certain parts of Canada, as in the United States, have very little potential water power. This includes the prairie provinces principally, also the extreme northwestern part of Ontario. As noted before, Canada is somewhat limited in its resources of coal and petroleum, at least in terms of a wide distribution. Coal and petroleum are both scarce in the eastern part of Canada, and it is here that water power is used as a cheap, even source of energy.

In MIDDLE AMERICA power production is small. Many areas, especially in northern Mexico and Yucatán, are dry. Others require very expensive dams before power can be satisfactorily developed. Mexico has some hydroelectric installations on the margins of the Central Plateau, and there are small power plants in most of the Central American countries.

SOUTH AMERICA has great potentials of water

FIGURE 35.4. *General view of Grand Coulee Dam on the Columbia River, Washington. Although this is primarily a power dam, by pumping from the reservoir it is possible to irrigate approximately 1,200,000 acres within the great bend of the Columbia River. From Bureau of Reclamation.*

FIGURE 35.5. *Water power plant on the Winnipeg River, Manitoba. This dam is rather long and low, but it impounds a large amount of water.*

power in some areas, but only about three per cent of the potential is developed. It should be noted that the Amazon with its various tributaries has very little power possibilities except in the upper reaches, in the Andes and to a limited extent in the Highlands of Guiana. On the west coast the rainfall is low at many places. Although steep gradients are available, the flow of the rivers is small and power, therefore, is limited. The best possibilities for development of power are on the east slope of the Andes in Colombia, Ecuador, Peru, and Bolivia, but this region is quite remote from centers of population. The greatest development of power is in southeastern Brazil where there is a good demand as well as many good sites.

AFRICA has the greatest potential for water power of any continent. The heavy rainfall in the equatorial regions combined with the plateau nature of the country, producing many waterfalls, rapids, and steep gradients, accounts for Africa's superiority in resources. The development though is very slight, less than one per cent of its potential. The best sites are in the equatorial region on the tributaries of the Congo River. The headwa-

ters of the Congo lie in the East African Highlands, so that the tributaries plunge down steep slopes to the lower plateau level and then, by a series of rapids, down to the sea. These tributaries, such as the Ubangi and Kasai, have large power potentials. The great falls of the Zambezi River are yet to be utilized, but the drop is very great. The upper Nile River also has many good power sites; and lakes, such as Lake Victoria, provide natural reservoirs to assure an even flow. The development of water power sites in Africa must await a greater market for the power. If power can be sent longer distances in the near future, it may be possible to send some of the surplus energy from Africa to western Europe, which has a large population and could use additional amounts of electrical energy.

WESTERN EUROPE has shown the greatest development of potential water power resources of any region on the earth (FIG. 35.6). The industrial development of the country, the dense population in many areas, and the relative ease with which small power sites could be developed have aided in this growth. This is true in spite of the fact that western Europe is generally well supplied with

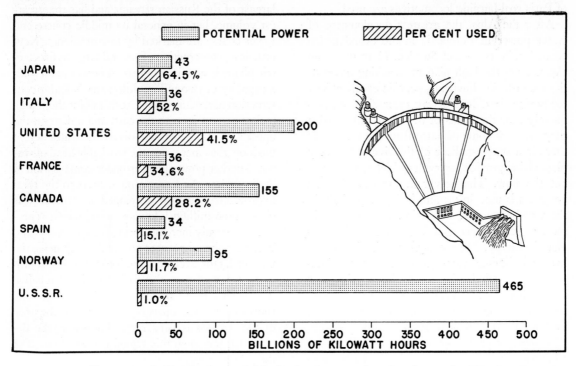

FIGURE 35.6. *Graph of potential hydroelectric power for selected countries. The data for potential power are based on minimum flow available 95 per cent of the time at 100 per cent efficiency.*

coal. The greatest development of water power in western Europe is in and on the margins of the Alps. The Alps receive much snow in winter and rain in summer, and on the various rivers draining the mountains are many sites for water power development. Switzerland is well known for its great development of water power resources partly because this country, unlike many of its neighbors, has very little coal. Many falls are utilized in the upper tributaries of the Rhine, the Rhone, and other rivers to furnish power for factories, especially ones that do not require large amounts of energy. Italy, like Switzerland, has very little coal and therefore depends largely upon hydroelectric energy for its factories, especially in the northern part of the country. Many of the tributaries of the Po River have medium-sized power plants which send the power to the Po Plain to such cities as Milano, Torino, and Verona. France also has many small and medium-sized hydroelectric plants in the French Alps, in the Central Massive, and on the north slope of the Pyrenees. These furnish sufficient power not only for domestic use in southern France but to run all the railroads as far north as Paris. North of Paris coal-burning locomotives are used.

After the Alps, the greatest development of water power in Europe is in the Scandinavian countries, Norway and Sweden. Here the steep slopes from the high plateau, reaching down to the sea or to the lowlands, provide excellent water power sites. In Norway these sites are frequently near the heads of the fjords. In Sweden they are back some distance from the sea where there is a steep gradient of the rivers. In many places lakes provide reservoirs which tend to even out the flow. The power in the Scandinavian countries is used in manufacturing, especially in the wood-processing industries. Lack of coal in most of Scandinavia stimulates the use of hydroelectric energy. Most other countries in Europe have only limited water power resources and development. Spain has just a few plants. Britain has many small plants, especially in the north, including Scotland, but the British Isles depend more on coal for energy in proportion to other sources than most other European countries. The Low Countries, Belgium and the Netherlands, also Denmark, have very limited supplies of water power. Germany has a high development of hydroelectric energy on the margins of the Alps in the southern part of the country, but Germany also has abundant coal. It is interesting to note that official statistics show Germany's *development* of water power is much greater than the *potential* water power existing in that country.

On the whole it should be noted that Europe is very well supplied with energy of some kind, derived either from coal or from water power. This offsets in part the lack of petroleum in most European countries. Because of the wide extent of industry in western Europe, the manufacture of hydroelectric machinery, including generators and turbines, is highly advanced in Europe. Supplies of these machines are exported to various parts of the world.

In RUSSIA conditions for hydroelectric development are not particularly favorable. The relief is low, and the precipitation is light. But a few of the large rivers have been developed by the construction of dams. The first construction was on the great bend of the Dnepr River in the Ukraine. (This dam and power plant are described in Chapter 39.) Another large installation is located to the northeast of Rybinsk, and the reservoir is one of the largest in Russia. The Volga River is the largest of the Russian streams and has the greatest volume, but in general its middle course and lower course are marked by low gradients. Nevertheless, construction of several large hydroelectric plants is now in progress. A power plant with a capacity of two million kilowatts is under construction near Kuibyshev. At this point the Volga makes a great loop to the east, and a dam on the upper arm of the loop will divert the water across the loop, thus increasing the workable head of water. Another power plant is under construction at Stalingrad on the lower Volga. In 1950 the total hydroelectric energy developed in Russia was about 1200 million kilowatt-hours, which represented a steady increase during the past ten years. The best sites for water power development, the market factor excluded, are located in the southeastern part of central Asiatic Russia, also called Turkestan. Here the mountains are high and snow-covered for a part of the year, and the drop of the streams is very rapid. However, the demand for power in this region is quite limited at the present time.

In INDIA the power potentials are large, but production is small. Recent developments include a large installation near Bombay on the slopes of the

Western Ghats where there is a drop of 1725 feet. Some power sites are being developed also on the east coast of southern India, particularly in the state of Madras. As noted previously, the monsoon rainfall of India is strongly seasonal, and if water power sites are to provide constant current, it is necessary to build large dams and to develop huge reservoirs. The largest reserves of power are in the Himalayan Mountains, where only one site has been developed. That is on the Jhelum River in Pakistan.

JAPAN's hydroelectric energy has been discussed briefly in Chapter 30. Japan, lacking coal and petroleum or having these in small quantities and in rather poor qualities, has made great efforts to develop its water power sites. In proportion to the small area of the country, Japan has rather large reserves of water power. As noted before, the surface is mountainous and the rainfall heavy. Furthermore, near these mountains are centers of dense population which can absorb the power. Therefore all the requirements for intensive development of hydroelectric energy are present. Japan has about 1500 hydroelectric generating stations which develop more than six million kilowatts of power. These stations are scattered widely so that very few parts of Japan lack electricity. Most of these hydroelectric plants are comparatively small units and are found in the valleys all the way from the southern tip of the country to the northern island of Hokkaido. Their capacity is usually less than 10,000 kilowatts; some have a capacity of less than 1000 kilowatts. It is to be noted, then, that development of water power in Japan is quite different from that of the United States and is comparable more perhaps to that of Switzerland, Norway, or the French Pyrenees. Although facilities for the interchange of power between the different parts of the main island of Honshu are adequate, there is very little opportunity for exchange in the islands of Hokkaido, Shikoku, and Kyushu. One handicap to exchange in the marginal areas is that both 50 and 60 cycle generation is used. A few trends in the use of power in Japan are to be noted. First, the basic manufacturing industries are consuming much more electricity than formerly. Industrial processes requiring more electricity may be essential if Japan is to be stabilized as far as its economy is concerned. Second, residential uses of electricity have increased so much that supplemental production from fuels has been necessary. Per capita residential consumption has about doubled in the last 20 years. This is mainly due to the shortage of household fuel. A third factor is the increase in urban population, as well as the overall increase in population. In general, Japan is fairly well supplied with power largely from hydroelectric sources, but also from coal. It is certainly much better supplied than any other Asiatic country. However, if the demand for power increases substantially, it will be difficult for Japan to supply it.

WATER SUPPLY IN THE UNITED STATES

A modern industrial nation needs vast quantities of water. In the United States alone nearly 200 billion gallons per day, or nearly 1200 gallons per capita, are used. Water for ordinary domestic purposes, both rural and urban, represents a very small proportion of the water consumed, probably not more than ten per cent. In some rural areas the consumption in homes may be as little as ten gallons per capita per day, while in cities it may reach 200 gallons. (Outside the United States the per capita consumption is much less, cities such as London, Paris, and Berlin averaging about 40 gallons per capita.) Irrigation and industry take most of the water, each accounting for approximately 45 per cent of the total. The consumption of water for all purposes, but most of all for irrigation, has increased rapidly in recent years.

Until recently water supply was taken for granted in most parts of the United States, excepting only the western section. But shortages of water are beginning to appear even in the humid regions, largely because of the increased consumption, but partly because of depletion of existing supplies. Irrigation, the largest consumer of water, shows increase not only in the western states where many large irrigation projects have been added in recent years, but also in the humid eastern states. Substantial amounts of water are being used for irrigation in the Atlantic Seaboard states, especially New Jersey, Virginia, and Florida. In many other states in the humid eastern half of the country, water for irrigation either from streams or from wells is being used. Irrigation is most important, however, in the western states, especially in California, Idaho, Colorado, and Arizona. In California 25 million acre feet of water are used for irrigation per year. (One acre foot per year equals 890 gallons per day.) This is equivalent to more than 2000 gallons per day per capita for irrigation alone.

Uses of water in industry are increasing most rapidly. A very large part of industrial water is used merely for cooling, especially in iron and steel mills and in other metallurgical industrial establishments. The manufacture of one ton of steel may require as much as 100,000 gallons of water. In other industrial processes large quantities of water are used for washing, grading, and for waste disposal. A food processing plant in New Jersey requires seven million gallons per day, enough to supply a city of 35,000 or more.

Both the supply and demand for water vary from region to region. Two main sources of supply are in current use—ground water obtained from wells and surface water obtained mostly from streams, lakes, and rivers. In both cases the ultimate source is precipitation, which ranges from nearly 150 inches annually in the Pacific Northwest to less than five inches annually in the most arid portions of the Southwest. The Pacific Northwest has the heaviest rains in the United States, but parts of this area have very light rainfall, especially the sections east of the Cascade Range. Nevertheless, this region has an average runoff of 600,000 gallons of water per day per square mile. In the country to the west of the Mississippi and to the south of Oregon and Idaho, the rainfall on the whole is the lightest of any part of the United States. Only a small part of this region, in Louisiana, northern California, and Arkansas, gets more than 50 inches of rain per year, whereas the driest parts receive under ten inches per year, in many places under five inches of precipitation per year. The average runoff here is about 150,000 gallons per day per square mile. In the northeastern part of the country, to the east of the Mississippi and to the north of the Ohio and the Potomac, the precipitation is fairly uniform, generally from 40 to 50 inches. The runoff here is 600,000 gallons per day per square mile. In the southeastern part of the country the runoff is the highest of any portion, about 750,000 gallons per day per square mile. This is based upon average high precipitation, ranging from over 60 inches per year in southern Mississippi and in the highest parts of the Appalachians,

down to 45 inches per year on the fringes, with no part having light precipitation.

An important factor in the precipitation picture of the United States is the variability of precipitation from time to time and the frequency of drought. Long periods with very light rainfall occur in all regions but affect more the regions of low rainfall. Drought reduces the supply of water for irrigation, for industry, for water power, and for domestic consumption. Since domestic water usually has priority over the others, there is usually adequate water for drinking and domestic purposes, but water for irrigation and for power may be seriously curtailed by a drought.

From time to time great efforts have been made to increase the rainfall by artificial means. Many methods have been tried including loud explosions and the release of various chemicals. In recent years rain making has been revived on a large scale, and most attention has been given to the seeding of clouds with dry ice or silver iodide. Small particles of these substances act as nuclei, around which the small water droplets in a cloud are concentrated. Obviously the success of the undertaking depends first of all on the occurrence of a suitable cloud. Many extravagant claims have been made for the success of these operations. Claims have been made also that rainfall can be prevented by heavily overseeding a threatening cloud (rainfall can cause serious damage to crops at harvest time). A conflict of interest sometimes arises. For example, a group of wheat farmers in a western state hired a rain maker who seeded some likely looking clouds. Possibly as a result of his efforts nearby fruit farms experienced a severe hailstorm. Suits for damages in such cases are very difficult to adjudicate since it is difficult to prove or disprove how much effect, if any, the rain-making efforts have had. Many meteorologists, including those of the United States Weather Bureau, have expressed doubt concerning the effectiveness of cloud seeding. As a step toward clarification of this subject a commission was appointed by President Eisenhower in 1953 to study various aspects of weather control, including some of the legal aspects of the subject.

Water becomes available when it reaches the surface but only under a wide variety of circumstances, conditions, and qualities. Some of the water evaporates immediately (FIG. 35.7); some

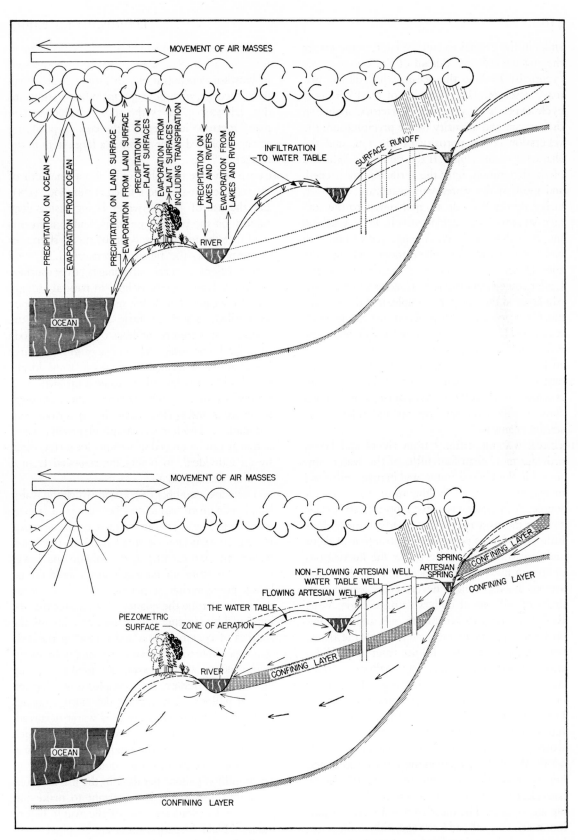

FIGURE 35.7. *The hydrologic cycle showing the relationships of precipitation, evaporation, surface runoff, and ground water circulation. From U. S. Geological Survey.*

sinks in the ground to emerge later; some enters the surface streams. But all of the water moves eventually back to the ocean, which is the primary reservoir. The behavior of the hydrologic cycle depends on a number of factors, including the amount and intensity of the precipitation, the vegetation cover, porosity of the soil, and the character of the slopes. If the rainfall is light and of short duration, only the surface is moistened, and most of the water will evaporate. A short, heavy rain will result in rapid runoff to the surface streams, with comparatively little reaching the ground-water level. A long, gentle rain will penetrate beneath the plant roots and into the zone of saturation known as the ground water. Under some circumstances, frozen soil or a hardpan layer in the soil, for example, it is difficult for much surface water to penetrate to the ground-water level. Once in the ground-water body, the water moves slowly through the pore space in the rocks, under the influence of gravity, seeking an outlet. Most ground water discharges into streams, either in the form of springs or through slow seepage from the bottoms and sides of the stream channels.

SURFACE WATER, mainly from rivers and lakes, provides more than four fifths of the water consumed in the United States, and in many hilly and mountainous regions is the most valuable resource. A satisfactory water supply from surface sources means a reasonably steady flow with as little pollution as possible. Construction of dams and reservoirs tends to level out the fluctuations of stream flow and to reduce the hazards of disastrous floods, which, nevertheless, cause hundreds of millions of dollars damage every year. Reservoirs tend to accumulate silt and thus improve the quality of the water below the dams, but in time the silt may fill the reservoir and destroy its storage capacity. The quality of surface water varies widely, and what is good water for one purpose may be unsatisfactory for another. For domestic uses water should be free of harmful organisms, low in mineral content (in other words, "soft"), and free of unpleasant tastes or odors. Water for papermaking must be clear and low in manganese and iron. In the textile industries clear water, low in iron is needed for bleaching and dyeing. The most common forms of pollution are silt, salt, and sewage. Silt is often related to soil erosion in the watershed of the streams and is frequently a serious problem in irrigated areas. Salt is more likely to be present in harmful concentrations in ground water than in surface streams. Sewage, including various industrial wastes, gives the most trouble, and in many metropolitan centers the cost of purifying sewage-polluted river water is a large item in the budget.

GROUND WATER furnishes only about one fifth of the requirements in the United States (FIG. 35.8). But the use of ground water is increasing very rapidly on the percentage basis, and it is in this field that the most serious problems of shortages exist so far as the future is concerned. Ground water offers several advantages over surface water. A large supply is held in natural storage and, by means of wells or springs, can be tapped as needed. There is little fluctuation of the ground-water supply, at least over short periods of time. To be sure, careless use of ground water has resulted in serious shortages in some localities. Pollution is less likely to be a problem with ground water than with surface water, although some wells and springs have shown serious contamination. Another advantage of ground water is that it can be tapped at various localities, often by an individual, in points far removed from a good surface supply.

There are a number of ways in which the water supply of a given region may be conserved or even increased. The available water may be increased by the construction of small dams in the headwaters and large dams in the middle and lower reaches to store up the excessive runoff during heavy precipitation or periods of melting snow. At the same time the quality of the water may be improved by treating before use or by finding the sources of contamination and removing them. It is also possible to conserve water supply by modifying industrial processes. A food-processing plant in New Jersey, for example, was using ten million gallons of water per day until a serious problem of disposing of the used water occurred. Then by a series of studies and economies, which did not interfere with the fundamental processes, the amount consumed was quickly reduced to seven million gallons per day. In the use and conservation of water it is important to make full provision for domestic use of the water before industrial and irrigation users are supplied.

Obviously the question of water supply in its

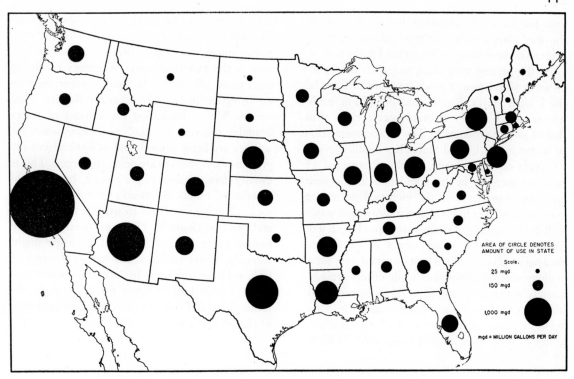

FIGURE 35.8. *The use of ground water in the United States. In general, the use of ground water is about 20 per cent of the total water used. In some western states, however, ground water supplies from 40 per cent to 60 per cent of the needs, most of which is for irrigation. From U. S. Geological Survey.*

particulars varies in different parts of the country and for different uses. In supplying a large city, such as New York, there are some special problems. New York City gets most of its water supply from the Catskill and Croton watersheds with a total reservoir capacity of about 284 billion gallons. In 1949 the New York region experienced a serious drought which reduced the city's water supply rather drastically. This condition stimulated demand for the extension of the water supply system for the city through the tapping of resources in the Delaware and Hudson rivers. The supply of water in the New York area is large. The only question is of engineering, in the form of dams and aqueducts, and in decreasing pollution. Supplying a city such as Los Angeles is quite a different problem. The rainfall in the vicinity of Los Angeles is very light, making it necessary to obtain water from Owens River on the east side of the Sierra Nevada Mountains and from the Colorado River. Both of these sources require long, expensive aqueducts. Fortunately,

the Lake Havasu Reservoir on the Colorado has a large surplus of water to take care of future demands. A part of the water from this reservoir is used by the city of San Diego also.

SUMMARY

The water power resources of the world are very unevenly distributed. Canada, the United States, Brazil, central Africa, and the mountainous parts of Russia and Asia have the largest reserves. The installed capacity, which is an index to water power produced but not an accurate measure of it, is limited by accessibility to market, since it is not profitable to transport hydroelectric energy more than a few hundred miles. Most of the production is located in a few countries: Canada, the United States, Norway, Sweden, France, Switzerland, Germany, Italy, Russia, and Japan. Some countries like Switzerland and Japan have developed a very large proportion of their potential power. Many other countries have developed more than half of their potential. The largest area for future development lies in the out-of-the-way places, such as central Africa, where at present there is very little market for the power.

At the present time the greatest strides in increasing water power production are in Canada, the United States, Russia, and India. The problem of water supply is even more serious than that of power production. The total consumption of water in the United States has doubled every 25 years on the average. With an expected 27 per cent increase in the population in the next 25 years, together with the increased per capita consumption, it is likely that withdrawal of water will double again and reach nearly 400 billion gallons per day. Since water cannot be distributed on a national basis, like wheat or petroleum, some regions will have shortages while others are adequately supplied. Many parts of the country are already experiencing serious shortages. In some western states eighty per cent of the available water resources are already being used. With so little reserve, periods of drought produce serious shortages, accompanied by crop failure and temporary migrations. On the brighter side of the picture is the fact that water resources are being used more efficiently. Industrial water supplies are being reclaimed and used again. Regulation of stream flow is increasing the amount of water available the year round. New ground-water resources are being tapped, and in some places the ground-water sources are being recharged. This is usually done by diverting a stream, by means of a series of canals, to an area of porous soil and rock, allowing the water to soak in and enter the underground channels. Either artificially induced rainfall or removal of salt from sea water might solve the water problem, but neither seems feasible at the present time. In the past the water supply has been largely taken for granted; in the future more and more citizens will become aware of the limited supply.

36

Manufacturing

ALTHOUGH brief references have been made to manufacturing in the previous chapters the emphasis, so far, has been on the production of raw materials. Many of the primary products of the farms, forests, and mines are not ready for consumption until they have undergone a more or less complicated process of manufacturing. Manufacturing calls to mind factories with smoking chimneys, noisy machinery, assembly lines, and streams of workers moving in and out in shifts at regular intervals. Steel mills, automobile factories, and textile mills are readily recognized by all as examples of manufacturing. Other forms are not so obvious to the casual observer. Is the printing plant of a city newspaper an example of manufacturing? A bakery? A meat packing plant? A local machine shop? The answer to each question is yes. Many kinds of light manufacturing such as clothing and jewelry factories are not conspicuous because they occupy small quarters in remote parts of the city or in the upper floors of downtown buildings. All things considered, manufacturing is much more varied in character than all the forms of primary production combined.

The fact that manufacturing is so intimately associated with all sorts of primary production makes it all the more difficult to define. Agriculture, mining, grazing, and forestry furnish raw materials. The regions of primary production afford a market for the finished products and, in addition, supply a never-ending stream of workers moving in from the rural areas to the industrial centers where usually the birth rate is not high enough to maintain the population. At the same time it should be pointed out that improved methods of agriculture, including the use of power

implements, such as the tractor and combine, have reduced the number of farm, forest, and mine workers necessary to supply the world's requirements of primary products.

A foolproof definition of manufacturing, one which will separate it from all other forms of production, is not easy to devise. Broadly speaking, every process which modifies the form and character of raw materials for human use and at the same time increases their value can be called manufacturing. The preparation of food and the making of clothing in the home are simple forms of manufacturing. It is obviously necessary to distinguish these simple home and community types of processing from the complex patterns of modern industries as represented by the modern factory.

The simple community types of manufacturing are widely distributed wherever modern civilized people exist. In every urban settlement there are small community shops, bakeries, print shops, repair shops, machine shops, and many others of a similar nature. On the other hand, the complex forms of manufacturing are restricted to localities where certain factors, such as raw materials and transportation, are available. The market may be regional, national, or even world wide. It is with this complex specialized form of manufacture that this and the three succeeding chapters are primarily concerned.

The concentration of manufacturing may be indicated on a map in several ways. One method shows the value added to raw materials by the processing, taking no notice of the original value of the raw materials. This is a good measure of the importance of manufacturing but does not distinguish the community from the complex type.

PERSONS ENGAGED IN MANUFACTURING

UNITED STATES TOTAL
11,758,000 ENGAGED IN MANUFACTURING OR
24.1 PERCENT OF ALL GAINFULLY EMPLOYED

*Each dot represents
500 people*

FIGURE 36.1. *A map showing the number of persons engaged in manufacturing indicates the
concentration in the northeastern part of the United States. During and following World
War II there was a sharp increase in manufacturing on the Pacific Coast and in the South.
From Bureau of Agricultural Economics.*

The amount of power used is also a good indicator of the distribution of manufacturing, stressing those industries which consume much power, such as aluminum refining, and minimizing those which use more labor and less power such as the clothing industries. The number of people engaged in industry, as determined by the census reports, is a useful indicator for marking out manufacturing regions. Some allowance can be made for those engaged in community industries. It is sometimes assumed that about 10 per cent of the population of large cities is engaged in community manufacturing. Therefore, a city of 500,000 population with only 50,000 workers engaged in industry would not be considered a manufacturing type. The percentage of gainful workers employed in manufacturing as compared to other productive activities is also useful. On a map, manufacturing can be best represented by the distribution of manufacturing cities, the importance of which is proportional to the number of persons engaged in manufacturing. On a small-scale map it may be desirable to mark out the regions in which most of the manufacturing cities are concentrated (compare FIGURES 36.1, 36.2, and 37.1). All methods based on the number of persons employed, however, are likely to minimize some industries such as flour milling where only a few men are needed to supervise a semiautomatic process.

LOCATION FACTORS

Raw materials, power, transportation, labor, and a market for the finished products are the chief location factors of industry. Many other influences are noted in certain areas, such as climate, tariffs, trade agreements, capital, invention (an inventor may start a factory in his home town in spite of the lack of raw materials, etc.), but the first five are usually the major ones. A little study will show that the various factors are interrelated and that industries can succeed without all being satisfactory. A factory which uses little raw material, a watch factory for example, or one which uses relatively light material, such as a textile mill, need not be located near the source of supply. Cheap transportation can offset in part the lack of raw materials and is most critical with the heavy industries where large quantities of coal, iron, and other materials must be moved. Labor can be attracted to an otherwise favorable location by high wages in many instances, but in some industries special skills are needed, thus giving an older industrial region a continuing advantage. A large market will attract industries, even though the other factors are not favorable; on the other hand, for light goods the principal market may be thousands of miles away.

Raw Materials

Of all the raw materials which go into industry, coal and iron ore are the most significant. In spite of the increasing use of water power and petroleum, it is difficult to find any well-established industries very far from coal. To be sure, the refining of some metals, aluminum and magnesium for example, needs so much cheap electric power that large establishments have been located at

Grand Coulee Dam on the Columbia River and at Hoover Dam on the Colorado. Originally neither of these had good transportation, labor, or market for the products. In wartime, when the cost-plus government contracts permit the usual rules of location to be set aside, industries are established which sometimes persist for many years in spite of certain unfavorable circumstances. With some exceptions, however, this is still the age of coal. Not only does coal supply most of the power for industry, but it is also a basic raw material in the production of iron and certain chemicals. Iron is hardly less important since so many secondary industries, like automobile manufacturing, use quantities of steel. Therefore, it is advantageous to be located near the sources of iron ore.

Most mineral raw materials, except coal, require refining or processing before they reach the manufacturer. Since the crude metal is usually much lighter in weight than the ore from which it is derived, smelters are located fairly near the mines. Refineries need not be so near, since the loss in weight from the crude metal to the pure

FIGURE 36.2. *Most of the wage earners in manufacturing are concentrated in cities. It is not difficult to identify many of the dots with cities even though the data were compiled by counties. From Bureau of the Census.*

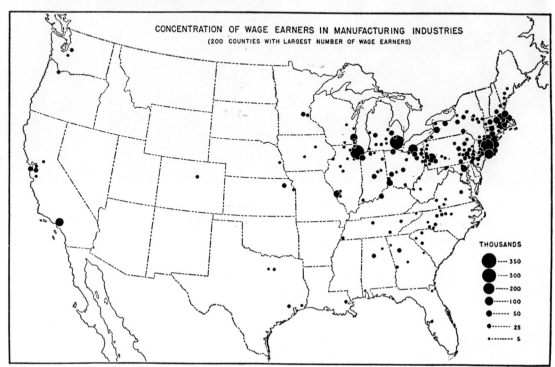

FIGURE 36.3. *A furniture factory in the southern Appalachian Hardwood Belt at Bassett, Virginia. Factories like this one are often inconspicuous and few passers-by realize their geographic significance. From N. and W. Railway.*

form is not significant in transportation. Indeed, refining is often near the point of consumption and far from the mines. The tin refineries using Malayan tin are in Wales, and the copper refineries near New York City obtain crude copper from Chile and Africa. The same principle applies to petroleum: some is refined in the field, some at the seaboard, and some in and near the large city markets. Whether the petroleum is carried by pipeline, tank car, or ocean-going tanker, it is equally easy to transport crude oil, gasoline, fuel oil, or other refined products.

The location of textile mills has little relation to supplies of cotton, wool, and other fibers since they are all readily and cheaply transported from one part of the world to another. The chief cotton mills of the world are located in New England, the English Midlands, and southern Japan, in none of which is raw cotton produced in any quantities. It is true that some of the textile mills of the southern Piedmont are in the Cotton Belt, but close examination of the district would indicate that the cheap power and water supply of the southern Appalachians are of more significance in the location of these textile mills than is the local supply of cotton.

The processing of cereal foods is like that of textiles. Flour mills are not usually located in the areas of greatest wheat production but rather near the market or on the way from producing area to market. Cheap power is likely to be the critical factor along with good transportation, since both flour and wheat keep well and also because comparatively little labor is needed in a flour mill. In the preparation of the more perishable foods which must be preserved quickly, the processing plants must be nearer the raw materials. This is especially true of canneries and drying or packing plants (FIG. 36.4). In most localities a part of the processing, enough to preserve the product or to reduce its bulk, is done near the source, leaving the final stages to the market areas. A good example is cane sugar, which moves from the plantation as crude sugar to be refined in the large import centers such as New York and San Francisco.

FIGURE 36.4. *The meat packing industry is widely distributed but the largest centers (circled) are in the western part of the Corn Belt. From Bureau of the Census.*

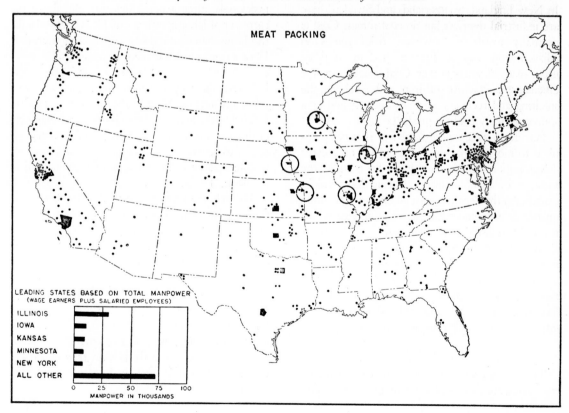

Power

The development and use of power from coal, petroleum, and water play a very important part in the location of manufacturing. Some areas of fairly dense population are unable to compete in the production of certain manufactured articles even though a few of the raw materials are at hand. The clearest instances are those in which a large amount of power is applied to small quantities of raw materials, in the refining of aluminum, for example. This is another way of saying that the raw material can sometimes be moved to the power. The concentration of aluminum refining in eastern Canada, at Alcoa (Tennessee) and Badin (North Carolina) is explained by the presence of cheap water power in those locations. Coal is the chief source of power for the world as a whole, and it can be transported for thousands of miles at comparatively low cost, if cheap transportation is available. However, the added cost of importing coal for manufacturing purposes puts a region at a disadvantage in the competition for a wide market. It is notable that the only manufacturing districts without coal are concerned with light industries or have very cheap hydroelectric energy. In New England, Switzerland, and Sweden there are industrial districts but no coal mines. Coal is normally available, however, from mines in adjacent countries or districts, and in all three use is made of water power. Coal is necessary for efficient manufacture of iron and steel, in the smelting and recovery of many metals, and as a source of many coal tar products.

Petroleum as a source of power is usually applied to moving machines and is thus of greater direct importance to transportation than in the location of manufacturing. Oil is less widely distributed than coal, at least so far as recoverable quantities are concerned, but it is also easier to transport in tankers, by pipelines, rail, and truck. Petroleum and its products have penetrated to remote parts of the earth where the people have never seen coal, simply because oil is so easy to transport and so significant to transportation. Oil, like coal, is also a raw material and as such enters into many manufacturing processes.

Transportation

The importance of transportation to an industry varies roughly according to the weight and bulk of the raw materials and the finished product. Since any well-rounded manufacturing district requires quantities of coal and iron ore as well as many lighter materials, it is obvious that good cheap transportation, including water, rail, and highway, is advantageous. Ocean, river, and lake routes play important roles in all the great manufacturing belts. A good harbor with connections to a broad hinterland is often the location for many types of manufacturing although its hinterland may possess few raw materials, little coal or water power. The New York Metropolitan District to be described in the next chapter is a good example. An excellent harbor and an easy route to the interior of the continent via the Hudson and Mohawk valleys and the Great Lakes more than offset the lack of coal and water power in the immediate vicinity. It will be observed, however, that heavy industries are not common in this district.

Labor

Any industry, whether light or heavy, requires an adequate labor supply with a variety of skills and knowledge. Some factories employ thousands of laborers, many of whom can perform their tasks only after a period of training. Since the turnover of labor is rather rapid it is necessary for the large manufacturers to recruit and train new laborers constantly. It is sometimes feasible, however, to induce skilled laborers to migrate to the industrial sites by the offer of higher wages or other advantages. Most of the larger factories are located in the areas of dense population where recruiting is much simpler. It would be easier, obviously, to secure suitable laborers for a new automobile factory in the vicinity of Detroit than in Houston, Texas.

The relative significance of the labor factor in the location of factories varies with different industries. In a modern flour mill, for example, the cost of labor is about two or three dollars per ton of grain. It is unlikely, then, that the labor factor would noticeably affect the location of this industry. On the other hand, in the textile industry, in watch making, and in many others where large amounts of skilled labor are applied to relatively small amounts of raw materials, labor rather than raw materials, power, transportation, or a convenient market may be the most critical factor.

FIGURE 36.5. *These photographs illustrate the various operations in the manufacture of iron and steel, the mining of iron ore and coal, the manufacture of coke, and the blast furnaces and converters. Further shaping and processing of the steel is necessary before it can be used. From Ford Motor Company.*

Market

The market factor in the location of industry is in many ways most difficult to evaluate. Other things being equal, the industry nearest its market has many advantages. Not only is transportation cheaper, in general, but the factory can keep in close touch with the changing demand of the consumers and alter the product accordingly. Obviously this is very important in the clothing industry where style plays an important role; it is less so in flour milling where tastes change more slowly. If an industry finds its chief market at other factories which further process the material, the location near the market may be critical. Thus a steel mill near Chicago finds a wide market in the nearby factories which turn out agricultural implements and automobile parts. This market is good enough to offset the advantages of a more distant steel mill which has better location with respect to raw materials.

THE MAJOR INDUSTRIES

Although the variety of manufactured goods is almost endless, most of the products can be grouped under a few main industries. In general, subsequent discussions will be concerned with the following:

Iron and Steel. Involving only the simpler and partially finished products.

Metal Refining. Production of pure metals, such as aluminum, copper, tin, lead, zinc, and silver.

Metal Manufacturing. Finished products made largely from metals, such as automobiles, machinery, ships, hardware.

Machine Tools (FIG. 36.6).

Chemical Industries. Fertilizers, drugs, coal tar products and plastics.

Glass.

Cement.

Wood Industries. Lumber, paper, furniture.

Leather. Shoes.

Textiles. Cotton, linen, wool, and synthetic fibers.

Clothing.

Food Processing.

In consideration of the various factors enumerated previously—raw materials, power, transportation, labor supply, and market—it will be worthwhile in the following chapters to examine how major types of manufacturing listed on this page are located. It is obvious that some forms of manufacturing are influenced more by certain location factors than by others. The heavy indus-

FIGURE 36.6. *The machine tool industry corresponds closely to the main Manufacturing Belt of the United States. From Bureau of the Census.*

tries are concentrated close to raw materials, cheap transportation, and the major markets. On the other hand, light industries such as cotton textiles are most frequently located with respect to cheap power and labor. The distribution of food processing industries is related closely to the market. A brief statement concerning several regions of industry will illustrate the variable effect of the location factors.

MAJOR MANUFACTURING REGIONS

Three major manufacturing regions are to be found in the world today, one in eastern North America, a second in western Europe, and a third which includes several distinct districts in Russia. The North American belt is about the same size as that of western Europe and is related directly to coalfields. From southern Maine to Baltimore on the east coast, the belt extends almost due west to Chicago and Milwaukee, including such major industrial cities as Boston, New York, Pittsburgh, Buffalo, Cleveland, Toronto, and Detroit. It is to be noted that all of this belt is either near coal or located on water so that coal can be imported cheaply. Outlying "islands" of manufacturing include Montreal and vicinity in eastern Canada, the southern Piedmont area, St. Louis, Los Angeles, San Francisco, Portland, Seattle, and many more. During periods of industrial expansion the outlying areas show great vigor, but the obvious advantages of the main belts become more apparent in dull times.

The region in western Europe, including parts of Great Britain, France, Belgium, the Netherlands, Germany, Czechoslovakia, and Switzerland, accounted for the greatest volume and variety of manufactured goods prior to World War II. Distribution is definitely related to the good coalfields and the excellent transportation provided by the marginal seas, rivers, and dense network of railroads. Such cities as Glasgow, Newcastle, Manchester, Leeds, Cardiff, London, Lille, Essen, Metz, Leipzig, and Breslau are typical of this industrial belt. Many of them are associated with specific industries. Outside the main manufacturing region are smaller concentrations of industry in and near certain cities: Paris, Lyon, Milan, and Barcelona, for example.

In Russia manufacturing is represented by a number of districts extending from Leningrad to the Black Sea and reaching into Asiatic Russia.

This wide dispersion is related to the distribution of resources in Russia, to the early stage of development, and to deliberate planning on the part of the Soviet Government. The district around Leningrad specializes in wood industries because of the proximity of the northern forest. The "Old Industrial District" in the vicinity of Moscow is highly diversified. The "Donbas" is a region of heavy manufacturing with excellent coal and access to the sea. The southern Urals region has diversified metal industries based on the occurrence of a variety of ores, while the "Kuzbas" in Asia is similar to the "Donbas" but in an earlier stage of development.

In addition to the industrial areas mentioned here, the manufacturing areas of Japan, eastern China, India, Australia, and a few districts in Latin America have been mentioned previously, because of their potential rather than their actual development. The present world distribution of manufacturing is based on complicated factors, some of which are constantly changing. The trend today is toward wider distribution and less concentration, as new sources of raw materials are exploited and as more and more regions approach industrial maturity.

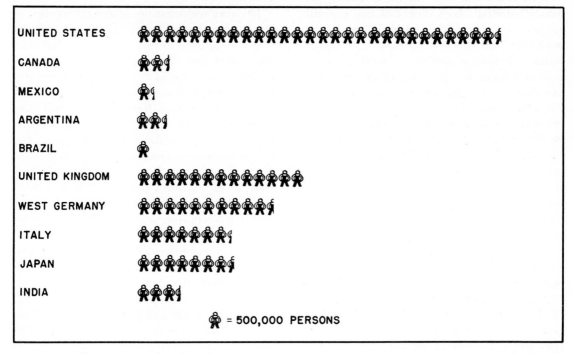

FIGURE 36.7. *Graph of the number of persons employed in manufacturing in selected countries. From* Statistical Yearbook, *United Nations. (See also Table 1, Appendix C.)*

37

The North American Manufacturing Region

MANUFACTURING, concentrated in one large region and several small districts, is a secondary form of production. In the United States far more of the wage earners are employed in manufacturing than in agriculture or in all other forms of primary production combined.

For a long time after the settlement of North America primary production—agriculture, forestry, and mining—were of greater importance than manufacturing. Industry has been continually growing, however, both in absolute and relative significance until at the beginning of World War II it could be said that the continent was mainly industrial. To a variety of raw material resources have been added human skill and power machinery, and although the number of skilled factory workers is smaller in North America than in Europe, the efficiency of the machines manufactured is higher on our continent. Never has such volume of goods been produced with so few workers as during the past decade. It was the fate of North Americans to develop their industrial economy at a time when technology was rapidly advancing. As a result, although there is in North America less than 9 per cent of the world's population, yet nearly one half of the world's industrial goods are produced and consumed there.

Manufacturing is concentrated, for the most part, in about four hundred counties in the United States and, in addition, around a dozen cities in Canada. This concentration is related to many of the location factors listed in the previous chapter, such as raw materials, transportation, labor supply, and market, and also to the fact that eastern North America was settled first. The location factors are continually changing, how-

ever, and shifts in manufacturing are frequent. There is a yearning in every town and city in the land for industrial development, but many localities are ill suited for manufacturing. A definite tendency for certain industries to migrate westward and southward can be noted: for example, cotton textiles from New England to the southern Piedmont and the aircraft industry to the Pacific Coast. The main Manufacturing Region of North America, however, is still supreme. Its advantages with respect to raw materials, transportation, labor supply, and market are still very evident.

In a very real sense the Manufacturing Belt of northeastern United States and the adjacent portion of Canada is superimposed upon the farm land, forest, and mines of this area. The region is mainly urban, whereas raw material production is largely rural. Raw materials for this manufacturing belt come not only from the vicinity but from all over the world, from almost every production region mentioned in the preceding chapters. The region occupies a comparatively small area of North America but from the standpoint of raw material uses, as well as markets, it belongs to the world. Yet it is not the only manufacturing region in North America; it is merely the largest and most diversified.

The best way to show the distribution of manufacturing on a map is by means of dots representing the manufacturing cities, but it is easier in the following discussion to mark out tentative boundaries of the region and to indicate several subdivisions. The northern boundary extends in an irregular east-west line from southern Maine to a point north of Milwaukee on the west shore of Lake Michigan. The boundary then trends southward to the west of Chicago, thence southeastward to Cincinnati, up the Ohio River to Wheeling and thence eastward to Baltimore and northeastward to New York. Not all of the region so outlined is dominantly manufacturing, as the discussion to follow will show. On the other hand, many significant areas of manufacturing lie outside the main region. These too deserve attention.

Volumes have been written about this great Manufacturing Region in order to explain its origin and growth. The fundamental location factors are coal, iron ore, transportation, and markets. It is difficult to overestimate the meaning of the Appalachian Coalfields to the factories of this region. Fuel, power, and raw materials come from these mines. Iron ore is not available in quantities within the belt but it is obtained cheaply from the Upper Lakes Region. The Great Lakes and various easy land routes provide excellent communication from the interior of the continent to the Atlantic despite the barrier effect of the Appalachians. Finally, the richest farming regions in North America, the Corn Belt and Dairy Belt, afford a market for a part of the factory products. The Manufacturing Region itself is a huge market as is any region of industrial urbanism. Many other minor location factors can be mentioned, such as settlement by a vigorous inventive people, a stimulating climate, and an abundant water supply. The magnitude and variety of manufacturing are clearly dependent on the development of North America as a whole.

The North American Manufacturing Belt is far too complicated for lengthy discussion as a unit. Each of the many products—steel, automobiles, airplanes, textiles, paper, hardware, machine tools, clothing, and printing, to mention just a few—tends to be concentrated in certain districts where raw materials, power, skills, or demand is most significant. Each subregion (FIG. 37.1) has a special function to perform, certain articles to produce, some of which are to be further processed by another subregion. However, it should be noted that certain kinds of manufacturing, such as machine tools, foundries, and clothing, are fairly evenly distributed throughout the whole region. The list of subregions follows:

SUBREGIONS OF THE MANU-FACTURING BELT

1. Eastern New England
2. Southwestern New England
3. New York Metropolitan Area
4. Southeastern Pennsylvania
5. Albany–Buffalo
6. Southern Ontario
7. Montreal–Ottawa
8. Pittsburgh–Cleveland
9. Southeastern Michigan
10. Inland Ohio–Indiana
11. Chicago–Milwaukee

FIGURE 37.1. *The Main Manufacturing Belt of North America. Subdivisions: 1. Eastern New England, 2. Southwestern New England, 3. New York Metropolitan Area, 4. Southeastern Pennsylvania, 5. Albany–Buffalo, 6. Southern Ontario, 7. Montreal–Ottawa (not shown), 8. Pittsburgh–Cleveland, 9. Southeastern Michigan, 10. Inland Ohio–Indiana, 11. Chicago–Milwaukee. Modified from a map by Richard Hartshorne.*

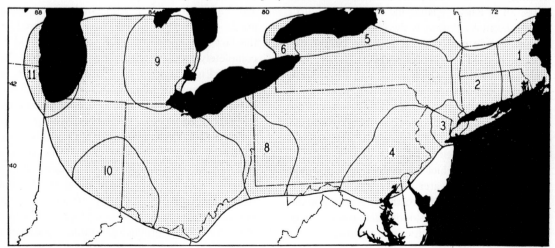

OUTLIERS

12. Southern Piedmont
13. St. Louis
14. Los Angeles
15. San Francisco
16. Portland
17. Seattle–Vancouver

EASTERN NEW ENGLAND SUBREGION

Settled early, New England was the first part
of North America in which manufacturing was
developed. Perhaps it was the difficulty of growing crops which turned the people to trade and
industry. At any rate, there are in New England
few of the raw materials which are ordinarily
considered necessary for an industrial economy.
There is no coal, iron ore, or petroleum in the
area. Metals, in general, are lacking. Industrial
crops, such as cotton and sugar beets, are not
grown. In the early days, as at present, New
Englanders had to depend on imported raw materials to supply their factories. As a result, heavy
industries have never succeeded, but most all
forms of light manufacturing are represented.

The general trend of industry in New England is downward in the face of keen competition
with other more favored areas. Cotton textiles
have migrated, in part, to the southern Piedmont.
The shoe industry in St. Louis, Chicago, and
other localities absorbs part of the market. The
paper industry, lumber, flour milling, and woolen
textiles are declining in New England for the
same reason—competition in other areas.

East of the Connecticut River industrial New
England includes a small part of southern Maine,
southeastern New Hampshire, eastern Massachusetts, all of Rhode Island, and the eastern fourth
of Connecticut. Boston is the chief financial and
administrative center as well as the largest importing port. This subregion specializes in light
industrial products which require skill in manufacturing but do not involve the handling of
heavy or bulky raw materials. Locally raw
materials are lacking—the area has no coal, no
ores, the forest is largely exhausted, and crops do
not contribute much in the way of raw material
to industry. The chief advantages of the region
are water power, water supply, the skill of the
people, and easy access to the sea. The population is dominantly urban, more than three fourths
of the people living in cities and towns.

In the immediate vicinity of Boston the shoe
industry is outstanding. Hides and tanning materials are imported through the port of Boston
and the leathers are distributed to the various
shoe cities. North of Boston, women's shoes are
important in the neighborhood of Lynn, Haver-
hill, and Salem, while to the south, Brockton and
Quincy produce men's shoes. Machinery for the
manufacture of shoes is also made in this region.

For many decades most of the cotton textiles
in the United States were produced in New England, and most of the woolen goods and certain
high qualities of cotton cloth are still produced
there. The advantages of the naturally damp air
(high humidity is necessary in the spinning of
cotton yarns), water power, and skilled labor
made New England supreme in the cotton textile
industry in the early days. The fact that all the
raw material had to be imported was no great
disadvantage. Cotton manufacturing is widely distributed over southeastern New England, but
most of the mills are in a zone stretching from
southern New Hampshire to Fall River, Massachusetts. The woolen industry is located in the
same region, concentrated especially in Lawrence
and Lowell in Massachusetts and Woonsocket in
Rhode Island. In southeastern New England a
variety of light metal goods, such as watches,
clocks, and hardware, are also produced. This
type of manufacturing is even more significant
in southwestern New England.

SOUTHWESTERN NEW ENGLAND SUBREGION

In the Connecticut Valley and the western part
of southern New England, industries are light
and highly diversified with emphasis on metal
goods. The variety of products is indicated by
the fact that a modern hardware store could be
completely stocked with goods produced in this
region. Light machinery of all kinds, such as
tools, firearms, electrical goods, clocks, watches,
jewelry, dyes, typewriters, sewing machines,
and rubber goods suggest the variety of products.
Springfield in the Connecticut Valley where the
Boston & Albany Railroad crosses the river is
noted for firearms, machine tools, radios, and refrigerators. There are paper mills in Holyoke
which specialize in fine paper (they long ago
ceased to compete in the coarse paper market) and
also textile mills producing cotton, woolen, and

FIGURE 37.2. *A pulp and paper mill at Groveton, New Hampshire. New England has exhausted a large part of its forest reserve but has access to the Canadian forests. Notice the small size of the logs in the pond. From U. S. Forest Service.*

rayon cloth. New Haven, at the southern end of the valley but not on the river, is best known as the home of Yale University and Yale locks. Various kinds of builders' hardware, clocks, toys, and railroad equipment are manufactured there. Many other cities and towns are well known for some special kind of light metal goods: New Britain for cutlery, Waterbury for clocks and watches, Hartford and Bridgeport for typewriters and sewing machines. The financial center for southwestern New England is New York City.

THE NEW YORK METROPOLITAN SUBREGION

New York City is easily the most significant manufacturing city in North America as well as a great port and financial center. In fact, the variety and quantity of its imported raw materials contribute to its industries. One half of the nation's commerce is handled in New York City where there is over 700 miles of water front. It is a region of extreme congestion, however, and industrial sites are expensive. As a consequence, heavy industries which require much space are not common. The lighter industries, which can function in a small space or in a multistoried building, are varied. Clothing, printing, light metal goods, textiles, soap making, and the refining of oil and sugar are typical. Some of these industries are not always classified as "light," but they require less space than steel mills or automobile factories.

Most of the clothing industry is located on Manhattan Island near the heart of the city. More than 7000 factories employ 250,000 workers in an area which totals no more than a good-sized farm. This district furnishes about one half the ready-made clothing of the nation. Printing, which is not so concentrated but occupies only slightly more space, includes book and magazine publishing as well as job printing and newspaper manufacturing. The refining industries are located on the Jersey side of the Hudson where space is not quite so dear. At Bayonne one single oil refinery occupies a square mile of land, an unusual size for an industry in this area. Metal refineries are located in the vicinity of Perth Amboy, New Jersey. Also on the west side of the Hudson are the large chemical industries which manufacture fertilizers partly from imported chemicals. Drug manufacturing is important on Long Island. The nearness of New York to the Appalachian Coalfields assures an abundant supply of power. The excellent rail connections with the interior provide outlets to a wide market.

SOUTHEASTERN PENNSYLVANIA SUBREGION

In southeastern Pennsylvania and adjacent portions of Maryland and New Jersey, a variety of both heavy and light industries are to be found. The anthracite coalfields and good water transportation encourage the heavy industries, such as iron and steel. Some of the iron ore, however, must be imported either from the Upper Lakes Region or from foreign sources, usually Chile and Newfoundland. This is the largest peacetime shipbuilding region in the United States since iron and steel are produced in quantities and access to tidewater is convenient. Oil refining and the chemical industries also profit by the tidewater locations. Textile industries include cotton, wool, and synthetic fibers, and the manufacture of woolen cloth, rugs, and carpets is outstanding in this subregion.

Philadelphia, Camden, Wilmington, Trenton, and Baltimore are all ocean ports which serve this region. The imports are often a key to the industries: Philadelphia imports raw sugar, crude oil, chemicals, wool, and wood pulp; other ports handle iron ore, clay for china, and various raw food materials. The region is noted for the canning and preserving of foods, some of which are produced on the well-kept farms. These farms were studied previously under the headings of the Corn Belt, Dairy Belt, and Horticulture.

THE ALBANY–BUFFALO SUBREGION

In a narrow belt which stretches from the junction of the Mohawk and Hudson rivers at Albany to Lake Erie lies the most important corridor in North America. This is variously called the Mohawk Valley, the Ontario Plain, or the Erie Canal Belt, although the canal of that name has long since ceased to function. The subregion is a long chain of manufacturing cities arranged along this important route, and in each city there is a tendency to specialize in one certain product although a number of others are produced to a lesser degree.

Albany, Troy, and Cohoes are close together at the eastern end of the corridor and are accessible to ocean-going freighters. Men's clothing, especially shirts and collars, is the best-known industry, but paper, light metal goods, and chemicals are also important. A few miles to the west in Schenectady electrical goods of all kinds and locomotives are manufactured. Still farther west is Gloversville, specializing in gloves of many kinds, one of the few instances in which a light industry gave its name to a city. Textiles and knit goods are produced in Utica, while a little farther west in Rome light metal articles, including wire, are made. There are in Syracuse a variety of industries which include automobile parts, foundry products, ceramics, and shoes.

In this subregion are found two raw materials, salt and soda, which are used in the chemical industries. The soda is also employed in glass making. Rochester is widely known as the chief center for the manufacture of optical goods in North America. The production of cameras, microscopes, field glasses, and various similar articles in Rochester has increased in both quantity and quality with the decline of the German industry in Saxony following World War II.

At the western end of the corridor is the Buffalo-Niagara industrial complex. This section differs markedly from the other cities mentioned in the Albany-Buffalo District because it has access to iron ores, coal, and grain by way of the Great Lakes. Producers in Buffalo lead the world in flour milling because of their favorable position with respect to wheat supplies and because of the agreement by which Canadian wheat is milled under bond (so that no import duties would be paid) for export. Iron and steel industries in the vicinity of Buffalo use iron ore from the Upper Lakes and coal from the nearby Appalachian Field. Manufacturers in the international city of Niagara Falls take advantage of cheap power to produce a variety of synthetic abrasives and to refine aluminum. Niagara power is consumed as far east as Rochester and westward to Hamilton, Ontario. It should be noted from these descriptions that little in the way of raw materials is produced in the Albany-Buffalo Subregion for the factories. There is no coal or iron, but only some deposits of salt and soda. The excellent transportation facilities, however, provide the necessary materials for the various factories.

SOUTHERN ONTARIO SUBREGION

The manufacturing of southern Ontario, from Toronto and Niagara Falls to Sarnia and Windsor, is similar to that of the subregion just described. It has few raw materials. Coal is transported from the northern Appalachian region of the United States and iron ore from the Upper Lakes District to supply the steel mills in Hamilton, Toronto, and Windsor. The Canadian industries are protected by tariffs on imported articles, which fact makes the selling price of foreign goods in Canada often greater than in the United States. The position of southern Ontario with respect to lake transportation and as a part of the great Manufacturing Belt of North America makes it the chief industrial area of Canada. Toronto manufacturers make clothing, electrical articles, and machinery, pack meat, and mill flour. Iron and steel, chemical soaps, and automobile parts are produced in Hamilton. Windsor is really a part of the Detroit area and specializes in automobile parts.

THE MONTREAL–OTTAWA SUBREGION

The manufacturing cities in the lower St. Lawrence Lowland—Ottawa, Montreal, and Three Rivers—are not favorably situated with respect to iron ore and coal, even though they are on or near tidewater. Coal is shipped up the St. Lawrence from Nova Scotia as far as Montreal during the ice-free season and iron is available from Newfoundland, but iron and steel industries are of little significance. Instead the abundant supplies of timber and water power contribute to a vigorous paper industry and to the refining of aluminum. One of the world's largest paper man-

ufacturing centers is the city of Three Rivers situated between Montreal and Quebec. It is on tidewater, there is a large supply of pulpwood in the immediate hinterland, and the St. Maurice River supplies both power and transportation for the pulpwood. Three Rivers is served by both the Canadian Pacific and Canadian National railways. In Montreal, at the head of freighter navigation, also there are paper mills and various other types of manufacturing such as textiles, clothing, flour milling, and sugar refining. At Ottawa, the capital of the Dominion, huge rafts of logs are received from the Gatineau River for lumber and paper mills located there.

THE PITTSBURGH–CLEVELAND SUBREGION

The Pittsburgh-Cleveland Subregion is the most vital part of the Manufacturing Belt of North America. Because of the central location and the diversity of the basic industries of this subregion, partially fabricated materials are transported from it to all the other subregions. It is dominant as a metallurgical center, but there are also chemical, glass, ceramic, rubber, paint, machine tool, and electrical industries. The major resource of this subregion, coal, has been described in a previous chapter. Water transportation on the Great Lakes is of great significance as are also the many railroads crossing the subregion in every direction.

The basic industry is iron and steel. Of the three raw materials needed in large quantities for iron and steel manufacture, two, coking coal and limestone, are found in the Pittsburgh-Cleveland Subregion. The third, iron ore, can be cheaply transported from the Upper Lakes Region. The first process is the manufacture of coke, which consists essentially of heating coal in the absence of air and driving off all volatile material. In the modern by-product coke plant all the volatile materials are saved—the gas, oils, and various chemicals. The coke, iron ore, and limestone in the correct proportions are then placed in a blast furnace. The purpose of the limestone is to absorb many of the impurities from the ore in the form of a slag which collects on top of the molten iron near the bottom of the furnace. The molten iron is drawn off from time to time from the very bottom. Iron as it comes from the blast furnaces is not suitable for most purposes;

FIGURE 37.3. *An open hearth furnace at the Rouge Plant near Detroit. The function of this furnace is to convert iron to steel. From Ford Motor Company.*

it is too soft. Most of the iron, therefore, is immediately converted to steel. Two processes are in common use depending on the nature of the impurities in the iron. In the Bessemer process hot blasts of air are blown through the molten iron to which some scrap and alloy metals, such as tungsten, nickel, chromium, or vanadium, have been added. Manganese is also added to aid in controlling the oxygen content of the steel. The Bessemer process requires only 15 or 20 minutes to produce 20 tons of steel. The open hearth method (FIG. 37.3) requires about 12 hours and also more fuel than the Bessemer method, but the product is of better quality, especially if certain types of impurities were present in the iron ore. A third process employs an electric furnace and is feasible only where power is cheap, coal scarce, and where the production of small quantities of high-grade steel is desired. The electric furnace may be used to refine further the steels from the Bessemer or open hearth converters.

By these processes manufacturers in the Pittsburgh-Cleveland Subregion and many other steel producing regions are able to turn out steel of varied qualities and shapes needed in the metal working industries, and also steel rails, boiler plates for the railroads, sheet steel, various castings for the automobile industry, and special quality tool steels to be used in the metallurgical industries. Mild steels for wire and nails, stainless steels for cutlery, and tough steels for drive shafts are a few examples of the varied products of the modern steel mill.

In the Pittsburgh-Cleveland Subregion there are large deposits of good clays which together with supplies of coal and natural gas form the basis of a widespread ceramics industry—brick, tile, pottery, porcelain, and sewer pipe. In some districts the clays are interbedded with coal, making very convenient sites for kilns. The location of good glass sands in central Pennsylvania has contributed to the establishment of industries in the vicinity of Pittsburgh, which is especially well located to distribute bulky glass articles to a wide market.

The chief rubber manufacturing city of North America, Akron, Ohio, lies within the limits of the Pittsburgh-Cleveland Subregion more or less by accident. There are no special location factors or other qualities in Akron which favor rubber manufacturing. It is, however, near fuel, good transportation, and the Automobile Subregion, but until the advent of synthetic rubber most of the essential raw materials had to be imported.

SOUTHEASTERN MICHIGAN SUBREGION

To most of the people of North America the most familiar manufacturing district is in southeastern Michigan and parts of Ohio and Indiana, the Automobile Subregion. Few of the 35 million owners of automobiles fail to realize the source of their vehicles and to understand, in general, how they are built. The subregion includes Detroit as the chief center with many other cities, such as Toledo, South Bend, Kalamazoo, Bay City, and Port Huron, on the margins of the main belt. In addition, parts flow to the automobile factories from more distant cities. The location of the industry, an accident of invention, is nevertheless justified by the good transportation of the Great Lakes and the many railroads, by nearness to the Pittsburgh-Cleveland steel producing subregion, and by easy access to a profitable market.

Once the early inventors, such as Ford, Haynes, and Olds, had decided to locate here, and the industry became well established, it was difficult if not impossible to produce automobiles on a competitive basis at any great distance from Detroit. Even the largest automobile manufacturers find it necessary to buy many parts from other factories. Some of the lighter accessories may be shipped for thousands of miles but the bulkier parts are produced in or near the subregion. In the early days of the industry, a half century ago, Detroit and vicinity possessed certain advantages because of industries already established. The vehicle industry was turning out buggies, carriages, and wagons of many kinds. On the shores of Lake St. Clair there were small factories producing motor boats. It required no great stretch of the imagination for someone to adapt the boat motor for use on a land vehicle, the buggy. The earliest automobiles were essentially that, a buggy with a small gasoline motor attached at some convenient point, front, side, or back, with a connection to the rear wheels, commonly a chain, and in addition a steering device. Today the industry is highly complicated, and the modern factory is carefully planned and arranged. As many as 5000 factories may contribute parts to one automobile (FIG. 37.4).

The workers in the cities of this subregion are engaged mainly in the manufacture of automobiles or parts, but other industries are present. The refining of sugar and petroleum is important. Diesel motors, pumps, compressors, paper, furniture, and glass are produced. Grand Rapids, on the northwestern margin of the Automobile Belt, is well known for its furniture, building hardware, and automobile parts. The furniture industry has shown signs of decline since the vast forests, the original advantage of this district, have been cut over and destroyed. In Toledo, on Lake Erie, large quantities of coal are handled and steel for the automobile factories is produced.

THE OHIO–INDIANA INLAND SUBREGION

This subregion is the only major district in the Manufacturing Region to which there is no access either to the Great Lakes or to tidewater. There is water transportation via the Ohio River, on which coal, steel, and other heavy materials are brought from the Pittsburgh-Cleveland district, and there are also good rail connections with the Cotton Belt to the south and the Great Lakes to the north. The chief manufacturing cities of this subregion are Cincinnati, Hamilton, Middletown, Dayton, Muncie, and Indianapolis. The industries are for the most part medium to light in character. Machine tools, electrical machinery, radios, refrigerators, soaps, shoes, clothing, and agricultural machinery are produced in this subregion. As in other subregions, each city possesses a few rather special industries. In Cincinnati soaps, machine tools, radios, and textbooks, along with many other items are produced. Dayton is especially noted for calculating machines, airplane parts, and refrigerators. In Hamilton and Middletown, just ten miles apart, most of the steel mills of this subregion are located, and there is specialization in sheet steel, tin plate, and other rustproof varieties of sheet steel. The industrial cities of the western margin, such as Indianapolis, Muncie, and Richmond, reflect the importance of agriculture in this part of the Corn Belt. Agricultural machinery, flour mills, packing plants, and canneries are found in many cities. The metal industries are represented by iron and steel, airplane and automobile parts, and machine tools.

THE CHICAGO–MILWAUKEE SUBREGION

Along the southern shores of Lake Michigan, in Wisconsin, Illinois, Indiana, and Michigan, and in the immediate hinterland of Chicago is a zone of intensive manufacturing. By means of the lake ready access to iron ore, coal, and limestone for the steel mills at Gary (Indiana) and vicinity is available. This subregion is the one place in the United States where steel is produced where none of the bulky raw materials are found within the subregion. The various industries in the district, however, provide a large market for steel, and the excellent water and rail transportation is favorable to the movement of the raw materials as well as of the finished product. Many excellent sites for factories are available along the lake plain.

Chicago occupies a most strategic position at the western end of the Manufacturing Region and the southern end of Lake Michigan where all the important east-west rail lines of the northern part of the United States must pass. The specific site of the city is on the lake plain where the small Chicago River provides a rather inadequate harbor. Many sorts of raw materials and partially finished goods arrive by rail and lake. Oil and gas are brought by pipeline and barge. In Whiting, near Chicago, there are large petroleum refineries. Chicago is the largest meat packing center in the world, because of its location on the margin of the Corn Belt and because of the good rail connections with the grazing lands to the west. Chicago producers also lead in the processing of corn. Flour milling and the manufacture of cereal foods are important. Agricultural implements, shoes, furniture, books, and printing are also of great significance. The population of metropolitan Chicago is approximately 5,000,000, a good-sized market in itself.

Milwaukee, 80 miles north of Chicago, would be a more important city but for the dominance of its larger neighbor. With use of a good harbor on Lake Michigan, large quantities of coal and grain are handled in Milwaukee, and a variety of industries, including agricultural and mining machinery, steam shovels, shoes, beer, and automobile parts are located there. Racine and Kenosha are somewhat similar in character, while Rockford, Illinois, on the west margin of this

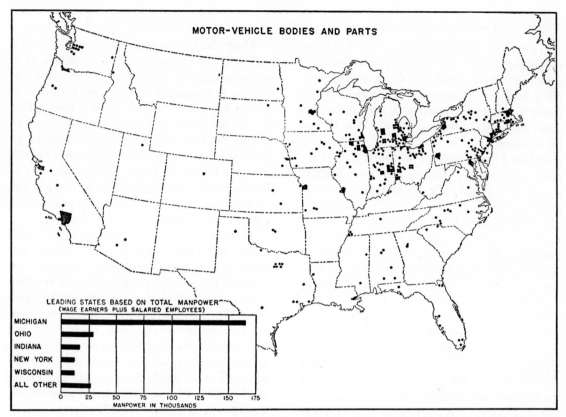

FIGURE 37.4. *A map of motor-vehicle bodies and parts production. Most of the vehicles are finished in southern Michigan and vicinity, but nearly every state contributes some parts. From Bureau of the Census.*

subregion, is best known for its furniture, Elgin for watches, South Bend for automobiles and parts.

THE OUTLYING DISTRICTS

Although manufacturing in North America reveals a constantly shifting pattern, there is no indication that the manufacturing districts outside the main region will ever be of more than secondary importance. During World War II, to be sure, a shift in industrial capacity, influenced by government "cost plus" financing, has had some permanent effects. The outlying districts, however, are limited in raw materials, transportation facilities, and markets compared to the major region. Some of these outliers have been mentioned briefly in previous chapters, the Southern Piedmont, for example, in Chapter 22. Others deserve at least a brief mention.

The St. Louis District

This district, partly in Missouri and partly in Illinois, is located on the Mississippi River near the confluence of the Ohio, Missouri, and Illinois rivers. It is also near the coalfields of southern Illinois which supply fuel in abundance, but not of the best quality, for metallurgical purposes. In the district are steel mills, petroleum refineries, bauxite processing plants, shoe factories, meat packing, glass, chemical, and beer industries. The fact that St. Louis ranks third in shoe production after New England and New York suggests that manufacturers in an outlying district may succeed in certain industries which do not require heavy or bulky raw materials. St. Louis manufacturers were at a decided disadvantage in making shoes, however, until a pool of skilled labor was built up.

The Los Angeles District

For many years the Pacific Coast districts were considered merely as warehouse and assembly points for eastern manufacturers. In recent years, many independent industries in southern California have advanced rapidly. A part of this advance has been the result of World War II, but by no means all of it. A number of factors have contributed to this growth, including a rapid increase in population resulting in a larger market, a climate favorable for photography (motion pictures) and aircraft testing, and the local supplies of petroleum. The war especially stimulated the heavier industries and resulted in constructions such as the steel mill at Fontana east of Los Angeles in a location where none of the raw materials for iron and steel manufacturing are available.

The aircraft industry uses some heavy materials which are sufficiently costly so that freight rates from distant points are not of great relative significance. Much of the steel and aluminum used by the aircraft factories is now produced on the Pacific Coast. In spite of the remoteness from the main Manufacturing Region it is probable that the most important airplane manufacturers in North America will continue to be in Los Angeles. Other industries include automobile assembly plants, automobile tires and tubes, petroleum refining, meat packing, and a very rapidly growing clothing industry.

The San Francisco District

The cities located on San Francisco Bay, San Francisco, Oakland, Alameda, Richmond, and other smaller ones, have the advantage of one of the world's best harbors with access to the various products of the Pacific. Hydroelectric energy is brought from the Sierra Nevada, oil from the southern part of the San Joaquin Valley, and the Central Valley supplies a variety of agricultural raw materials. This district resembles in some respects Metropolitan New York in that light industries are stressed. Refining of oil and of sugar is important, also printing and publishing. Except for its wartime boom in shipbuilding, the San Francisco Bay Region is not highly industrialized. As Pacific trade expands, however, more and more raw material will pour into this port for processing.

The Portland District

Along the Columbia River, from the confluence with the Willamette River to the sea, is an industrial district which includes Portland and Astoria in Oregon, Vancouver and Longview in Washington, and several smaller cities. This district has good local water transportation, although the Columbia offers some difficulties to large ships. Abundant hydroelectric power comes from the Bonneville Dam about 50 miles east of Portland, and from Grand Coulee in eastern Washington. A part of this power is used in aluminum refineries at Troutdale and at Vancouver.

The chief industry is the processing of wood: lumber mills, plywood mills, paper making, furniture manufacturing, and various associated industries. Paper mills in the vicinity of Portland produce everything from newsprint to book paper. The furniture industry utilizes large quantities of softwood, especially Douglas fir, and also some of the local hardwoods, such as oak, maple, and alder, while tropical hardwoods are imported from South America and the Philippines. The woolen industry, based primarily on wool produced in the Pacific Northwest, is concentrated in the Willamette Valley near Portland, but additional mills are located in eastern Oregon, and even in northern California. Portland is the largest market for domestic wool in the United States. Linen mills are also located in the Willamette Valley. Food processing is also important.

The Seattle–Vancouver District

The cities around Puget Sound—Seattle, Tacoma, Bremerton, Bellingham, and Vancouver (British Columbia)—have good harbors and an excellent outlet to the sea. Access to the eastern hinterland is not satisfactory, although two railroads cross the Cascades with the aid of tunnels. The industries of Washington include woodworking, lumber, millwork, shingles, paper, and furniture. Shipbuilding, the aircraft industry, light metal manufacturing, machine tools, and machine shops represent the mechanical trades. The processing and canning of fruits, the canning and quick-freezing of fish, and the refining of sugar are the chief items in the foodstuffs industries. The manufacture of clothing, especially types suitable for loggers, fishermen, and for sportswear, is expanding. Approximately forty

FIGURE 37.5. *A general view of the Rouge Plant of the Ford Motor Company at Dearborn, Michigan. Notice the numerous smoking chimneys, the railway yards, parking lot for employees, and administration building in the foreground. From Ford Motor Company.*

plants are engaged in the production of women's clothing. Manufacturing in and near Vancouver, British Columbia, does not differ markedly from that of the Pacific Northwest. Wood industries, lumber, pulp, paper, and plywood are outstanding. Fish curing and canning, the preserving of fruits, shipbuilding, and the manufacturing of aircraft follow the same general pattern as in Seattle or Portland.

TRENDS

As the result of rapid expansion during World War II and severe damage to many European industrial areas, North America now leads the world in manufacturing. No other people in a comparable area in the world has the variety of resources, material and human, necessary to produce the quality and quantity of goods the world wants and needs. The implications of this fact are far reaching and not a little disturbing to the thoughtful citizen. From now on the surplus of industrial products of North America will be more valuable than the excess of agricultural goods. Therefore, we must export manufactures and import raw materials, and our economy, trade agreements, and governmental policy must be adjusted to these ends. Now, or in the immediate future, we must import petroleum, iron ore (perhaps), wood products, many minerals, fibers, vegetable oils, meat, coffee, and many other items. To pay for these imports we must export industrial goods. Tariffs and other trade barriers must not interfere with this process, however much protection they may give to specific products which are manufactured within the boundaries of this continent.

38

The Manufacturing Region of Western Europe

For nearly two centuries Western Europeans have been processors to most of the outside world. Into their ports and inland cities have poured an unbelievable variety of raw materials: phosphate and iron ore from North Africa; petroleum from Indonesia, the Persian Gulf, and America; cotton and grain from the United States; meat and apples from Canada; wool from Australia and Argentina, to mention but a few. Not all of these articles were processed for export but many of them were. A flood of manufactured articles left the ports of Western Europe bound sometimes for the same countries where the raw materials were produced. The world was dependent on Western Europeans for many products because of their skill.

Europeans were dependent on the rest of the world and now are even more so. People in a region can get along for a time with a limited amount of highly processed manufactured goods or even with none at all. But when imports of foods and other basic materials to Europe are cut off by war or conditions of world economy the people feel the pinch immediately. By manufacturing and trade Western Europeans have lived. Without these activities they face at worst economic and literal starvation, at best a serious upheaval and readjustment of their productive structure.

Following World War II many of the factories of Europe were piles of battered rubble. This was momentarily important but not fundamental. Factories can be rebuilt, if the world is demanding their products. However, the market has changed. Producers in Western Europe have lost some of their best customers simply because the buyers have gone into the business of making

things for themselves. Having discovered what they can do, former customers may expect further progress in the same direction. Do Brazilians need to buy steel from English or German manufacturers? No, indeed. There is now a modern steel mill in Brazil. Do Australians have to purchase farm implements from the British? The Australians too have set up factories to supply many of their needs. The same holds true in greater or less degree in Argentina, Canada, South Africa, and Russia. The workers of Western Europe, to be sure, still retain some of their former superior skill and in all probability will continue to manufacture many articles for the home market and for export. But it seems almost certain that the changing pattern of world production will continue to affect the industrial position of Western Europe adversely. In the discussion of manufacturing to follow it is important to keep in mind the changing relation of Western Europe to the outside world.

The Manufacturing Region in Western Europe resembles that in North America in many fundamental respects. The concentrated areas are in or near the coalfields. The relationship to water transportation is even more pronounced, and the adjacent agricultural areas furnish some raw materials and a large market. The European region differs in that a very large proportion of the raw material is brought from outside the continent, and a very large share of the market lies outside the industrial countries. The European Belt is the older of the two and is somewhat more diversified and concentrated. On the other hand, the small industry and the home industry play a greater role in the European area.

Like the North American Belt, manufacturing

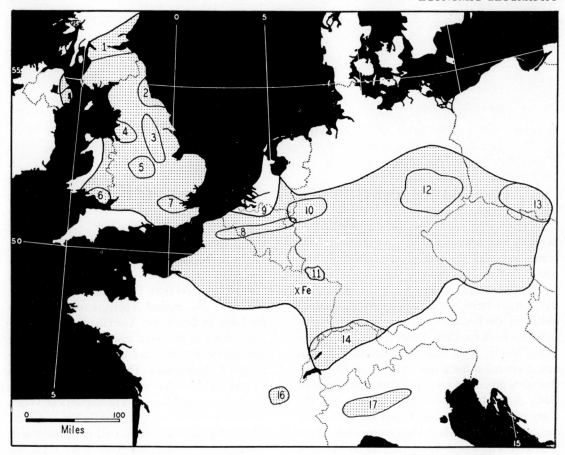

FIGURE 38.1. *A map of the Manufacturing Region of Western Europe. The manufacturing belts are shaded, and the chief districts of concentration indicated by numbers. Abbreviation: iron, Fe. 1. Scottish Lowland (to which northeastern Ireland may be added), 2. Northeastern England, 3. Yorkshire, 4. Lancashire, 5. The Midlands, 6. Southern Wales, 7. London District, 8. The French–Belgian Coalfield, 9. The Low Countries, 10. The Ruhr, 11. The Saar, 12. The Saxon Plain, 13. Upper Silesia, 14. Northern Switzerland. Outliers: 15. Central Sweden (not shown), 16. Lyon District, 17. The Po Plain.*

in Europe is best represented on a map by the distribution of the manufacturing cities (see page 444). It is convenient to mark the approximate borders of the region (FIG. 38.1) prior to the discussion of the individual districts and cities. In Great Britain the belt begins with the Scottish Lowland; from Glasgow and Edinburgh it extends southward to London and Bristol. The Channel Coast of England is not industrial because of its remoteness from coal, but the major coalfields, Ayrshire (Glasgow), Cleveland (Newcastle), Yorkshire (Leeds and Bradford), Lancashire (Manchester), Birmingham, South Wales (Cardiff and Swansea), are represented by con-

centrated industries. London, although not close to a coalfield, is strategically situated on the Thames Estuary opposite the Rhine Delta, and in London there are many diversified industries except for the heavier types. On the continent the industrial belt extends from northern France through the Low Countries, thence into Luxembourg, northern Switzerland, central Germany, western Czechoslovakia, and western Poland. The most concentrated part is the "triangle," the corners of which are located approximately at Lille in northern France, Essen in the German Ruhr, and Nancy in the Lorraine iron ore district of eastern France. Outside the main belt several outlying "islands" of manufacturing are to be found, as in southern France and northern Italy, but the coal supplies and the volume of production in these districts are comparatively small.

TRANSPORTATION

It is essential for producers in the European Manufacturing Belt, with their widespread commitments overseas, to be located near ocean transportation. Much of the local traffic is seaborne and many of the great industrial centers are also ports, some, to be sure, by virtue of ship canals or by the deepening of rivers. Particularly fortunate are the areas in which the coal is near the sea as in southern Wales and the Newcastle District of northeastern England. Those centers which are not on salt water have, for the most part, good water transportation by river and canal to the sea. The main function of the canal system of Western Europe is to connect and supplement the rivers by providing connections from one river to another and extending the upper reaches of the rivers. The best example of such a canal is the *Mittelland*, which cuts across the German rivers from the Rhine to the Oder, providing east-west transportation. An elaborate network of canals connects the various rivers so that it is possible to take a barge from Paris to Warsaw or from Marseille to Hamburg without reaching the sea. It should be noted that the lowlands of Western Europe, including northern Germany, are well adapted for water transportation. The rivers have even gradients with few falls or rapids, and remarkably steady flow. Old abandoned channels of the rivers provide sites for easy canal construction. All this is in strong contrast to the North American Belt, in which inland waterways have limited use, except for the Great Lakes.

Most of the great seaports of Western Europe have grown up on the estuaries of rivers in or near the manufacturing regions. The typical site is that of London, Glasgow, or Hamburg, at the head of the estuary where the river is easily bridged. There the port is accessible to the hinterland on both sides of the river. The depth in the upper estuary, however, is often insufficient for the larger modern freighters, and dredging is necessary. The growth of the various ports has been in proportion to the resources of the hinterland for manufacturing. The chief function of the port is to receive raw products from overseas and to export manufactured goods. Liverpool, at the lower end of the Mersey Estuary, is in a good position to receive cotton from America; London on the Thames looks toward the North Sea and the Rhine Delta, and chemicals from Germany are unloaded from freighters at the docks in this great port. Many other ports are in a good position to receive goods, but coal and other resources are lacking in the vicinity for first rank manufacturing. In addition to raw materials imported from distant lands, large quantities of raw materials and manufactured goods are interchanged through the ports of Western Europe.

The inland waterways, the rivers and canals, are almost as important as the port districts. At the head of navigation for the ocean freighters, the river steamers and barges load and discharge their freight. The Rhine, with its tributaries the Maas, Moselle, Ruhr, Main, and Neckar, not to mention the many connecting canals, taps a vast hinterland which contains abundant coal, iron ore, chemicals, and various agricultural raw materials. The Weser River is navigable to Minden on the eastern margin of the Ruhr Coalfield. The Elbe carries freight to and from the heart of the Bohemian Basin, and the Oder, with a connecting canal, reaches the industrial district of Upper Silesia. The Seine River is marginal to the main Manufacturing Belt, but some of its tributaries and connecting canals are included in the belt.

It is easy to paint a bright picture of water transportation in Europe because conditions are generally more favorable than in North America. But the railroads, which were built after the waterways were well established, are gradually taking more and more of the traffic. In World War II the railways were heavily damaged but were easily repaired. However, canal barges and steamers were sunk at strategic points to block the canals, and locks were heavily damaged. For this reason waterborne inland traffic has been slow to recover. Water for the operation of the locks is not too plentiful, partly because of the increasing use of water for power. The waterways of Western Europe, however, are heavily subsidized by the various governments and will continue to function, carrying a smaller proportion of the freight.

The railway system of Western Europe is so

well developed that few points in the Manufacturing Belt are farther than ten miles from a railroad station. A great east-west system connects southwestern France to eastern Germany with standard gauge ($56\frac{1}{2}$ inches). (In Spain and in Russia the gauges are wider.) North-south railway routes connect the Channel and North Sea coasts with the Mediterranean via the Rhone Valley, various Alpine passes, and Vienna. Even in the mountainous districts rail lines are well distributed, the spiral tunnels of the Swiss Alps being wonders of railroad engineering. Although the roadbeds and the rolling stock of the European roads are lighter than those in North America, the total traffic carried is very great.

On the basis of natural resources—minerals and climate—and lines of communication Western Europe is well suited for manufacturing, but the various resources are by no means equally distributed. Coal, iron, water power, wool, and various chemicals are found within the Manufacturing Belt. From outside must come additional supplies of iron ore, cotton, vegetable oils, and petroleum as well as many other raw materials. The divergent patterns of industry in the following subregions are related to variations in resources, access to outside resources, and to the habits and heritage of the peoples.

SUBREGIONS OF THE MANUFACTURING BELT

1. Scottish Lowland
2. Northeast England
3. Yorkshire
4. Lancashire
5. The Midlands
6. Southern Wales
7. London District
8. The French–Belgian Coalfield
9. The Low Countries
10. The Ruhr
11. The Saar
12. The Saxon Basin
13. Upper Silesia
14. Northern Switzerland

OUTLIERS

15. Sweden
16. Lyon District
17. The Po Plain

THE SCOTTISH LOWLAND SUBREGION, with Glasgow as a focal point, includes a variety of industries, of which iron and steel, shipbuilding, and textiles form the major part. It may be said that the nature of the Scottish industries is related mainly to natural resources which have been supplemented by imported materials. Coal, small quantities of iron ore, wool, linen, and clays are produced in the region. The iron ore and coal supply the basic materials for the steel mills and in turn for the shipbuilding industry. Wool and linen formed the original basis for the textile industry although imported cotton and linen have now become of primary importance. Glasgow, the largest industrial city, is located on the Clyde River, somewhat above the estuary. In spite of improvements in the river the largest ocean freighters must be unloaded several miles below Glasgow. The port is well situated with respect to the northern Atlantic route which lies to the north of Ireland. It is connected by canal with the Firth of Forth on the east side of Scotland. Clays which can be turned into brick, tile, and earthenware occur in the lowland. In the eastern part of the lowland the industries are somewhat lighter. Here linseed oil and linen from the flax plant were combined more than a century ago to make the first oilcloth. Later ground cork from Spain and Portugal was added to make the first linoleum. Jute from India eventually replaced the linen backing and modern linoleum was achieved.

THE NORTHEAST ENGLAND SUBREGION includes a coalfield near the sea, and for nearly two centuries coal has been exported from the port of Newcastle-on-Tyne. "Carrying coals to Newcastle" is notoriously not a profitable venture, but the coal is more and more difficult to mine and the demands of other parts of England leave very little for export. Northeastern England is in a good position to receive iron ore from Sweden via the Norwegian port of Narvik. The iron and steel mills along the Tyne produce material for the shipbuilding industry in which this district rivals that of the Clyde. Lead refining (based on imports of ore and crude metal), glass making, flour milling, and food processing are also of importance. Along the navigable portion of the Tyne River, about 15 miles in length, lie several industrial cities with a total population of more than one million.

THE YORKSHIRE SUBREGION, to the east of the Pennine Range, is another industrial subregion based on coal. The shallow, easily mined coal near the Pennines has long been virtually ex-

FIGURE 38.2. *A steel mill in the English Midlands. By no means all of the English factories are in the large manufacturing centers. Notice the lack of agriculture. From London "Times."*

hausted, and deep shaft mines farther east are now the chief sources. Some of the mine tunnels reach out under the North Sea and attain depths of almost a mile. In the southern part of the Yorkshire Subregion, in the vicinity of Sheffield, iron and steel is the chief industry. This district has been favored since the early days for the production of cutlery. Coal, iron ore, water power, and hard sandstone for grinding were available nearby. Today much of the iron ore comes from Sweden and Spain and synthetic abrasives are used for grinding. Therefore, many of the original advantages are no longer functional.

The northern part of the Yorkshire Subregion, in the vicinity of Leeds and Bradford, is noted chiefly for its woolen goods. Originally most of the wool was brought from the Pennine Range, the upper slopes of which are used mostly for sheep raising, but for many decades heavy imports of wool have come from Australia, New Zealand, South Africa, and Argentina. Various articles are made from wool for domestic use and for export, including yarns, woolen cloth, "shoddy" from reworked wools, carpets, blankets, and various types of woolen clothing. Since more coal is produced in Yorkshire than in any other field in Britain, the metal industries such as iron and steel, locomotives, machine tools, and printing also thrive.

THE LANCASHIRE SUBREGION, on the west side of the Pennine Range, has been for many decades the chief cotton textile district of the world. Originally the spinning and weaving of cotton was favored by the moist climate, by the abundant coal and water supply, and by the good communications with the Americas via Liverpool. All of these factors are significant today except climate, since air conditioning makes it feasible to spin cotton anywhere. Manchester, the center of an urban district which includes Bolton, Bury, Oldham, and Stockport, is connected to the Mersey River Estuary by a ship canal. It is the distributing center of raw cotton and the collecting center of the finished cloth, much of which is ordinarily exported. Before World War II manufacturers in Lancashire faced very keen competition from the Japanese textile mills and will probably continue to do so. The Japanese mills are not so favorably situated with respect to coal, but the labor costs, a decisive factor in the textile industry, are much lower.

THE MIDLAND SUBREGION lies to the south of the Pennines in the vicinity of Birmingham and is sometimes called the "Black Country" because of the coalfields. Birmingham, with good rail lines to all parts of central and southern Britain, has no water routes to the sea. The presence of coal and the importation of ores form the basis of both heavy and light metal industries. Iron and steel, formerly important, have declined but lighter industries, particularly hardware, automobiles, motorcycles, bicycles, machine tools, radios, rayons, and ready-made clothing have enjoyed comparative prosperity.

THE SOUTHERN WALES SUBREGION, like the Northeast England Subregion, has a good coalfield on the sea and formerly much coal was exported to France, Spain, and Italy, and in smaller quantities to more distant lands. Iron and steel mills are of some importance, but the outstanding industry of Wales is the refining of metals, especially tin, copper, and zinc, and the plating of thin sheets of steel with these metals. Ores, crude metals, and petroleum are the chief imports; metals and coal are the principal exports. Prior to World War II, when more and more ships were being converted to oil and the French were getting large quantities of coal from Germany, the export of coal declined. But the scarcity of coal in Western Europe, including England, following the war has again put a premium on Welsh coal.

THE LONDON SUBREGION is as unique in British industry as is New York in United States industry. There is no coal in the immediate vicinity of London but it is a great commercial city with a rather extensive and varied industry. Heavy industries, such as iron and steel, are of minor importance, but chemicals and soapmaking, tanning, printing, and clothing industries employ thousands of workers. In the eastern part of the city the chemical industries, soap factories, petroleum refineries, machine shops, and shipyards are located. Farther inland and to the north of the commercial core ("the City") are the lighter industries—clothing, printing, watch and instrument making, furniture factories, and glassworks. Most of the products manufactured in London, to be sure, are designed to be consumed locally, since a city of eight million population is a large market in itself. The metal industries usually employ more than 50,000 workers, most of them engaged in the repair of machines.

THE FRENCH–BELGIAN SUBREGION occupies the margins of a long narrow coalfield which reaches from the vicinity of Calais on the English Channel through Lille and Roubaix in France and via Mons, Charleroi, and Liége in Belgium to the southern tip of the Netherlands. The coal

FIGURE 38.3. A rayon factory near St. Quentin, France. Many of the French factories have a rural setting with vegetable gardens in the vicinity. From USAF.

is of good quality, and the sea, rivers, and canals are available for the importation of iron ore from Lorraine in eastern France or from other sources. Besides steel and machinery this subregion is outstanding for the production of cotton, rayon (FIG. 38.3), and woolen textiles. Imports include cotton, wool, metals (partly in the crude form), chemicals, timber, and hides. Refined metals, machinery, clothing, iron and steel, and coal are exported. This subregion constitutes the northwestern limb of the great industrial triangle of western continental Europe, one corner of which is near Lille, France, one in the Ruhr, and the third in Lorraine near Nancy. In this triangle there is abundant coal, most of it easier to mine than that of Britain, and plentiful iron ore. The Lorraine ores are not the richest in the world, but their high lime content makes them self-fluxing. Excellent inland transportation, including the lower Rhine, the Moselle, and the Meuse rivers and a network of canals, has made this triangle in the past the most important industrial district of its size in the world.

THE LOW COUNTRIES SUBREGION, the coastal fringe of Belgium and the Netherlands, is a manufacturing district in its own right, distinct from the coalfields of those countries. Both countries have overseas colonies which supply raw materials for processing, and both have a tradition of manufacturing. In central and northern Belgium, in the vicinity of Bruxelles, Antwerp, Bruges, and Roulers, textiles are dominant. During the Middle Ages Flanders was the chief region where woolen cloth was manufactured in Europe. Today the volume of cotton goods is greater than that of wool. Linens and rayons are produced for export. Belgian lace, more and more of it machine made, brings an excellent price on the world market. Most of the industry in the Netherlands is located on the estuaries of the Rhine and Scheldt rivers in the general vicinity of Rotterdam and along the ship canal connecting Amsterdam with the North Sea. The importation of large quantities of raw sugar, petroleum, rubber, copra, metals, chemicals, and textiles sets the stage for many of the industries. The refining of sugar, manufacture of alcohol, and the processing of chemicals and foodstuffs account for a large share of the industry. Other manufactures include soap, fertilizers, electrical machinery, wool,

FIGURE 38.4. *A ball-bearing plant near Stuttgart, Germany. This and many similar factories use hydroelectric power and are, therefore, devoid of the smoking chimneys so characteristic of the large industrial centers. From USAF.*

linen, cotton, synthetic textiles, pottery, earthenware, chocolate, paper, ships, furniture, and leather goods.

THE RUHR SUBREGION, east of the Rhine and north of the Ruhr River, includes the best coalfield in Western Europe and several industrial centers, such as Essen, Dortmund, Duisburg, Gelsenkirchen, and many smaller ones. The coal is of high quality and comparatively easy to mine. Canals and rivers bring abundant iron ore, chemicals, and other raw materials to the district. The Ruhr may be divided into three belts running eastward from the Rhine. The southernmost belt lies along the Ruhr River, which is significant mainly for water supply and power. A few of the smaller industrial centers are located on the river, but most of the land is wooded hills with small farms. The middle belt includes the larger cities mentioned previously together with the main part of the coalfield. There the coal is close to the surface and can be mined by means of drift tunnels and shallow shafts. The northernmost belt lies in the plain where the coal can be reached only by relatively deep shafts.

Before World War II the Ruhr was one of the most important districts of heavy industry in the world. Iron and steel mills, with their coke plants, blast furnaces, and rolling mills, were crowded into the middle belt, especially on the western margin near the Rhine. Factories depending on the abundant supply of steel included various kinds of heavy engineering, steel rails, locomotives, boilers, and railroad cars. Solingen and Remscheid were cutlery centers, comparable to Sheffield; Stolberg was associated mostly with brass. Other centers produced textiles, chemicals, and paper. The Ruhr was so badly damaged during World War II and is so dependent on a prosperous Germany for a market that many years will elapse before the prewar industrial capacity can be restored. But the basic resource—coal—and the favorable position remain.

THE SAAR SUBREGION is a small but strategically located industrial district on the northern border of Lorraine. It is connected by rail and canal with the iron mines of Lorraine and the Rhine, so that iron ore and metallurgical coke are readily available. Coal is produced from mines in the Saar but the quality is not suitable for making metallurgical coke, at least not without blending with higher grade coal. Formerly iron and steel were produced in the Saar on a small scale on the basis of local ore and coal. More recently additional iron ore has been imported from Lorraine. The iron and steel mills have expanded in the Saar Valley near Saarbrücken, and various types of iron and steel are sent out from this subregion to other industrial districts for further processing.

THE SAXON BASIN SUBREGION has long been considered the second industrial district of Germany after the Ruhr. Leipzig is near the center, Dresden on the east, Plauen on the south, and Gotha on the west. On the north the subregion reaches Magdeburg. There are large reserves of lignite in Saxony but only limited quantities of good coking coal so the heavy industries are of minor significance. The industrial growth is related to the varied resources of the district, including the lignite, which is useful as a fuel and in the chemical industries. Small amounts of various metals in the Ore Mountains and glass sands and various chemicals in other parts of the subregion were influential in the establishment of industry. As in many parts of Britain, Saxony continued to manufacture many articles made of metals and other materials long after local supplies of the raw materials had been exhausted. The Saxon Basin is also a rich farming region and some of the crops, such as sugar beets, barley, and hops, contribute to manufacturing. Imports of textiles via the Elbe River are also important.

A typical industry of Saxony is the manufacture of optical glass and instruments, such as microscopes, telescopes, and cameras. Based on local supplies of glass sands and a high degree of skill, the optical industry of Jena and vicinity was unequaled anywhere in the world until the end of World War II. The lignite and salt mines both contribute to the chemical industries. The lignite is converted by distillation to tar from which benzene, nitrogen, fuel oil, and paraffin are obtained. The nitrogen is used in the fertilizer industry together with other chemicals obtained from the vicinity of Staszfurt on the northwest margin of the basin. The lignite is also a source of power, which is transmitted as far as Berlin. At Dresden deposits of good clay form the basis of the porcelain and china industry. In Leipzig there are chemical works, textile mills, and an extensive printing industry.

THE UPPER SILESIA SUBREGION, centering around Gleiwitz, includes good deposits of coking coal, lead, zinc, some silver, and glass sands. As a result of boundary changes agreed upon in a plebiscite held in 1922, most of this region became a part of Poland. Producers in the district import cotton, wool, and flax, and the textile industry has been important in the past. On the basis of local raw materials, however, Upper Silesia is best suited for heavy industry. After those in the Ruhr and in Donbas of Russia, the coalfield is the best on the continent of Europe. The excellence of the situation of Silesia is attested by the fact that the Germans relocated most of their heavy industry there when the Ruhr was heavily bombed during World War II. Now that Silesia is entirely in Poland and Germany is industrially divided, it will be interesting to note the reorientation of the industries. Silesia is on the eastern margin of the main Manufacturing Belt and its greatest market formerly lay to the west in central Germany, which never produced much steel. Political boundaries, however, are rarely complete barriers to trade.

THE NORTHERN SWITZERLAND SUBREGION, of all the subregions of the European Manufacturing Belt, is the poorest in basic raw materials for manufacturing. But like New Englanders in the United States, the Swiss long ago developed the technical skill to offset this handicap. An ingenious, energetic people, faced with long periods of idleness in winter, learned to apply long hours of labor to small amounts of raw materials. A stream of tourists from northern Europe and the United States provided a ready market for many types of handicraft, and by their spending for goods and services provided foreign exchange, so that raw materials of various kinds could be imported. Abundant water power helps offset the lack of coal.

Although some types of manufacturing, such as wood carving, use local raw materials, the dominant textile industries—spinning, weaving, printing and dyeing of silk, rayon, and cotton cloth—are based on imported fibers. Most of the cotton spinning and weaving is in the northeastern part of the plateau, in and near Zürich and St. Gallen. Watches, clocks, scientific instruments, toys, and electrical and agricultural machinery are also produced in Switzerland. The cheap water power encourages the refining of aluminum. Many of the factories are small and home industries still survive.

OUTLIERS

The Swedish District

In Sweden, like Switzerland, there are limited raw materials but many articles can be manufactured on the basis of skill, abundant water power, and some imports. The value of the forest in Sweden has been discussed previously. In addition to many sawmills, paper and pulp mills and match and furniture factories are to be found on the north shore of Lake Väner and along the middle portion of the Gulf of Bothnia, north of Stockholm. The iron ore of northern Sweden is mostly exported, but the ore of central Sweden, extending from Lake Väner eastward to the Gulf of Bothnia, is used in local industries. There is no good coking coal in Sweden but small quantities can usually be imported for the smelting of this ore. Wood charcoal is still used instead of coke in some establishments. The cost of steel production under these circumstances is high, but most of the steels have special qualities. Swedish steel has been famous throughout the world for more than a century. Woolen goods are manufactured at Norrköping, and cotton textiles are made at Göteborg on the west because of its favorable location for the import of raw cotton. Although nearly one third of Sweden's population is engaged in industry, the chief exports are raw or slightly processed materials, such as ore, lumber, pulp, and paper. The imports include foods, textiles, and coal.

The Lyon District

Although Lyon, at the confluence of the Rhone and Saône rivers, is essentially a commercial center, it is also important for manufacturing. The silk industry, started by Italian immigrants and supported at first by local production of raw silk, is of first rank. Prior to World War II the silk mills employed more than 300,000 people, making fabrics of various kinds, mostly from Japanese raw silk. As in Switzerland, the tourist trade furnished a good market, and silks from Lyon are sold in large quantities in Paris and in many other European cities. Chemicals (especially for photographic purposes), explosives, drugs, and leather goods are also manufactured. It should be noted that only a small part of the factories are in Lyon or the immediate vicinity. The district spreads out into the lower Rhone Valley, reaches into the Central Plateau, and even into the Jura Mountains. The marginal mountains furnish water power, which is supplemented by coal from the vicinity of St. Étienne, southwest of Lyon. The coal is used also to produce iron and steel, and munitions.

The Po Plain District

There are a number of important industries in the Po Plain, although it is evident that the basic requirements for heavy manufacturing and for many of the lighter types are missing. The scarcity of coal is the most serious limiting factor, all the more critical in the light of the general postwar shortage of coal in Western Europe. To a limited extent the extensive water power of the southern Alps compensates for the lack of coal, especially in the textile industries. In spite of handicaps some iron and steel are produced in Italy. This is made possible by the import of scrap, pig iron, and coking coal, and also by the use of electric furnaces for the production of high-grade steel. Most of the iron and steel industries are located on the island of Elba and at Genoa,

both of which have ready access to the Po Plain.

In general, the textiles, especially cotton, silk, and rayons, are the chief manufactures in the Po Plain. Cotton cloth and clothing, based on imports of cotton from the United States, Brazil, and Egypt usually lead in volume. The silk industry is based partly on local supplies of raw silk, in part on imports. In recent years the manufacturing of rayons has made rapid progress. Light metals, hats, wine, and food processing are also important. One belt of manufacturing cities— Turin, Bergamo, Brescia, Verona, and Udine— is situated at the foot of the Alps with access to Alpine passes and water power. A second line of cities lies between the edge of the Alps and the Po River. Milan is the largest of this second group and is the chief industrial center of Italy. The manufacturing of textiles, light metals, automobile and airplane parts, and the processing of foods are all in the vicinity. Of all the Mediterranean countries, Italy has the densest population with respect to its arable land. This makes manufacturing for export imperative if the Italians are to enjoy even a moderately high living standard. Under the circumstances it is not difficult to understand the Italian gamble for an overseas empire, which it was hoped would supply raw materials and a market for manufactured goods.

39

Manufacturing in Russia

MORE than one seventh of the land area of the earth and one eleventh of the people are in Russia. Until World War I, in spite of the varied resources which favored industry, Russians made little progress in manufacturing. However, following the war, progress was rapid until interrupted by World War II. In some respects this great conflict was an advantage, since it stimulated Russian war industries and through it Russian technicians were brought into contact with many technicians of other countries. In recent years progress has continued on an even greater scale. Russian economy advances according to plan. The best industrial sites are selected only after considerable study, the factories are financed by government banks, and the administration is by government bureaus. The successive five-year plans have resulted in enormous percentage increases in production, but much remains to be done before the 200 million people of Russia are supplied with the comforts and conveniences of modern industrialization. How the Russian government achieves its goals and what relation it will bear to other countries are the most important questions facing the world at the present time. See FIGURE 39.1.

RESOURCES

Many of the raw materials used in Russian industry have been mentioned in the preceding chapters. A brief review with some additions will be useful at this point. The farms, forests, and mines all make valuable contributions. The industrial crops include sugar beets, potatoes, sunflower seed, cotton, and flax, to mention only the more important ones. The forests supply lumber, pulp for paper, and cellulose for synthetic fibers. It is from the mines, however, that the most signifi-

cant raw materials are taken. Russia is well supplied with good coal, although some parts of the country are too remote from the mines to make use of this resource with the present limitations of transportation. Petroleum is abundant but its distribution and use are limited by the scarcity of drilling equipment, pipelines, and tankers. Iron ore, manganese, potassium salts, and phosphate are plentiful. Gold, copper, zinc, lead, aluminum, uranium, asbestos, and potash are also available. Tin, antimony, diamonds, and a few other minor minerals are lacking in Russia. Compared to those in the United States, Russia's mineral deposits are somewhat more varied, but the quality of the ores is in general poorer.

INDUSTRIAL GROWTH

Russian industrial production has increased sharply since 1913. Thousands of new factories and power plants have been constructed, and raw material production has been increased to keep pace. The growth of heavy industry has been especially rapid, while the manufacture of consumers goods has expanded slowly. The enormous expansion of truck and tractor production, for example, is in sharp contrast to the small output of passenger automobiles. Machine tools, jet airplanes, and synthetic rubber, all designed to build up the nation's military strength, are now in large-scale production. The distribution of manufacturing has also changed. Forty years ago most of the industries were located in the Leningrad, Moscow, and Donbas districts. More recently industrial growth has been rapid in the eastern districts, the Urals, Kuzbas, Far East, and Central Asiatic Russia (Turkestan). This represents a deliberate effort to distribute industry more evenly, but it also reflects the vast extent of Russian resources.

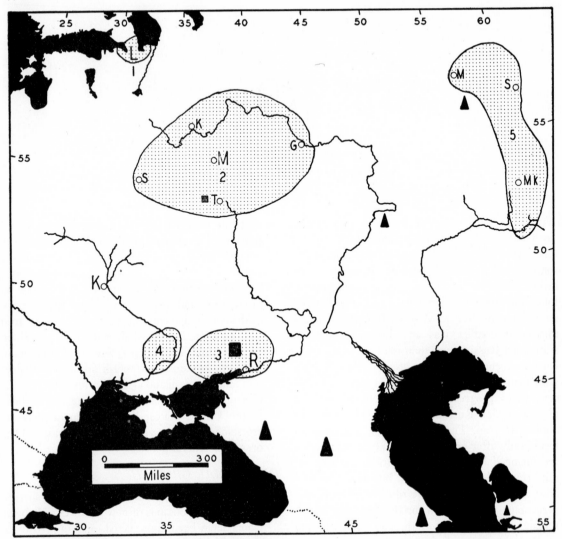

FIGURE 39.1. *A location map of the chief industrial regions of Russia.* 1. *The Leningrad Region with Leningrad (L) the chief city.* 2. *The Central Industrial Region, Moscow (M) in the center and the cities of Kalinin (K), Gorki (G), Tula (T), and Smolensk (S) on the periphery.* 3. *In the Donbas are the largest and best coal deposits and several seaports including Rostov (R).* 4. *The Dnepr Bend Region.* 5. *The Southern Urals, in which Molotov (M), Sverdlovsk (S), and Magnitogorsk (Mk) are important centers. Three additional industrial regions are shown on the opposite page.*

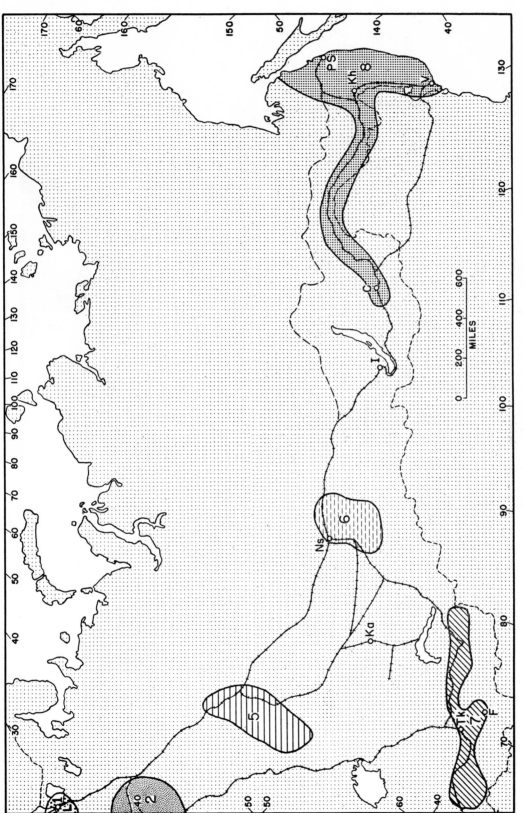

FIGURE 39.2. *Map showing the location of the northern and eastern industrial regions of Russia. 1. Leningrad. 2. The Central (Moscow) Industrial Region. 5. The Southern Urals. 6. The Kuzbas. 7. Central Asiatic Russia. 8. The Far East. Important industrial cities, some of them outside the regions listed, are indicated by letters: Fergana (F), Tashkent (Tk), Novosibirsk (Ns), Karanganda (Ka), Chita (C), Irkutsk (I), Khabarovsk (Kh), and Vladivostok (V). (Broken line indicates that railroad is under construction or not in use.)*

FIGURE 39.3. *An electrified iron ore mine at Tashtagol near Gornaya Shoria. This district supplies part of the ore for the Kuzbas industrial district. From "Sovfoto."*

THE MANUFACTURING DISTRICTS

Manufacturing in Russia is more widely dispersed than in Western Europe or North America. Instead of a major "manufacturing belt" there are eight districts, each with a different history and function. In a measure the eight districts are supplementary and the whole represents a well-rounded industrial development. But the distances between some of them are so great that a certain amount of duplication is necessary. Only state planning prevents further duplication and competition. The eight major districts and the chief products manufactured in them are:

Leningrad. Wood products, chemicals, textiles, clothing.

The Central Industrial District (Moscow and environs). Textiles, food, chemicals, automobiles, agricultural machinery.

The Donbas. Steel, machinery, shoes, clothing, ships, chemicals.

The Dnepr Bend. Iron and steel, machinery, sugar, flour, chemicals.

The Southern Urals. Iron and steel, machinery.

The Kuzbas. Iron, steel, zinc.

Central Asiatic Russia (Turkestan, in the vicinity of Tash- kent *and* Fergana). Water power, cotton textiles, and light industries.

Far East (Lake Baikal to Vladivostok). Petroleum refining, fish canning and processing, wood products, and metal working.

Leningrad

At one time the industries in and near Leningrad (then St. Petersburg) were the most progressive and prosperous in Russia. Access to Western Europe, with its supplies of coal (when Russians mined little of their own coal), cotton, leather, other raw materials, and machinery was largely responsible. Leningrad gradually grew in industrial importance but other districts advanced even faster. Today Leningrad owes its industrial production to the resources of its hinterland in northern Russia rather than to imports, although small amounts of imported raw materials still enter. With rail connections to Arkhangelsk, Murmansk, and the Pechora River west of the northern Urals, Leningrad taps the timber, ores of aluminum, nickel, and iron of the north country. Potassium salts and phosphate, valuable for fertilizer and in the chemical industry in general, are mined in the hinterland and brought to Leningrad via the Baltic–White Sea Canal. Lumber, paper, matches, cotton cloth and clothing, shoes, machinery, and chemicals of various kinds including drugs are produced in Leningrad. Although the Leningrad District lost many of its factories by removal to the east during World War II, the city continues to be one of the most important industrially in the Soviet Union. Wood products and furs are the chief exports, most of the other products being restricted to the home market. The chief disadvantage of Leningrad is its distance from coal. The use of large quantities of peat for fuel and power compensates in part for the lack of coal.

The Central Industrial District

The Central Industrial District lies in the heart of western Russia, with Moscow as the chief city. It is often called the Old Industrial Belt because of the early development of a variety of industries. It is not a compact manufacturing subregion such as that of Western Europe or North America but consists of scattered urban areas with vast expanses of farming land between. The location is to be explained by history and transportation rather than by resources. A rather limited supply of coal and good supply of lignite and peat are available on the south in the vicinity of Tula. Also some local iron ore, phosphate, and an abundance of clay contribute to the raw materials. But most of the raw materials used in the factories must be imported from outside the district, for example, coal and steel from the Donbas, timber from the north, cotton from Turkestan, ores and metals from the Urals, and petroleum from the Caucasus. The relation of this region to the Volga is rather obvious from study of a map. The cities of the middle and eastern portions of the Central Industrial District especially are located on the Volga or its tributaries.

Moscow itself is a city of five million people and accounts for about one eighth of the industrial production in Russia by value. From the standpoint of modern transportation, its location is far from ideal. Situated on the small, shallow Moscow River, which is not navigable in the vicinity, the city leans heavily on its canal connection to the upper Volga. Rail transport is good, however, and since many of the industries are of a lighter nature, the cost of transportation is not excessive.

There are both light and heavy industries in the city. In the first category textiles take first place and have done so for more than a century. Moscow's first reputation as an industrial center was based on cotton print. Linen and woolen fibers are of increasing importance. Gradually other industries have come to the fore, such as iron and steel, chemicals, ceramics, flour milling, and food processing.

Many industries have grown in outlying cities, and a dozen of these cities are now rated as industrial centers. Kalinin on the west is noted for its textiles, especially cotton and linen. More flax is grown in the vicinity than in any other part of Russia, and modern methods of sowing, harvesting, and retting the flax have been introduced. Yaroslavl, to the northeast of Moscow, is one of the oldest cities on the Volga. Linen, rubber goods made partly from synthetic rubber, and agricultural machinery are produced there. To the east of Moscow is the city of Gorki, formerly called Nizhni Novgorod, located at the junction of the Oka and Volga rivers. Gorki has access by river to the coal of the Donbas and the iron ores of the Urals, but its steel mills use large quantities of scrap because of the great distance from ore and coal. The steel is used to make automobiles, river boats and barges, agricultural machinery, and railroad cars. The forested regions of the north are not distant, and paper and other wood products are manufactured in Gorki. Chemicals, household implements, shoes, and other leather goods contribute to the well-rounded development of Gorki's industries. Near Tula, south of Moscow, the best coal of the Central Industrial District is mined. This city is also nearest the coal of the Donbas. Coal from both sources is used in the iron and steel industries of Tula and vicinity, although local coals are used chiefly for fuel and power. Rifles, guns, sewing machines, and the famous Russian samovars are manufactured in Tula. The cities mentioned in this paragraph form a circle which marks out in a rough manner the limits of the Central Industrial Belt, in which Moscow is slightly to the left of the center. This is by far the most diversified of all the manufacturing districts in the Soviet Union.

The Donbas

The Donbas (FIG. 39.4), or Donetz Coal Basin to use a longer name, is perhaps better endowed

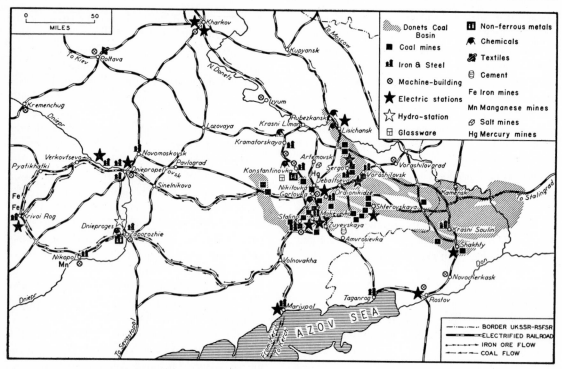

FIGURE 39.4. *A map of the Donbas and Dnepr Industrial Regions. From "Land of the Soviets"*
by Mikhailov with permission of The Citadel Press.

by nature for the development of heavy industries than any other region in the world. In its natural setting and the availability of raw materials, it is equal, if not superior, to the Northern Appalachians or the Ruhr. Abundant coal, both anthracite and high-grade bituminous, is comparatively easy to mine. Iron ore and manganese are obtained from the Krivoi Rog District in the great Bend of the Dnepr River and can be brought to the coal either by rail or by water. Cheap water power and abundant petroleum are also available. The position of the Donbas on the Sea of Azov permits ocean vessels to enter the district, which is not true of most iron and steel districts, such as the Ruhr or the Pittsburgh-Cleveland district. The Russians have not been able to make full use of this district, however, since it was occupied by the Germans during World War II. Because much of the heavy machinery was removed before invasion, it was necessary to rebuild the whole industrial structure after the close of the war.

Because of the technical lag in Russia, the iron ore and coal resources in southern Russia were slow to be exploited. As late as 1934 Russians were importing quantities of steel, part of which came from Germany, and part from the United States. Iron ore production increased from six million tons to 28 millions in the period from 1928 to 1938, and prior to World War II some iron and steel were exported from Russia. Since the war, the vast domestic needs for rebuilding the wrecked industries has allowed little for export. Then too, the best potential customers for Russian exports were impoverished by the war and therefore able to buy little.

In Donbas there are, in addition to coal, deposits of limestone which can be used as flux in the blast furnaces. Salt and mercury are also mined, and although these have little relation to the iron and steel production, they do contribute along with the by-products of the coking plants to the chemical and drug output. The blast furnaces of the Donbas include some of the smaller types of the old days together with modern types, some of which have a capacity of more than 40,000 cubic feet. Most of the converters are also of recent construction. Many of the factories of the Donbas are engaged in shaping the iron and steel into useful machines. Machine tools, heavy drills and presses, locomotives, ships, and mining machinery are examples. Brick from local clays, glass, shoes, clothing, and refined petroleum products are also produced in the Donbas District.

The Dnepr Bend

The Dnepr Bend District is a sort of counterpart of the Donbas, furnishing iron ore, manganese, and power. Coal from the Donbas supplements the local minerals and heavy industry is set up here also. Iron, steel, and metal-working plants, similar to those of the Donbas, are found on the banks of the Dnepr. On the river, 60 miles below Dnepropetrovsk, is the great dam which transforms the rapids of the river, formerly only an interruption to navigation, into power and quiet water. The original dam was 200 feet high and 2500 feet long, and the power plants had an

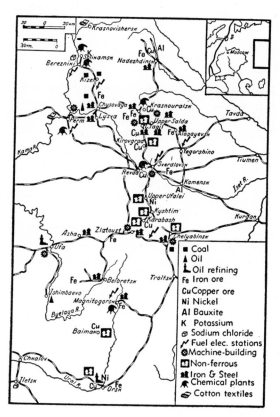

FIGURE 39.5. *A map of the southern Ural Industrial Region. Notice the variety of raw materials in and near the region. From "Land of the Soviets" by Mikhailov and with the permission of The Citadel Press.*

installed capacity of 500,000 kilowatts. The dam was partially destroyed during World War II by the retreating armies of Russia and Germany, but has subsequently been rebuilt. Pig iron, ordinary steel, electric steel, aluminum, and magnesium are produced and refined there, and from these metals many kinds of machinery are made.

The Southern Urals

The Southern Urals (FIG. 39.5) and the Kuzbas are of more recent development than the districts previously described. In a general way, the two bear the same relation to each other as the Dnepr Bend and the Donbas districts. In detail, however, there are many differences. The Urals are rich in iron ore but have little metallurgical coal, whereas the Kuzbas has abundant high quality coal. Although more than 1400 miles apart, the two districts have functioned as a "team" since their development as industrial centers.

The Urals probably contain a greater variety of mineral wealth than any other area of the same size in the world. In addition to iron ore which includes high-grade magnetite, ores of copper, gold, nickel, bismuth, tungsten, and aluminum are found. Other minerals include metallic platinum, asbestos, quartz crystal, and also salt, potassium, and pyrites. The minerals of the Urals are chiefly close to the surface, and their existence has been known for centuries. Iron ores were exploited on a small scale, with the aid of wood charcoal, more than three centuries ago. As an industrial region the Urals are handicapped by the lack of good coal and by the sparse population. Its markets are far away in the Central Industrial District. The iron ore of the southern Urals together with the Kuzbas coal forms the basis of the iron and steel industry, and from the steel many machines and other metal products are derived. The chemicals are used to make fertilizer; the potassium salts and the pyrites make a good combination for this purpose. Paper and textile mills are also found, the former being supplied with raw material from the north, the latter getting raw cotton from the fields of Turkestan.

The Kuzbas

The Kuzbas is located in the foothills of the Altai Mountains about 200 miles to the southeast of the city of Novosibirsk and not far from the

Trans-Siberian Railway. The reserves of good quality metallurgical coal are very large, easy to mine, and in recent years iron ore deposits have been developed in the vicinity. The largest iron and steel mills are at Stalinsk, which is connected with the Trans-Siberian by rail. Steel rails, frame steel for general construction, and a variety of other shapes are produced here for delivery all along the Trans-Siberian Railway. Water power from the nearby mountains contributes to industry, and a part of the railway line is electrified. The Kuzbas is a new industrial district with a remote location. Its distance from large centers of consumption, obviously a disadvantage for peacetime trade, is considered an advantage in the event of war because of the distance from the Russian frontiers.

Central Asiatic Industrial District

This long narrow district lies to the south and southwest of Lake Balkhash largely in Uzbek, Tadzhik, and Kirghiz republics. It is marginal to several mountain ranges, including the lofty Tien Shan Range. As previously noted, this is one of the most favored regions in all Russia for the development of water power, because of the great relief rather than the heavy rainfall, however. The mountains contain valuable minerals including salt, coal, and the ores of various metals. The irrigated lands (see FIGURE 11.6) in the Sir Darya, Amu Darya, and Ili river valleys produce most of the cotton of Russia. The combination of abundant water power and large supplies of raw cotton sets the stage for a large-scale textile industry. The cities of Tashkent, Fergana, and Ashkhabad have large textile mills. Coal and salt are the basic raw materials for the chemical industries. Woodworking and leather goods are also of importance. The mountain forests supply wood for lumber, furniture, and wood chemicals. Leather is obtained in part from the grazing regions to the north (see page 172) and from the more humid pasture lands on the margin of the mountains. The Turk-Sib Railway connects this region with the Caspian on the west and with the Trans-Siberian Railway on the north at Novosibirsk, and another line leads to Kuibishev on the Volga.

The Far East Industrial District

Between Lake Baikal and the Pacific Ocean, and along the Trans-Siberian Railway, is the most remote of the Russian industrial regions, the Far East. It is connected with other parts of the U.S.S.R. by the long, thin thread of the railroad or by sea, but it is evident that this region has great strategic importance, largely because of its nearness to China, Japan, and the Pacific. The raw material base includes petroleum on Sakhalin Island, coal on the same island and in the vicinity of Vladivostok, and numerous small deposits of iron and gold. The forests supply both hardwood and softwood to the lumber mills and woodworking establishments. The fisheries of the coastal waters are excellent, and a portion of the catch is canned. The agriculture is as diversified as climate will permit, with greatest emphasis on grains, hay, and livestock. The chief industries are petroleum refining, metal working, woodworking, and food processing. Although the long, cold winter is a handicap, this pioneer industrial region has sufficient resources for continued growth, especially if trade with China and Japan can be increased.

CONCLUSION

It is apparent from the foregoing brief statements that Russia has great industrial potentialities. How far the development will go and in what directions is not clear at the present time. The official Soviet reports are optimistic but incomplete. The first years following World War II had to be devoted largely to rehabilitation of the devastated areas, and therefore comparatively little progress could be shown in terms of consumer goods production. In spite of the lack of specific recent information and statistics of production it must be recognized that Russia is in a good position to become a great industrial power. The population is increasing at the rate of about three million per year, and by 1970 it will reach 250 millions (by 2000, 300 millions) if the present rate of increase continues. Russian raw materials, as noted previously, are varied and abundant. A considerable number of the people have a strong desire to increase industrial production and will make great sacrifices to do so. In technological skill and industrial organization Russians still lag behind the workers of Western Europe and North America. The Russians are not and never will be completely self-sufficient, and their industrial maturity, therefore, depends on peaceful trade with the rest of the world.

40

World Trade

FREQUENT references have been made in the preceding chapters to trade and transportation. It has been pointed out that commercial production often depends on established trade routes. A coffee plantation in Uganda, Africa, for example, can succeed only by virtue of water transportation on Lake Victoria, the railroad to the coast, and a sea route via the Suez Canal. In remote regions with resources, there is often no production. From another point of view it can be stated that world trade depends fundamentally on the variety of production in different regions and on the desires of many people to possess things which they cannot produce at home. In previous discussions it has been noted that the nature of production in various parts of the world depends on the natural resources, including the climate, and on the skills and culture of the various peoples. Production is variable. Trade is even more variable since a small change in production in one region may have serious repercussions in trade thousands of miles away. The rapidity and far-reaching effect of such changes are indicated by a brief history of trade. See FIGURE 40.1.

HISTORY OF TRADE

No one knows when the first trade, in the form of barter, began, but it is known that the Phoenicians introduced regional sea trade about the year 1000 B.C. From their base in the eastern Mediterranean, now the coast of Syria and Palestine, the Phoenicians were in the most strategic locality of that time. From the east they could import dyes and jewels and from Africa gold and ivory. The sea routes in the Mediterranean provided markets for the gold and silver of Spain and, with the addition of the land routes, the tin of Brittany

and Cornwall. For the first time towns were founded primarily for the purposes of trade, for example, Carthage near Tunis and Cadiz in southern Spain.

As the Phoenicians declined in sea power, Greece emerged as a trading state. Athens became an important trade center, and Athenians even depended on wheat from the north coast of the Black Sea. This is the earliest record of the movement of grain long distances by sea. During the ascendancy of Rome trade advanced very little although many new routes, which later became lines of trade, were opened up for military purposes. Wheat moved into Rome from the north, but the city was never an important trade center. In the Middle Ages sea trade was limited and means of transportation on the land were slow and expensive. Many hazards awaited the trader. Roads were poor, bridges few, and heavy tolls, if not robbers, harassed the trading parties.

Coastwise trade escaped many of the hazards of land routes. The Hanseatic League was organized in northern Europe to protect and foster trade. At first it was a league of merchants but later became a coalition of trading towns: Königsberg, Danzig, and Lübeck on the Baltic; Bruges and London on the North Sea; and Bergen on the west coast of Norway. The merchants of these towns traded in fish, salt meat, timber, skins and furs, wheat, wine, beer, cloth, and many other commodities. This is the first instance of large-scale trading in a variety of heavy necessities. Hitherto the long trade routes had carried only expensive luxuries such as gems, metals, dyes, silks, and spices.

In spite of such regional trade as that of the Hanseatic League, world trade began only after the

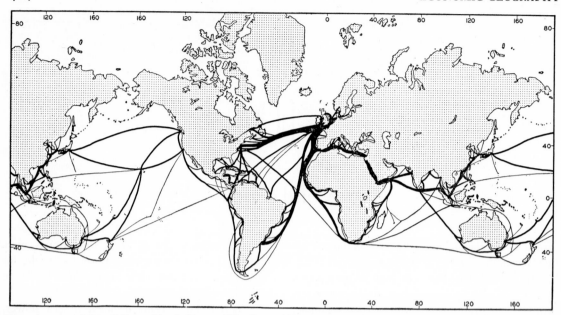

FIGURE 40.1. *Map of Ocean Trade Routes. The line width is proportional to tonnage.*

Age of Discovery had brought the products in distant lands to the attention of the European merchants. Improvements in navigation made this possible. The introduction of the ship keel, making it possible to tack against a prevailing wind, was one of these inventions. Large casks for storing water to be used on long voyages were just as necessary. The magnetic compass, first used about the year 1300, enabled the mariner to steer a fairly constant course, although out of sight of land. Columbus worked out the variation of the compass, making it more useful and accurate. The astrolabe, precursor of the modern sextant, allowed the navigator to determine his latitude simply (although rather roughly) from the Pole Star. The determination of longitude came much later with the invention of the chronometer.

The motive in the Age of Discovery, as noted in the chapter on Plantations, was trade and profit. As the new lands were discovered and their products appeared on the market the pattern of trade constantly changed. Trade centers rose and fell (they still are doing so), and likewise production and trade routes shifted. Venice was the great *entrepot* (collecting and distributing center) of world trade as long as most of the traffic was via the eastern Mediterranean and the sea route around the Cape of Good Hope was unknown.

After the Portuguese rounded Africa, Lisbon enjoyed a brief period of pre-eminence, only to be succeeded in turn by Amsterdam and London, as the British and Dutch traders replaced the Portuguese in the distant colonies.

The great expansion in trade occurred in the 17th and 18th centuries. Plantations were established in many parts of the world, and cheap textiles, sugar, coffee, and tea poured into the middle latitudes. Ships were improved and the chief source of power, the wind, gave way to coal and later to oil. New navigation instruments—sextants and good chronometers—helped to speed up the reliability and swiftness of the sea voyages. In more recent times harbor facilities have been greatly improved and extended. The radio, ice patrols, and many other inventions and precautions have contributed to the safety and efficiency of ocean carriers, but no important new areas of trade have been developed.

Trade routes of the land, railroads, highways, and inland waterways were slower in developing than the sea routes. Most of the expansion came in the 19th century, which was a period of railroad, highway, and canal construction. Canals antedated the railroads in many parts of the world where the low gradient made construction fairly easy. Water has little friction, and therefore canals could be used to move heavy goods cheaply. Railroad construction began in England in 1829, in the United States in 1830. The tracks have pushed across all types of terrain, over and through mountains, and across wide rivers and swamps. Cheap land transportation has contributed to the growth of inland trade centers such as Chicago in the United States and Moscow in Russia, and has, therefore, added to the amount of sea trade.

CARRIERS AND COMMODITIES

The goods of the world are transported by a variety of means, from human porters and pack animals, which can negotiate rough terrain and live off the country, to speeding aircraft. Carts and wagons carry heavier loads at a low cost but must have some kind of road. Highways for efficient truck traffic have a high initial cost and are practicable only where large amounts of goods are to be moved. The railroad is a cheap form of transport where the volume is great and the hauls at least several hundred miles long. The ocean freighter is the cheapest form of transport of all. The best way to compare the efficiency of the various carriers is to study the costs per ton-mile. In the following table the approximate cost only is given, and it should be remembered that costs change frequently. Other factors such as speed must be considered, especially if the goods are perishable.

Carrier	Cost per ton-mile (in dollars)
Ocean freighter	0.001
Inland water carriers	0.002
Pipelines	0.003
Railroads	0.01 to 0.05
Truck	0.06
Pack mule	0.10 to 1.00
Human porter	0.10 to 1.00
Dog sled	up to 10.00
Airplane	0.15 to 0.50

It is obvious that each of the carriers listed in this table has special virtues and also inherent weaknesses. A truck, for example, is cheaper than rail transportation for short hauls, since it can usually pick up the load at the origin and deliver it to its exact destination. If rail transportation were used, a short truck haul would often be necessary at each end. An ocean freighter is most efficient when bulky goods, such as coal or iron ore, are involved and is less suited to a variety of package freight. The airplane is most used where speed is essential or where other means of transport are not available. If a cargo of several hundred tons were to be transported from the upper Amazon to Rio de Janeiro, one large four-motored cargo plane could carry as much freight as 25,000 pack animals and probably at about the same cost, assuming that landing facilities are available. Since neither animals nor good trails are available in this region, the plane would be employed, but only for goods which would justify a markup of approximately 15¢ per pound. Most of the carriers listed above are confined to land routes and are, therefore, best discussed on a continental basis. Although railroads and pipelines often carry international traffic, it is the ocean carriers and airlines which have the greatest intercontinental significance.

SHIPS are the cheapest means of transporting heavy commodities and carry a large proportion of the goods which enter into international trade, as well as much coastwise internal trade. Three types of ships—tramps, tankers, and liners—carry most of the freight, although much freight is moved for short distances by smaller craft. Each type of ship has its own special advantages, in terms of structure, schedule, and character of the cargo.

The tramp is a free-lance freighter, one which has no fixed schedule or route but calls at any port at which it can pick up a cargo. Tramps are comparatively small, as ocean ships go, averaging only about 5000 gross tons. The average tramp can be described as a floating box designed to handle bulk cargoes, especially those which have a low value in proportion to their weight and bulk. Coal, ore, lumber, fertilizer, grain, and sugar are typical cargoes.

TYPICAL OF TRAMP VOYAGES AND CARGOES ARE THE FOLLOWING:

FROM	TO	CARGO
Havana	Oslo	Sugar
Houston	Liverpool	Cotton
Casablanca	Rotterdam	Phosphate
Lourenço Marques (Mozambique)	Buenos Aires	Coal
Hamburg	Yokohama	Potash
Buenos Aires	Rotterdam	Corn

The tramp owner usually books a series of cargoes each way on the voyages and avoids, if possible, sailing even for short distances in ballast.

But some ports are primarily one way in character. Exports of raw materials such as nitrate may be heavy while imports of goods are light, and some tramps therefore must make long voyages in ballast. Tramps move along all the ocean routes (FIG. 40.1) and visit all the great ports of the world as well as many minor ones. Narvik, Norway, is a highly specialized port for the export of iron ore; Bahia Blanca, Argentina, for wheat. Many tramps call at places not ordinarily known as ports.

The tanker is a specialized freighter adapted to the transport of liquids or semiliquids, mainly petroleum and its products, also vegetable oils and molasses. Most tankers are engaged in transporting crude oils from the producing fields to refineries and in delivering the finished products, gasoline, fuel oil, etc., to the markets. In the latter service tankers call at most of the world ports. On inland waterways tankers help distribute petroleum products to the interior of many countries. The tankers both supplement and compete with pipelines. The construction of more pipelines from the Texas oilfields to the eastern seaboard reduced tanker traffic. Pipelines from Arabia to the Mediterranean shorten the tanker voyage to western Europe and reduce the number of tankers in service. Since world trade in petroleum products has been increasing rapidly in recent years, there has been very little actual decrease in the number of tankers. FIGURE 40.2 shows the world trade in crude petroleum and in petroleum products.

The cargo liner is a ship which sails a definite route on a regular schedule, with or without passengers. Most cargo liners range from 5000 to 10,000 gross tons, but the large liners, such as the *Queen Elizabeth*, reach 83,000 tons. Unlike the tramp or tanker, the liner usually does not carry bulk cargo, but instead all sorts of goods in bags, boxes, crates, bundles, drums, or articles which do not require packaging, such as automobiles, crude metal in the form of ingots, or various shapes of steel. Many liners are equipped to handle special cargoes which must be refrigerated, such as bananas, meat, and butter. Passengers and mail also represent, in a sense, a special class of cargo. Liners often call for mail and passengers at ports which do not have good dock facilities, in which case tenders or lighters are used between the anchored ship and the land. Queens-

town (Cobh), Ireland, and Toulon, France, are examples of such ports.

Some ports are known as "liner ports" because of the frequent calls by cargo liners. A good liner port has facilities for assembling cargoes from its hinterland, as well as a good harbor. Once liners begin to call at a port, other liners are attracted, and nearby ports may be neglected. Liners often call at "outward ports," however, to pick up late mail and passengers. Liners outward bound from Le Havre, for example, call at Cherbourg; those from Hamburg call at Cuxhaven. In addition to the liner ports where most of the cargo is received and discharged, there are many "ports of call." These are usually ports with limited hinterlands, near to the regular routes but usually not at the end of the voyage. Aden, Suez, Singapore, Capetown, Colombo, Karachi, and Brisbane are good examples of such ports.

In addition to the tramps, tankers, and cargo liners described above, many other types of seagoing craft follow the trade routes, especially for short distances. Small coastwise freighters of various tonnages and seagoing barges carry most of this traffic. These smaller craft are often able to enter the inland waterways and reach ports not accessible to the larger ships. A brief description of some of the inland waterways will be found in the following chapters.

AIRLINES are competing more and more for the mail, passenger, express, and light freight traffic of the world, especially for long hauls. The transoceanic airlines compete with the ocean liners, and the transcontinental and local airlines are rivals of the railroads, buses, trucks, and automobiles. Planes have the advantage of speed, the ability to fly over isolated regions without roads, and are able to serve coastal districts without harbors. Planes do require airports which are becoming more and more expensive as the speed and size of the aircraft increase. The cost of air transportation, per ton mile, is high and the plane cannot now, and probably never will, carry much heavy freight except in emergencies.

The most important transoceanic airlines follow approximately the same routes as the ocean ships, using the great circle courses more effectively than can ships. The heaviest traffic is between New York and western Europe (FIG. 40.3) via Gander, Newfoundland, and Shannon, Ireland, along a route used by at least a dozen air-

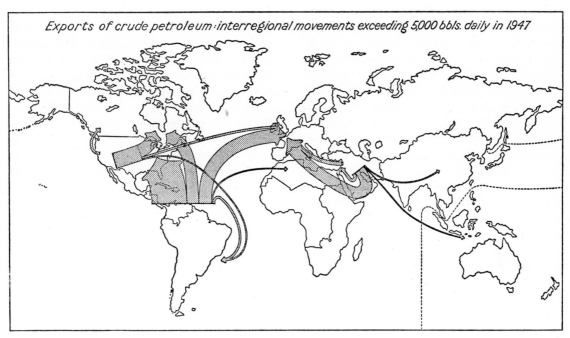

FIGURE 40.2. *Maps showing world trade in crude petroleum and petroleum products. The lower map indicates the large refining capacity in the United States, northern South America, and the Middle East. From* The Geography of Petroleum, *American Geographical Society.*

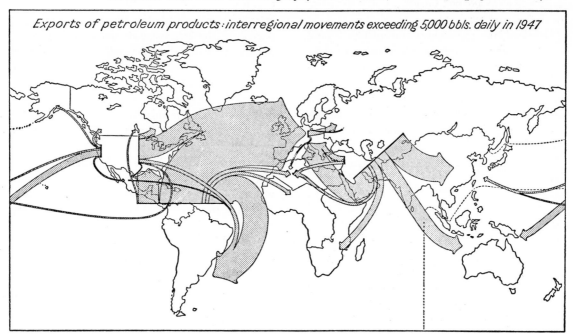

lines. These two airports illustrate the importance of "outports" and island ports for refueling and servicing of airplanes, since neither Gander nor Shannon contributes very much traffic. A second route connects New York via the Azores to Lisbon and northwestern Europe, and a third via

Bermuda and the Azores, both being longer than the northern route. Bermuda also serves as a convenient stopping place between New York and northern South America. The island and coastal airports are supplied with fuel by ocean tankers.

Another important transatlantic route connects

the eastern coast of South America with western
Europe via the Cape Verde Islands and Dakar, in
French West Africa. Dakar is also connected
with Capetown, although the main north-south
transcontinental lines from Europe to South
Africa go via Algiers and Cairo. The "Suez"
route is followed, with many variations, by nu-
merous airlines via Athens, Cairo, Damascus,
Karachi, Bombay, Calcutta, Singapore, Darwin,
Hongkong, Manila, and Tokyo.

In the Pacific, passenger, mail, and express
traffic has been taken over, in large measure, by
the airlines. Only one passenger ship, at this writing, sails between the west coast of the United
States and New Zealand, and the voyage, one
way, requires three weeks. Three airlines serve
the same route and make the journey in three
days with stopovers of several hours at Honolulu,
Canton Island, and Fiji. The great circle route
from western North America to the Orient goes
via Alaska, the Aleutian Islands, and Japan. It is
rarely far from land but sometimes encounters
unfavorable weather. In the longer crossing of the
North Pacific it is evident that Hawaii, and to a
lesser extent Wake and Guam, are key localities
for fueling and servicing.

Overland, the transcontinental airlines follow
the same general routes as the transcontinental
railroads with minor variations. In North America, which leads the continents in airway mileage,
the principal lines run east-west. The north-south
lines are shorter and less regular. The table below gives the airways mileage for various countries but does not indicate the traffic density.

Country	Thousands of miles	Country	Thousands of miles
United States	471	Canada	29
Mexico	26	Colombia	19
Brazil	33	Argentina	6
United Kingdom	48	France	29
Netherlands	20	China	14
India	19	Australia	46

Some airways have several flights daily; others
may have only one or two per month. South
America has two transcontinental lines, from
Buenos Aires to Santiago and from Rio de Ja-
neiro to Lima. Otherwise most of the airlines hug
the coast with short feeder lines into the interior.
In the U.S.S.R. the main air routes follow the
Trans-Siberian Railroad from Kaliningrad and

Leningrad, via Moscow, Sverdlovsk, Omsk, and
Irkutsk to Vladivostok, with several branch lines
to the Arctic coast and to the south. Australia has
two transcontinental lines, one from Sydney to
Perth and another from Sydney to Darwin, connecting with the "Suez" route to western Europe.
Most of the transoceanic and transcontinental airlines mentioned above carry passengers, mail, express, and light freight on regular schedules. In
addition charter service is available to any point
on the earth with a landing surface, either natural
or man-made.

THE TRADE CENTER AND ITS HINTERLAND

A trade center is an urban agglomeration engaged
in the handling of goods (FIG. 40.4). It is located
at the focus of trade routes in a convenient situation with respect to its hinterland or trade territory. Many varieties of trade centers exist, depending on their special functions. Some trade
centers are engaged in the production of goods for
commerce. Virginia, Minnesota, for example, is
important chiefly because of the mining of iron
ore in the immediate vicinity. Other centers are
engaged principally in the transfer of goods, especially if the location calls for a change in the
mode of transportation. At Duluth, Minnesota, at
the head of the lakes, ore, grain, and other commodities are transferred from rail to water carriers. It is obvious then that Duluth has a larger
hinterland than Virginia. On the other end of the
Great Lakes Waterway, Montreal functions in
much the same manner as Duluth with many interesting variations. Some trade centers such as
Louisville, Kentucky, are located at portages
where a temporary interruption in traffic occurs.
Another common type of location is a bridgehead,
an easy crossing of a river, preferably near the
sea. London, Glasgow, and Hamburg are located
on their respective rivers at the lowest point that
can be easily bridged. As a result their harbors are
a little shallow for the largest modern ships.

One of the clearest examples of a trade center is
the seaport. Located at the point where the mode
of carrier changes and where sea and land routes
converge, the primary function is the handling of
goods. A great seaport must have first of all a
productive and consuming hinterland with good
land transportation. Many of the best harbors of
the world have insignificant ports because of the

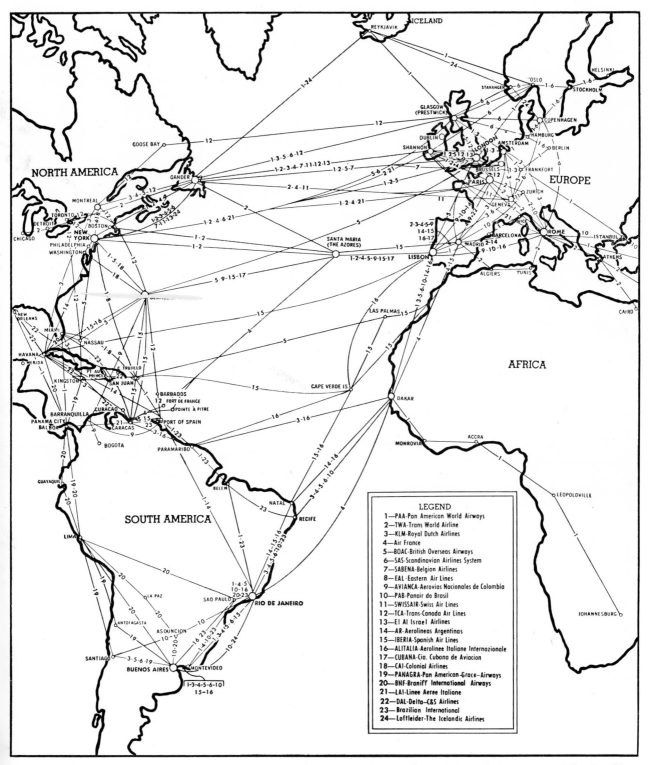

FIGURE 40.3. *The major airlines of the Atlantic Ocean. Notice the importance of Gander, Shannon, Bermuda, the Azores, Lisbon, Dakar, and Natal. From American Aviation Publications, Incorporated.*

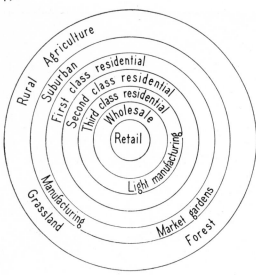

FIGURE 40.4. *The diagram represents in general the concentric aspect of a trade center. At the focus of the trade center is the "commercial core," the retail and wholesale districts. Beyond is the poorest (third class) residential district and light manufacturing. (In many trade centers manufacturing is not conspicuous.) First and second class residence districts are farther out. On the margins of the center are suburban areas (some with manufacturing), market gardens, farms, forest, and grasslands.*

lack of production in the back country. On the other hand, a rich hinterland calls for the construction of an artificial harbor if no natural one exists. Los Angeles constructed an artificial harbor because of the large quantities of goods produced and consumed by the people in the vicinity.

It is an advantage, of course, for a port to be located on a good natural harbor protected from wind and waves, with deep water (about 50 feet) to accommodate the largest ships, a low tidal range, and freedom from ice and fog. A low shoreline with soft rock permits the construction of dock facilities and affords an easy approach by railroads and other land routes. San Francisco is an example of a good natural harbor. The entrance, the Golden Gate, is narrow and deep. The bay is deep and spacious enough to accommodate all the ships of the world, and the tidal range is small, about six feet. There is no ice, but fog is a handicap at times. The site of San Francisco on a peninsula is not too favorable for access to the

hinterland but the construction of two bridges, the Golden Gate and the Bay Bridge, has improved the land transport system.

It is obvious that cities perform many functions in addition to trade. Some, like Washington, D.C., are primarily administrative in character. Mecca, in Arabia, is a religious center. Small cities with large universities could be described as educational, while others are primarily resorts, or recreational centers. Usually in the large cities, however, the main function is the gathering of products from the surrounding country and the distribution of the products from other regions. Briefly, the trade center collects and distributes. Marketing is the chief function.

The hinterland of a trade center is not easy to define and delimit with even a reasonable degree of exactness. This is true because the functions of most centers are varied and because of the competition with other trade centers. Several methods have been suggested for mapping the hinterland. One of the simplest involves the plotting of newspaper distribution. It is assumed that if a majority of the readers subscribe to the Denver newspapers, for example, that territory is in Denver's hinterland. Maps showing the density of traffic flow are sometimes used to mark out the hinterland. Study of the movements of commodities usually results in a variety of hinterland boundaries depending on the nature of the commodities. It could be argued, for example, that the Canadian Wheat Belt is in the hinterland of Portland, Maine, because that port in the winter season handles a large part of the wheat exports from the Canadian Wheat Belt. In reality the Canadian Wheat Belt is the hinterland of Winnipeg (FIG. 40.5). In spite of the difficulty of mapping the hinterland exactly, and in spite of ambitious chambers of commerce who extend the hinterland of their trade centers indefinitely, a careful study of the trade territory is necessary in order to understand the function of a city.

THE TRADE CENTER AND THE PRODUCTION REGION

Since the function of a trade center depends on the character of its hinterland and since nearby centers compete with each other, it is important to organize the discussion of trade on a regional basis. The production regions as set forth in the preceding chapters provide a pattern for such

FIGURE 40.5. *An aerial view of Winnipeg, Canada, showing the railroad yards with hundreds of wheat-laden box cars. The chief function of Winnipeg is to collect and distribute grain by the carload. See Figure 12.3. From National Film Board of Canada.*

discussion. In plantation regions, for example, all ports and trade centers have somewhat similar functions; the commodity may vary from bananas to coffee but the main function of the port is to gather the surplus products from the surrounding plantations and export them. Likewise, the trade centers of the world wheat belts are all similar in function and furthermore often very similar in appearance.

It should be noted, however, that trade routes often cut across production regions. Vancouver, B.C., lies in a dairy region and has a forested hinterland, but large quantities of wheat are exported through it from the Canadian Plains. An even larger amount of Canadian wheat is exported from the ports of Montreal, Portland, Maine, Boston, New York, and Baltimore. Inland areas are

dependent on adjacent or even distant regions for an outlet to the sea, a handicap which causes considerable concern to the people of these inland regions. Because of the competition in world trade there is a constant struggle to improve and cheapen transport, but there is also a struggle against it. Cities on the eastern seaboard of the United States, for example, have opposed the improvements in the St. Lawrence Waterway because they have feared a loss of traffic. They have been able to block approval of the project for many years. Thus the trade routes and centers are influenced in their growth and function, not merely by the nature of production and by the natural features, but by political considerations, tariff barriers, customs regulations, and many other nonmaterial factors.

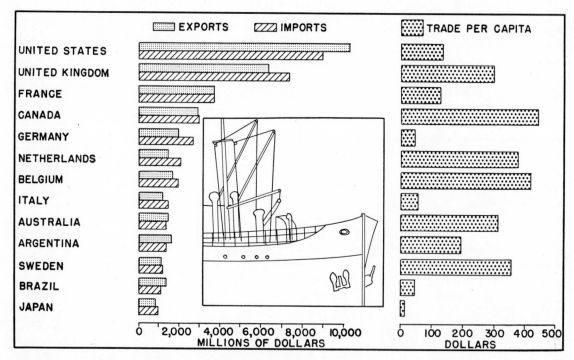

FIGURE 40.6. *Graph of imports and exports of leading countries in millions of dollars and the total trade per capita in dollars.*

41

Trade Centers and Trade Routes of the Americas

WITH the decline of Western Europe during and following World War II, North America became the greatest trading continent both for internal and external trade. The internal trade routes have two main functions: first to carry the goods from the producing regions to the areas of consumption, second to reach the main ports. North America is favored for trade by its excellent harbors, inland waterways (especially the Great Lakes), and its excellent rail system and highways. Air transport is also well developed. We shall not discuss all the trade centers and trade routes of North America. Discussion will be limited largely to such topics as the Great Lakes, the railroads, pipelines, and airways. Each of these should be studied in terms of the production regions which they serve.

The Great Lakes

The Great Lakes serve all the eastern interior of North America directly or indirectly, but they are of special significance to the wheat belts of Canada and the United States, to the Northern Forest with its timber and minerals, to the Northern and Middle Appalachian Coalfields, and to the Manufacturing Belt. Indeed, it may be stated that the very existence of the Manufacturing Belt depends as much on Great Lakes transportation as it does on the coalfields and iron mines.

The Great Lakes with their connecting waterways constitute the largest fresh water navigable waterways in the world. To a very great extent the route is a natural one with comparatively few improvements. From Montreal, where the route really begins, to Duluth at the head of the lakes, the distance is 1340 miles. From Montreal to Chicago, the most important trade center in the

interior of North America, the distance is 1260 miles. Along this route or parts of the route a variety of carriers are used: lake freighters, railroad car-ferries, tankers, passenger ships, and many smaller craft. The chief commodities handled are iron ore, coal, grain, oil, limestone, cement, and package freight.

A few difficulties in the navigation of the lakes are being overcome with a view to making the waterways fully accessible to ocean freighters. See FIGURE 41.1. Beginning at the upper end, the first difficulty encountered is the rapids of St. Marys River which flows from Lake Superior to Lake Michigan and Lake Huron involving a 20-foot drop. Locks on both the Canadian and United States sides of the rapids permit the passage of lake freighters. However, the Canadian locks with a depth of only 18 feet will not accommodate the largest loaded vessels. The next difficulties, little ones to be sure, are in the St. Clair River where rocky shoals exist at a depth of 20 feet, and in the Detroit River which requires some dredging. The greatest obstacle of all, Niagara Falls, has been by-passed by the Welland Canal. The drop from Lake Erie to Lake Ontario, 326 feet, is accomplished by this canal in 26 miles with the aid of 25 locks. The depth of the canal is about 27 feet. From the western end of Lake Ontario to Ogdensburg, New York, there is little obstruction to navigation. Between Ogdensburg and Montreal, rapids in the St. Lawrence River present a formidable barrier to navigation. The canals which bypass the rapids have a depth of only 14 feet and the shortest lock is only 270 feet long. Large lake steamers cannot be accommodated, but specially built ocean-going ships ascend the lakes to Chicago and other ports.

FIGURE 41.1. *The Soo Locks at Sault Ste. Marie, Michigan. The annual shipping through the Sault Ste. Marie Canal is greater in tonnage than that through the Suez Canal. From Fairchild Aerial Surveys, Inc.*

Diesel-powered ships under Dutch, Swedish, Norwegian, French, and German flags, carry package freight, including wines, liquors, cork, and many other items at a saving of ten to twenty per cent, compared with the rail-water route via New York. With the completion of the St. Lawrence Seaway the tonnage will be increased many times, since most ocean freighters will then be able to reach the upper lakes. Grain from the upper lake ports, Port Arthur, Fort William, Duluth, and Chicago will move directly to Europe without a break in

bulk. Iron ore from the newly developed field in Labrador can be moved to the Lake Erie ports and thus transported to coal. Improvements in the seaway have long been opposed by shippers on the eastern seaboard of the United States, who held back for many years improvement of the waterway. The seaway has some handicaps, however, which cannot readily be overcome. The St. Lawrence is frozen from four to five months of the year, although the use of icebreakers has extended the effective season. Another handicap is the lack of large rivers entering the Great Lakes, making it necessary to use railroads as feeders and also to break the bulk at the lake ports. See FIGURE 41.2, a map of inland waterways.

The greatest tonnage carried on the lakes is iron ore from the shores of Lake Superior to the Lake Erie ports. Most of the ore is shipped through the locks at Sault Ste. Marie. Some of it then is moved across Lake Michigan to Chicago and Gary; some is unloaded at Detroit; while the greater amounts are moved to the northern Appalachian Coalfields via the ports of Cleveland, Ashtabula, and other Lake Erie ports. More ships and a greater tonnage pass through the upper lakes than through the Panama and Suez canals combined. The cost of movement of the ore on the lakes is less than the rail hauls at each end of the route. The returning ore steamers carry coal to the upper lakes although the tonnage is somewhat less than that of the ore. The grain shipments originate mainly in the Canadian ports of Port Arthur and Fort William, in Duluth-Superior, and in Chicago. Some of the grain is destined for export, and because of the late harvest in the Spring Wheat Belt the shipments arrive in the lower lakes just as the freeze begins. For this reason large quantities of grain are transshipped by rail from Buffalo and other ports. The Great Lakes provide cheap transportation for oil, stone, gravel, automobiles, and various kinds of package freight. Large-scale navigation of the lakes by ocean freighters will greatly extend the use of this inland waterway.

The Railroads

In most parts of North America no adequate waterways are available to handle the traffic. As a result railroads serve all the production regions of the continent, even those which have waterways. The rail pattern is densest in eastern North America (FIG. 41.4), especially in the vicinity of the Great Lakes, where railroads supplement the water-borne traffic. For the purposes of this brief discussion the railroads may be classed according to function as Trunk Lines, Coal Roads, Southern Roads, Southwestern Roads, and Transcontinental Lines. Such a classification does not include all lines but will illustrate the variety of function of the railway system as a whole.

The Trunk Lines, the main function of which is to connect Chicago with the eastern seaboard ports of New York, Philadelphia, and Baltimore,

parallel and complement the Great Lakes. The Trunk Lines feed the lake ports and also carry goods from the lakes to the sea where water transport is not available. Trunk Lines include the Grand Trunk, which lies partly in Canada; the New York Central, which uses the Mohawk Valley and the Hudson River Valley to cross the Appalachians; the Pennsylvania Railroad passing through the heart of the northern Appalachian Coalfields; and the Baltimore and Ohio, which runs through the southern part of the same field. These roads carry large quantities of ore, coal, grain, and general freight. All have connections to Lake Erie as well as Chicago, and most have terminal facilities in New York, Philadelphia, and Baltimore. The New England railroad system could be considered as an extension of the Trunk Lines, also reaching the lower St. Lawrence ports.

The Coal Roads, exemplified by the Chesapeake and Ohio and the Norfolk and Western, are primarily engaged in hauling coal from the northern and middle Appalachian Field to the Great Lakes and to the Atlantic Seaboard. The Southern Roads, represented by the Atlantic Coast Line and the Illinois Central, carry goods north and south from the Gulf of Mexico to both ends of the Trunk Line Route, that is, Chicago and New York. The Southwestern Roads connect Chicago and the upper lakes with the Winter Wheat Belt and the western end of the Cotton Belt.

The Transcontinental Lines do not all connect the two oceans as the name implies. Most of the lines so classified connect Chicago with the Pacific Coast and via the Trunk Lines with the East Coast. Only one Transcontinental Line in the United States, the Southern Pacific, which reaches from New Orleans to Los Angeles, fails to come into Chicago. The Santa Fe, the Union Pacific, the Northern Pacific, the Great Northern, and the Milwaukee connect Chicago with the west coast ports of Los Angeles, San Francisco, Portland, and Seattle. Only the Canadian railroads, the Canadian Pacific and the Canadian National, are truly transcontinental, reaching from Quebec and Montreal to Vancouver, B.C. and Prince Rupert.

Pipelines

Pipelines have proved to be highly efficient carriers of petroleum and natural gas as well as other fluids and gases, provided the quantities

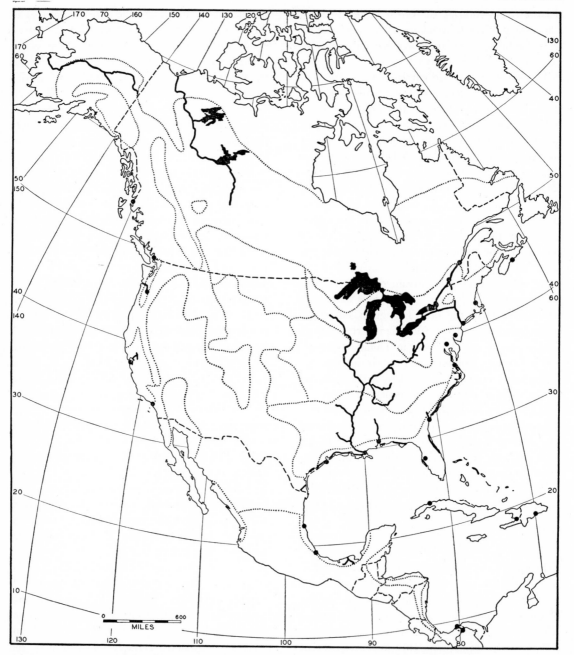

FIGURE 41.2. *Inland Waterways of North America. Lakes, rivers, and canals are used for trans-*
portation. Dots indicate important ports. The boundaries of production regions are shown by
dotted lines (compare End Paper 1).

FIGURE 41.3. *The Intercoastal Waterway, when completed, will provide an inland passage for small craft all the way from New York to the Mexican border. The uncompleted section across northern Florida presents the greatest difficulty. Construction of a canal was abandoned several years ago, partly because of the high cost. The Okeechobee Waterway provides a route across southern Florida. From Corps of Engineers, U. S. Army.*

produced justify the cost of the pipelines. Where volume is large the pipelines are second to the ocean tanker as a cheap means of transportation. Since the largest supplies of petroleum and natural gas come from the Mid-Continent and Gulf fields, most of the pipelines connect this area with the Great Lakes and with the Eastern Seaboard. The "Big Inch" and "Little Inch," two large pipelines constructed during World War II, reach from northeastern Texas, via southern Illinois, to New Jersey. After the war these lines were sold to private companies to be used in transporting oil and gas. Other lines reach Chicago, Cleveland, Minneapolis, and St. Paul. In California there are pipelines reaching from Los Angeles and San Francisco to the oilfields, and Wyoming is connected to the Mid-Continent system. The pipeline is especially suited to the transmission of natural gas, which is highly compressible and cannot readily be stored in large quantities near the points of consumption. It is obvious that coastwise tankers, plying between Port Arthur, Texas, and New York, offer keen competition to the pipelines for the transport of petroleum.

Airways

Now that a fairly complete network of airlines covers North America, it is beginning to be clear what role airplanes will play in competition with the railroads, highways, and other forms of transportation. In the United States the airlines have made a vigorous bid for mail, passenger, express, and even freight traffic. They have succeeded most where other forms of transportation are unavailable, as in certain parts of northern Canada, and where speed is essential as with airmail and passengers. North America has several transcontinental airlines in Canada, the United States, and Mexico. Extensions of these lines reach across the Atlantic and Pacific oceans to Europe, Asia, Africa, and South America. North America is the hub of a series of overseas routes which include the north Atlantic route to Europe, the south Atlantic route to South America and Africa, the Caribbean route to the West Indies, Central America, and the northern coast of South America, and the north Pacific route to Japan, China, and Indonesia.

Because of the numerous improvements during recent years, the airlines find themselves technically advanced in many ways, particularly with respect to speed and long nonstop flights, but with something less than a desirable standard of safety. Following a number of fatal crashes passenger traffic declines, causing losses to most airlines. It appears that the greatest future of the airline is in mail and passenger service, plus a limited amount of express and freight service. The high cost per ton-mile is a serious handicap to the airlines when the routes parallel rail lines or highways.

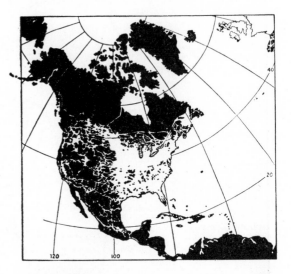

FIGURE 41.4. *Railroads of North and South America. The white bands are 20 miles wide and therefore all white areas are within 10 miles of a railroad. Courtesy of Mark Jefferson.*

FIGURE 41.5. *Pipelines bring oil to this refinery at Talara on the northern coast of Peru. A pipeline is used to bring water to this desert locality. From Standard Oil Company of New Jersey.*

FIGURE 41.6. *Inland Waterways of South America. Because of the limited distribution of rail-roads, some rivers such as the Amazon and its tributaries play a dominant role in transporta-tion. Notice the breaks in water transportation caused by rapids in the Magdalena River (Colombia), in the Madeira (western Brazil), and in the São Francisco (eastern Brazil). Production regions are outlined by dotted lines (compare End Paper 2). Important ports are indicated by dots.*

FIGURE 41.7. *The Rio Negro and the Amazon at Manaus, Brazil. In the center a small river steamer is towing a "river train" of small craft. At Manaus, a thousand miles from the ocean, the elevation of the river is only 100 feet above the sea. From USAF.*

SOUTH AMERICA

It might appear to the casual observer that South America is similar to North America with regard to trade routes. Both continents are wide at the north and narrow at the south. Both have lofty ranges of mountains along the west coast and lesser ranges near the east coast. But the resemblance is superficial. The great bulk of South America is undeveloped tropical forest supplying little in the way of goods to the outside world. Obviously because of its tropical nature, much of South America is still in an early stage of production. As a result, trade routes and trade centers are fewer and smaller (FIG. 41.6).

Several navigable rivers in South America help to make up for the deficiency of railroads. Of these the Amazon and its tributaries is the largest with nearly 20,000 miles of water navigable by river steamer. See FIGURE 41.7. Because of the limited production in Amazonia, the river is little used. The Paraná River and its estuary La Plata, on the other hand, carry rather heavy traffic. The Paraná is navigable by ocean freighters to Santa Fé, Argentina, and by river steamers to Asunción, Paraguay.

South America is well served by railroads in only a few areas. The best network radiates from the La Plata cities—Buenos Aires, Rosario, and Santa Fé—and to Chile by a transcontinental line. The principal lines lead northward to Brazil, Uruguay, and Paraguay, northwestward to Bolivia, and westward to Valparaíso, Chile. Most of the traffic from this net focuses on the ports mentioned plus Montevideo and Bahía Blanca. Except for the crossing of the Andes, all these lines have easy routes. Another smaller network of rails serves the Coffee Belt of Brazil, the chief ports of which are Santos and Rio de Janeiro. Rail lines extending toward the west from these ports encounter the steep escarpment of the Brazilian Highland. Once this escarpment is ascended the roads find fairly easy routes in the valleys, a situation somewhat similar to the Allegheny Front and the plateau of western Pennsylvania. The third net of rail lines in South America extends from northern Chile to the city of Puerto Montt at the southern end of inhabited Chile. This system is in the form of a trellis with a main line following the Great Valley of Chile while branch lines extend to the coastal ports, such as Arica, Iquique, Antofagasta, Valparaíso, and Valdivia, and into the Andean valleys. Except for the "transcontinental" line to Buenos Aires and two rail lines leading to the Bolivian

Plateau the Chilean railroads are isolated. In addition to these rail nets, there are a number of short spurs in South America leading from the coast inland to reach a plantation or mining district. Riverlinks, rail portages around rapids, connect the different points of the Magdalena and Madeira rivers. Rail lines are being slowly extended along the fringes of South America and in the interiors of the middle latitudes. Southern Brazil will soon be connected with Bolivia, and the Peruvian lines are expected to reach the eastern lowland in the near future.

A few years ago it was said that South America would pass directly into the Air Age without going through a period of large-scale railroad building as did North America. What appears more likely is that the rails, waterways, and airlines will develop simultaneously, each serving the purpose for which it is best suited. At present the airlines serve both coasts effectively for mail and passenger service and local lines reach some points in the interior. In some places these lines carry freight, but where heavy goods in large quantities are to be carried either water or rail transportation is necessary.

42

Trade Centers and Trade Routes of Africa, Europe, and Asia

SINCE Africa is located near Europe and has been skirted for centuries by sea routes, it would seem that the trade routes of Africa would be in a more advanced stage of development than those of South America. Such is not the case. The coasts of Africa, to be sure, have been known for centuries, but the difficulties of communication to the interior have delayed and limited commercial development. Africa is essentially a plateau, and in many places this plateau comes down to the very edge of the sea. As a result the rivers do not always afford good lines of communication to the interior. The Congo, for example, is navigable less than 100 miles from the sea (FIG. 42.1), and in its middle and upper courses rapids and falls require several portages. In the Nile there are a series of cataracts which hinder navigation, and this is true for most of the other rivers. Another barrier to communication is the Sahara. Of course, the Sahara can be crossed by camel, rail, automobile, or plane, but such a vast expanse of unproductive territory does not invite modern lines of communication.

In spite of handicaps, the rivers and lakes of Africa are used for commercial transportation. The Nile is used by river boats extensively as far as Khartoum with the aid of rail riverlinks and a railroad to Port Sudan on the Red Sea. Unfortunately much of the middle watershed of the Nile is unproductive and navigation does not extend to the Plateau of East Africa. The Congo is navigable, once the lower falls have been passed, to Stanley Falls about 1000 miles from Leopoldville. Steamers and barges are used on this long stretch, fueled with oils brought by pipeline from the coast. A rail link around Stanley Falls gives access to another stretch of navigable water 1200 miles in length, which is connected by rail with

Lake Tanganyika and the Katanga copper country. Altogether the Congo and its tributaries provide over 6000 miles of water navigable by river steamers, but falls and rapids necessitate many breaks in bulk. The construction of locks and canals could weld the various parts into a very useful waterway. The upper Niger, connected by rail with the port of Dakar, is navigable as also is its tributary the Benué. Lakes Victoria, Tanganyika, and Nyasa are used for local traffic but unfortunately are not connected with each other.

Africa is poorly served by rail lines except in the eastern part of South Africa and in the northwest. No net of rails resembling that of the Humid Pampa of South America is to be found. Short spurs are located along the coast at various points. Lakes Tanganyika and Victoria are connected by rail with the Indian Ocean ports of Mombasa and Dar es Salaam. There is a line from Lake Nyasa to the port of Beira on the coast of Mozambique. The Katanga copper district of southern Belgian Congo is reached by a line from the Portuguese port of Benguela and is also connected with South Africa. Most of the rail lines are used for the purpose of getting minerals, plantation products, wool, and mohair out to the coast. Many years ago it was proposed to build a railroad from the "Cape to Cairo," a distance of about 6000 miles, but the project was abandoned since little traffic would move over such an expensive route. The sea routes via the west coast and the Suez Canal offer cheap transportation from South Africa with which the rails cannot compete.

EUROPE

Until recently Europe was the center of world trade. From this small continent all the major sea

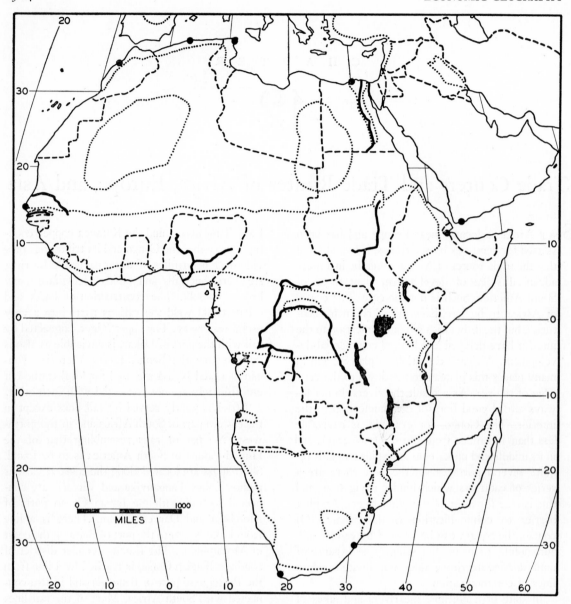

FIGURE 42.1. *Inland Waterways of Africa. Numerous rapids handicap inland navigation in Africa. Traffic on the Congo is interrupted less than 100 miles from the sea. Several cataracts on the Nile necessitate portages. Much of the continent is too dry for navigable rivers of any kind. Victoria, Tanganyika, and Nyasa Lakes are used for local traffic. Each lake is connected with the sea by rail. Outlines of production regions are shown with dotted lines (compare End Paper 3). Dots represent important ports.*

FIGURE 42.2. *A battery of huge cranes unload ships at Durban, Natal, South Africa. The ships are at the extreme right, scarcely visible in this picture. The crane at the left is lifting a large bus over the cranes at the right. From Information Office, Union of South Africa.*

routes originated. In addition there was a very active internal trade between different countries. World War II struck a severe blow to Europe's trade as well as disturbing world trade in general, and it is doubtful if this small continent will ever dominate trade so completely again. The Continent of Europe has a great advantage for trade because of the nature of its coastline and its many excellent harbors. Internal communications are good also, although the Alps, Pyrenees, and other mountains present some handicaps. The mountains of Europe are not long, continuous ranges such as the Andes, but are short enough to be skirted by the major land routes.

Western Europe has been the focus of most of the world's commerce. From all parts of the productive world goods have moved in by sea, across the North Atlantic, from South America and Africa, from Asia and Oceania. The raw materials from overseas together with a variety of manufacturing provided the basis of internal trade, as previously noted. The system of inland waterways, coastwise waterways, rivers, and canals have greatly facilitated this inland trade. See FIGURE 42.3. Much of the traffic between the various countries and ports of Europe moves through the inland and marginal seas, such as the Mediterranean, North, and Baltic seas. This is a cheap and efficient form of transportation in which small steamers and barges are freely used. Car-ferries are employed to transport trains across narrow passages such as the English Channel and from Denmark to south Sweden. The marginal seas provide excellent natural waterways without artificial improvements except in the facilities of the harbors. Only storm and fog interrupt or hinder the use of the marginal seas.

The rivers perform two main functions. Their estuaries provide sheltered harbors for the ocean steamers and the upper courses are used by river steamers and barges to haul heavy goods to and from the interior. In the first instance, the harbors of London, Lisbon, Le Havre, Hamburg, and many others lie near the heads of river estuaries. Except the Thames at London, these upper rivers carry heavy traffic. Not all rivers are useful in their middle upper courses for inland transport. In general, the rivers of the Iberian Peninsula are too shallow and too uneven in flow to be of more than local use. In the British Isles the rivers are small and only the estuaries are used to any great extent. But in France, the Low Countries, Germany, the Danube States, and Russia the rivers play a major role in commerce.

In France rivers and connecting canals extend to most parts of the country. The Garonne reaches back from the port of Bordeaux which is on the estuary known as the Gironde. The Garonne is connected with the Rhone by the Canal du Midi which crosses the gap of Carcassone with the aid of bridges and tunnels. The Rhone and Saône are navigable by river boats although the Rhone Delta is not usable and the upper river is connected to the Mediterranean by canal. From the upper Saône a canal connects with the Seine, another with the upper Rhine. The Seine and its tributaries, the Oise and Marne, are used by river boats and barges with connecting canals to the Meuse and thence into the lower Rhine. Canal traffic is heaviest on the north and east where large quantities of coal and iron ore are handled. In the south the canals are generally smaller and have rather light traffic, particularly since the war.

In Germany the main navigable rivers—the Rhine, Weser, Elbe, and Oder—flow toward the northwest more or less parallel to each other. This is valuable for the exchange of goods between the highland of southern Germany and the North German Plain. Canals cut across the rivers and provide transportation in an east-west direction. The German Plain is especially favorable for the use of rivers and canals because of its relatively smooth surface and loose sediments which can be readily dredged. Old abandoned river channels are advantageous locations for the construction of canals. The Danube is navigable as far as Ulm in southern Germany and is connected with the Rhine by a canal which functions with difficulty because of the numerous locks. The rivers and canals of western Europe have an adequate water supply for most of the year.

The fact that Europe has excellent coastal and inland waterways does not mean that railroads and highways are neglected. There are excellent networks of rails in the British Isles, France, Germany, and Italy, while southern Scandinavia and the Danube states are also well served. In Spain and Russia there are fewer rail lines in proportion to area, but even in these countries most places are within a short distance of a railroad.

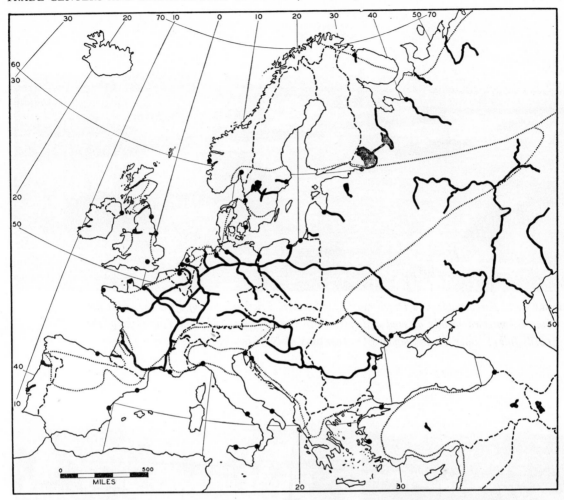

FIGURE 42.3. *Inland Waterways of Europe, including a part of Russia. Rivers and canals are more widely used in Europe than in any other continent in spite of the hilly nature of parts of the continent and the freezing of the waterways in the north and east. Outlines of production regions are indicated with dotted lines (compare End Paper 3). The dots represent important ports. The long dry season in the Mediterranean Lands limits the use of inland waterways.*

In general, the cars and locomotives of Europe's railroads are lighter than those of North America, but the average distances between large cities are much shorter in Europe and the rails are considered to be efficient carriers.

The network of rails on the map of Western Europe is so dense (FIG. 42.6) that it is difficult to distinguish the main routes. London, Paris, and Berlin are centers from which several main routes radiate. From London there is fast train service to Scotland, to Liverpool, to Paris (with a channel crossing by steamer), and to various other points on the Continent. From Paris fast train service is available to the Channel ports—Le Havre, Cherbourg, and Brest—to Bordeaux and Madrid, to Marseille, Zürich, Munich, and Berlin. It is noteworthy that the Manufacturing Belt of Western Europe is especially well served by rail. Because of the scarcity of automobiles and gasoline in Europe, the railroads carry a very large part of the passenger traffic. The numerous highways, most of them narrow and winding, are used by trucks, wagons, and carts for local traffic.

FIGURE 42.4. *Barge traffic on a Dutch canal near Sneek in Friesland, east of Ijssel Sea. This flat land is composed mainly of sand and clay which is easily excavated. The rainfall keeps the canals full of water. From Standard Oil Company of New Jersey.*

FIGURE 42.5. *The best way to study trade is to examine a small port and its hinterland. This view shows a portion of the port of Bayonne in southwestern France on the Adour River. On the wharfs and in the warehouses are barrels of rosin, bales of cork, and lumber from the forests to the north. Casks of wine and piles of iron ore and coal are also present. The river and its tributaries provide access by means of small boats to the hinterland. Rail and highway transport are also available. From "Yvon."*

TRANSPORTATION

It has been apparent from the studies of the manufacturing belts of North America and Europe that a very important role is played by transportation. In Russia this role is of even greater significance because of the immense distances, the unequal distribution of raw materials, and the dispersed pattern of industry inherited from earlier times. Transportation is still the greatest handicap to further industrial progress in Russia. Russia is essentially an inland country although her territory touches four oceans. Coastwise shipping is limited largely to the Black and Baltic seas, although efforts are being made to develop the Pacific and Arctic coastal trade. Inland the network of railroads is rather open and inadequate.

Good roads are few but the moderate to light rainfall and the level character of the land make it possible to use many thousands of trucks without paved roads. Rivers and canals are important even though some of them are closed several months every year by ice.

In Russia seven major ocean ports handle most of the foreign commerce. Three of the ports are on the Baltic—Kaliningrad, Riga, and Leningrad; one—Arkhangelsk—is on the Arctic; three are on the Black Sea—Odessa, Mariupol, and Rostov. More tonnage is handled in the Caspian seaports of Astrakhan and Baku than in some of the ocean ports mentioned.

Kaliningrad and Riga, acquired by the occupation of the Baltic States and East Prussia, give the Russians much better access to the Baltic

FIGURE 42.6. *The railways of Europe, Asia, Africa, and Australia. The white bands are 20 miles wide and all white areas are within 10 miles of a railroad. Courtesy of Mark Jefferson.*

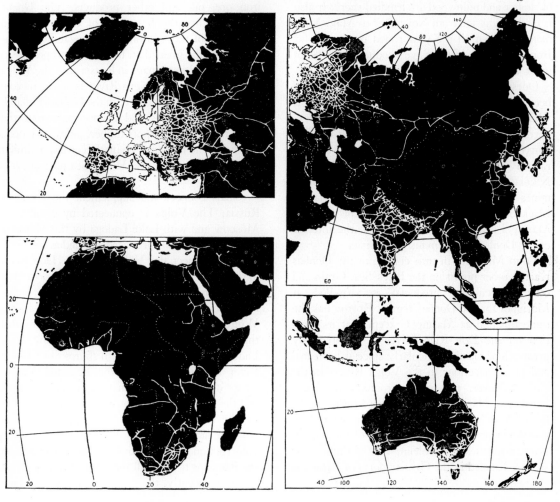

than was furnished by Leningrad alone, since Kaliningrad and Riga are free of ice for a longer period and are much closer to Western Europe. It is difficult at present to estimate what the ultimate function of these ports will be, but Kaliningrad is well situated to become the western terminal of the Trans-Siberian Railroad which reaches to Vladivostok on the Pacific. Kaliningrad and Riga will grow in importance as trade between Russia and the west increases. The role of Leningrad is much clearer. Leningrad is the major port and trade center for much of the Northern Forest Area of western Russia. It also functions as the major import point for textiles, coal, and machinery from the west. Leningrad is frozen from November to April but can be used with the aid of ice breakers all the year. See FIGURE 42.7.

Arkhangelsk on the White Sea is the only Arctic port of consequence, and large quantities of timber and pulpwood are handled there. It also is hindered by ice from November to May. Murmansk is open all the year round but is too far from any areas of intensive production to be of great value.

Odessa, the chief port of the Black Sea, has been greatly improved in recent years. From it wheat, sugar, machinery, and metal ores are exported. Oil, coal, tobacco, fish, and salt are imported. Odessa is near the outlet to the Mediterranean via the Bosporus and the Dardanelles. Nikolaev is the port for the iron and manganese mines to the north. The ores are moved via the Black Sea and the Sea of Azov to the ports of Mariupol and Rostov and thence to the interior of the Donbas heavy industrial district.

From Mariupol in turn coal from the Donbas reaches other points on the Black Sea. Grain and other agricultural products are handled at Mariupol for the Donbas region. Rostov has the same function as Mariupol except that its location on the Don River gives it a potentially greater hinterland, particularly since it has canal and rail connections to the Volga River. In the past, however, the greater tonnage has been handled at Mariupol. Both of these ports on the Sea of Azov are hindered by ice from one to four months, depending on the severity of the winter. Large quantities of petroleum, cotton, timber, and salt are handled in the Caspian ports of Baku and Astrakhan.

In western Russia five rivers—the Volga, Don, Dnepr, Neva, and northern Dvina—carry most of the inland traffic. Of these the Volga and its tributaries account for more than half the total tonnage of inland waterborne freight. See FIGURE 42.8. The Volga is navigable from the Caspian Sea to Moscow, to which the upper river is connected by canal. Tributaries reach the southern Urals and other parts of central Russia. The Volga has a fairly even flow and good depth throughout most of its 10,000 miles of navigable water. It has two disadvantages; it is frozen for a number of months and it flows into an inland sea which is 85 feet below sea level. Its chief function is to distribute oil from the fields around the Caspian to central Russia and to bring timber from the north into southern Russia which is poorly supplied with wood. The Don River reaches back into and partly around the Donbas Coal Basin, and carries large quantities of coal, iron ore, oil, and other products. The Dnepr River touches the best part of the wheat and sugar belt of the Ukraine. Its navigability is improved by the great dam below Dnepropetrovsk, and it is third in tonnage in Russia after the Volga and the Neva. The Neva River is short, merely connecting Lake Ladoga with the Gulf of Finland. With its tributaries and connecting canals the Neva is used to transport timber, pulpwood, ores, and fish. The northern Dvina River has a similar function but reaches the White Sea port of Arkhangelsk.

Canals connect and supplement the rivers of Russia. The Volga is connected by canal with Moscow and with Lake Ladoga by the Mariinsk Canal. Other canals proposed and under construction will connect the Volga with the Don River in the south and with the Dvina in the north. The Baltic–White Sea Canal (Stalin Canal) reaches from Leningrad on the Gulf of Finland to the White Sea via Lake Onega. It is noteworthy that this canal does not go through shallow Lake Ladoga but skirts its southern shores. The Dnepr River is connected with the Bug and Vistula rivers of Poland by a canal 127 miles in length and the Vistula, as previously noted, is connected by the Mittelland Canal with the Rhine. The Russian landscape lends itself readily to canal construction and it is obviously an advantage for the Russians to have all their major rivers joined.

Until recently the railroads in Russia have

been of limited service to the country as a whole because of the vast distances, the limited amount of rolling stock, the open network, and the use of broad gauge (5 feet) which made it difficult to transfer freight to the lines of neighboring countries. The system is being improved steadily, however, and the southwestern part of the country now is well served. The Russian terrain offers little difficulty for the construction of railroads. Tunnels are almost unknown in the west and even through the Ural Mountains there are easy passes. The heaviest rail traffic in the Soviet Union is in the south between the Donbas and the neighboring industrial districts, especially Kharkov and the Dnepr Bend Region. A network of rails radiates from Moscow like the spokes of a wheel, reaching Leningrad, Arkhangelsk, and Sverdlovsk on the eastern end of the Ural Gateway. Moscow is connected with the Volga by rail at Gorki, Kazan, and Kuibishev, with Astrakhan on the Caspian, with all the Black Sea ports, with Kiev on the southwest, and with Minsk on the west.

Less important but more spectacular are the lines which join western Russia with the East. Best known is the Trans-Siberian reaching from Leningrad to Vladivostok on the Pacific. This line, 6000 miles long, is double-tracked and is of great strategic importance, but long stretches provide little revenue at the present time. In building the Trans-Siberian Railway, the Russian engineers for the first time encountered real mountainous terrain. Unaccustomed to the construction of tunnels, the line was at first laid out in sweeping curves to avoid as many elevations as possible. Later, tunnels were added and the tracks shortened. The Trans-Siberian extends into the Siberian Wheat Belt (the Pioneer Agricultural Belt, as the Russians call it) and also passes through or near valuable mineral deposits which contribute to the industrial establishments of the west. Another railroad, the "Turk-Sib," connects the southern part of Turkestan and the Caspian Sea with the Trans-Siberian Railway. It reaches many of the cotton producing oases of Turkestan and also carries petroleum from the

FIGURE 42.7. *A map of the cities of Russia. Compare with Figure 39.1. From Chauncy D. Harris and the "Geographical Review."*

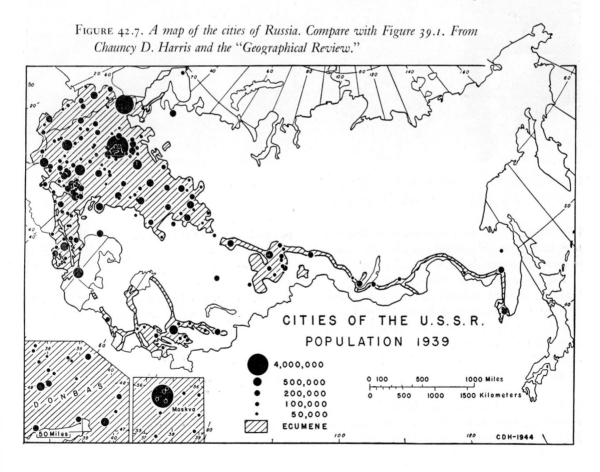

CITIES OF THE U.S.S.R.
POPULATION 1939

4,000,000
500,000
200,000
100,000
50,000
ECUMENE

0 100   500   1000 Miles
0   500   1000   1500 Kilometers

CDH-1944

FIGURE 42.8. *River transport on the Volga River at Stalingrad. This river carries a large tonnage in spite of ice conditions in winter. From "Sovfoto."*

Caspian fields. All the major industrial districts now have good rail connections with the source of their raw materials and with each other.

The great distances, vast expanses of level land, and favorable weather all suggest the extensive use of air transport in Russia for mail, passengers, and express. A network of airlines connects all parts of the country, and has a total length of nearly 90,000 miles. Not all lines have regular or frequent schedules, however.

The Russian transport system carries great quantities of coal, timber, ores, building materials (including stone and cement), grain, and oil. Most of these materials are moved from the point of production to the large industrial districts or to the ports. Foreign trade is small, confined largely to grain and timber exports and to imports of a few of the materials, such as machinery, copper, aluminum, cotton, gasoline, and wheat for the Far East, which are lacking in Russia.

ASIA

Asia, the largest of the continents, has the greatest handicaps to internal communication. Vast deserts, lofty mountains, and tropical jungles have proved to be too difficult for even the billion people of Asia to overcome. Much of Asia can still be reached only by caravan, rough truck

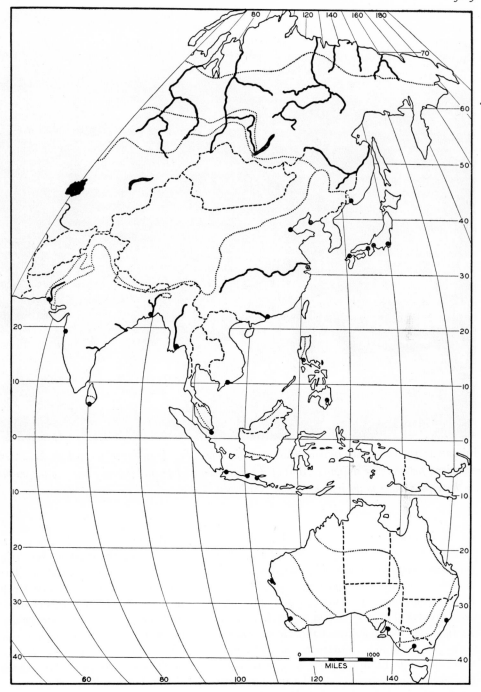

FIGURE 42.9. *Inland Waterways and principal ports of Asia. Only a few of Asia's rivers are navigable and those in the far north are closed by ice for a large part of the year. As a result, the burden of transportation is thrown on the inadequate railroads, highways, and trails. The Yangtze River of China, however, carries a large volume of traffic, probably more than any other river in the world. Boundaries of production regions are shown with dotted lines (compare End Paper 4). Dots indicate important ports.*

FIGURE 42.10. *Naval Base in Kure Harbor on the Inland Sea, Japan. Harbors such as this are excellent for coastwise shipping. Most of the small plains of Japan have easy access to the sea but have poor routes to the interior. From Northwest Airlines.*

routes, human porters, or chartered plane. The lack of airports in the rough terrain is a decided handicap. The only reasonably satisfactory rail development is in India, Japan, parts of China and Korea, and along the Turk-Sib and Trans-Siberian routes. The chief inland routes (FIG. 42.9) are related to the great marginal sea lane from the Suez Canal via India, Singapore, and Shanghai to Vladivostok. From the ports along this route, the rivers, railroads, trails, and caravans carry most of the produce to and from the interior.

The river valleys of Asia provide the oldest and in many places the most important routes to the interior, but not many of the streams are navigable. The rivers of India are little used for transport since rail lines have been constructed along their courses. The plains of the Indus and the Ganges are productive, but even the heaviest

goods move by rail. The large amounts of water taken from these rivers for irrigation interfere with their use for navigation. The low gradients and the abundant silt carried are also unfavorable factors. The rivers of Indochina—the Irrawaddy, Mekong, and Menam—are navigable to a limited extent by small craft and are very useful in getting the surplus rice crops down to the seaports of Rangoon, Bangkok, and Saigon.

The Yangtze River of China is the most useful river on the continent and probably carries more traffic than any other river in the world. For more than 7000 miles from the sea its course is navigable although with some difficulties. From the greatest port in China, Shanghai, located on a small tributary in the delta of the Yangtze, ocean steamers can be used as far as Hangkow. From that point river steamers and various kinds of small craft take over the cargo. Above Ichang the river flows in a gorge and the current makes it difficult for craft moving upstream. A few dams and locks would greatly improve the navigation of the Yangtze, but these are by no means easy to construct. Other rivers of China, notably the Si and the Hwang, are used to a limited extent for transport.

The railroad nets of India and Japan are the brightest spots in the transportation map of Asia. In India there are more than 40,000 miles of track serving all parts of the country. The ports of Karachi, Bombay, Madras, and Calcutta are especially well served. The lines are handicapped by the scarcity of coal in some parts of India. In Japan a network of narrow gauge lines covers most of the main island. There the mountainous character of the land is the greatest handicap. Steep grades, sharp curves, and numerous tunnels are frequent. As in India, where automobiles are very scarce, the railroads in Japan have a heavy passenger traffic. Coastwise shipping takes care of most of the heavy goods. See FIGURE 42.10.

THE FUTURE OF WORLD TRADE

As stated previously, no new areas of trade have been opened up for nearly two centuries. Throughout this book frequent references have been made to changes in trade and production, and further changes, perhaps even greater, ones may be expected. It appears at this writing that significant modifications will occur in the next decade in certain regions.

Europe has lost its position of pre-eminence in manufacturing and trade. This will benefit North Americans most because of their technical resources but will also benefit the Russians, who are advancing in production and manufacturing. Many countries are expanding and diversifying their production and as a result will purchase less from the great trading nations. Brazil, Argentina, South Africa, Australia, and Canada are outstanding in this regard. China and India possess vast resources, raw materials and labor, which may easily result in large-scale industrial development. One of the most fascinating questions for the future of world trade concerns the development of the tropical lands. If their resources can be utilized as effectively as those of the middle latitudes the whole character of world trade will be changed. The ultimate question, however, is one of world political organization. The pattern of world trade will vary sharply from that of the past if a reasonably harmonious world organization can be established. It will be even more divergent if the world resolves itself into two or more distinct areas of influence, each of which sets up trade barriers against the others.

Climates

*A BRIEF OUTLINE OF KÖPPEN CLIMATES**

OF all the factors in geography which tend to limit production and to fix the regional limits of certain types of production, climate is the most far-reaching and the most useful from the standpoint of explanation and classification. It is everywhere a potent factor. In a given region the land form may be of negligible importance to production. There may be no useful minerals; the natural and cultural conditions may permit a variety of production types; but undoubtedly the climate in some manner exercises a limiting influence. Climate alone is not a satisfactory means of distinguishing the productive possibilities of small regions, but in a general study of world production it is an extremely useful device, even though it presents only a partial explanation.

The early Greeks took the first step in the study of climatic regions when they divided the earth into three zones—torrid, temperate, and frigid. This was a theoretical division in which the assumption was made that boundaries of climates corresponded precisely to parallels of latitude. This elementary system did not provide for variations in moisture. If the element of moisture is added to the system and the zones defined more carefully, we obtain the skeleton of the widely used climatic system devised by W. Köppen (*Die Klimate der Erde*, 1923).

A. The tropical, winterless zone near the equator, mean temperature of no month under 64° F.
B. The dry zones, arid and semiarid areas in which evaporation exceeds precipitation.
C. The temperate humid zones with warm summers and mild winters, mean temperature for coldest month 32° to 64° F.
D. The continental high latitude areas with warm summers and long severe winters, with the mean temperature of the warmest month above 50° F. and that of the coldest month below 32° F.
E. The summerless polar regions, with the warmest month averaging under 50° F.

On a world map these broadly defined regions are represented as large irregular areas. The regions are so large that subdivision is necessary if they are to be useful. The subdivisions may be based on the amount and seasonal distribution of precipitation, including the concept of moisture efficiency. In addition, the temperature of the warmest month and the length of the growing season may be critical factors. In the subdivision of the five types, the following characteristics are considered:

a. Hot summers, warmest month over 72° F.
b. Mild summers, warmest month under 72° F.
c. Short growing season, less than four months over 50° F.
f. Always moist, that is, each month has precipitation.
s. Summers are dry and winters rainy.
w. Winters are dry and summers rainy.

The five principal zones, represented by the upper case letters, and the six secondary zones occur in the following combinations. [The meaning of individual letters is constant. A few symbols are derived from German words as: W from *Wuste* (desert) and f from *feucht* (humid). S is the symbol for Steppe, T for Tundra, and F for "frozen all year."]

Af	Rainforest
Aw	Savanna
B	Dry climates
BS	Steppe
BW	Desert
Cfa	Humid Subtropical, hot summer
Cfb	Rainy Temperate, cool summer
Cs	Mediterranean
Cw	Winter Dry Temperate
Da	Humid Continental, hot summer
Db	Humid Continental, cool to warm summer
Dc	Taiga, short summer
E	Polar climates
ET	Tundra, treeless

It should be noted that other types and combinations occur. However, the fourteen types and combinations listed above are usually sufficient unless detailed explanations are required. Either the names or the symbols may be used in designating a climate, but if the names are used the student should keep in mind the quantitative definition of each type.

A brief outline of the principal climates follows. Refer to Figures A1, A2, and A3.

---

* Modified with permission from Hartshorne, R., and Dicken, S. N., *Syllabus for the Introductory Course in Economic Geography*. Edwards Brothers. Ann Arbor, Michigan, 1939.

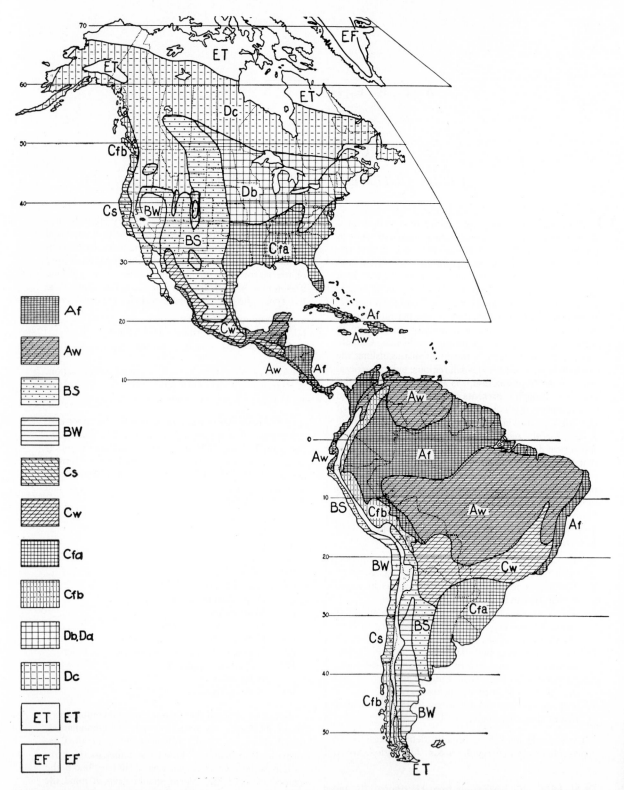

FIGURE A1. (Figures A2 and A3 on pages 520 and 521.) Generalized maps of Köppen climates.
*From "Syllabus for the Introductory Course in Economic Geography" by Richard Hartshorne and
S. N. Dicken.*

I. *TROPICAL CLIMATES* (A)
Always hot—coolest month over 64° F.

A. TROPICAL RAINFOREST CLIMATE. (Shown on map as Af.)

Type Area: Amazonia

1. Always hot. Growing season unbroken; 12 months long.
2. Always moist. No prolonged dry season. (If the total rainfall is great, 80 to 100 inches, a short rainless period is scarcely significant.)
3. Little seasonal variation in temperature; annual range less than 19° F.
4. Maximum rain at the time of vertical sun, minimum with low sun. Many stations near the equator show two maxima and two minima.
5. Cloudiness, humidity, and sensible temperature high.
6. Luxuriant, stratified, rainforest vegetation. Lianas, Epiphytes, etc.
7. Soils: Red lateritisch tropical soils; some laterites.
8. Location: Belt near the equator 0–10 degrees wide; windward margins of highlands in the trade wind belt; highlands exposed to monsoon winds. In the latter there is a marked dry season, but because the total rainfall is so great, rainforest conditions exist to a large extent.

NOTE: To distinguish Tropical Rainforest (Af) from Winter Dry Tropical (Aw):

If the total annual
rainfall is   40   60   80   100   inches,
the driest month
must have over   2.4   1.6   0.8   0.0   inches.

B. WINTER DRY TROPICAL CLIMATE. (Aw) Savanna.

Type Area: The Sudan

1. Always hot. Growing season (temperature aspects) unbroken; 12 months long.
2. Distinct dry season at time of lowest sun, maximum rain at time of highest sun. Rainy season may be divided by a short dry season.
3. Rainforest conditions in the wet season; desert conditions in dry season.
4. A transition from forest to steppe; dry season forests or grassy vegetation with drought-resistant trees, isolated in groves or near streams.
5. Soils: Red lateritisch tropical soils; perhaps some chernozems in drier portions.
6. Location: On poleward margin of Tropical Rainforest; the lee side of highlands in the trade wind belt.

II. *THE DRY CLIMATES* (B)
Areas of deficient moisture

(The exact measurement of "moisture deficiency" is based not only on amount of rainfall but also on evaporation as determined by seasonal temperatures and rainfall. The formulas are too complicated to be given here.)

A. DESERT CLIMATE. (BW) Arid.

Type area: Sahara

1. Extreme drought; moisture supply insufficient for grass.
2. Temperature conditions similar to those of adjacent humid regions; growing season anywhere from 1 to 12 months.
3. Subdivisions: hot desert and cold desert, separated by 32° F. isotherm for coldest month.
4. Plants adapted to extreme aridity: Cactus, agave, creosote bush, saltbush. Few vegetationless areas except the moving sand dunes.
5. Soils: Gray and brown desert soils.
6. Location: West coasts in lee of trade winds, latitude 20°–30°; remote interiors of continents, latitude 35°–45°.

B. STEPPE CLIMATE. (BS) Semiarid.

Type area: The Great Plains

1. Rainfall sufficient for closed grass formation but not for trees.
2. Effect of rainfall depends on the temperature and seasonable distribution of rain (this is true of all climates) so that a given amount of rain is more effective if accompanied by low temperatures.
3. Rainy season and temperature conditions (but not the amount of rain) similar to adjacent humid regions; growing season anywhere from 1 to 12 months. Two subdivisions: Hot Steppe and Cold Steppe, separated by isotherm of 32° F. for the coldest month.
4. Vegetation: Grass; tall grass in the more humid areas, short grass elsewhere.
5. Soils: Dark brown soils and chernozems.
6. Location: Transition zones between the arid and the humid areas, especially in the continental interiors.

III. *TEMPERATE MESOTHERMAL CLIMATES* (C)
Coldest month 32°–64° F.

(These climates are distinguished by having a *mild* cool season [winter] without permanent frost. In the first three the winters are generally very short, the warm season much longer and except in highlands as hot as in the tropical climates.)

A. WINTER DRY TEMPERATE CLIMATE. (Cw)

Type areas: Abyssinia, Ganges, Gran Chaco

1. Dry, mild winter; rainy, hot summer. (Rainiest month must have at least ten times the rain of the driest month.)
2. Growing season between 7 and 11 months.
3. Park Landscape: Scattered trees with grass.
4. Soils: Red and yellow subtropical loams.
5. Location: Adjacent to Winter Dry Tropical (Aw) in higher latitudes or in elevated areas.

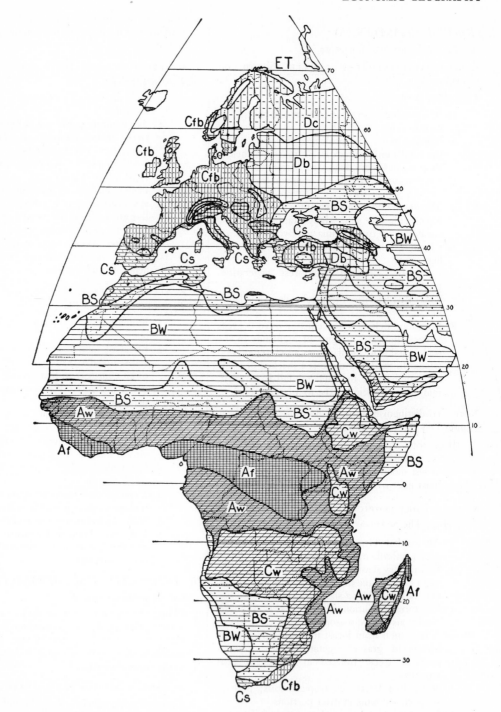

FIGURE A2.

B. SUMMER DRY TEMPERATE CLIMATE. (Mediterranean) (Cs)

Type area: Lands bordering Mediterranean Sea

   1. Dry summer, rainy mild winter. (Rainiest month has at least three times the rain of driest month.) Regions near the sea usually have cool summer; inland the summers are hot.

   2. Growing season between 7 and 11 months.

   3. Grassy vegetation with forest in favorable location; "maquis," "scrub," or "chaparral" developed locally.

   4. Soils: Red and yellow subtropical loams; *terra rossa.*

   5. Location: West coasts of continents, latitude 30°–40°.

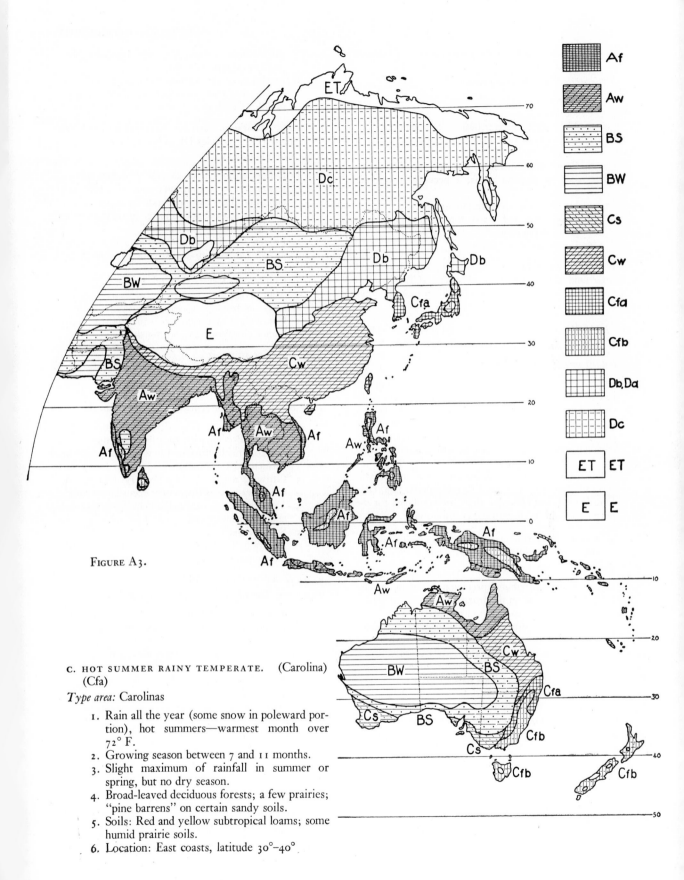

FIGURE A3.

Legend:
- Af
- Aw
- BS
- BW
- Cs
- Cw
- Cfa
- Cfb
- Db, Da
- Dc
- ET ET
- E   E

C. HOT SUMMER RAINY TEMPERATE. (Carolina) (Cfa)

Type area: Carolinas

1. Rain all the year (some snow in poleward portion), hot summers—warmest month over 72° F.
2. Growing season between 7 and 11 months.
3. Slight maximum of rainfall in summer or spring, but no dry season.
4. Broad-leaved deciduous forests; a few prairies; "pine barrens" on certain sandy soils.
5. Soils: Red and yellow subtropical loams; some humid prairie soils.
6. Location: East coasts, latitude 30°–40°

D. COOL SUMMER RAINY TEMPERATE.   (Puget Sound) (Cfb)

Type areas: Puget Sound, British Isles

1. Rain all the year with winter maximum in most localities.
2. Mild summer; warmest month under 72° F. Growing season generally between 4 and 6 months.
3. Range of temperature less than any types outside of tropical areas; especially low along coasts.
4. Deciduous and coniferous forests.
5. Soils: Gray and brown forest soils; podzols in poleward portions.
6. Location: West coasts, 38°–62°.

NOTE: In terms of growing season, vegetation, and soils (and also agriculture), this type (Cfb) is much more like the following type (Db) than like the other C climates.

IV. HUMID MICROTHERMAL CLIMATES (D)

Warmest month over 50° F.

Coldest month under 32° F.

(These are the humid continental climates, characterized by a shorter warm season, which may include truly tropical hot spells, and a longer cold season including a continuous frozen season which may have truly polar cold spells. At all seasons the weather is influenced by cyclonic storms and is more fluctuating and uncertain than in any other type.)

Based on rainfall distribution and summer temperatures the following types can be recognized: Dfa, Dfb, Dfc, Dwa, Dwb, Dwc, but these are combined for the purposes of this book into the two following:

A. WARM SUMMER MICROTHERMAL CLIMATE. (Db—includes Dfa, Dfb, Dwa, Dwb.)

Type area: Great Lakes Region

1. Evenly distributed precipitation; snow in winter remains on the frozen ground for at least a few weeks up to 4 or 5 months.
2. Cyclonic storms frequent in winter, sudden changes in the weather, blizzards.
3. At least four months above 50° F. Growing season, 3 to 6 months, is therefore long enough for cultivation of at least hardier grains.
4. Hardwood and mixed forests with local prairies; coniferous forests in poleward portions.
5. Soils: Gray and brown forest soils; humid prairie soils; chernozems on drier margins; podzols on poleward margins.
6. Location: In the northern hemisphere only; interiors and east coasts of continents; higher middle latitudes.

B. SHORT SUMMER MICROTHERMAL CLIMATE. (Taiga) (Dc—includes Dfc, Dwc.)

Type area: Hudson Bay

1. Differs from Db in shorter growing season, longer frozen season, and generally less precipitation. Less than four months above 50° F.; frost-free season much shorter; growing season 1 to 3 months.
2. Frozen period usually more than half the year; includes areas with lowest winter temperatures observed on earth's surface.
3. Coniferous forest, thin on northern margin. Many bogs.
4. Soils: Podzols.
5. Continental location 50°–70° north, also higher elevations 40°–60° north.

V. COLD CLIMATES (E)

Warmest month below 50° F.

A. TUNDRA CLIMATE. (ET)

Type areas: Coast of Greenland, Northern Canada

1. Warmest month 32°–50° F. Too cold for tree growth. Precipitation mostly in summer.
2. Soil continually frozen; a few inches or more at surface thaws in summer.
3. Growing season: From a few days to a month, but never sure as frosts may occur at any time.
4. Vegetation: Mosses and lichens; some grasses and flowering plants.
5. Soils: Tundra.
6. Location: Lowlands in poleward regions; high plateaus and mountains just below snowline.

B. GLACIAL CLIMATE. (EF)

Type areas: Interior of Greenland, Antarctica

1. Warmest month below 32° F. Too low to melt accumulated snow and ice. No growing season whatever.
2. Almost lifeless; some algae and bacteria.
3. No soil; ground permanently covered with ice and snow; bare rock where blown clear.
4. Location: Only in high altitudes; chiefly in polar regions, but in highest mountains in any latitude, even on equator.

Soils*

I. CHARACTERISTICS

A. COLOR—unimportant in itself, but indicative of important characteristics, and most obvious.

1. Dark: Dark brown or black. Indicates high percentage of organic material (humus), high percentage of nitrogen; usually fertile and easily tilled.

   a. Exception: Raw humus (undecomposed) on surface of very humid forest areas (especially coniferous and tropical Rainforests).

   b. Exception: Undrained soils, such as muck and peat.

2. Light: Brown, grayish brown, red, yellow, gray, white. Indicates low humus content, hence lower fertility unless fertilized.

   a. Tints of red result chiefly from iron compounds. Locally, these colors are caused by iron in the parent materials or by the reduction of impure limestones which are low in clay. This color is characteristic of mature soils in humid tropics.

   b. Yellow soil is due to the presence of iron and the lack of organic matter.

   c. Gray and white soils indicate reduced quantities of iron together with anaerobic decay of organic matter under conditions of poor drainage and limited aeration.

   d. Brown and grayish brown soils usually contain some iron and are mixed with black from humus.

B. TEXTURE—mixture of different size particles. Texture is the most thoroughly studied characteristic, but not most important.

1. Size of individual particles, in order (after Wentworth):

   Boulders greater than 256 mm.
   Cobbles 64 to 256 mm.
   Pebbles 4 to 64 mm.
   Granules 2 to 4 mm.
   Very coarse sand grains 1 to 2 mm.
   Coarse sand grains $\frac{1}{2}$ to 1 mm.
   Medium sand grains $\frac{1}{4}$ to $\frac{1}{2}$ mm.
   Fine sand grains $\frac{1}{8}$ to $\frac{1}{4}$ mm.
   Very fine sand grains $\frac{1}{16}$ to $\frac{1}{8}$ mm.
   Silt particles $\frac{1}{256}$ to $\frac{1}{16}$ mm.
   Clay particles, including colloids,
       less than $\frac{1}{256}$ mm.

_____
* Modified with permission from Hartshorne, R., and Dicken, S. N., *Syllabus for the Introductory Course in Economic Geography*. Edwards Brothers. Ann Arbor, Michigan, 1939.

2. Always found in mixtures of various sized particles. Sands and sandy loams are subdivided according to the size of the sand particles; from coarse to very fine. There are also gravelly and stony loams.

| | *Percentage of* | | |
	Sand	Silt	Clay
Sands	over 80	(together—under 20)	
Sandy loams	50–80	(together— 20–50)	
Loams	30–50	30–50	under 20
Silt loams	under 30	over 50	under 20
Clay loams	20–50	20–50	20–30
Clays	(together—under 70)		over 30

C. STRUCTURE—arrangement of particles into aggregates into which the soil breaks up in cultivation. Structure can be blocklike, cloudy, nutlike, granular, columnar, plastic, etc.

1. In medium-textured soils, like loams, structure is favorable for plant growth.

2. In heavy-textured soils, like clays, structure is unfavorable for plant growth.

   a. Soil is hard and refractory when dry; plastic and intractable when wet.

   b. Soil makes a poor seed bed.

   c. Soil is unresponsive to fertilizer.

   d. Natural drainage of such soil is poor.

3. In light-textured soils, like sands, structure is unimportant since these soils are made up of grains, not aggregates.

D. CHEMICAL COMPOSITION.

1. Acid condition of soil is caused by low lime content either from parent materials low in lime or from loss of lime in soil formation or cultivation.

   a. Acid soils, if caused naturally, are usually low in humus content.

   b. Acid soils are often coarse or of structure not suitable for cultivation.

   c. Soils of high acidity require "sweetening" with lime fertilizer.

2. Alkaline condition of soil is caused by high lime content.

   a. More humus is retained than in acid soils because as water percolates through soil, the lime does not dissolve as rapidly as the humus forms.

b. Structure is better than for acid soils because lime particles dissolve in upper horizons. See Figure 3.10.

c. The advantages in "a" and "b" remain in such soils even though soil formation and cultivation cause the soil to become neutral or acid. Such soils may then require the addition of lime.

E. "SOIL FERTILITY."—The value of a soil depends on the use to which it is to be put. Soils that are "good" for one crop, such as apples, may be very "poor" for another, wheat. However, most of the cultivated land of the world is used for crops, such as grains, which were domesticated from wild grasses of steppe lands (rice is a possible and important exception). Consequently, the most desirable soil characteristics for most important crops are those which are similar to the characteristics of steppe soils. But since the steppe climate provides a low and uncertain yield of these same crops, they are grown to a much greater extent in the more humid climates, that is, in forest soils. The improvement of these soils, therefore, by cultivation and fertilizing, is essentially for the purpose of making and maintaining them as much like the steppe soils as is possible.

II. PROCESSES IN SOIL FORMATION FROM UNDERLYING ROCK (residual soils)

A. DEVELOPMENT OF REGOLITH (loose material from parent rock).

1. Physical decomposition—chiefly from temperature changes, especially freezing and thawing. Forms coarse material, rock fragments, and sand.

2. Chemical decomposition—chiefly from water, especially marked in tropical areas. Forms fine material, clay.

B. SOIL FORMATION ON TOP OF REGOLITH—three processes. Percolation of water causes two processes; these are especially rapid in very humid regions and in very coarse regoliths.

1. Leaching—soluble materials carried down to ground water level. These materials may be carried out to rivers and so lost.

2. Eluviation—fine particles carried down and deposited in lower levels. In extreme cases eluviation leaves sandy surface and clay hardpan below.

Humus accumulation—organic litter provided by vegetation and insects. This is greater in grasslands than in forests, and is practically nil in deserts. Bacterial action tends to destroy humus; this effect is greatest in hot humid areas, as in the tropical rainforest.

III. MATURITY OF SOIL FORMATION (See Figure 3.10 on page 46.)

A. MATURE SOILS—on smooth, level areas.

1. Arrangement in "soil horizons," labeled from surface.

a. "A" horizon—zone of dissolution. Coarse texture, usually contains humus (dark); chemically different, usually acid.

b. "B" horizon—zone of deposition. Heavy texture, light color.

c. "C" horizon—unweathered, broken parent material.

2. Depth of different horizons varies even locally, from a few inches to several feet.

B. IMMATURE (YOUNG) SOILS—with rudimentary horizons.

1. Soils on steep slopes, where A horizon is eroded as it forms.

2. Soils recently uncovered by ice.

3. Recent volcanic deposits.

4. Undrained soils, in swamps and bogs.

C. ALTERED SOILS—due to change in environment.

1. Flood plain soils and loess (wind-blown) soils.

a. Chiefly accumulations of materials of A horizon of soils originally formed elsewhere.

b. Such soils develop new A', B', and C' horizons on terraces.

2. "Degraded soils," where forest succeeds grass.

3. Alterations from cultivation.

D. OLD SOILS.

1. Often have tough, indurated B horizon.

2. Usually have coarse A horizon.

IV. GEOGRAPHIC CLASSIFICATION OF MATURE SOILS

A. MAJOR DIVISION OF WORLD SOILS. See Figure B1.

1. Pedocals—have zone of lime carbonate accumulation usually in lower B.

a. Subhumid and arid areas; grasslands and deserts.

b. Generally alkaline or neutral.

c. Little contrast between horizons.

d. High humus content (dark) except in deserts.

2. Pedalfers—without zone of lime accumulation.

a. Found in humid areas; forests usually, also humid prairies.

b. Strong contrast between horizons.

c. Little humus, except in prairies.

d. Inclined to be acid, except on limestone rock.

e. Require fertilization and cultivation; but more used because located in areas of greater rainfall.

B. MAJOR WORLD TYPES, resulting from broad environmental conditions (chiefly climate and vegetation).

Pedalfers

1. Red lateritisch tropical soils.

2. Laterites.

3. Red and yellow subtropical forest soils.

4. Gray-brown podzolic soils.

5. Podzols.

6. Tundra soils.

7. Humid prairie soils.

Pedocals

8. Chernozem (black) soils (steppe and subhumid).

9. Dark brown or chestnut brown soils (steppe).

10. Brown desert soils.

11. Gray desert soils.

C. VARIATIONS within the major soil types.

1. Gradational changes between major soil types, corresponding to gradational changes in climatic types.

2. Differences in maturity—the various kinds listed under III: mature, immature, altered, and old soils.

3. Differences in relief—related to heading 2.

a. Soils on steep slopes are generally immature, as sheet erosion tends to carry off A horizon.

b. Thin, rocky soil on very steep slopes.

c. At foot of slopes coarse gravelly soil may overlie fine material.

4. Differences in drainage—related to previous headings.

a. Poorly drained soils: muck, peat.

b. Well-drained soils: sand, silt.

5. Differences in character of underlying rock.

a. Physical character of regolith formed.

(1) Coarse sandy soils are likely to remain immature almost indefinitely; accumulate little humus; remain coarse in texture; leach rapidly.

(2) Soils formed from transported materials may be
(a) Very fine texture to great depths; flood plains and loess (wind deposited).
(b) Coarse sand or gravel; glacial outwash or deposits of swift mountain streams.
(c) Sands, loams, or clays mixed with boulders of all sizes; glacial moraine.

V. DESCRIPTION OF MAJOR WORLD TYPES OF SOILS

THE PEDALFERS

1. Red lateritisch tropical soils.

a. Occurrence—humid tropics (Af, part Aw).

b. Description—thin humus layer; coarse A horizon; B horizon heavy in iron content; leached of most soluble minerals. Chemical character of soil makes readily available the large annual addition of mineral foods and humus, although soil will not retain these. Structure is good and fertilizers can therefore be used annually.

c. Subtype—degraded forest due to cultivation (Africa). Native clearing of forest by burning; later fields left to brush and that burned repeatedly for salts; iron concretions form plates; only reed grass grows, and steppe fires make soil type permanent.

2. Laterites—extreme of conditions in previous type.

a. Occurrence—probably much less widespread than formerly thought; limited to small parts of previous humid tropical areas.

b. Iron in B horizon forms crustations, which may appear on surface; may even be low-value iron ore.

3. Red and yellow subtropical forest soils.

a. Occurrence—subtropical forest areas (Cfa, Cw, Cs).

b. Description—general character similar to tropical soils, but less extreme. Thin gray humus layer; lower A light yellow, B horizon red, or yellow (on sand); A horizon much coarser than B. Low in mineral foods as well as humus (leached); soon require fertilizers or fields are abandoned; acidic. Structure fair, but does not hold up with cultivation, except in lime areas, or on sand (granular).

c. Subtypes.

(1) On sand, tends to be very rapidly leached; low fertility.
(a) On mature sand soils (middle Coastal Plain in U. S.); fine B horizon retains mineral foods and fertilizers well.
(b) On immature sands (coastal margin) fertilizers are rapidly carried off by ground water.

(2) Limestone soils (including terra rossa of Mediterranean). Poor in humus but fine texture; clay or loam; high in mineral food. Especially rich where it has accumulated in karst basins (east coast of Adriatic).

(3) Calcareous loess soils (east of Mississippi River).

(4) Eroded red soils of Piedmont (southeastern U. S.). Most of coarse A horizon has been eroded, leaving clay loams.

(5) Flood-plain soils. Usually deep accumulations of humus-bearing A horizon. The Mississippi flood-plain consists chiefly of such rich materials from the western prairies. In central and southern China most cultivation (rice) is limited to these fertile soils.

4. Gray-brown podzolic soils.

a. Occurrence—mid-latitude deciduous forest lands (Cfb, Db), chiefly in northeastern United States and western Europe.

b. Description—more humus than any other forest soil; lower A horizon less leached; grayish brown or pale yellow; more soluble minerals; difference between A and B horizons less than in previous types. Mildly acidic.

c. Structure best of forest soils; nutlike.

d. Variations.

(1) Sandy soils (Northern Coastal Plain, glacial sands in Upper Lake States). Low in humus, more leached, tend to be podzolized.

(2) Calcareous (large parts of eastern Corn Belt, Ontario Plain, Lancaster Co., Penn.). Heavy texture; responds to fertilizer; now low in lime.

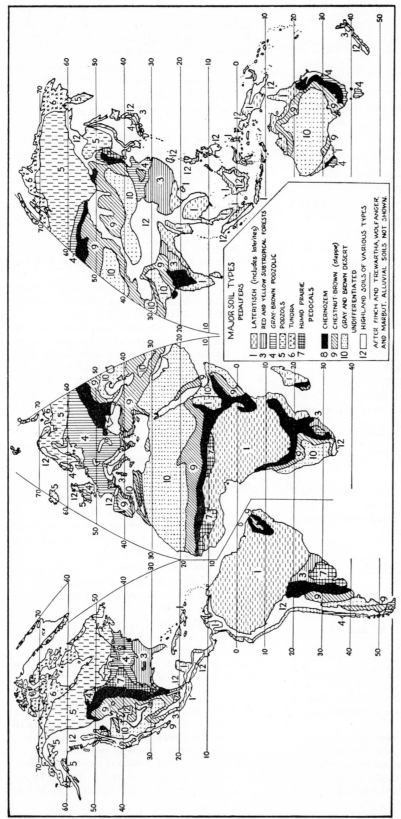

FIGURE B1. The major soil areas of the world. *From "Syllabus for the Introductory Course in Economic Geography" by Richard Hartshorne and S. N. Dicken.*

(3) In immature forms, limestone content is especially important. Acidic immature soils (Southern Appalachians, much of New England) are among poorest.

(4) Abnormal—hardpan areas (Southern Illinois and Indiana).

5. Podzols (ash-colored soils).

a. Occurrence—high latitude forest areas (Dc, part Db and Cfb); chiefly under coniferous forests; farther south on sands.

b. Description—surface is layer of raw humus (undecomposed, little value); lower A horizon is bleached, gray to white, with little or no humus; coarse, acidic, and structureless; highly leached. B horizon is darker brown; richer in minerals and even some humus; may be indurated; structure poor, plastic, when dry bakes into hard clods.

c. Variations.

(1) Extreme conditions form "heath" (many districts northwestern Europe, none in U. S.).

(2) With careful cultivation, lower A horizon (bleached) is slowly changed to more fertile soil.

(3) On slopes, A horizon is eroded, leaving B horizon with humus, but with poor structure.

(4) Calcareous (Aroostook Valley, Maine, and northeastern Vermont). Poorly developed podzol profile; nonacidic.

6. Tundra soils.

a. Occurrence—areas of Tundra climate; polar margins and high altitudes anywhere.

b. Description—soils necessarily immature; no profiles. Subsoil frozen all year; upper soil generally poorly drained. Cultivation may aid drainage and permit thawing of subsoil.

7. Humid prairie soils.

a. Occurrence—grassland areas in mid-latitude forest land areas; especially on drier margins (western part of Db and Cfa areas in U. S.; scattered elsewhere), chiefly on limestone or marl—Black Belts in Alabama and Texas.

b. Description—A horizon is dark brown to black (high humus content); B horizon brown; little difference in texture; structure granular or nutty; neutral or only slightly acidic. Very similar to chernozem, but not lime-accumulating; otherwise a steppe soil in a humid climate.

THE PEDOCALS (lime-accumulating)

8. Chernozem (black earths).

a. Occurrence—more humid parts of steppe regions (BS); chiefly in the tall grass areas, but overlaps into short grass. (Especially developed and studied in steppes of southeastern Russia, continuing across Siberia, and in Great Plains of North America—western Canada to Texas.)

b. Description—A horizon very dark to black; B horizon brown, with lime carbonate accumulation at low level. Unleached. Structure nutlike (best of any soils for most grains). Both horizons very deep. This type soil will not develop on sands (western Nebraska).

9. Dark brown (chestnut) soils.

a. Occurrence—drier portions of steppe regions (BS), chiefly in the short grass areas. (Found parallel to the chernozem belts listed previously, on the drier side.)

b. Description—less humus in A horizon than chernozems; B horizon is brownish gray to gray; carbonate layer. Unleached. Cloddy structure, imperfect, but improves with cultivation.

10. Brown desert soils (a gradation from previous type).

a. Occurrence—less arid portions of deserts (BW).

b. Description—small amount of humus in A horizon, which is structureless. Lime carbonate level near or at surface; shallow soil.

11. Gray desert soils.

a. Occurrence—deserts (BW).

b. Description—surface horizon (A) thin, of "desert crust" or of pebbles, forming "desert pavement"; very low humus content, but unleached of soluble minerals. Porous brown subsoil. Lime carbonate layer close to surface; in older soils may form hardpan.

c. Local variation—salt soils (alkali); infertile even when watered.

APPENDIX C
Statistical Tables

I~N~ the preceding chapters frequent quantitative references, usually in rounded form, have been made to the data of economic geography, without which a study of production is likely to be quite general if not vague. The tables which follow are intended to supplement the statements made in the text in a somewhat more explicit and comparable form. Even here, however, some rounding of cumbersome data will be noted, and most figures are expressed in "thousands" or "millions."

It is necessary, perhaps, to warn some students of the limitations of statistics. The methods of collecting data vary from country to country and from time to time. Most collection methods are subject to error, although in many cases the errors are not significant. Definitions of commodities, political units, and units of measurement are by no means constant. Between the collection of the data and the publication much time may elapse, and all statistics are more or less out of date. For this and other reasons it is not worthwhile to remember specific production figures. Nevertheless, the study of specific data gives a clearer and more lasting impression of production than can be obtained without them.

In most cases the statistics presented below are for the year 1950, but in some cases it was necessary to use data for earlier years. Lack of space precludes the inclusion of data for previous years, which would show trends of production. For such data the original sources should be consulted. It may be noted that some of the statistics in the Appendix are at variance with data mentioned in the main body of the text, where average or representative figures are often given. Comparison of two or more standard sources also reveals some discrepancies, which are generally of insignificant magnitude. Dashes indicate that data are uncertain and unknown.

The usefulness of statistics will be enhanced if they are expressed in visual form, on maps, diagrams, or graphs. If the student is provided with graph paper and base maps, additional visual aids may be prepared to supplement the maps and graphs in the text, and at the same time the student will gain a greater appreciation for the subject matter. It is recommended that some of the statistical sources listed in the REFERENCES be consulted, since only a sampling of the data of economic geography can be presented in this Appendix.

Table 1. ACTIVE POPULATION, INCOME, AND OCCUPATIONS

COUNTRY	a	b	c	d	e	f	COUNTRY	a	b	c	d	e	f
Canada	5,415	870	21.0	25.5	16.0	8.5	Poland	15,006	300	65.0	15.5	5.5	2.5
United States	59,583	1,453	13.0	26.5	18.5	8.0	Czechoslo-						
Mexico	5,858	121	65.5	9.0	9.5	2.5	vakia	5,852	371	38.0	35.0	6.5	5.0
Guatamala	1,086	77	—	—	—	—	Hungary	4,503	269	47.5	23.5	6.0	3.0
Nicaragua	353	89	73.0	10.0	—	0.5	Romania	10,458	—	78.5	6.0	3.5	1.5
Panama	265	183	50.0	7.0	7.5	3.0	Bulgaria	3,433	—	80.0	8.0	2.5	1.5
Cuba	1,521	296	41.5	12.5	10.0	2.0	Yugoslavia	9,509	146	75.0	—	—	—
Puerto Rico	602	—	38.0	17.5	8.5	3.0	Greece	2,995	128	—	—	—	—
Jamaica	505	—	45.5	11.5	7.5	—							
							Japan	36,280	100	47.5	15.5	11.5	5.0
Brazil	14,020	112	67.5	10.0	5.5	3.5	Philippines	7,347	44	73.0	10.0	5.0	3.5
Argentina	6,267	346	—	—	—	—	Thailand	6,824	36	89.0	2.0	5.0	1.0
Chile	1,742	188	35.5	17.0	9.5	4.5	Malaya	1,905	—	64.0	7.0	8.0	3.5
Peru	2,475	100	62.5	15.0	4.5	2.0	India	148,817	57	67.5	10.5	5.5	1.5
Colombia	4,566	132	72.5	9.5	3.5	1.5	Turkey	7,540	125	76.0	7.5	3.5	2.0
Venezuela	1,241	322	51.0	16.5	8.0	5.0	Cyprus	165	—	37.5	21.0	4.0	4.0
United King.	22,579	773	5.0	37.5	14.0	9.5	Egypt	6,729	100	65.5	10.5	9.0	3.0
France	20,520	482	36.5	22.0	12.0	6.5	So. Rhodesia	33	101	14.5	17.5	17.0	8.5
Belgium	3,481	582	12.0	37.5	13.5	7.0	Union of So.						
Luxembourg	135	553	26.0	39.5	—	18.5	Africa	5,160	264	46.5	7.0	5.0	4.0
Netherlands	3,866	502	19.5	24.0	14.0	7.0							
Italy	18,755	235	47.0	21.0	8.5	4.0	Australia	3,196	679	15.5	25.0	15.0	10.0
Spain	9,254	—	51.5	18.5	6.5	3.5	New Zealand	679	856	20.0	26.0	14.5	10.0
Portugal	3,050	250	48.5	15.5	6.5	3.0	Hawaii	166	—	20.0	12.5	18.5	8.5
Eire	1,298	420	46.0	10.5	7.5	4.5							
Finland	2,017	348	57.5	16.0	5.5	3.5							
Sweden	2,988	780	24.5	29.5	12.0	8.0							
Norway	1,394	587	26.5	26.0	11.0	11.0							
Denmark	2,173	689	25.0	29.0	14.0	6.5							
Iceland	54	57	45.5	16.5	7.5	8.5							
Germany	19,374	320	30.0	38.0	—	15.0							
Saar	300	—	12.5	27.5	9.0	10.0							
Switzerland	1,992	849	21.0	36.0	10.0	4.0							
Austria	3,352	216	31.5	40.5	—	13.5							

a. Total economically active population (000's).
b. National income per capita, in dollars.
c. Percentage of active population engaged in agriculture.
d. Percentage of active population engaged in manufacturing.
e. Percentage of active population engaged in trade and commerce.
f. Percentage of active population engaged in transport.

Condensed from John C. Weaver and Fred E. Lukermann, *World Resource Statistics*. Burgess Publishing Co. Minneapolis, 1953

Table 2. UNITED STATES, POPULATION AND LAND USE, 1950

STATE	a	b	c	d	e	f
NORTH	83,938	91.3	32,678	447,415	—	
New England	9,938	147.5	3,613	14,497	96.4	
Maine	914	29.4	312	4,613	109.4	16,788
New Hampshire	533	59.5	203	2,017	107.4	4,800
Vermont	378	40.7	137	3,931	148.4	3,835
Massachusetts	4,691	596.2	1,827	2,078	56.2	3,310
Rhode Island	792	748.5	305	265	73.5	453
Connecticut	2,007	409.7	829	1,593	71.3	1,907
Middle Atlantic	30,164	300.1	11,838	34,406	90.0	—
New York	14,830	309.3	5,944	17,568	117.5	13,500
New Jersey	4,835	642.8	1,963	1,818	69.3	2,348
Pennsylvania	10,498	233.1	3,931	15,020	87.4	15,228
East North Central	30,399	124.1	11,873	115,564	121.2	—
Ohio	7,947	193.8	3,060	21,928	99.4	4,831
Indiana	3,934	108.7	1,518	20,027	113.8	3,445
Illinois	8,712	155.8	3,546	31,602	154.7	3,396
Michigan	6,732	111.7	2,394	18,392	104.9	19,000
Wisconsin	3,435	62.8	1,355	23,615	132.9	17,000
West North Central	14,061	27.5	5,354	283,248	274.5	—
Minnesota	2,982	37.3	1,144	33,140	175.4	19,700
Iowa	2,621	46.8	1,002	34,454	164.9	2,248
Missouri	3,955	57.1	1,522	35,278	145.2	19,142
North Dakota	620	8.8	224	41,001	589.8	621
South Dakota	653	8.5	242	43,032	626.3	1,979
Nebraska	1,326	17.3	512	47,753	427.3	1,112
Kansas	1,905	23.2	708	48,589	344.1	1,121
SOUTH	47,197	53.4	16,499	377,794	—	
South Atlantic	21,182	79.0	7,656	96,601	92.6	
Delaware	318	160.8	127	923	99.3	442
Maryland	2,343	237.1	895	4,200	101.8	2,742
District of Columbia	802	13,150.5	373	2	46.4	—
Virginia	3,319	83.2	1,150	16,358	94.5	14,832
West Virginia	2,006	83.3	628	8,720	89.3	9,954
North Carolina	4,062	82.7	1,463	18,618	64.8	18,400
South Carolina	2,117	69.9	755	11,022	74.6	10,611
Georgia	3,445	58.9	1,255	23,676	104.8	21,432
Florida	2,771	51.1	1,010	13,084	213.9	23,478
East South Central	11,477	63.8	3,839	76,198	79.4	—
Kentucky	2,945	73.9	955	19,725	82.7	11,857
Tennessee	3,292	78.8	1,136	17,789	75.9	12,165
Alabama	3,062	59.9	1,031	19,068	85.4	18,878
Mississippi	2,179	46.1	717	19,617	74.4	15,889
West South Central	14,538	33.8	5,004	204,995	233.5	—
Arkansas	1,910	36.3	616	17,456	87.8	20,036
Louisiana	2,684	59.4	876	10,040	77.6	16,196
Oklahoma	2,233	32.4	754	36,162	219.4	10,646
Texas	7,711	29.3	2,758	141,338	367.1	36,553
WEST	19,562	16.6	7,067	316,106	—	
Mountain	5,075	5.9	1,748	244,577	1,150.8	
Montana	591	4.1	218	58,787	1,557.4	24,238
Idaho	589	7.1	206	12,503	301.3	18,813
Wyoming	291	3.0	108	33,117	2,532.6	8,878
Colorado	1,325	12.8	477	36,218	760.6	19,902
New Mexico	681	5.6	207	49,608	1,670.6	20,001
Arizona	750	6.6	239	37,856	2,880.6	19,538
Utah	689	8.4	229	10,309	391.7	8,494
Nevada	160	1.5	64	6,178	1,801.7	4,720
Pacific	14,487	45.3	5,319	71,529	253.7	
Washington	2,379	35.6	840	16,720	209.3	24,100
Oregon	1,521	15.8	577	19,754	312.9	29,755
California	10,586	67.5	3,902	35,054	252.3	45,515
UNITED STATES	150,697	50.7	56,241	1,141,615	194.8	623,828

a. Population (000's)
b. Population density per square mile
c. Employed (000's)
d. Total farm land (000's acres)
e. Average acres per farm
f. Forest land (000's acres)

Source: *Seventeenth Census of the United States.*

Table 3. FISH LANDINGS FOR SELECTED COUNTRIES, 1950 (In thousands of metric tons)

COUNTRY	LANDINGS	COUNTRY	LANDINGS	COUNTRY	LANDINGS
United States	2,652	Belgium	60	Poland	66
Canada	927	Denmark	251	Sweden	203
Mexico	55	France	432	United Kingdom	988
Argentina	65	Finland	65	Soviet Union	1,560
Brazil	155	Germany	555	China	220
Chile	86	Italy	190	Japan	3,794
Peru	83	Netherlands	244	Philippines	220
Venezuela	75	Norway	1,467	Australia	39
		Portugal	307	New Zealand	32
		Spain	576		

Sources: United Nations, *Statistical Yearbook*, 1952, pp. 82–83; Food and Agricultural Organization, *Fisheries Bulletin*, 1952.

Table 4. WOOD PRODUCTION, LEADING NATIONS, 1949 (In millions of cubic meters)

COUNTRY	a	b	c	d	COUNTRY	a	b	c	d
World	1,600.0	—	—	—	Nyasaland	5.7	—	—	5.6
					Gold Coast	5.0	0.5	—	4.0
United States	282.0	160.5	45.7	51.5	Switzerland	3.2	1.4	0.3	1.5
Soviet Union	270.0	—	—	—	Spain	8.0	1.6	—	5.5
Brazil	101.4	6.8	.2	90.0	French Cameroons	3.6	0.3	—	3.3
Canada	94.4	37.8	31.0	23.0	Newfoundland	—	—	—	—
Japan	42.8	11.0	1.3	12.8	Greece	4.4	0.2	—	4.0
Finland	31.2	10.9	8.3	8.8	New Zealand	3.4	2.5	—	0.8
Sweden	33.8	12.4	9.5	8.7	United Kingdom	3.8	2.2	—	0.6
Germany	40.4	19.8	3.8	10.8	Mexico	—	—	—	—
France	25.5	7.7	0.7	13.5	Southern Rhodesia	3.5	—	—	3.2
China	—	—	—	—	Bulgaria	—	—	—	—
Romania	—	—	—	—	Thailand	2.3	1.3	—	0.6
Italy	14.7	2.7	0.3	6.5	Sierra Leone	2.6	—	—	2.5
Yugoslavia	28.0	6.4	0.6	18.0	Korea (South)	1.0	0.1	—	0.7
Australia	15.7	6.0	0.3	8.5	Puerto Rico	2.3	—	—	2.3
Poland	11.0	—	—	—	Belgian Congo	3.2	0.3	—	2.9
French Eq. Africa	1.0	0.7	—	0.2	Belgium	2.2	0.9	0.2	0.3
India	27.9	9.9	1.0	14.8	Indonesia	2.8	1.3	—	1.4
Czechoslovakia	11.0	5.4	1.8	3.0	Philippines	3.0	2.9	—	0.1
Portugal	0.2	—	—	—	Hungary	—	—	—	—
Norway	6.9	3.0	3.0	0.5	Denmark	1.6	0.9	—	0.6
Chile	0.6	0.3	—	0.1	Haiti	—	—	—	—
Burma	1.5	0.4	—	0.8	Union of S. Africa	—	—	—	—
Turkey	6.1	0.5	0.1	5.3					
Austria	6.5	4.1	1.2	1.0					

a. Total wood produced   c. Pulpwood
b. Sawlogs   d. Fuel wood

Source: United Nations, *Yearbook of Forest Products Statistics*, 1951.

Table 5. MILK PRODUCTION AND USE IN SELECTED COUNTRIES, 1950
(Milk cows in 000's; production per cow in pounds per year; milk production and use in millions of pounds.)

COUNTRY	PRODUCTION			UTILIZATION					
	Milk cows	Production per cow	Milk production	Fluid milk	Butter	Cheese	Canned milk	Other uses	Feed
Canada	3,609	4,554	16,437	5,852	7,228	1,148	597	559	1,053
United States	22,779	5,292	123,381	58,450	33,345	11,680	6,940	9,584	3,382
Austria	1,170	3,674	4,299	2,055	1,267	287	—	2	688
Belgium	950	7,309	6,944	1,951	3,968	132	20	8	865
Denmark	1,577	7,566	11,931	1,592	8,578	913	291	48	509
France	8,400	4,057	34,079	8,770	11,905	5,680	—	454	7,270
Netherlands	1,521	8,385	12,754	3,433	5,125	2,468	834	228	666
Norway	766	4,678	3,582	1,656	1,080	551	—	75	220
Sweden	1,664	6,482	10,798	3,763	5,346	1,012	—	126	551
Switzerland	858	6,349	5,534	2,359	794	1,422	—	99	860
United Kingdom	3,765	6,136	23,103	17,582	1,380	1,298	762	526	1,555
Australia	2,354	5,508	12,966	2,625	8,449	1,034	317	541	—
New Zealand	1,850	5,623	10,403	937	6,767	2,112	—	309	278

Source: *Agricultural Statistics*, 1951, p. 401.

Table 6.   WHEAT: ACREAGE AND PRODUCTION FOR SELECTED COUNTRIES, 1950

COUNTRY	1,000 ACRES	1,000 BUSHELS	COUNTRY	1,000 ACRES	1,000 BUSHELS
North America			Asia		
Canada	27,021	461,664	Iran	—	79,000
Mexico	1,515	20,210	Iraq	1,606	20,210
United States	61,741	1,026,755	Lebanon	173	2,020
			Syria	—	27,560
Estimated total	90,330	1,509,000	Turkey	10,500	150,000
			India	24,000	231,500
Europe			Pakistan	10,715	153,180
Austria	585	14,500	Japan	1,883	49,160
Belgium	430	20,110			
Denmark	209	10,990	Estimated total	114,260	1,550,000
Finland	500	11,200			
France	11,150	280,000	South America		
Western Germany	2,530	95,500	Argentina	14,000	200,000
Other Germany	—	—	Brazil	—	15,500
Greece	2,097	31,230	Chile	1,989	38,130
Hungary	—	—	Uruguay	1,040	14,020
Ireland	375	12,000			
Italy	12,100	285,000	Estimated total	19,200	275,000
Luxembourg	46	1,300			
Netherlands	235	12,000	Africa		
Norway	78	2,510	Algeria	3,820	38,500
Poland	—	—	Egypt	1,424	41,000
Portugal	1,720	19,470	French Morocco	2,900	25,000
Romania	—	—	Tunisia	1,720	16,900
Spain	9,900	130,000	Union of S. Africa	3,108	20,250
Sweden	837	26,860			
Switzerland	216	8,100	Estimated total	14,600	153,000
United Kingdom	2,476	94,000			
Yugoslavia	—	—	Oceania		
			Australia	11,700	183,000
Estimated total	70,700	1,520,000			
			Total	11,840	188,000
U.S.S.R. (Europe and Asia)	107,000	1,110,000			
			Estimated world total	427,930	6,310,000

Table 7.   WHEAT ACREAGE AND PRODUCTION IN THE UNITED STATES, 1950

STATE	1,000 ACRES	1,000 BUSHELS	STATE	1,000 ACRES	1,000 BUSHELS
New York	435	12,585	Kentucky	260	3,900
New Jersey	78	1,677	Tennessee	270	3,375
Pennsylvania	872	19,184	Alabama	12	180
			Mississippi	6	126
North Atlantic	1,385	33,446	Arkansas	19	285
			Oklahoma	4,846	43,614
Ohio	2,118	46,596	Texas	2,839	22,712
Indiana	1,479	31,798			
Illinois	1,376	27,538	South Central	8,252	74,192
Michigan	1,141	29,666			
Wisconsin	86	2,073	Montana	4,862	93,958
Minnesota	921	15,410	Idaho	1,342	37,350
Iowa	262	5,740	Wyoming	334	6,218
Missouri	1,362	24,516	Colorado	2,362	39,924
North Dakota	8,706	120,724	New Mexico	149	955
South Dakota	3,278	33,978	Arizona	28	672
Nebraska	3,879	84,788	Utah	408	8,008
Kansas	12,280	178,060	Nevada	17	471
			Washington	2,547	67,582
North Central	36,888	600,887	Oregon	952	23,693
			California	651	13,671
Delaware	61	1,037			
Maryland	329	6,086	Western	13,652	292,502
Virginia	425	7,862			
West Virginia	66	1,221	United States	61,741	1,026,755
North Carolina	375	5,438			
South Carolina	156	2,184			
Georgia	152	1,900			
South Atlantic	1,564	25,728			

Sources: (Table 6) *Agricultural Siatistics*, 1951, pp. 12 and 13; (Table 7) *Agricultural Statistics*, 1951, p. 9.

Table 8.   WORLD ACREAGE AND PRODUCTION OF OATS, BARLEY, RYE, AND TOBACCO, 1950

CONTINENT AND COUNTRY	OATS		BARLEY		RYE		TOBACCO	
	Acres (000's)	Bushels (000's)	Acres (000's)	Bushels (000's)	Acres (000's)	Bushels (000's)	Acres (000's)	Pounds (000's)
World	131,890	4,200,000	116,790	2,435,000	110,040	1,675,000	8,085	7,100,000
North America	53,700	1,886,000	18,320	480,000	2,990	36,310	2,020	2,375,000
South America	2,420	67,000	2,450	47,000	—	—	480	400,000
Europe	31,460	1,340,000	23,290	690,000	29,480	685,000	885	750,000
U.S.S.R.	37,000	750,000	21,500	325,000	74,000	910,000	—	—
Asia	4,120	95,000	39,900	740,000	1,180	20,830	3,600	2,850,000
Africa	1,330	24,000	10,170	125,000	—	—	560	245,000
Oceania	1,860	35,300	1,160	28,350	—	—	9	9,355
Algeria	460	10,250	2,664	38,000	—	—	53	41,887
Anglo-Egyptian Sudan	—	—	—	—	—	—	—	—
Argentina	1,900	55,000	1,500	29,900	1,975	19,680	82	73,193
Australia	1,800	32,000	1,100	26,000	—	—	5	3,855
Austria	544	16,500	330	11,500	680	16,500	—	—
Belgian Congo	—	—	—	—	—	—	—	—
Belgium	438	34,680	207	12,000	219	9,380	4	10,000
Brazil	—	—	—	—	—	—	297	218,026
Bulgaria	—	—	—	—	—	—	—	44,092
Burma	—	—	—	—	—	—	137	63,000
Canada	11,575	419,930	6,625	171,393	1,168	13,333	102	120,298
China	2,322	50,000	15,200	305,000	—	—	1,200	1,200,000
Colombia	—	—	—	—	—	—	49	43,650
Cuba	—	—	—	—	—	—	117	72,400
Czechoslovakia	1,421	69,000	1,425	50,000	1,790	51,000	14	17,684
Denmark	688	57,250	1,219	74,084	381	13,110	—	—
Dominican Republic	—	—	—	—	—	—	47	33,000
Egypt	—	—	130	4,500	—	—	—	—
Finland	1,125	49,500	335	9,200	375	9,200	—	—
Formosa	—	—	—	—	—	—	12	21,065
France	5,678	222,000	2,362	72,200	1,260	24,000	71	112,435
French Cameroons	—	—	—	—	—	—	—	—
French Morocco	119	3,060	4,950	55,000	—	—	4	4,189
French Togoland	—	—	—	—	—	—	—	—
French West Africa	—	—	—	—	—	—	—	—
Gambia	—	—	—	—	—	—	—	—
Germany	2,860	175,000	1,520	67,600	3,335	118,000	27	63,933
Greece	363	8,270	510	9,186	135	1,890	253	127,646
Hungary	—	—	—	—	—	—	47	50,706
India	—	—	7,641	103,000	—	—	790	500,000
Indochina	—	—	—	—	—	—	25	14,330
Indonesia	—	—	—	—	—	—	48	21,000
Iran	—	—	1,977	36,740	—	—	44	33,186
Iraq	—	—	2,470	35,000	—	—	10	17,000
Ireland (Eire)	650	38,000	125	6,000	—	—	—	—
Italy	1,169	38,130	613	13,370	250	5,700	144	147,333
Japan	212	8,500	2,515	80,200	—	—	134	218,864
Korea	—	—	—	—	—	—	49	60,000
Manchuria	—	—	—	—	—	—	—	—
Mexico	100	1,400	507	7,120	—	—	64	59,000
Mozambique	—	—	—	—	—	—	—	—
Netherlands	334	25,500	171	10,580	445	16,500	—	—
Nigeria	—	—	—	—	—	—	—	—
Pakistan	—	—	563	7,200	—	—	167	150,000
Paraguay	—	—	—	—	—	—	12	13,000
Philippine Islands	—	—	—	—	—	—	141	71,000
Poland	—	—	—	—	—	—	35	43,651
Portugal	851	8,800	353	6,050	684	7,440	—	—
Portuguese Guinea	—	—	—	—	—	—	—	—
Romania	—	—	—	—	—	—	69	37,037
Southern Rhodesia	—	—	—	—	—	—	174	88,200
Spain	1,600	36,200	3,950	75,000	1,581	21,000	32	34,028
Sweden	1,242	55,550	232	9,650	313	9,650	1	772
Tanganyika & Uganda	—	—	—	—	—	—	—	—
Tunisia	74	1,720	934	9,200	—	—	2	2,380
Turkey	747	21,740	4,700	94,020	1,180	20,830	317	186,229
United Kingdom	3,105	183,000	1,779	75,000	71	2,220	—	—
United States	42,027	1,465,134	11,191	301,009	1,822	22,977	1,604	2,032,450
Union of S. Africa	600	8,000	80	1,412	—	879	—	45,484
Uruguay	250	4,600	70	1,100	—	—	1	661
Yugoslavia	—	—	—	—	—	—	85	68,000

Source: *Agricultural Statistics*, 1951, pp. 24, 49, 55, 112, and 113.

Table 9. ACREAGE AND PRODUCTION OF OATS, BARLEY, RYE, AND TOBACCO, 1950

STATE	OATS		BARLEY		RYE		TOBACCO	
	Acres (000's)	Bushels (000's)	Acres (000's)	Bushels (000's)	Acres (000's)	Bushels (000's)	Acres	Pounds (000's)
United States	42,027	1,465,134	11,191	301,009	1,822	22,977	1,603,800	2,032,450
Maine	98	4,802	6	210	—	—	—	—
New Hampshire	5	210	—	—	—	—	—	—
Vermont	37	1,295	1	27	—	—	—	—
Massachusetts	7	231	—	—	—	—	8,200	13,675
Rhode Island	1	33	—	—	—	—	—	—
Connecticut	5	190	—	—	—	—	19,200	27,412
New York	787	33,841	75	2,550	18	360	500	700
New Jersey	43	1,677	16	512	14	245	—	—
Pennsylvania	788	29,944	159	5,644	13	202	39,600	61,365
North Atlantic	1,771	72,223	257	8,943	45	807	67,500	103,152
Ohio	1,147	41,292	26	728	35	665	20,600	24,610
Indiana	1,421	52,577	25	675	59	826	10,100	12,850
Illinois	3,911	166,218	48	1,344	62	868	—	—
Michigan	1,480	58,460	115	3,910	65	1,040	—	—
Wisconsin	2,924	141,814	216	8,856	92	1,150	21,100	30,645
Minnesota	5,101	188,737	1,252	36,934	162	2,349	400	520
Iowa	6,457	264,737	60	1,920	14	224	—	—
Missouri	1,782	55,242	80	1,720	36	468	4,900	5,390
North Dakota	2,126	59,528	2,112	50,688	234	2,808	—	—
South Dakota	3,311	87,742	1,148	18,942	420	5,250	—	—
Nebraska	2,644	66,100	304	4,864	210	2,415	—	—
Kansas	960	21,120	254	3,556	42	441	200	240
North Central	33,264	1,203,567	5,640	134,137	1,431	18,504	57,300	74,255
Delaware	8	224	12	348	18	234	—	—
Maryland	55	1,870	89	2,759	18	252	50,000	40,000
Virginia	160	5,200	95	2,898	26	390	118,800	165,496
West Virginia	55	1,568	14	392	2	28	3,100	3,379
North Carolina	402	11,859	37	888	18	207	650,500	875,990
South Carolina	678	18,984	22	440	9	90	114,000	150,480
Georgia	597	16,119	5	110	4	44	93,200	102,120
Florida	16	288	—	—	—	—	22,200	23,268
South Atlantic	1,971	56,112	274	7,835	95	1,245	1,051,800	1,360,733
Kentucky	118	2,832	63	1,480	21	242	322,400	361,655
Tennessee	239	5,975	66	1,221	22	220	104,000	132,105
Alabama	158	4,108	2	40	—	—	400	400
Mississippi	249	7,719	1	25	—	—	—	—
Arkansas	212	6,254	4	84	—	—	—	—
Louisiana	71	1,952	—	—	—	—	400	150
Oklahoma	838	14,665	92	1,242	45	338	—	—
Texas	1,386	27,027	133	1,729	28	196	—	—
South Central	3,271	70,532	361	5,821	116	996	427,200	494,310
Montana	444	15,984	849	23,772	20	250	—	—
Idaho	212	9,540	386	13,896	4	52	—	—
Wyoming	162	5,184	163	4,564	6	72	—	—
Colorado	190	4,940	490	9,555	28	238	—	—
New Mexico	33	759	38	836	4	24	—	—
Arizona	10	300	163	6,520	—	—	—	—
Utah	47	2,186	120	5,520	6	54	—	—
Nevada	8	360	30	1,050	—	—	—	—
Washington	167	8,183	250	8,750	20	230	—	—
Oregon	281	8,992	370	12,210	35	385	—	—
California	196	6,272	1,800	57,600	12	120	—	—
Western	1,750	62,700	4,659	144,273	135	1,425	—	—

Source: *Agricultural Statistics*, 1951, pp. 23, 48, 54, and 109.

Table 10. ROUGH RICE, ACREAGE AND PRODUCTION, 1950

	1,000 ACRES	MILLION POUNDS		1,000 ACRES	MILLION POUNDS
North America			South America		
Costa Rica	35	49.2	Argentina	112	308.6
El Salvador	37	50.7	Brazil	4,500	6,600.0
Mexico	292	502.6	British Guiana	100	241.0
Panama	143	189.7	Chile	58	107.1
United States	1,608	3,797.1	Ecuador	—	300.0
Cuba	130	143.0	Paraguay	25	44.1
Dominican Republic	116	134.1	Peru	111	330.0
			Surinam	44	110.0
Total	2,562	5,131.8	Uruguay	35	98.8
			Venezuela	50	55.1
Europe					
France	28	101.4	Total	5,697	8,773.0
Greece	24	70.5			
Italy	357	1,631.4	Africa		
Portugal	122	298.1	Egypt	727	2,587.0
Spain	147	661.4	French West Africa	1,860	1,111.5
			Madagascar	1,553	1,703.1
Total (excl. U.S.S.R.)	764	2,918.8			
			Total	7,358	8,099.4
Asia					
Iran	550	981.0	Oceania		
Iraq	525	551.2	Australia	38	179.2
Turkey	60	170.0	Fiji	35	58.0
Burma	10,000	12,000.0			
China	46,000	98,000.0	Total	105	270.3
Taiwan	1,898	4,087.0			
Manchuria	850	1,530.0	World total	230,464	342,125.0
Indochina	11,250	12,150.0			
India	74,000	70,000.0	United States	1,608	3,797.1
Japan	7,940	26,443.0	Louisiana	545	1,047.0
Korea	2,500	6,467.6	Texas	481	1,130.0
Federation of Malaya	908	1,375.0	Arkansas	343	793.0
Java and Madura	10,000	14,000.0	California	232	760.0
Pakistan	22,300	28,500.0			
Philippine Republic	5,700	5,589.1			
Thailand	9,100	13,500.0			
Total (excl. U.S.S.R.)	213,553	316,121.7			

Source: *Agricultural Statistics*, 1951, p. 29.

Table 11. ACREAGE AND PRODUCTION OF CORN FOR SELECTED COUNTRIES, 1950

COUNTRY	1,000 ACRES	1,000 BUSHELS	COUNTRY	1,000 ACRES	1,000 BUSHELS
Canada	306	13,389	Turkey	1,446	24,720
United States	81,817	3,057,803	China	12,300	255,220
Mexico	9,880	98,420	Manchuria	6,680	130,000
Cuba	410	6,500	Indochina	1,053	22,365
			India	7,600	70,000
Argentina	4,400	103,000	Pakistan	950	14,720
Brazil	11,560	237,000	Japan	150	3,300
Chile	137	3,700	Korea	321	4,177
Colombia	1,710	23,030	Java	5,150	79,976
Uruguay	460	6,100	Philippines	2,246	22,587
Bulgaria	1,879	26,174	Belgian Congo	823	13,000
France	803	16,500	Egypt	1,535	51,000
Greece	614	7,650	French Morocco	1,290	6,000
Hungary	3,091	81,067	French West Africa	1,500	19,200
Italy	3,260	98,000	Madagascar	197	2,900
Portugal	1,220	18,960	Angola	1,435	12,900
Romania	9,870	172,000	S. Rhodesia	258	4,891
Spain	925	24,000	Union of S. Africa	8,000	97,000
Yugoslavia	6,615	176,600			
			Australia	182	4,450
U.S.S.R.	9,000	150,000			
			World Total	211,060	5,145,000

Source: *Agricultural Statistics*, 1952, pp. 39–40.

Table 12. UNITED STATES ACREAGE AND PRODUCTION OF CORN, 1950

STATE	1,000 ACRES	1,000 BUSHELS	STATE	1,000 ACRES	1,000 BUSHELS
Maine	13	455	Kentucky	2,130	78,810
New Hampshire	14	630	Tennessee	2,141	72,794
Vermont	68	3,060	Alabama	2,845	64,012
Massachusetts	38	1,520	Mississippi	2,282	60,473
Rhode Island	7	280	Arkansas	1,430	38,610
Connecticut	45	1,935	Louisiana	866	19,918
New York	740	30,340	Oklahoma	1,269	31,725
New Jersey	177	9,558	Texas	3,130	65,730
Pennsylvania	1,337	60,834			
			South Central	16,093	432,072
North Atlantic	2,439	108,612			
			Montana	202	3,838
Ohio	3,364	174,928	Idaho	35	1,645
Indiana	4,319	213,790	Wyoming	68	1,156
Illinois	8,234	419,934	Colorado	604	14,496
Michigan	1,683	64,796	New Mexico	101	1,414
Wisconsin	2,544	104,304	Arizona	36	396
Minnesota	5,111	194,218	Utah	24	960
Iowa	9,865	463,655	Nevada	3	105
Missouri	4,158	187,110	Washington	15	870
North Dakota	1,318	25,042	Oregon	28	1,036
South Dakota	3,747	99,296	California	86	2,924
Nebraska	6,775	250,675			
Kansas	2,625	93,188	Western	1,202	28,840
North Central	53,743	2,290,936			
Delaware	146	5,256			
Maryland	473	18,920			
Virginia	1,117	54,733			
West Virginia	251	9,287			
North Carolina	2,215	81,955			
South Carolina	1,446	33,258			
Georgia	3,465	57,172			
Florida	712	9,968			
South Atlantic	9,825	270,549			

Source: *Agricultural Statistics*, 1951, p. 38.

Table 13. COTTON ACREAGE AND PRODUCTION, LEADING COUNTRIES AND STATES, 1950

COUNTRY	1,000 ACRES	1,000 BALES	STATES	1,000 ACRES	1,000 BALES
Mexico	1,804	1,120	Missouri	449	254
United States	17,843	10,012	Virginia	23	4
			North Carolina	610	181
U.S.S.R.	5,600	2,700	South Carolina	879	405
			Georgia	1,054	488
Iran	321	129	Tennessee	644	409
Turkey	1,100	542	Alabama	1,327	575
Burma	193	35	Mississippi	2,084	1,322
China	7,650	2,430	Arkansas	1,728	1,090
India	13,859	2,695	Louisiana	739	426
Pakistan	3,011	1,227	Oklahoma	965	242
			Texas	7,048	2,946
Argentina	1,137	482	California	586	978
Brazil	4,700	1,550			
Peru	383	380			
Anglo-Egyptian Sudan	539	442			
Belgian Congo	815	197			
Uganda	1,535	289			
Egypt	2,050	1,754			
French Eq. Africa	600	93			
Mozambique	700	120			
World Total	66,825	27,740			

Source: *Agricultural Statistics*, 1952, pp. 77–79.

Table 14.   ACREAGE AND PRODUCTION OF POTATOES, 1950

COUNTRY	1,000 ACRES	1,000 BUSHELS	COUNTRY	1,000 ACRES	1,000 BUSHELS
North America			**Asia**		
Canada (incl. Newfound-			Cyprus	9	1,300
land and Labrador)	517	98,895	Israel	4	900
El Salvador	2	100	Lebanon	11	1,176
Guatemala	10	470	Syria	9	919
Honduras	4	150	Turkey	186	22,238
Mexico	82	4,960	Japan	466	64,157
Panama, Republic of	1	70	North Korea	260	16,000
United States	1,847	439,500	South Korea	120	7,000
Bermuda	1	40	Indonesia	18	1,000
Cuba	25	3,300	Philippine Republic	1	8
Dominican Republic	3	72			
Jamaica	3	80	Total	1,084	114,698
Total	2,495	547,637	**South America**		
			Argentina	514	55,115
Europe			Brazil	370	27,500
Albania	3	150	Chile	127	12,125
Austria	454	95,165	Colombia	250	16,000
Belgium	242	84,826	Ecuador	60	4,000
Bulgaria	45	3,000	Peru	482	45,929
Czechoslovakia	1,500	275,000	Uruguay	29	1,727
Denmark	255	67,938	Venezuela	12	650
Finland	210	44,459			
France	2,748	551,150	Total	1,844	163,046
Germany					
Western Zone	2,800	1,027,000	**Africa**		
Eastern Zone	2,000	480,000	Algeria	50	8,063
Greece	85	12,879	Belgian Congo	7	500
Hungary	680	45,000	Egypt	36	7,500
Iceland	2	367	Eritrea	2	75
Ireland	337	106,773	Madagascar	50	3,210
Italy	947	87,553	Mauritius	1	130
Luxembourg	20	3,000	Mozambique	1	120
Malta	7	480	Nigeria and Cameroons	1	40
Netherlands	410	148,878	Southern Rhodesia	4	400
Norway	146	41,006	Tunisia	5	700
Poland	6,400	1,140,000	Union of S. Africa	170	10,000
Portugal	233	35,682			
Romania	450	30,000	Total	327	30,738
Spain	882	102,881			
Sweden	322	60,443	**Oceania**		
Switzerland	137	44,092	Australia	130	22,000
United Kingdom	1,235	359,781	New Zealand	18	4,200
Yugoslavia	770	50,000			
			Total	148	26,200
Total (excl. U.S.S.R.)	23,320	4,897,503			
			World total	52,618	8,679,822
U.S.S.R. (Europe and Asia)	23,400	2,900,000			

Source: *Agricultural Statistics*, 1951, pp. 257 and 258.

Table 15. RAW SUGAR PRODUCTION, CANE AND BEET, 1950

CONTINENT AND COUNTRY	1950	CONTINENT AND COUNTRY	1950	CONTINENT AND COUNTRY	1950
	1,000 short tons		*1,000 short tons*		*1,000 short tons*
North America (cane)		Eastern Zone	882	Colombia	175
British Honduras	2	Hungary	281	Ecuador	61
Canada (beet)	160	Ireland	108	Paraguay	26
Costa Rica	22	Italy	670	Peru	465
El Salvador	30	Netherlands	453	Surinam	5
Guatemala	34	Poland	1,164	Uruguay (beet)	6
Honduras	6	Romania	123	Venezuela	65
Mexico	800	Spain	224		
Nicaragua	30	Sweden	344	Total South America	3,355
Panama	17	Switzerland	31		
United States (beet)	2,009	United Kingdom	847	Africa (cane)	
United States (cane)	564	Yugoslavia	104	Belgian Congo	16
Antigua	27			Kenya	14
Barbados	177	Total Europe (excl. U.S.S.R.)	10,023	Tanganyika	10
Cuba	6,300			Uganda	50
Dominican Republic	600	U.S.S.R. (Europe and Asia)		Egypt	198
Grenada	1	(beet)	2,400	Madagascar	15
Guadeloupe	78			Madeira Islands and Azores	8
Haiti	64	Asia (cane)		Mauritius	503
Jamaica	315	Iran (beet)	68	Mozambique	90
Martinique	58	Turkey (beet)	168	Angola	58
Puerto Rico	1,280	Burma	6	Reunion	115
St. Kitts	49	China	300	Union of S. Africa	686
St. Lucia and St. Vincent	15	Manchuria (beet)	10		
Trinidad and Tobago	182	Indochina	6	Total Africa	1,763
Virgin Islands of the U.S.	14	India	1,445		
		Indonesia	465	Oceania (cane)	
Total North America	12,842	Japan (beet and cane)	48	Australia	1,043
		Pakistan	35	Fiji	112
Europe (beet)		Philippine Republic	981	Hawaiian Islands	1,050
Austria	134	Taiwan	400	Japanese Mandated Islands	0
Belgium	488	Thailand	40		
Bulgaria	50			Total Oceania	2,205
Czechoslovakia	970	Total Asia (excl. U.S.S.R.)	3,972		
Denmark	410			World total (cane)	21,720
Finland	29	South America (cane)			
France	1,592	Argentina	676	World total (beet)	14,840
Germany		Brazil	1,646		
Western Zone	1,119	British Guiana	230	World total (cane and beet)	36,560

Source: *Agricultural Statistics*, 1951, p. 93.

Table 16. MANUFACTURE OF WHEAT FLOUR, MARGARINE, MALT BEVERAGES, AND CIGARETTES FOR SELECTED COUNTRIES, 1950

COUNTRY	a	b	c	d	COUNTRY	a	b	c	d
United States	10,201	425	10,420	391,956	Eire	352	6	306	5,667
Canada	1,869	43	809	17,311	Sweden	373	81	173	3,993
Mexico	341	—	495	28,000	Norway	143	66	62	1,280
Colombia	52	—	333	10,261	Denmark	214	59	284	4,436
Brazil	1,032	—	319	27,197	Western Germany	2,460	364	1,706	23,646
Argentina	1,971	—	389	—	Czechoslovakia	817	71	816	12,984
Chile	530	—	92	7,665					
					Japan	1,688	20	171	62,436
United Kingdom	4,262	378	4,118	97,145	India	485	—	4	23,629
Belgium	756	65	1,049	10,208					
France	—	54	785	51,096	Australia	1,369	31	709	4,805
Netherlands	667	176	141	8,180	New Zealand	149	—	157	1,454
Spain	2,840	—	46	9,813					

a. Wheat flour, 000's metric tons
b. Margarine, 000's metric tons
c. Malt beverages, million liters
d. Cigarettes, millions

Source: United Nations, *Statistical Yearbook*, 1952, pp. 157–158, 162, 168–173, 188–189, and 193.

Table 17. CATTLE, SHEEP, AND HOGS IN SELECTED COUNTRIES, 1950
(In thousands)

Country	Cattle	Sheep	Hogs
Canada	8,243	1,259	5,413
U.S.A.	77,963	29,826	58,852
Mexico	14,500	5,100	5,600
Cuba	4,550	—	1,800
Argentina	39,000	47,000	2,600
Brazil	52,655	14,251	25,000
Chile	2,331	6,000	600
Colombia	15,513	1,198	2,240
Paraguay	3,865	18,000	—
Uruguay	8,600	23,000	259
Austria	2,203	375	1,927
Belgium	1,902	121	1,361
Czechoslovakia	4,140	480	3,242
Denmark	2,886	61	1,944
France	15,404	7,510	6,424
Germany (west)	10,833	2,020	9,698
Italy	8,162	10,376	4,375
Netherlands	2,723	390	1,795
Norway	1,237	1,812	422
Spain	3,900	24,921	5,568
Sweden	2,648	311	1,278
Switzerland	1,530	—	908
United Kingdom	10,620	19,943	2,986
U.S.S.R.	56,000	78,000	19,000
India	180,000	28,900	3,700
Turkey	11,118	23,303	—
China	25,000	21,000	—
Japan	2,489	—	716
Indonesia	6,370	1,740	1,234
Philippines	2,601	—	3,899
Algeria	765	4,531	137
Kenya	5,550	3,350	—
Uganda	2,525	1,066	—
Egypt	2,366	1,729	—
Ethiopia	20,000	—	—
French Morocco	1,762	9,149	103
Madagascar	5,412	204	405
S. Rhodesia	3,004	315	107
Union of S. Africa	11,513	31,361	1,450
Australia	14,640	112,891	1,123
New Zealand	4,949	33,857	552
World Total (estimated)	791,000	749,100	281,000

Source: *Agricultural Statistics,* 1952, pp. 387–388; 408–409; 424–425.

Table 18. CATTLE, SHEEP, AND HOGS IN THE UNITED STATES, 1950. Numbers and value per head (calves, lambs, and pigs included)

State	Cattle		Sheep		Hogs	
	Thousands	Dollars	Thousands	Dollars	Thousands	Dollars
Maine	216	121.00	21	13.20	34	24.50
New Hampshire	118	145.00	7	14.70	13	26.10
Vermont	433	147.00	12	14.30	21	21.70
Massachusetts	179	196.00	8	14.60	94	24.60
Rhode Island	27	211.00	2	14.00	9	25.80
Connecticut	171	191.00	6	14.00	30	23.50
New York	2,226	174.00	158	19.10	212	25.30
New Jersey	226	234.00	10	18.50	72	28.10
Pennsylvania	1,790	159.00	217	13.80	704	25.90
North Atlantic	5,386	168.00	441	15.80	1,189	25.70
Ohio	2,149	132.00	930	15.30	3,176	25.30
Indiana	1,760	131.00	370	17.30	4,611	27.00
Illinois	3,159	137.00	396	18.20	6,285	30.10
Michigan	1,914	144.00	336	18.50	927	26.60
Wisconsin	3,804	170.00	205	18.50	1,733	30.30
East North Central	12,786	146.00	2,237	16.90	16,732	28.20
Minnesota	3,276	140.00	571	17.00	3,498	32.40
Iowa	4,960	128.00	623	17.40	11,920	32.00
Missouri	3,107	118.00	1,054	16.30	4,429	25.10
North Dakota	1,527	132.00	346	15.90	413	34.00
South Dakota	2,454	126.00	730	17.90	1,442	34.70
Nebraska	3,920	124.00	168	16.60	2,499	32.00
Kansas	3,627	117.00	336	16.60	1,253	25.00
West North Central	22,871	126.00	3,828	16.90	25,454	30.70
North Central	35,657	133.00	6,065	16.90	42,186	29.70
Delaware	61	145.00	2	18.50	37	22.70
Maryland	449	151.00	47	18.40	270	21.20
Virginia	1,108	124.00	293	20.20	752	20.30
West Virginia	548	113.00	296	17.30	256	20.70
North Carolina	710	99.70	35	18.10	1,120	20.70
South Carolina	360	91.10	3	10.70	663	20.50
Georgia	1,220	83.30	13	9.80	1,700	20.60
Florida	1,392	71.60	12	8.30	619	19.50
South Atlantic	5,848	99.30	701	18.30	5,417	20.90
Kentucky	1,608	107.00	700	20.90	1,668	23.30
Tennessee	1,462	101.00	265	17.20	1,371	22.30
Alabama	1,330	80.40	22	10.70	1,225	18.70
Mississippi	1,674	78.30	104	8.00	965	17.10
Arkansas	1,209	86.90	55	11.70	974	17.50
Louisiana	1,439	86.30	140	7.90	731	16.30
Oklahoma	2,630	104.00	105	14.50	835	18.00
Texas	8,574	104.00	6,638	15.40	1,701	20.80
South Central	19,926	98.00	8,029	15.70	9,470	19.90
Montana	1,712	128.00	1,623	19.40	192	25.00
Idaho	939	124.00	990	21.40	209	25.20
Wyoming	1,001	124.00	1,901	18.50	80	23.70
Colorado	1,800	125.00	1,198	21.30	351	24.60
New Mexico	1,166	118.00	1,343	18.90	73	22.50
Arizona	849	111.00	405	17.80	24	26.60
Utah	549	128.00	1,326	20.40	83	22.20
Nevada	552	122.00	449	20.40	28	25.40
Washington	851	125.00	305	18.50	155	24.80
Oregon	1,107	110.00	671	18.20	166	25.50
California	2,709	139.00	1,652	20.30	879	26.30
Western	13,235	125.00	11,863	19.70	2,240	25.30
United States	80,052	123.00	27,099	17.80	60,502	27.10

Source: *Agricultural Statistics,* 1951, pp. 324, 342, and 354.

Table 19. WORLD PRODUCTION OF IRON ORE, IMPORTS AND EXPORTS, 1950
(In thousands of metric tons)

COUNTRY	PRODUCTION	IMPORTS	EXPORTS	COUNTRY	PRODUCTION	IMPORTS	EXPORTS
North America				**Asia**			
Canada	3,271	2,804	2,045	Burma	—	—	—
Cuba	12	—	29	Hongkong	169	—	169
Mexico	420	—	192	India	3,005	—	—
United States	99,619	8,348	2,591	Japan	910	1,461	—
				Malaya	507	—	529
Total	103,322			Philippines	599	—	599
				Portuguese India	131	—	71
South America				Turkey	234	—	—
Argentina	40	—	—				
Brazil	1,900	—	900	Total	5,555		
Chile	2,976	—	2,611				
Venezuela	190	—	—	**Africa**			
				Algeria	2,574	—	2,566
Total	5,106			French Morocco	319	—	314
				Sierra Leone	1,185	—	1,161
Europe				Southern Rhodesia	57	—	—
Austria	1,859	372	—	Spanish Morocco	860	—	953
Belgium-Luxem-				Tunisia	758	—	698
bourg	3,891	8,254	103	Union of S. Africa	1,189	—	—
Finland	—	93	—				
France	30,203	168	7,545	Total	6,941		
W. Germany	10,882	4,870	52				
Greece	5	—	41	**Oceania**			
Italy	465	184	9	Australia	2,403	17	—
Netherlands	—	812	58	New Caledonia	15	—	8
Norway	430	16	283	New Zealand	4	—	—
Spain	2,079	239	939				
Sweden	13,927	—	12,949	Total	2,422		
Switzerland	55	—	54				
United Kingdom	13,145	8,548	1				
Yugoslavia	1,000	—	250				
Total	77,941						

Source: *Resources For Freedom*, Washington, 1952, p. 188.

Table 20. WORLD PRODUCTION OF PRIMARY ALUMINUM, IMPORTS AND EXPORTS, 1950
(In metric tons)

COUNTRY	PRODUCTION	IMPORTS	EXPORTS	COUNTRY	PRODUCTION	IMPORTS	EXPORTS
North America				Denmark	—	3,112	239
Canada	360,043	57	304,564				
United States	651,920	160,369	601	**Asia**			
				India	3,650	1,865	—
Total	1,011,913			Israel	—	6,942	—
				Japan	24,764	1,321	22,508
Europe							
Austria	17,988	—	—	Total	28,414		
Belgium-Luxem-							
bourg	—	8,682	3,340	**Oceania**			
France	60,715	799	15,815	Australia	—	6,600	—
Germany	30,000	—	10,000				
Greece	—	546	—				
Italy	37,070	5,570	2,939				
Norway	46,622	—	42,339				
Spain	2,338	1,660	—				
Sweden	4,038	12,200	—				
Switzerland	21,000	2,745	9,563				
United Kingdom	29,941	143,467	5,508				
Yugoslavia	2,500	—	—				
Total	252,212						

Source: *Resources For Freedom*, Washington, 1952, p. 186.

Table 21. WORLD PRODUCTION OF COPPER, IMPORTS AND EXPORTS, 1950
(In metric tons, crude metal content)

COUNTRY	PRODUCTION	IMPORTS	EXPORTS	COUNTRY	PRODUCTION	IMPORTS	EXPORTS
North America				Asia			
Canada	247,158	—	29,301	India	7,000	—	—
Cuba	18,600	—	18,600	Cyprus	22,933	—	22,933
Mexico	61,701	—	13,224	Japan	39,324	—	—
United States	822,812	97,089	559	Philippines	10,384	—	10,384
				Turkey	13,000	—	—
Total	1,150,271			Total	92,641		
South America				Africa			
Bolivia	5,240	—	5,240	Belgian Congo	175,920	—	—
Chile	362,751	—	16,746	Northern Rhodesia	297,500	—	—
Peru	27,852	—	7,523	South-West Africa	10,460	—	10,648
Other	581	—	581	Union of S. Africa	33,975	—	436
Total	396,424			Total	517,855		
Europe				Oceania			
Austria	1,635	—	—	Australia	15,912	700	—
Finland	15,600	—	—				
France	156	—	—				
Germany	1,012	266,192	—				
Italy	54	—	—				
Norway	15,400	—	13,000				
Portugal	418	—	—				
Spain	4,212	—	—				
Sweden	16,099	—	—				
Yugoslavia	40,006	—	—				
Total	94,592						

Source: *Resources For Freedom*, Washington, 1952, pp. 192–193.

Table 22. PRODUCTION OF COAL AND PETROLEUM, 1950
(In thousands of metric tons. One metric ton of petroleum is approximately
equal to seven U. S. barrels)

COUNTRY	COAL	PETROLEUM	COUNTRY	COAL	PETROLEUM
Algeria	258	3.4	Japan	38,459	298
Belgian Congo	160	—	Korea	568	—
Morocco	368	39.3	Malaya	422	—
Nigeria	594	—	Pakistan	444	—
S. Rhodesia	2,218	—	Turkey	4,361	17
Union of S. Africa	26,473	—			
Egypt	—	2,343.0	Austria	183	1,500
			Belgium	27,304	—
Canada	15,634	3,749.0	Czechoslovakia	18,456	—
Mexico	912	10,296.0	France	50,843	127
United States	505,319	270,353.0	Saar	15,091	—
			Germany	110,755	1,119
Argentina	26	3,394	Hungary	1,400	530
Brazil	1,959	443	Italy	1,031	—
Chile	2,181	801	Netherlands	12,247	704
Colombia	534	4,497	Poland	73,001	178
Peru	196	2,004	Romania	—	5,350
Venezuela	—	78,235	Spain	11,042	—
			United Kingdom	219,795	46
China	13,800	—			
India	32,825	—	U.S.S.R.	264,000	32,321
Indochina	499	—			
Indonesia	804	6,414	Australia	16,809	—
Iraq	—	6,479	New Zealand	934	—
Iran	—	32,259			
Kuwait	—	17,291	World	1,771,000	486,000
Saudi Arabia	—	26,904			

Sources: United Nations, *Statistical Yearbook*, 1952, pp. 102–104, 107–108.
Minerals Yearbook, 1953, pp. 343–344, 1000–1001.

Table 23.   ELECTRIC ENERGY, INSTALLED CAPACITY, HYDRO AND THERMAL, 1950
(In thousands of kilowatts)

COUNTRY	HYDRO	THERMAL OR TOTAL*	COUNTRY	HYDRO	THERMAL OR TOTAL*
Algeria	28	208	Belgium	25	2,915
Morocco	103	53	Denmark	—	1,073
Mozambique	—	25	Finland	658	406
Northern Rhodesia	—	132	France	6,160	8,806
Union of S. Africa	—	2,405	Germany	—	11,245
			Italy	6,929	1,387
Canada	—	9,960	Netherlands	—	2,275
Cuba	—	166	Norway	2,903	112
Mexico	—	1,235	Spain	1,711	644
United States	18,675	64,176	Sweden	3,660	1,003
			United Kingdom	544	16,351
Argentina	—	1,444			
Brazil	1,134	281	Australia	284	2,194
			New Zealand	640	85
India	562	1,738			
Japan	6,559	3,984			
Turkey	—	408			

* If hydroelectric energy is not reported separately, the total production is listed in the thermal column.

Source: United Nations, *Statistical Yearbook*, 1952, pp. 244–247.

Table 24.   MANUFACTURING OF IRON AND STEEL, 1950
(In thousands of metric tons)

COUNTRY	PIG IRON	STEEL	COUNTRY	PIG IRON	STEEL
Australia	1,101	1,400	Mexico	249	320
Austria	883	947	Netherlands	454	490
Belgium	3,693	3,788	Norway	220	70
Brazil	704	764	Poland	1,250	2,305
Canada	2,260	3,070	Spain	680	779
China	1,022	540	Sweden	848	1,438
Czechoslovakia	1,883	2,736	Turkey	116	90
France	7,844	8,052	South Africa	733	755
Saar	1,682	1,896	U.S.S.R.	19,500	27,000
Germany (west)	9,480	12,121	United Kingdom	9,785	16,555
Germany (east)	288	1,156	U.S.A.	60,217	87,848
Hungary	500	1,022	Yugoslavia	210	420
India	1,689	1,437			
Italy	445	2,362	World total		
Japan	2,286	4,848	(estimated)	133,000	186,000
Luxembourg	2,499	2,440			

Source: *Minerals Yearbook* (1953), pp. 662–663.

Table 25.   TEXTILES, WOOD PULP, AND NEWSPRINT, SELECTED COUNTRIES, 1950
(In thousands of metric tons)

COUNTRY	a	b	c	d	COUNTRY	a	b	c	d
Canada	96.0	7.2	7,483	4,803	Sweden	28.0	17.3	3,146	325
United States	1,715.0	363.7	13,450	923	Norway	4.4	7.4	1,017	161
					Denmark	8.7	11.7	—	
Mexico	6.5	—	49	—	Germany	282.4	85.0	823	170
					Switzerland	—	—	143	40
Brazil	168.2	—	—	36	Austria	19.4	11.0	343	71
Argentina	75.6	—	—	—	Poland	92.1	41.9	230	28
					Czechoslovakia	75.8	35.4	320	28
United Kingdom	386.9	252.1	130	553	Hungary	—	12.0	—	3
France	251.0	127.0	496	305					
Belgium	98.4	40.2	77	62	Yugoslavia	29.4	13.1	—	—
Netherlands	60.3	26.8	89	80	Greece	—	3.8	—	—
Italy	183.0	—	266	92					
Spain	57.8	10.0	—	—	Turkey	30.2	7.5	12	4
Portugal	35.6	3.9	—	—	Egypt	31.7	—	—	—
Finland	2.0	1.8	1,912	420					
					Union of S. Africa	—	—	15	—
					Japan	238.3	32.5	74	132
					India	534.3	—	—	—
					Pakistan	9.6	—	—	—
					Australia	12.1	21.9	131	31
					New Zealand	—	0.9	23	—

a. Cotton yarn
b. Woolen yarn
c. Wood pulp
d. Newsprint production

Source: United Nations, *Statistical Yearbook*, 1951, pp. 205–206, 209, 221, and 222.

Table 26.   INTERNATIONAL TRADE FOR SELECTED COUNTRIES, 1950
(In millions of dollars)

COUNTRY	IMPORTS	EXPORTS	$ PER CAPITA TOTAL TRADE 1948	COUNTRY	IMPORTS	EXPORTS	$ PER CAPITA TOTAL TRADE 1948
Anglo-American				Austria	332.0	305.0	65.00
Canada	2,926.0	2,910.0	442.35	Poland	516.0	533.0	43.90
United States	8,964.0	10,285.0	134.93	Czechoslovakia	788.0	806.0	121.50
				Yugoslavia	236.0	159.0	39.10
Gulf-Caribbean				Greece	428.0	90.0	58.40
Mexico	509.0	466.0	40.85	French N. Africa	909.5	619.9	83.75
Cuba	515.0	642.0	248.25				
Colombia	336.0	394.0	59.00	U.S.S.R.	—	—	—
Venezuela	537.0	1,239.0	379.15				
				Middle East			
South America				Turkey	285.6	263.4	24.20
Brazil	1,098.0	1,347.0	46.90	Egypt	564.0	504.0	64.50
Argentina	1,342.0	1,613.0	193.90				
Chile	248.0	284.0	105.70	Southern Africa			
				Union of S. Africa	859.0	695.0	167.60
Europe-N. Africa				Southern Rhodesia	164.5	116.9	145.35
United Kingdom	7,305.0	6,331.0	298.95				
France	3,066.0	3,066.0	128.45	So. & E. Asia			
Belgium-(Lux.)	1,936.0	1,648.0	420.90	Japan	973.0	820.0	11.60
Netherlands	2,055.0	1,413.0	375.35	China	451.0	216.0	0.87
Italy	1,442.0	1,199.0	56.15	India	1,188.0	1,264.0	8.30
Spain	392.0	389.0	30.35	Pakistan	414.5	591.5	8.29
				Indonesia	404.0	724.0	10.70
Portugal	274.0	186.0	70.05	Malaya	952.0	1,311.0	274.65
Finland	388.0	354.0	221.05				
Sweden	1,182.0	1,103.0	357.90	Oceania			
Norway	679.0	390.0	363.80	Australia	1,354.0	1,482.0	313.45
Denmark	853.0	665.0	304.35	New Zealand	443.0	512.0	519.55
Germany	2,697.0	1,977.0	43.70				
Switzerland	1,052.0	907.0	425.50				

Source: United Nations, *Statistical Yearbook*, 1951.

Questions

CHAPTER 1. *The New World*

1. From a study of Chapter 1 what continent has the greatest resources per capita? The least resources per capita?

2. From the list of important products (page 9) select those which you use every day. Which of these are made from raw materials derived from a foreign country?

3. What are the most important strategic materials to-day? Have there been any changes in this list during the last ten years?

4. Do you favor a high tariff, a low tariff, or free trade? What would be the effect on the United States of removing all import restrictions on meat? From which states would the loudest protests come? What countries would benefit by the free trade? What would these countries purchase with their dollars?

5. With what countries did people of the United States do most of their trading before World War II? What products were exchanged?

6. Discuss briefly the changes in foreign trade since World War II. Keep this topic in mind and discuss again at the end of the course.

CHAPTER 2. *The Major Types of Production*

1. Define and distinguish *units*, *types*, and *regions* of production. Give two or three examples of each.

2. How many kinds of production *units* have you observed? What types do these represent?

3. Where are the most important fishing banks of the world? Why do some banks produce more than others?

4. Suggest a definition to be used in drawing a boundary between areas of forest production and agriculture. Would the same definition apply to both the hardwood forests and the softwood forests?

5. Distinguish Commercial Grazing from Nomadic Herding. Is there any Nomadic Herding in the Americas?

6. What is Commercial Agriculture? Subsistence Agriculture? Does either exist in a pure form?

7. Define an animal unit. What is the basis of this definition? Purpose?

8. Are there any areas outside the Corn Belt which grow much corn? Explain.

9. Distinguish between the Small-Grain and Livestock type and Commercial Dairying on the basis of crops and the use of livestock.

10. Name four distinct regions of Mediterranean Agriculture. In what latitudes do these regions occur?

11. Distinguish between Horticulture, Mediterranean Agriculture, and Oases.

12. Define a plantation. Are plantations limited to tropical lands? What plantation crops must be grown near the coast?

13. Name three types of Oriental Agriculture and list distinctive crops for each.

14. Compare rice and wheat as food crops. Do any areas outside of the Orient produce rice in quantity?

15. What are the most important minerals from the standpoint of production value? From the standpoint of strategic use?

16. What important minerals are scarce? Relatively abundant?

17. List the kinds of factories in your community or near by. Are these a part of a manufacturing belt or do they represent community manufacturing only?

CHAPTER 3. *The Geographic Background of Production in the Americas*

1. Discuss the position of North America with respect to the sources of goods which it lacks. From the standpoint of markets. From the standpoint of surplus commodities.

2. What type of production is associated with the Continental Shelf?

3. What are the main divisions of the Appalachian Highland from west to east? Which of these are most important for farming? Mining?

4. Do the lakes of the Laurentian Upland have any significance for production?

5. Is the Great Plains region all smooth level land? What is the source of water for irrigation in the Great Plains?

6. List the main divisions of the Pacific Borderlands. Discuss the production relationships of mountains and basins.

7. List six or seven important inland ports on the Great Lakes. What products do these ports handle? How large are their hinterlands?

8. What part of South America has a climate similar to southern California? To South Carolina? To Arizona? To central Mexico?

9. Contrast the usefulness for navigation of the Mississippi and Amazon rivers. What are some disadvantages of each?

10. Locate the areas of densest population in Argentina, Brazil, Chile, and Colombia. Explain.

11. What are the greatest handicaps to industrial development in South America? Lack of raw materials? Skills? Power? Market?

CHAPTER 4. *The Geographic Background of Production in Other Continents*

1. Rank the seven "continents" according to area and population. Explain the anomalies.

2. In what climates and in which production regions do most of the people of Africa live?

3. What is the basis of western Europe's superiority in manufacturing?

4. Can the U.S.S.R. support a larger population and at the same time increase the standard of living substantially? In which direction would territorial expansion be of greatest value to the U.S.S.R.?

5. Contrast "Dry Asia" and Monsoon Asia. Suggest some possible solutions to the problem of over-population in India and China.

6. What part of the Northern Hemisphere is similar to New Zealand in climate? Peoples? Products? Make the same comparisons for southeastern Australia (Melbourne) and northern Australia (Darwin).

7. Which continents are at the present time showing the greatest percentage increase in population? Production? Which are showing the least percentage increase? Explain.

CHAPTER 5. *Products of the Seas*

1. What country consumes most fish products per capita? Explain.

2. Why is there little large-scale exploitation of fish in tropical waters?

3. Explain the delayed exploitation of the rosefish.

4. What fish are used chiefly for fertilizer and oil?

5. What kind of sea bottom is favorable for oysters? Are oysters sometimes transplanted? Farmed?

6. What is the most important fish of the north Pacific Coast? Why are most of the fish canned in this region?

7. Where are the most important inland fisheries of North America?

8. Why is the shark so valuable?

9. Where is Dogger Bank? What varieties of fish are caught on this bank and by the fishermen of what countries?

10. What is the major bottom-feeding fish of the North Sea? Surface-feeding?

11. What European country derives the largest share of its national income from fish? Explain.

12. What are the chief fishery products of Brittany? Why do Bretons catch more fish than the fishermen of other coastal districts of France?

13. What are the chief fishing waters of Russia? Are these near areas of dense population?

14. Does Russia have important inland fisheries? Where?

15. Explain the large per capita consumption of fish in Japan. What unusual variations of sea food do the Japanese consume?

16. What are some of the chief products of fish farming? What countries practice fish farming?

17. How widely do the Japanese fishermen range?

18. Why have Australia and New Zealand produced so few fish?

CHAPTER 6. *The North American Forest Region*

1. Explain the small blank areas within the general forest belt in Figure 6.1. Why should Canada have more blank area than the United States in the Rocky Mountains?

2. In the Upper Peninsula of Michigan there are copper and iron mines, agriculture, and forest products. Which will probably be of greatest importance in 1975?

3. Of the various kinds of production in the North American Forest, which are most interrelated? Which is most independent of the others?

4. Make a list of the major products of this region. How many of the product groups listed in Chapter 1 are included?

5. What forms of production in this region might be difficult to classify according to the types studied in Chapter 2?

6. Is the production of lumber or pulpwood more important in New England today? Explain.

7. Where is the Aroostook Region? Explain its significance for agriculture.

8. What factors make the Laurentian Shield suitable for water power development? Are all parts of the Shield available for power production?

9. List the chief softwoods of the Pacific Northwest. Why is this the most important lumber region of the United States?

10. What minerals are produced in the Rocky Mountains? Is coal production large in proportion to the resources?

11. Describe the natural setting of Grand Coulee. What area can be irrigated from Grand Coulee Dam?

CHAPTER 7. *The Softwood Forests of Other Lands*

1. What parts of the softwood forest region of Europe have the best access to markets?

2. Does the United States obtain any forest products from northern Europe?

3. Discuss the variation in climate from Bergen to Okhotsk.

4. In what north European countries are the forest industries most advanced?

5. What is meant by the Norwegian term "fjeld?" For what is the fjeld used?

6. What is the chief hardwood of the north European forest? Uses?

7. Explain the significance of rivers to north European forest production.

8. Why is such a small part of China forested? What do the Chinese use for building materials?

9. What types of trees grow in southern Japan?

10. Define and delimit the areas of softwood forest in South America. What is the market for each of these?

CHAPTER 8. *The Tropical Hardwood Forests*

1. Why are the tropical hardwood forests not more thoroughly exploited?

2. What are the chief woods of the tropical forest? Are you familiar with articles made from these woods? Are tropical hardwoods superior in any way to temperate belt hardwoods?

3. Discuss the distribution of kapok, chicle, and cinchona.

4. Discuss the future of Amazonia in terms of its forest, resources, and agricultural possibilities.

5. Why did the Ford Motor Company dispose of its rubber plantations in Amazonia? Were these plantations a success? Explain.

6. Compare the Congo region of Africa with Amazonia as to climate, relief, transportation, and in terms of possible settlement by mid-latitude peoples. In which region would you prefer to live?

7. What does it mean to "girdle" a tree? Is this practiced in the temperate belt as well as in the tropics?

8. Is bamboo a cultivated crop or a natural forest product?

CHAPTER 9. *Commercial Grazing and Oases in North America*

1. What are the three most important grazing animals in North America? In what regions is each dominant?

2. How many acres of Great Plains grassland are needed to support one cow?

3. What products of Commercial Grazing in the United States are protected by tariff? What are the competing regions in each case?

4. In what climate is the greatest density of grazing animals found? Is this commercial grazing or agricultural land?

5. What is the relation of the grazing lands to the oases? To dry farming areas? To the Corn Belt?

6. What is meant by transhumance? Where is it practiced?

7. What are the chief products of the Imperial Valley on the United States side of the border? On the Mexican side of the border? Explain.

8. Would you expect more sheep per acre in northern England or in western Montana?

9. What minerals are produced in the grazing lands of North America?

10. By what routes does cotton move from the Imperial Valley to Mexico City? Explain.

CHAPTER 10. *Commercial Grazing in Other Lands*

1. Compare the Dry Pampa and Patagonia with the Great Plains grazing region. Which is more productive? Are the same kinds of animals represented? What is the difference in marketability of meat, wool, and hides?

2. Why are parts of the Humid Pampa still used for grazing? Is this good farming land?

3. What are the chief products of the Argentine oases— Tucumán, Jujuy, and Mendoza?

4. What are the disadvantages of the Savanna grazing region? Which is more favorably located, the Llanos of Venezuela or the Campos of Brazil? Could these regions be used for agriculture?

5. Where are the Little Karroo and the Great Karroo? What products are exported from these districts?

6. Where is the "Maize Triangle"? Does it bear any definite relationship to the grazing lands of South Africa?

7. What are the handicaps to grazing in the interior of Australia?

8. Describe the greatest concentration of cattle in Australia. Are they in commercial grazing lands?

9. What pests have interfered with grazing in Australia? How have these been controlled?

10. What are some of the chief minerals of the Australian grazing region?

11. Does the discovery of mineral resources aid in the introduction of ranching?

CHAPTER 11. *Nomadic Herding and the Oases*

1. Compare the life of the nomad on the desert borderlands to that of the Eskimo.

2. Why are there no large areas of Nomadic Herding in the Western Hemisphere?

3. Why are some deserts almost unused? Assuming the same amount of rainfall, would the northern or southern margin of the Sahara be more favorable for herding? Which season is best in each area?

4. Name three districts where grass is available to nomadic herders only in winter. Name two where grass is satisfactory only in summer.

5. What factors influence the efficiency of rainfall?

6. Contrast the life of a nomad with that of an oasis dweller. Which makes a better living? Which has a more interesting life?

7. Is the Gobi a desert or a steppe? Compare a climatic map with an ordinary Atlas map.

8. In Palestine and North Africa which have the better claim to the steppe borderlands, the nomads or the agriculturists? Reasons?

9. Make a check list of items with which to compare the oases of lower Egypt, of Iraq, Turkestan, and the Indus. Include crops, water supply, accessibility, character and size of the population, and any other relevant factor.

CHAPTER 12. *The Commercial Wheat Belts of North America*

1. What is a wheat belt? Develop a definition which will enable an observer in the field or an office worker with suitable statistical material to distinguish a wheat belt from adjacent types of production.

2. Under what conditions does wheat grow best? How many of these conditions are found in the wheat belts?

3. Discuss the relative qualities of the three wheat belts of North America.

4. What are the relative advantages of Winnipeg, Minneapolis, and Buffalo as flour milling centers?

5. In what parts of the various wheat belts is crop failure most likely? Consider drought, frost, winterkilling, insects, and other factors. Do these same parts have the lowest average yields?

6. What is dry farming? What does "fallowing" mean?

7. List the types of production other than wheat farming in the various wheat belts.

8. To what cities do the wheat belt farmers look for markets, flour milling, and the supply of farm machinery? Are most of these cities in or marginal to the wheat belts?

9. Where is the Peace River district? Explain its advantages and disadvantages as a wheat growing district.

10. Discuss the effect of high prices, unemployment, and variations in rainfall on the wheat acreage.

CHAPTER 13. *The Wheat Belts of Argentina, Australia, and Russia*

1. What districts, other than those described in this and the previous chapter, sometimes produce surplus wheat?

2. What is the usual harvest month for each of the wheat belts? Which belts have the longest harvest season?

3. Which belt has the best location with respect to market?

4. Which belts have the most distinct types of land ownership?

5. Where is wheat irrigated? Why is there so little irrigation of wheat?

6. What is a "collective" farm? Advantages? Disadvantages?

7. Define "chernozem." What wheat belts lie partly in this soil zone?

8. Construct a matching question of 25 items, using the six major wheat belts in the answer column. Do not use place names.

9. How long has wheat been cultivated in each of the major wheat belts? Is there any evidence of declining yields?

10. Discuss the differences between a large wheat farm and a plantation.

11. List three cities associated with each wheat belt, including at least one port through which the grain is exported.

CHAPTER 14. *The Mediterranean Lands of Europe, Asia, and North Africa*

1. What are the dominant European peoples in Tunisia, Algeria, and Morocco, respectively? Which group has the largest proportion of farmers?

2. What parts of the Mediterranean lands have the heaviest rainfall?

3. What products are exchanged between different Mediterranean districts? Explain.

4. Which parts of the Mediterranean lands are best suited for livestock? Why so few cattle and horses? So many more sheep and goats? Are any livestock products exported to the United States?

5. Is any Mediterranean country self-sufficient in wheat? Explain.

6. What are the possible effective solutions to Italy's population problem? Colonies? Emigration? Others?

7. Can Palestine support many more people without risk of serious overcrowding? Is the conflict between the Arabs and the Jews fundamentally economic, religious, or political?

8. Are the Mediterranean resort districts more popular in summer or winter? Why?

9. German engineers once proposed to construct a huge dam across the Strait of Gibraltar. Discuss some of the effects of such a project. What would be the effect on the level of the Mediterranean Sea? On the present harbors? On the climate?

10. What parts of the Old World Mediterranean Lands have the least water for irrigation?

11. Where is corn grown in the Mediterranean Lands? Why not more?

CHAPTER 15. *The New Mediterranean Lands*

1. Which of the Mediterranean regions has the best market for its distinctive products? What other regions compete for this market?

2. Explain the distribution of oranges, grapes, prunes, and apples in California. Which is the most valuable crop?

3. What are the three main stages in the evolution of Mediterranean Agriculture? Is there a fourth stage yet to appear?

4. Explain the variation of precipitation from the coast of California across the middle of the San Joaquin Valley to the crest of the Sierra Nevada. What climates occur on this profile? What types of land use occur?

5. Compare production in Mediterranean California and Middle Chile. What would Chile need to enable her to produce as much as California? More water? More land? More people? A better market?

6. Would the opening of South Africa to Asiatic immigration increase the home market for grapes and citrus fruits from the Cape District?

7. What are the forest resources of the Mediterranean Lands?

8. Compare the livestock of California with that of the Old World Lands. Explain the differences.

9. Compare the Mediterranean Agriculture districts of California and Italy as to area, population, exports, and per capita income. Which is more commercial?

10. Compare California and Florida from the standpoint of citrus fruit production. Compare the two as winter resorts. As summer resorts.

11. Describe the effects of a large mountain range such as the Sierra Nevada of California on the character of the Mediterranean Agriculture in the adjacent region.

12. What kinds of natural vegetation and crops would be encountered in ascending a mountain range in southern California, beginning in the bottom of the Los Angeles Basin?

13. Why does California produce less wheat than Spain?

14. What Mediterranean crops have the most valuable yields per acre? What items enter into the cost of producing an acre of oranges?

15. Which Mediterranean region lays greatest stress on dairy products? Explain.

16. Where could Chile find additional outside markets for Mediterranean crops? Olives? Grapes? Citrus fruits?

17. Why has Australia so little Mediterranean Agriculture?

18. Make a list from memory of the countries which have some Mediterranean Agriculture. Which country has the most people in the area of Mediterranean Agriculture? Which has the best mineral resources? Which is most likely to develop large-scale manufacturing?

Which regions produce coal? Petroleum? Has mining in South Africa helped or hindered the agriculture of the Cape District?

CHAPTER 16. *Dairy Regions of North America*

1. Explain the boundaries of the Dairy Belt of North America. What types of production compete for the use of the land? Is the Dairy Belt to be explained largely by negative factors such as cool summers and rough land, or by positive ones such as the nearness of large cities?

2. Compare the products of the extremities of the Dairy Belt, Minnesota and the Canadian Maritime Provinces. Which has the better market? Better climate? More all round resources?

3. How can the Dairy Belt be defined quantitatively and what data are needed to mark it out on a map?

4. What parts of the Dairy Belt specialize in the marketing of whole milk? Butter? Cheese? Dried milk?

5. What are some of the *by-products* of an average dairy farm?

6. Why did New York State fall behind Wisconsin in dairying?

7. What limits the Dairy Belt on the northern side? Climate? Surface? Soil? Transportation? Are there any small districts of dairying north of the main belt?

8. What is the nature of the "milkshed" of New York City? Chicago? Do cities compete with each other for whole milk? How is whole milk transported?

9. If there were no Manufacturing Belt in North America would the Dairy Belt exist?

10. What are the chief crops of the Dairy Belt other than hay and forage? Does the belt excel in any of these?

11. What part of the Dairy Belt of Canada supplies the most milk to the United States?

12. Outside of the main Dairy Belt and the Pacific Northwest are there any small districts of intensive dairying in North America? Where?

13. Why is southeastern United States (the Cotton Belt) deficient in dairy production?

14. How do soybeans and cotton compete with dairy products? Are there any restrictions on the use of vegetable oils for food?

CHAPTER 17. *Dairy Regions of Europe, Australia, and New Zealand*

1. Locate the dairy regions of Europe. Is there very much dairying carried on outside of these regions?

2. What countries share in the Alpine Dairy Region?

3. Describe the "three-storey" farm of the Alps.

4. Why are the flat floors of the Alpine valleys so poor for agriculture?

5. Define "May pasture" and "Alp."

6. Is irrigation practiced in the Alps? Explain.

7. What are some of the products of the home industries in the Alpine region? Are these related to dairying?

8. Are the animals of the Alps used for milk production only? Other uses?

9. What are the chief crops of the northwestern European Dairy Belt other than hay and forage?

10. Are the dairying regions of the British Isles self-supporting?

11. What are the advantages of the north coast of France and the Low Countries for dairying?

12. Explain the use of land reclaimed from the sea for pasture. Does this pay?

13. Is meat production important in the dairy regions of the British Isles? Explain.

14. What part of the British Isles is best suited for agriculture? Is this a dairy region?

15. Describe the location of the dairy belts of Australia and New Zealand. Do these belts have a large urban market nearby?

16. List five breeds of dairy cattle and give the place of origin of each breed.

17. Discuss the movement of butter and cheese in world trade. Why the great variety of cheeses?

18. Name several large cities in the world which have very little dairying in the immediate vicinity.

CHAPTER 18. *The United States Corn Belt*

1. What is a corn belt? Is much corn produced outside the corn belts? If so, where?

2. What are the optimum conditions of soil and climate for growing corn? Where found?

3. What state in the United States produces the most corn? The least corn?

4. Explain the expression "corn for grain." For what other purpose is corn grown?

5. List at least ten ways in which corn is consumed as food.

6. What is the average size of a Corn Belt farm? Is the size changing? Why?

7. Why are horses still used as draft animals on some Corn Belt farms?

8. What is the basic crop rotation in the Corn Belt?

9. Explain the northern, western, and southern boundaries of the Corn Belt. Are these boundaries based on climatic factors or on the competition of other crops?

10. What are the chief secondary cash crops of the Corn Belt? Has the importance of any of these crops changed in the last decade?

11. What proportion of corn in the United States is used for human food? Other uses?

12. What is the Inner Corn Belt? How could this sub-region be defined quantitatively?

13. What is hybrid corn? Did its introduction have any effect on corn production?

14. Does the United States Corn Belt compete with the Corn Belt of Argentina? Of Brazil? Of the Po Plain?

15. Why is the volume of foreign trade in corn less than that in wheat?

16. What has happened to the average size of the corn belt farm in the last two decades? Explain.

17. What is a subsistence hill farm? Is the area of this subtype increasing or decreasing?

18. Describe the corn belt farms of southeastern Pennsylvania. How do these differ from those of Iowa?

19. What is the proportion of tenants on corn belt farms? Compare with the Cotton Belt and Dairy Belt.

CHAPTER 19. *Corn Belts of Other Lands*

1. How do the corn belts of other lands differ from the United States Corn Belt? Are the differences due to natural factors such as climate and soil or to cultural factors such as market?

2. In which corn belt outside of the United States do you think the highest proportion of the crop is used for human food? Why?

3. In which corn belt is flax an important crop? The sugar beet?

4. Describe the pioneer agriculture of the Brazilian Corn Belt and compare with that of the United States a century or more ago.

5. Why does Argentina grow "flint" corn?

6. Why are the corn belt farms of Argentina larger on the average than those of the United States?

7. Explain the relation of the South African "Maize Triangle" to mining.

8. What is kaffir corn? Is it suitable for human food? For livestock feed?

9. Which corn belt has a larger acreage of wheat than of corn? Does this justify calling the region a wheat belt?

10. Which Danubian countries have corn belts? Do these regions produce meat for export?

11. Describe several areas of hill farms in the corn belts outside the United States. Are most of these on a subsistence basis?

CHAPTER 20. *Small-Grain and Livestock Regions*

1. What other kind of production is similar to the Small-Grain and Livestock type?

2. Which portions of the Small-Grain and Livestock region of northern Europe are most commercial? Explain.

3. Why is southeastern England more favored for grain production than other portions of the British Isles?

4. What is the driest part of the European Small-Grain and Livestock region? Does the low rainfall limit production?

5. Define *landes*, *campagne*, and *bocage* as these terms are used in France.

6. What are the chief crops of the Paris Basin?

7. Are dairying and livestock production important in the vicinity of Paris?

8. Does the North German Plain have fertile soils? Which portion is most fertile? Is this variation in fertility apparent in the distribution of certain crops?

9. Where is the Central Agricultural Belt of Russia? Define approximately in terms of cities or towns located on or near the margins.

10. Is wheat the chief crop in central Russia?

11. What type of soil is the podzol? Is it fertile?

12. Explain the origin of Small-Grain and Livestock Agriculture in southern Middle Chile. What peoples settled this area?

13. Describe the Small-Grain and Livestock Agriculture of New Zealand. With what part of western Europe can it be compared?

CHAPTER 21. *Extensive Subsistence Agriculture and the Plantation*

1. Describe the origin of the plantation in Virginia, the West Indies, and Indonesia.

2. What are the requirements for plantation cultivation?

3. Is the United States Cotton Belt a pure or a transition plantation region?

4. What are the chief cash crops grown on plantations? Are some of these crops grown also on middle latitude small farms?

5. What are the principal subsistence crops on the plantations? Can a single crop be both commercial and subsistence?

6. How is the plantation related to Subsistence Agriculture? To Oriental Agriculture?

7. Locate the chief plantation areas on a world map.

CHAPTER 22. *The United States Cotton Belt*

1. What fibers compete with cotton for clothing? For other uses?

2. Why is cotton planted early?

3. What equipment does a tenant farmer need to grow cotton?

4. What is the labor bottleneck of cotton production?

5. Why has the foreign market for United States cotton been declining? What lands are competing for the world market?

6. Why is more cotton grown in the western part of the United States Cotton Belt than in the eastern part? How long has this been true?

7. In what part of the Cotton Belt does the boll weevil do the most damage? Least damage?

8. What other cash crops are grown in the Cotton Belt? Forage crops?

9. Is lumbering important in the Cotton Belt? Mining?

10. Why is cotton of slight importance in the lands immediately adjacent to the Gulf and Atlantic?

11. Compare the Black Belt and the Black Prairie. Which is more productive?

12. Explain the variation in crops as represented in the graphs of Figure 22.4.

13. What are the chief ports of the Cotton Belt?

14. What are the chief differences in climate and soil between the Cotton Belt proper and the coastal margins of the Cotton Belt?

15. List the important crops in the coastal margins. Where are each of them found?

16. Discuss the farm pattern of the coastal margins. Compare with the Cotton Belt proper.

17. In what part of the coastal margins of the Cotton Belt is sugarcane production most important? Why?

18. Discuss the plantation system in the Louisiana "Sugar Bowl."

19. Where is rice grown in the coastal margins? Why?

20. What minerals are important in the Cotton Belt?

CHAPTER 23. *Plantations and Extensive Subsistence Agriculture in Middle America*

1. What is the average elevation of the Central Plateau of Mexico? What part of the United States has a similar summer climate?

2. What crops are grown on the Central Plateau of Mexico? Are these mainly for subsistence or commercial purposes?

3. What crops are grown on the Mexican Coastal Lowland from Tampico to Yucatán? Are these crops grown for export?

4. What is the chief cash crop on the highlands of Central America? Subsistence crop?

5. Describe a typical sugar plantation in Cuba. What is the "central"?

6. Can the sugar beet compete with cane sugar without protective tariffs or embargoes?

7. In what way is the climate of Cuba favorable for cane sugar production? In what months is sugar harvested?

8. Where is cane sugar refined?

9. What products other than sugar are ordinarily exported from Cuba?

10. What are the chief subsistence crops on the plantations of Middle America? Is there a variation with climate and altitude?

CHAPTER 24. *Plantations and Subsistence Agriculture Regions in South America*

1. At what extreme altitude in the Andes would each of the following crops ripen or mature: corn, white potatoes, cacao, wheat. rubber, rice, and coffee? Suggest a specific location for the upper limit of each.

2. In which areas would the following animals be of the greatest relative importance: swine, goats, sheep, and llamas?

3. Make a list of twelve products important in the internal trade of South America. For each product suggest the chief importing and exporting countries.

4. Describe the schemes used by Brazil to valorize coffee.

5. On a map divide Peru into three main regions, coastal, sierra, and selva. Which has the densest population? List the chief surplus products for each.

6. Discuss the location of Brazil's new steel mill at Volta Redonda. Discuss its relationship to supplies of coal and iron ore.

7. What countries compete with Brazil in coffee production? Has production increased recently in some of these countries? In Brazil?

8. What is *terra roxa?* Why is it favorable for coffee production?

9. When does the harvest of coffee begin in São Paulo?

10. In what part of the world has coffee consumption decreased in the last decade? Why?

CHAPTER 25. *Plantations and Subsistence Agriculture Regions in Africa*

1. Why does most of Africa belong to European nations? Which countries hold the largest areas?

2. What are the chief exports of West Africa? Are they derived from plantations, small farms, or the forest?

3. What are the uses of palm oil?

4. What are the chief commercial and subsistence crops of the Sudan? Is livestock important here? Compare with Equatorial Africa.

5. Describe the climate of the East African Plateau in the vicinity of Lake Victoria. Does any part of the United States have a similar summer climate?

6. Discuss the African Plateau as a possible home for surplus European population.

7. Discuss the coordination of lake and rail traffic in East Africa.

8. What is the chief product of Katanga? How does it reach the coast?

9. What are the chief crops of the East African Lowland? By what non-African people was this lowland settled?

10. What are the chief crops of Madagascar? What is the chief mineral?

CHAPTER 26. *Oriental Agriculture*

1. Define the area of Oriental Agriculture. Is this the same as Monsoon Asia?

2. Describe the monsoon climate. How does it differ from the rainforest climate of Amazonia or the Congo?

3. What is the population of Monsoon Asia?

4. Describe the principal concentrations of population. What areas of India and China are sparsely populated?

5. Why is rice so important in Monsoon Asia?

6. In what areas are two crops of rice grown on the same land in one year?

7. Discuss the subdivisions of Oriental Agriculture. Suggest additional subdivisions for more elaborate study.

CHAPTER 27. *Indonesia, Malaya, the Philippines, and Indochina*

1. What is meant by the term "Indonesia"? Does it have the same meaning as the "Dutch East Indies"?

2. What countries formerly had colonies in Indonesia other than the Netherlands?

3. What is meant by Inner Indonesia? Outer Indonesia?

4. Explain the dense population of Java. Are other tropical lands capable of supporting such dense population?

5. What are the chief crops on the plantations of Java?

6. What proportion of the cropped land of Java is in plantations? Native farms?

7. What is meant by the "Great East"? Does it support very many people? Explain.

8. Where are the chief petroleum fields of Indonesia? What are the nearest competing fields?

9. What areas produce tin? Where is the tin refined?

10. Why does Indonesia produce so much natural rubber? What advantage does Indonesia have over Amazonia?

11. What effect has Philippine Independence had upon crop production?

12. What minerals are exported from the Philippines?

13. What is abacá? Uses?

CHAPTER 28. *India, Pakistan, and Ceylon*

1. Compare the Deccan Plateau of India with the Columbia Lava Plateau, with respect to surface, soils, climates, and crops.

2. Why are the yields of rice so low in India?

3. What factors limit the amount of cotton grown in India? Soil? Climate? Market?

4. How could mineral production in India be greatly increased?

5. What crops are grown in the non-rice areas of India?

6. Where is jute grown? Uses?

7. List the chief industrial cities of India, with the principal manufactures.

8. Does India have plantations? Where? What crops?

9. What is the effect of the new status of India and Pakistan on production?

CHAPTER 29. *Humid China*

1. What ocean routes connect eastern United States and western Europe with China? Which is in the best position to trade with China?

2. Suggest criteria for the delimitation of each of the nine agricultural regions of China. Would the statement "soybeans occupy more than 20% of the crop land" serve to distinguish the Manchurian Region?

3. Assume that the railroad facilities, tracks, rolling stock, etc., could be doubled, where would be the best site for iron and steel industries in China?

4. Where are the best sites in China for hydroelectric development? Can one large dam contribute power, flood control, and water for irrigation at the same time?

5. What farm land in China is most productive of calories per acre, per year? Why?

6. What is Shantung or Pongee silk? Where produced? What kind of leaves do the silkworms eat in this district?

7. Make a matching question with the nine agricultural regions of China in the answer column.

8. What resources do the Chinese lack?

9. Do any Chinese crops or minerals find a market in the United States? Elaborate.

10. Suggest possible solutions of China's overpopulation problem.

CHAPTER 30. *Japan's Production Regions*

1. What percentage of the surface of Japan can be cultivated? What factors prevent cultivation of the remainder?

2. Compare Japan with the British Isles as to population, resources, relation to the sea and to the adjacent continent. Which is more favorably situated?

3. In what part of China is the agricultural production similar to that of southern Japan?

4. Where is most of the rice of Japan grown?

5. Approximately how many people live on the Kwanto Plain?

6. What was Japan's chief export before World War II? Was the war alone responsible for its decline?

7. Is Japan primarily a manufacturing country? What kind of manufacturing is dominant?

8. List the chief mineral resources of Japan.

9. Do the Japanese have enough coal, iron ore, and petroleum for domestic needs?

10. From what foreign localities could additional supplies be obtained?

11. What is the chief source of power in Japan? Explain.

12. Describe the internal communications of Japan.

13. Does the sea play a part in domestic transportation?

CHAPTER 31. *Metallic Minerals*

1. What are the most strategic minerals? Sources?

2. Discuss the substitution of one metal for another, aluminum for copper, stainless steel for gold, etc.

3. What are the trends in iron ore production? Where are the greatest reserves close to cheap transportation?

4. What are the ferroalloys. Where obtained?

5. What is the most important factor in locating an aluminum refinery?

6. Discuss the chief uses of copper, lead, and zinc.

7. Could we do without the precious metals? Are there some uses for which there are no substitutes?

8. What are the possible practical uses for uranium and its derivatives?

CHAPTER 32. *Nonmetallic Minerals*

1. Suggest a method of classifying nonmetallic minerals other than the "use" classification used in this book.

2. What are the chief ingredients of cement? What is aggregate? Is there a cement plant in your vicinity? A sand or gravel pit?

3. The figures 10-8-6 on a sack of fertilizer represent the percentages of what minerals?

4. List three important uses for mica, asbestos, graphite, and quartz.

5. What are the four most precious stones? Can any of these be reproduced synthetically?

6. What are "culture" pearls? Where produced?

7. What is pumice, corundum, diatomite, tripoli, and gypsum? Uses?

8. Which of the nonmetallic minerals are scarce in the United States?

CHAPTER 33. *Coal*

1. What are the three chief sources of energy? Does the order of importance vary from continent to continent?

2. Why is coal easy to mine in the Appalachian Plateau? Is it as easy to mine in the Anthracite Field? Explain.

3. What part of Canada exports coal to the United States? What part of the United States exports coal to Canada?

4. Compare anthracite and bituminous coal as to heating value, cleanliness, and use in metallurgical industries.

5. Which have the greater reserves of coal, the Appalachian or Rocky Mountain fields?

6. List two areas of coal production in Canada. Are these well located to supply the Canadian market?

7. Describe the location of Latin America's coal resources. How many fields are in production?

8. Are the coals of Latin America generally suitable for smelting iron ore?

9. Describe the chief coalfields of western Europe.

10. What countries have surplus coal for export?

11. What are the difficulties in mining coal in Britain at the present time?

12. Is coal ever exported from the United States to western Europe?

CHAPTER 34. *Petroleum and Natural Gas*

1. What are the major uses of petroleum?

2. How does the value of oil production compare with that of other minerals in the United States?

3. Where are the chief oilfields of the United States?

4. Is production of petroleum increasing or declining? How long will the reserves last?

5. Is petroleum found in the margins of the sea? Where? Who owns this oil?

6. Where are the chief natural gas fields of the United States?

7. How are oil and gas transported? Which method is cheapest?

8. Is the United States a net exporter or a net importer of petroleum? What are the best sources of supply outside the continental borders of the United States?

9. Which countries have the largest reserves of petroleum and natural gas? What important countries have almost none?

10. Describe the new oilfields in western Canada. Where is the market for this oil and how is it transported?

11. What countries control the oil production of the Middle East? What is the destination of most of this oil?

12. Where is the greatest market for Russian oil? How is the oil transported to this market from the following fields: Baku, Grozny, Sakhalin?

13. Discuss the relative importance of oil, coal, and water power in California, Switzerland, and England.

CHAPTER 35. *Water Power and Water Supply*

1. Discuss the changes in relative energy sources in the last few decades. What are the trends?

2. What is the significance of the following terms: head, gradient, run-off, silt, kilowatt?

3. Describe the conditions which favor the development of a power plant suitable for a city of 50,000 population.

4. Discuss the relative merits of one large dam versus several small dams. List several power sites without dams.

5. What factors are involved in estimating the water power resources of a stream at a given point? Of a state such as New York or California?

6. Is water power always cheaper than steam power?

7. Which rivers in South America and Africa have the greatest potential water power? In what parts of the rivers?

8. Where are railways electrified? Why?

9. Why has western Russia so little water power in proportion to its size? Where are the largest dams?

10. Why does a power plant in southern India need a large reservoir?

11. Explain the wide use of power in Japan.

12. Distinguish between potential and developed water power. Why are statistics from different sources often at variance?

13. How far can hydroelectric energy be transmitted efficiently?

14. Would it be possible to develop power from the tides? What are some of the difficulties?

15. Does the development of water power interfere with the other uses of a stream?

16. What is the chief water supply source for your community?

17. Explain the hydrologic cycle.

CHAPTER 36. *Manufacturing*

1. What is a manufacturing region? Do all cities have some manufacturing?

2. Suggest several methods for delimiting the manufacturing region. Discuss the weaknesses of each method.

3. What are the location factors in manufacturing?

4. Explain the fact that individual location factors may have varying importance in different regions.

5. What raw materials are needed for a steel mill? A synthetic textile factory? A shoe factory?

6. What are the three major manufacturing regions of the world? Which has the best location with respect to raw materials and markets?

7. List six smaller manufacturing districts.

CHAPTER 37. *The North American Manufacturing Region*

1. Explain the location and boundaries of the North American Manufacturing Region.

2. Are all parts of the region as outlined on Figure 37.1 used for manufacturing?

3. What agricultural belts overlap the manufacturing region?

4. What is the chief financial center for each of the subregions of the North American Manufacturing Belt? Does each subregion contain its own financial center?

5. What are the chief "outliers" of the manufacturing region? Explain the significance of each.

6. What are the advantages and disadvantages of New England as a manufacturing region?

7. What are the chief industries of the New York metropolitan district? Does this include much heavy industry?

8. List four cities in the Albany-Buffalo subregion and give the manufacturing specialty for each.

9. Explain the effect of the tariff on Canadian industry.

10. What is meant by the ceramic industries? Where important?

11. Describe a typical site for a steel mill in the Pittsburgh district. Are some of these subject to flood? Explain the choice of site.

12. Describe the distribution of the machine tool industry. The automobile parts industry.

13. What are the chief products of the Lake Michigan manufacturing district?

14. Discuss the advantages and disadvantages of the West Coast industrial regions.

CHAPTER 38. *The Manufacturing Region of Western Europe*

1. Why is western Europe suited for manufacturing? What has been the nature of the foreign market? Has the market changed since World War II?

2. Where are the principal coalfields of western Europe? Are these related to industry? Is there any important industrial development remote from the coalfields?

3. What countries were the largest producers of steel before World War II?

4. Explain the importance of colonial possessions of European countries to their manufacturing economy. Has this factor changed since World War II?

5. What parts of western Europe have adequate canal transportation?

6. What parts of western Europe have abundant water power?

7. Do the subregions of the Manufacturing Belt of Europe have outstanding financial centers comparable to those of North America?

8. List the chief cities in each of the fourteen subregions.

9. What are the chief manufactured products of the Scottish Lowland? Are these based on local raw materials?

10. What coalfields of Britain formerly exported large quantities of coal? Explain.

11. What foreign country gave Lancashire the keenest competition before World War II?

12. What are the specialties of southern Wales? Explain the origin of these specialties.

13. Compare London and New York as manufacturing centers.

14. What is meant by the "manufacturing triangle" of continental Europe? What cities are located near the corners of the triangle?

15. Discuss the "outliers" of the European Manufacturing Belt. Are their industries based upon local raw materials or other factors?

CHAPTER 39. *Manufacturing in Russia*

1. How long has Russia been an important manufacturing country? Explain the late development.

2. Is Russia more or less self-sufficient than the United States from the standpoint of modern industry?

3. What is the greatest handicap to inland waterways in Russia?

4. Explain the difficulties of constructing the Volga-Don Canal.

5. What are Russia's major ocean ports? Did she acquire some new ones following World War II?

6. Explain the location of each of the six major industrial districts of Russia and list their chief products.

7. What is the chief source of power in Russia? Is water power important? Where?

8. Compare the Donbas with the Ruhr and the Pittsburgh district in terms of local raw materials, transportation, and market.

9. What is the greatest handicap to the iron and steel industry of the southern Urals? What steps have been taken to overcome this handicap?

10. What is the Kuzbas? What are its chief resources?

CHAPTER 40. *World Trade*

1. Describe the expansion of world trade giving special attention to the "Age of Discovery."

2. What were the first great *entrepôts* of trade? Explain the rise and decline of each.

3. What was the effect of the development of the plantation on world trade?

4. What is the relative cost per ton mile of the chief trade carriers?

5. How do these facts limit trade in certain parts of the world?

6. Are there any resources in the world today which cannot be exploited because of poor transportation?

7. Describe a typical trade center on the coast and in the interior of the United States. What functions do these centers perform? How are they related to the trade routes?

8. What are the most desirable qualities of a good port?

CHAPTER 41. *Trade Centers and Trade Routes of the Americas*

1. Compare the trade routes of North and South America Which continent has the better harbors, inland waterways, and railroad routes?

2. Why does South America have such a limited railroad pattern? What parts are adequately served by rail?

3. Discuss the difficulties in the construction of the St. Lawrence Waterway. Would this make the Great Lakes navigable by ocean freighter? Does the recent development of efficient icebreakers have any bearing on these questions? In what part of the United States are the people opposed to the St. Lawrence Waterway? Explain.

4. What are the main trunk lines and what function do they perform?

5. List the chief coal roads and the coalfields which they reach.

6. Are there any truly transcontinental railway lines in North America?

7. Discuss the terminals of the principal pipelines including the "Big Inch" and the "Little Inch."

8. California and Texas are connected by pipeline. In which direction does the oil flow?

9. In what part of South America have rail lines been constructed recently? Is further railroad building contemplated? Where?

10. Describe the rail nets of Chile, Argentina, and southern Brazil. What are the chief commodities carried on each?

CHAPTER 42., *Trade Centers and Trade Routes of Africa, Europe and Asia*

1. Explain the fact that Africa was the last continent to be exploited.

2. What are the chief handicaps to river transportation in Africa? What rivers are actually used?

3. Why has the projected Cape to Cairo Railroad failed to materialize? Difficulties of construction? Political questions? Lack of potential freight?

4. What are the chief ports of western Europe? Is their importance related to the quality of the harbor or to the products of the hinterland or both?

5. Define the hinterland of Hamburg. Does it include the head of navigation of the Elbe?

6. What inland waterways would be traversed in shipping goods from Marseille, France, to Warsaw, Poland?

7. What are the chief navigable rivers of Germany?

8. How does the Mittelland Canal make these rivers more effective?

9. What parts of Asia have the best inland transportation? Explain the development of railroads in some sections and not in others.

10. What is the most important inland waterway of Asia? Why does it carry such heavy traffic?

11. What products are exported from Karachi, Bombay, Calcutta, Rangoon, Shanghai, and Dairen?

12. Discuss recent changes in world trade.

Selected References

GENERAL

ISAIAH BOWMAN. *The New World*. World Book Co. New York, 1928.

JEAN BRUNHES. *Human Geography*. Rand McNally and Co. New York, 1952.

"Climate and Man," *Yearbook of Agriculture*. U. S. Dept. of Agriculture. Washington, 1941.

ROBERT B. HALL. "American Raw-Material Deficiencies and Regional Dependence," *Geogr. Rev.*, 30:177–186, 1940.

RICHARD J. RUSSELL and FRED B. KNIFFEN. *Culture Worlds*. Macmillan. New York, 1951.

"Soils and Men," *Yearbook of Agriculture*. U. S. Dept. of Agriculture. Washington, 1938.

NICHOLAS J. SPYKMAN. *America's Strategy in World Politics*. Harcourt, Brace and Co. New York, 1942.

J. RUSSELL WHITAKER and EDWARD A. ACKERMAN. *American Resources*. Harcourt, Brace and Co. New York, 1951.

ERICH W. ZIMMERMANN. *World Resources and Industries* (Revised edition). Harper and Brothers. New York, 1951.

ATLASES

The American Oxford Atlas. Oxford University Press. New York, 1951.

Atlas Internationale Larousse. Librairie Larousse. Paris, 1950.

JOHN BARTHOLOMEW. *Advanced Atlas of Modern Geography*. McGraw-Hill Book Co., Inc. New York, 1950.

J. PAUL GOODE. *Goode's World Atlas*. Rand McNally and Co. New York, 1953.

WILLIAM VAN ROYEN and OLIVER BOWLES. Vol. I, *The Agricultural Resources of the World*. Vol. II, *The Mineral Resources of the World*. Prentice-Hall, Inc. New York, 1954 and 1952.

PERIODICALS

The Geographical Review. The American Geographical Society of New York.

The National Geographic Magazine. The National Geographic Society. Washington.

The Journal of Geography. A. J. Nystrom and Co. for the National Council of Geography Teachers. Chicago.

Annals of the Association of American Geographers. Lancaster, Pennsylvania.

Economic Geography. Clark University. Worcester, Mass.

Yearbook: Association of Pacific Coast Geographers, Cheney, Washington.

The Professional Geographer. The Library of Congress. Washington.

The Geographical Journal. Royal Geographical Society. London.

The Scottish Geographical Magazine. The Royal Scottish Geographical Society. Edinburgh.

Geography. The Geographical Association. Manchester.

The Geographical Magazine. Chatto and Windus for the Geographical Magazine, Ltd. London.

Japanese Journal of Geology and Geography. National Research Council of Japan. Tokyo.

The South African Geographical Journal. South African Geographical Society. Johannesburg.

The Australian Geographer. The Geographical Society of New South Wales. Sydney.

The New Zealand Geographer. New Zealand Geographical Society. Auckland.

STATISTICAL

Agricultural Statistics, 1927–1952. U. S. Dept. of Agriculture. Washington.

Census of Agriculture: 1950. Bureau of the Census. U. S. Dept. of Commerce. Washington, 1952.

Census of Manufactures: 1947. Bureau of the Census. U. S. Dept. of Commerce. Washington, 1950.

Coal Resources of the United States. Geological Survey Circular 94. U. S. Dept. of the Interior. Washington, 1950.

Demographic Yearbook of the United Nations, 1948–1952. Statistical Office of the United Nations. New York.

Fishery Statistics of the United States, 1946. Fish and Wildlife Service. U. S. Dept. of the Interior. Washington, 1950.

Foreign Commerce Yearbook, 1948–1950. Office of International Trade. U. S. Dept. of Commerce. Washington.

Forests and National Prosperity. Forest Service. U. S. Dept. of Agriculture. Misc. Publ. No. 668. Washington, 1948.

Graphic Summary of Land Utilization in the United States. U. S. Dept. of Commerce and U. S. Dept. of Agriculture. Washington, 1947.

Handbook of Regional Statistics. Joint Committee on the Economic Report. S. Con. Res. 26, 81st Congress. Washington, 1950.

International Yearbook of Agricultural Statistics, 1941/42–1945/46. International Institute of Agriculture. Bureau of Food and Agriculture Organization. Rome.

Minerals Yearbook, 1932–1950. Bureau of Mines. U. S. Dept. of the Interior. Washington.

Proceedings of the United Nations Scientific Conference on the Conservation and Utilization of Resources. Vol. II, Mineral Resources. Vol. III, Fuel and Energy Resources. United Nations. New York, 1951.

Seventeenth Census of the United States: 1950, Preliminary

Data. Bureau of the Census. U. S. Dept. of Commerce. Washington.

The State of Food and Agriculture. Food and Agricultural Organization of the United Nations. Washington, 1952.

Statistical Abstract of the United States (Annual). Bureau of the Census. U. S. Dept. of Commerce. Washington.

Statistical Yearbook of the United Nations, 1948–1951. Statistical Office of the United Nations. New York.

JOHN C. WEAVER AND FRED E. LUKERMANN. *World Resource Statistics: A Manual of Data Selected Especially for Students of Economic Geography*. Burgess Publishing Co. Minneapolis, 1953.

World Energy Supplies in Selected Years, 1929–1950. United Nations. New York, 1952.

World Iron Ore Resources and Their Utilization. United Nations. New York, 1950.

World Oil, February 15, July 15, 1949–1952. Gulf Publishing Co. Houston.

WOYTINSKY, W. S. and E. S. *World Population and Production*. The Twentieth Century Fund. New York, 1953.

Yearbook of Fisheries Statistics, 1947, 1948–49. Food and Agricultural Organization of the United Nations. Washington.

Yearbook of Food and Agricultural Statistics I. Production, 1948–1951. Food and Agricultural Organization of the United Nations. Washington.

Yearbook of Food and Agricultural Statistics II. Trade—Commerce, 1948–1951. Food and Agricultural Organization of the United Nations. Washington.

Yearbook of Forest Products Statistics, 1949–1951. Food and Agricultural Organization of the United Nations. Washington.

REGIONS

L. S. BERG. *Natural Regions of the U.S.S.R.* Macmillan. New York, 1950.

CYRUS T. BRADY, JR. *Africa Astir*. Georgian House. Melbourne, 1950.

GEORGE B. CRESSEY. *Asia's Lands and Peoples* (Second edition). McGraw-Hill Book Co., Inc. New York, 1951.

ARCHIBALD W. CURRIE. *Economic Geography of Canada*. Macmillan. New York, 1946.

ALBERT DEMANGEON. *British Isles* (Revised by E. D. Laborde). Heinemann. London, 1950.

S. DE SILVA. *The New Geography of Ceylon*. Colombo Apothecaries Co., Ltd. Colombo, 1948.

The Economy of Turkey. International Bank for Reconstruction and Development and Government of Turkey. International Bank. Washington, 1951.

WALTER FITZGERALD. *Africa* (Revised edition). E. P. Dutton and Co., Inc. New York, 1952.

OTIS W. FREEMAN (Editor). *Geography of the Pacific*. John Wiley and Sons, Inc. New York, 1951.

THOMAS W. FREEMAN. *Ireland; Its Physical, Historical, Social, and Economic Geography*. Methuen and Co. London, 1950.

JAMES S. GREGORY and D. W. SHAVE. *The U.S.S.R.: A Geographical Survey*. George G. Harrap and Co. London, 1944.

SIMON G. HANSON. *Economic Development in Latin America*. Inter-American Affairs Press. Washington, D. C., 1951.

GEORGE W. HOFFMAN (Editor). *A Geography of Europe*. The Ronald Press Co. New York, 1953.

PRESTON E. JAMES. *Latin America*. The Odyssey Press. New York, 1950.

Japanese Natural Resources. Prepared in General Headquarters in 1948. Hosokawa Printing Co. Tokyo.

GEORGES JORRE. *The Soviet Union*. Longmans, Green and Co., Ltd. London, 1950.

RICHARD U. LIGHT. *Focus on Africa*. Amer. Geogr. Society. New York, 1941.

NICHOLAS T. MIROV. *Geography of Russia*. John Wiley and Sons, Inc. New York, 1951.

T. G. A. MUNTZ. *Turkey: Economic and Commercial Conditions in Turkey*. Philosophical Library, New York, 1951.

DORE OGRIZEK (Editor). *Italy*. McGraw-Hill Book Co., Inc. New York, 1950.

DOUGLAS L. OLIVER. *The Pacific Islands*. Harvard Univ. Press. Cambridge, 1951.

ROBERT S. PLATT. *Latin America: Countrysides and United Regions*. McGraw-Hill Book Co., Inc. New York, 1942.

ELLEN C. SEMPLE. *The Geography of the Mediterranean Region*. Henry Holt & Co., Inc. New York, pp. 83–101, 297–405, and 433–473, 1931.

MARGARET R. SHACKLETON. *Europe: A Regional Geography*. Longmans, Green and Co., Ltd. London, 1950.

J. RUSSELL SMITH and M. OGDEN PHILLIPS. *North America*. Harcourt, Brace and Co. New York, 1940.

J. E. SPENCER. *Land and People in the Philippines*. Univ. of California Press. Los Angeles, 1952.

L. DUDLEY STAMP. *Africa: A Study in Tropical Development*. John Wiley and Sons, Inc. New York, 1953.

L. DUDLEY STAMP. *Regional Geography—Asia*. Longmans, Green and Co., Inc. New York, 1952.

GLENN T. TREWARTHA. *Japan*. Univ. of Wisconsin Press. Madison, 1945.

S. P. TURIN. *The U.S.S.R.: An Economic and Social Survey*. Methuen and Co. London, 1944.

ANNE WELSH (Editor). *Africa South of the Sahara: An Assessment of Human and Material Resources*. (South African Institute of International Affairs.) Oxford Univ. Press. London, 1951.

C. LANGDON WHITE and EDWIN J. FOSCUE. *Regional Geography of Anglo-America*. Prentice-Hall, Inc. New York, 1953.

FISHERIES

A. W. ANDERSON and E. A. POWER. *Fishery Statistics of the United States, 1948*. Statistical Digest 22. Fish and Wildlife Service. U. S. Dept. of the Interior. Govt. Printing Office. Washington, 1951.

ADA ESPENSHADE. "A Program for Japan's Fisheries," *Geogr. Rev.*, 39:76–85, 1949.

REGINALD H. FIEDLER. "Fisheries of North America with Special Reference to the United States," *Geogr. Rev.*, 30:201–214, 1940.

REGINALD H. FIEDLER. "Peruvian Fisheries," *Geogr. Rev.*, 34:96–119, 1944.

Fish and Shellfish of the Middle Atlantic Coast. Conservation Bulletin No. 38. U. S. Dept. of the Interior. Washington, 1945.

Fish and Shellfish of the South Atlantic and Gulf Coast. Conservation Bulletin No. 37. U. S. Dept. of the Interior. Washington, 1944.

Fishery Resources of the United States. (Prepared by Fish and Wildlife Service. U. S. Dept. of the Interior.) U. S. Senate Doc. No. 51, 79th Congress, 1st Session. Washington, 1945.

ELON JESSUP. "Pastures of the Sea," *Natural History*, pp. 16–21, 1943.

GLENN T. TREWARTHA. *Japan.* Univ. of Wisconsin Press. Madison, pp. 245–256, 1945.

LIONEL A. WALFORD (Editor). *Fishery Resources of the United States.* Public Affairs Press. Washington, 1947.

CARL ZIERER. "Fishing Industry of California," *Scottish Geogr. Mag.*, 51:65–83, 1935.

FORESTS

LOYAL DURAND, JR. "The West Shawano Upland of Wisconsin: A Study of Regional Development Basic to the Problem of Part of the Great Lakes Cut-over Region," *Ann. Assoc. Amer. Geogr.*, 34:135–163, 1944.

IVAN ELCHIBEGOFF. "Special Report on the Far Eastern Timber Trade," *Far Eastern Survey*, 7:92–97, 1938.

Forest Resources of the World. Food and Agriculture Organization of the United Nations. Washington, 1948.

Forests and National Prosperity. Forest Service. U. S. Dept. of Agriculture, Misc. Publ. 668. Washington, 1948.

Gauging the Timber Resource of the United States. Forest Service. U. S. Dept. of Agriculture. Washington, 1946.

CARYL PARKER HASKINS. *The Amazon.* Doubleday Doran and Co., Inc. Garden City, New York, 1943.

V. KATKOFF. "Timber Industry of the U.S.S.R.," *Econ. Geogr.*, 16:390–406, 1940.

WILLIS B. MERRIAM. "Forest Situation in the Pacific Northwest," *Econ. Geogr.*, 14:103–108, 1938.

HUGH M. RAUP. "Forests and Gardens along the Alaskan Highway," *Geogr. Rev.*, 35:22–48, 1945.

Trees. Yearbook of Agriculture. U. S. Dept. of Agriculture. Washington, 1949.

A. TSYMEK. *The Forest Wealth of the Soviet Far East and Its Exploitation.* U.S.S.R. Council of the Institute of Pacific Relations, 1936.

J. B. WOODS. "The Forests of Maine," *American Forests*, 54:266–268, 285–287, 1948.

GRASSLANDS

B. W. ALLRED. "Range Conservation Practices for the Great Plains," U. S. Dept. of Agriculture, Misc. Publ. No. 410, U. S. Govt. Printing Office. Washington, 1940.

ROBERT G. BOWMAN. "Prospects of Land Settlement in Western Australia," *Geogr. Rev.*, 32:598–621, 1942.

R. OGILVIE BUCHANAN. *The Pastoral Industries of New Zealand.* Philip. London, 1935.

MARION CLAWSON. *The Western Range Livestock Industry.* McGraw-Hill Book Co., Inc. New York, 1950.

MERIAN C. COOPER. *Grass.* G. P. Putnam's Sons. New York, 1925.

KENNETH B. CUMBERLAND. "High Country 'Run.' The Geography of Extensive Pastoralism in New Zealand," *Econ. Geogr.*, 20:204–220, 1944.

JEAN GOTTMAN. "New Facts and Some Reflections on the Sahara," *Geogr. Rev.*, 32:659–662, 1942.

Grass. Yearbook of Agriculture. U. S. Dept. of Agriculture. Washington, 1948.

IRENE A. MOKE. "New Zealand: Marketing a Pastoral Surplus," *Econ. Geogr.*, 23:248–255, 1947.

RAGNAR NUMELIN. *The Wandering Spirit: A Study of Human Migration.* Macmillan. New York, 1937.

PAUL O. NYHUS. "Argentine Pastures and the Cattle Grazing Industry," *For. Agr.*, 4:3–30, 1940.

G. ROSEVEARE. *The Grasslands of Latin America.* Bulletin No. 36. Imperial Bureau of Pastures and Field Crops. Aberystwyth, 1948.

BERTRAM THOMAS. *Arabia Felix.* Charles Scribner's Sons. New York, 1932.

C. WARREN THORNTHWAITE. "The Great Plains," offprinted from *Migration and Economic Opportunity*, Chap. 5, pp. 202–250, by C. Goodrich, B. W. Allen, C. W. Thornthwaite, and others. Univ. of Penn. Press. Philadelphia, 1936.

H. C. TRUMBLE. "The Development of Pastures in South Australia," *Scottish Geogr. Mag.*, 53:10–16, 1937.

AGRICULTURE

MERRILL K. BENNETT. "International Contrasts in Food Consumption," *Geogr. Rev.*, 31:365–376, 1941.

L. J. BRASS. "Stone Age Agriculture in New Guinea," *Geogr. Rev.*, 31:555–569, 1941.

JAN O. M. BROEK. "The Economic Development of the Outer Provinces of the Netherlands Indies," *Geogr. Rev.*, 30:187–200, 1940.

JOHN LOSSING BUCK. Land Utilization in China. Univ. of Chicago Press. Chicago, 1938.

LOUISE E. BUTT. "Belgian Agriculture," *For. Agr.*, 11:90–98, 1947.

RAYMOND E. CRIST and CARLOS E. CHARDON. "Changing Patterns of Land Use in the Valencia Lake Basin," *Geogr. Rev.*, 31:430–443, 1941.

Crops in Peace and War. Yearbook of Agriculture, 1950–1951. U. S. Dept. of Agriculture. U. S. Govt. Printing Office. Washington.

ALDEN CUTSHALL. "Reconstruction of Philippine Agriculture," *Econ. Geogr.*, 23:308–310, 1947.

LOYAL DURAND, JR. "Cheese Region of Northwestern Illinois," *Econ. Geogr.*, 22:24–37, 1946.

LIU ENLAN. "Climate and China's Agricultural Industry," *Journ. of Geogr.*, 45:90–95, 1946.

HELEN C. FARNSWORTH and V. P. TIMOSHENKO. *World Grain Review and Outlook.* Food Research Institute. Stanford University, Calif., 1945.

RICHARD HARTSHORNE and SAMUEL N. DICKEN. "A Classification of the Agricultural Regions of Europe and

North America on a Uniform Statistical Basis," *Ann. Assoc. Amer. Geogr.*, 25:99–120, 1935.

HALENE HATCHER. "Dairying in the South," *Econ. Geogr.*, 20:54–64, 1944.

E. C. HIGBEE. "The Agricultural Regions of Guatemala," *Geogr. Rev.*, 37:177–201, 1947.

HU HUAN-YONG. "A New Cotton Belt in China," *Econ. Geogr.*, 23:60–66, 1947.

NAUM JASNY. "Unirrigated Cotton in Southern Russia and the Danubian Countries," *For. Agr.*, 11:2–12, 1947.

K. H. W. KLAGES. *Ecological Crop Geography.* Macmillan. New York, 1942.

WALTER C. LOWDERMILK. *Palestine: Land of Promise.* Harper and Brothers. New York, 1944.

SHANNON MCCUNE. "Southeastern Littoral of Korea," *Econ. Geogr.*, 23:41–50, 1947.

JAMES C. MALIN. *Winter Wheat in the Golden Belt of Kansas: A Study in Adaptation to Subhumid Geographical Environment.* Univ. of Kansas Press. Lawrence, 1944.

J. K. MATHESON and E. W. BOVILL. *East African Agriculture.* Oxford University Press. London, 1950.

PEVERIL MEIGS. "Current Trends in California Orchards and Vineyards," *Econ. Geogr.*, 17:275–286, 1941.

OSCAR K. MOORE. "Argentina's Foreign Agricultural-Trade Policy," Part II, *For. Agr.*, 11:25–32, 1947.

ROBERT L. PENDLETON. "Land Utilization and Agriculture of Mindanao, Philippine Islands," *Geogr. Rev.*, 32:180–201, 1942.

W. L. POWERS. "Soil Development and Land Use in Northern Venezuela," *Geogr. Rev.*, 35:273–285, 1945.

H. F. RAUP. "Piedmont Plain Agriculture in Southern California," *Yearbook of Assoc. Pac. Coast Geogr.*, 6:26–31, 1940.

KATHLEEN ROMOLI. *Colombia: Gateway to South America.* Doubleday Doran and Co., Inc. New York, 1940.

WILLIAM E. RUDOLPH. "Agricultural Possibilities in Northwestern Venezuela," *Geogr. Rev.*, 34:36–56, 1944.

CARL ORTWIN SAUER. *Agricultural Origins and Dispersals.* Bowman Memorial Lectures, Ser. 2, American Geographical Society. New York, 1952.

LEO J. SCHABEN. "The Bread-Grain Picture in Europe," *For. Agr.*, 12:20–21, 1948.

EARL B. SHAW. "Banana Trade of Brazil," *Econ. Geogr.*, 23:15–21, 1947.

T. H. SHEN. *Agricultural Resources of China.* Cornell University Press. Ithaca, 1951.

L. DUDLEY STAMP. *Land for Tomorrow, the Underdeveloped World.* Indiana University Press. Bloomington, 1952.

GEORGE P. STEVENS. "Agricultural Methods in the Lower Nile Valley and Delta of Egypt," *Journ. of Geogr.*, 46:327–337, 1947.

F. S. STRAUS. "Austrian Agriculture," Part I, *For. Agr.*, 11:50–59, 1947.

GRIFFITH TAYLOR. "Agricultural Climatology of Australia," *Quar. Journ. of Royal Meteorological Soc.*, 46:331–356, 1920.

GRIFFITH TAYLOR. "Settlement Zones of the Sierra Nevada de Santa Marta, Colombia," *Geogr. Rev.*, 21:539–558, 1931.

RUPERT B. VANCE. *Human Geography of the South.* Univ. of North Carolina Press. Chapel Hill, 1932.

JOHN C. WEAVER. "United States Malting Barley Production," *Ann. Assoc. Amer. Geogr.*, 34:97–131, 1944.

DAVID WEEKS. "Bolivia's Agricultural Frontier," *Geogr. Rev.*, 36:546–567, 1946.

KENNETH WERNIMONT. "Trends in Brazilian Agriculture," *For. Agr.*, 11:14–16, 1947.

VERNON D. WICKIZER and MERRILL K. BENNETT. *The Rice Economy of Monsoon Asia.* Food Research Institute, Stanford Univ. Press. Calif., 1941.

J. R. WHITAKER. "Peninsular Ontario: A Primary Regional Division of Canada," *Scottish Geogr. Mag.*, 54:263–284, 1938.

C. LANGDON WHITE. "The Argentine Meat Question," *Geogr. Rev.*, 35:634–646, 1945.

C. LANGDON WHITE and EDWIN J. FOSCUE. "Hennequin: The Green Gold of Yucatán," *Journ. of Geogr.*, 38:151–155, 1939.

DERWENT S. WHITTLESEY. "Major Agricultural Regions of the Earth," *Ann. Assoc. Amer. Geogr.*, 26:199–240, 1936.

KATHRYN H. WYLIE. "Food Production and Supply in Mexico," *For. Agr.*, 11:106–112, 1947.

MINERALS

ALAN M. BATEMAN. *Economic Mineral Deposits* (Second edition). John Wiley and Sons, Inc. New York, 1950.

JAMES E. COLLIER. "The Aluminum Industry of Europe," *Econ. Geogr.*, 22:75, 1946.

JAMES E. COLLIER. "Aluminum Industry of the Western Hemisphere," *Econ. Geogr.*, 20:229, 1944.

JOHN B. DEMILLE. *Strategic Minerals.* McGraw-Hill Book Co., Inc. New York, 1947.

HOWARD N. EAVENSON. *The First Century and a Quarter of American Coal Industry.* Privately printed. Pittsburgh, 1942.

LEONARD M. FANNING. *Our Oil Resources.* McGraw-Hill Book Co., Inc. New York, 1950.

OTIS W. FREEMAN and HALLOCK F. RAUP. "Pacific Northwest Minerals in Wartime," *Journ. of Geogr.*, 42:121–129, 1943.

CHAUNCY D. HARRIS. "The Ruhr Coal-Mining District," *Geogr. Rev.*, 36:194–221, 1946.

Investigations of Petroleum Resources in Relation to National Welfare, 80th Congress, 1st Session, Senate Report No. 9. Washington, 1947.

CHARLES K. LEITH, JAMES W. FURNESS, and CLEONA LEWIS. *World Minerals and World Peace.* The Brookings Institution. Washington, 1943.

T. S. LOVERING. *Minerals in World Affairs.* Prentice-Hall, Inc. New York, 1943.

E. WILLARD MILLER. "Some Aspects of the United States Mineral Self-Sufficiency," *Econ. Geogr.*, 23:77–84, 1947.

RAYMOND E. MURPHY and HUGH E. SPITTAL. "A New Production Map of the Appalachian Bituminous Coal Region," *Ann. Assoc. Am. Geogr.*, 34:164–172, 1944.

DALE NIX. "Oil Developments in Saudi Arabia," *Mines Mag.*, 36:533–535, 1946.

Petroleum in the Western Hemisphere. Report of the Western Hemisphere Oil Study Committee. Independent Petroleum Assoc. of Amer. Washington, 1952.

Petroleum Productive Capacity. A Report of the National Petroleum Council. Washington, 1952.

N. J. G. POUNDS. *The Ruhr: A Study in Historical and Economic Geography.* London, 1952.

WALLACE E. PRATT and DOROTHY GOOD (Editors). *World Geography of Petroleum.* Spec. Publ. No. 31, American Geographical Society, 1950.

STEWART SCHACKNE and N. D'ARCY DRAKE. *Oil for the World.* Harper and Brothers. New York, 1950.

DEMITRI B. SHIMKIN. *Minerals, A Key to Soviet Power.* Harvard Univ. Russian Research Center, Studies No. 9. Harvard University Press. Cambridge, 1953.

WALTER H. VOSKUIL. "Oil after the War," *Geogr. Rev.,* 34:655–660, 1944.

WALTER H. VOSKUIL. "Postwar Issues in the Petroleum Industry," *Univ. of Illinois Bull., Business Studies,* 43:1–32, 1946.

KUNG-PING WANG. "Mineral Resources of China," *Geogr. Rev.,* 34:621–635, 1944.

CLIFFORD M. ZIERER. "Broken Hill: Australia's Greatest Mining Camp," *Ann. Assoc. Amer. Geogr.,* 30:83–108, 1940.

WATER POWER AND SUPPLY

H. K. BARROWS. *Floods, Their Hydrology and Control.* McGraw-Hill Book Co., Inc. New York, 1948.

Energy Resources and National Policy. National Resources Committee. Washington, 1939.

BERNARD FRANK and ANTHONY NETBOY. "Dams Are Not Enough," *American Forests,* January, 1950.

Headwaters: Control and Use. U. S. Dept. of Agriculture. Washington, 1937.

C. L. MCGUINNESS. *The Water Situation in the United States with Special Reference to Groundwater.* U. S. Dept. of the Interior. Geol. Survey, Circular 114. Washington, 1951.

PEVERIL MEIGS. "Water Planning in the Great Central Valley, California," *Geogr. Rev.,* 29:252–273, 1939.

U. S. President's Water Resources Policy Commission Report. Vol. 1. *A Water Policy for the American People.* Vol. 2. *Ten Rivers in America's Future.* U. S. Govt. Printing Office. Washington, 1950.

ALBERT N. WILLIAMS. *The Water and the Power.* Duell, Sloan and Pearce, Inc. New York, 1951.

MANUFACTURING

E. B. ALDERFER and H. E. MICHL. *Economics of American Industry* (Second edition). McGraw-Hill Book Co., Inc. New York, 1950.

JOHN W. ALEXANDER. "Geography of Manufacturing: What Is It?" *Journ. of Geogr.,* 40:284–287, 1950.

JOHN E. BRUSH. "Iron and Steel Industry in India," *Geogr. Rev.,* 42:37–55, 1952.

J. HERBERT BURGY. *The New England Cotton Textile Industry: A Study in Industrial Geography.* Waverly House. Boston, 1932.

WILLIAM G. CUNNINGHAM. *The Aircraft Industry: A Study in Industrial Location.* Lorrin L. Morrison. Los Angeles, 1951.

J. G. DUDLEY. "A Paper on the Growth, Trade, and Manufacture of Cotton," *Bull. of the Amer. Geogr. and Statistical Society,* 1: No. 2, 105–194, Jan., 1853.

MAZAFFER ERSELCUK. "Iron and Steel Industry in Japan," *Econ. Geogr.,* 23:105–129, 1947.

GEORGE W. HOFFMAN. "Austria: Her Raw Materials and Industrial Potentialities," *Econ. Geogr.,* 24:45–52, 1948.

PRESTON E. JAMES. "The Significance of Industrialization in Latin America," *Econ. Geogr.,* 26:159–161, 1950.

ROBERT G. LONG. "Volta Redonda: Symbol of Maturity in Industrial Progress of Brazil," *Econ. Geogr.,* 24:149–154, 1948.

GLEN E. MCLAUGHLIN. "Industrial Expansion and Location," *Ann. Amer. Academy of Political and Social Science,* 242:25–29, 1954.

HOWARD J. NELSON. *Localization of Manufacturing in Iowa.* Unpublished M. A. thesis, Univ. of Chicago, Dept. of Geography, 1947.

JAMES J. PARSONS. "California Manufacturing," *Geogr. Rev.,* 39:229–241, 1949.

JAMES J. PARSONS. "Recent Industrial Development in the Gulf South," *Geogr. Rev.,* 40:67–83, 1950.

THOMAS T. READ. "Economic-Geographic Aspects of China's Iron Industry," *Geogr. Rev.,* 33:42–55, 1943.

ALLAN RODGERS. "Industrial Inertia—A Major Factor in the Location of the Steel Industry in the United States," *Geogr. Rev.,* 42:56–66, 1952.

ALLAN RODGERS. "The Manchurian Iron and Steel Industry and Its Resource Base," *Geogr. Rev.,* 38:41–54, 1948.

ALFRED J. WRIGHT. "Recent Changes in the Concentration of Manufacturing," *Ann. Assoc. Amer. Geogr.,* 35:144–166, 1945.

ROBERT L. WRIGLEY. "Organized Industrial Districts with Special Reference to the Chicago Area," *Journ. of Land and Public Utility Economics,* 23:180–198, 1947.

GEORGE WYTHE. *Industry in Latin America* (Revised edition). Columbia University Press. New York, 1949.

TRADE AND TRANSPORTATION

D. F. ALLEN. *Report on the Major Ports of Malaya.* Govt. Printer. Kuala Lumpur, 1951.

W. W. ATWOOD. "Graphic Summary of Trade between the United States and the Other Americas," *Econ. Geogr.,* 20:102–115, 1944.

LAUCHLIN CURRIE. "Trade Policies after Victory," *For. Commerce Weekly,* 17:3–5, 1944.

GEORGE F. DEASY. "The Harbors of Africa," *Econ. Geogr.,* 18:325–342, 1942.

JOHN H. FREDERICK. *Commercial Air Transportation.* R. D. Irwin, Inc. Chicago, 1946.

KAREN J. FRIEDMAN. "Denmark's Postwar Agricultural Export Trade," *For. Agr.,* 11:45–48, 1947.

HUGH B. KILLOUGH and L. W. KILLOUGH. *Economics of International Trade* (Second edition), McGraw-Hill Book Co., Inc. New York, 1948.

HAL B. LARY and Associates. "The United States in the World Economy: The International Transactions of the United States during the Interwar Period." Econ. Series, No. 23, U. S. Bur. of Foreign and Domestic Commerce. Washington, 1943.

SIR HARRY O. MANCE. *International Sea Transport*. Royal Inst. of Int. Affairs. Int. Transport and Communications. Oxford Univ. Press. London, 1945.

F. W. MORGAN. *Ports and Harbours*. Longmans, Green and Co., Inc. New York, 1952.

G. ETZEL PEARCY. "Air Transportation—World Coverage," *Journ. of Geogr.*, 28:105, 1949.

WALTER A. RADIUS. *United States Shipping in Transpacific Trade, 1922–1938*. Stanford Univ. Press, Calif., 1944.

W. E. RUDOLPH. "Strategic Roads of the World," *Geogr. Rev.*, 33:110–131, 1943.

HENRY SAMPSON. *World Railways*. Sampson, Low, Marston and Co. London, 1950.

A. J. SARGENT. *Seaports and Hinterlands*. Adam and Charles Black, Ltd. London, 1938.

EDWARD L. ULLMAN. "The Railroad Pattern of the United States," *Geogr. Rev.*, 39:242–256, 1949.

J. PARKER VAN ZANDT. *The Geography of World Air Transport*. The Brookings Institution. Washington, 1944.

Index

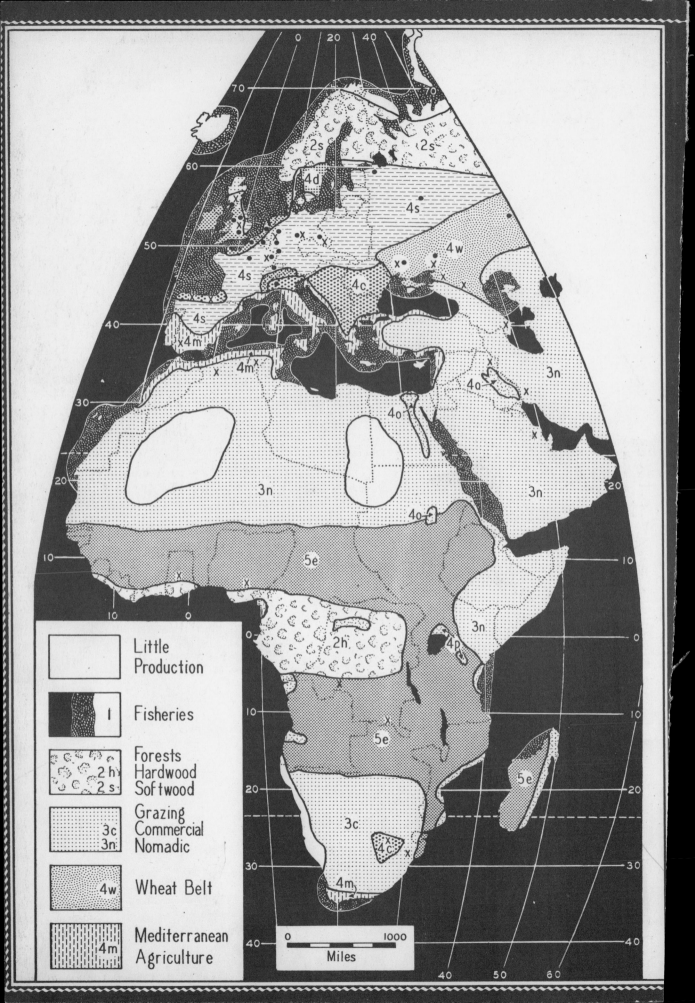